INTRODUCTION TO
ELECTRICAL ENGINEERING

INTRODUCTION TO ELECTRICAL ENGINEERING

GEORGE V. MUELLER

Registered Professional Engineer
Development Engineer
Robbins & Myers, Inc.

THIRD EDITION

McGRAW-HILL BOOK COMPANY, INC.

New York   Toronto   London

1957

INTRODUCTION TO ELECTRICAL ENGINEERING

Library of Congress Catalog Card Number 56-8869

VI

43958

THE MAPLE PRESS COMPANY, YORK, PA.

PREFACE

This book presents the principles of electric and magnetic circuits and fields. Applications of these principles to the solution of typical problems are considered. It is intended that the theoretical discussions be rigorous and consistent with modern engineering practice.

At an early stage the nonlinear relations that exist in certain electric circuits are considered. Practice in solving problems related to these circuits is utilized as preparation for solving others that relate to magnetic circuits containing materials of variable permeability.

The physical relations involved in the transient responses of electric and magnetic circuits are introduced. An understanding of these principles is useful when one considers special cases such as those in a-c circuits that are in a steady-state condition.

The rationalized mks system of units is the basic one used. The relations of certain other systems to the mks system are shown for certain quantities.

The topics have been arranged in an order based upon suggestions received from users of the previous editions. For a one-semester course Chaps. 1 to 9 include the material desired by most users. The material in the remaining chapters is suitable for a subsequent course or as reference material.

The abbreviations and the graphical symbols agree with the latest standards published by the American Standards Association and are used with its permission.

The inclusion of many numerical examples has proved to be a popular feature of the book. Additional examples are included in this edition to augment some explanations. The treatment of network theorems is more extensive than in the earlier editions.

No instructions for laboratory experiments are included since a survey has shown that most instructors prefer to write their own instructions to apply specifically to equipment available in their own laboratories.

In writing the earlier editions, the author was particularly indebted to the late Dr. C. F. Harding, former Head of the School of Electrical Engineering at Purdue University; to Dr. D. D. Ewing, Emeritus Professor of Electrical Engineering at Purdue University; and to Dr. T. J. Higgins, Professor of Electrical Engineering at the University of Wisconsin for counsel and suggestions. In preparing this edition, he is indebted to colleagues at Purdue University and to other teachers elsewhere for valuable suggestions.

GEORGE V. MUELLER

v

CONTENTS

ABBREVIATIONS AND SYMBOLS

Except for those denoted by (ns), all abbreviations and symbols agree with American Standard Abbreviations for Scientific and Engineering Terms, Z 10.1—1941, and Letter Symbols for Electrical Quantities, Z 10.5—1949.

Term or quantity	Letter symbol	Abbreviation
Alternating-current (as adjective)	. . . .	a-c
Ampere	. . . .	amp
Angular velocity	ω	
Arctan	. . . .	$\tan^{-1}$ (ns)
Audio frequency	. . . .	af (ns)
Average	. . . .	avg
Calorie	. . . .	cal
Capacitance	C	
Cent	. . . .	¢
Centimeter	. . . .	cm
Centimeter-gram-second (system)	. . . .	cgs
Charge	Q, q	
Circular mils	. . . .	cir mils
Conductance	G, g	
Cosine	. . . .	cos
Coulomb	. . . .	coul (ns)
Coupling coefficient	k	
Cubic centimeter	. . . .	cu cm
Cubic meter	. . . .	cu m
Current	I, i	
Current density	S	
Cycles per second	. . . .	c
Decibel	. . . .	db
Degree centigrade	. . . .	C
Degree Fahrenheit	. . . .	F
Degree Kelvin	. . . .	K
Diameter	. . . .	diam
Direct-current (as adjective)	. . . .	d-c
Dielectric constant	ϵ	
of free space	ϵ_v	
Dielectric flux	Ψ, ψ	
Dielectric flux density	D	
Efficiency	η	eff
Elastance	S	
Electric potential gradient	$\mathcal{E}$	

Term or quantity	Letter symbol	Abbreviation
Electromotive force	E, e	emf
Energy	W, w	
Equation	....	eq
Farad	....	f
Flux density, electric	D	
Magnetic	B	
Flux, dielectric	Ψ, ψ	
Magnetic	Φ, ϕ	
Foot	....	ft
Force	F, f	
Frequency	f	
Gauss	....	gs (ns)
Gilbert	....	gb (ns)
Gram	....	g
Henry	....	h
Horsepower	....	hp
Hour	....	hr
Impedance	Z	
Inch	....	in.
Inductance, mutual	M (ns)	
Self-	L	
Joule	....	j
Kilocycles per second	....	kc
Kilogram	....	kg
Kilovolt	....	kv
Kilovolt-ampere	....	kva
Kilowatt	....	kw
Logarithm, common	....	log
Natural	....	ln
Magnetic flux	Φ, ϕ	
Magnetic flux density	B	
Magnetic potential gradient	H	
Magnetomotive force	....	mmf
Maxwell	....	mx (ns)
Meter	....	m
Meter-kilogram-second (system)	....	mks
Microampere	....	μa
Microfarad	....	μf
Micromicrofarad	....	$\mu\mu$f
Microvolt	....	μv
Microweber	....	μwb (ns)
Mile	....	mi (ns)
Milliampere	....	ma
Milliampere-second	....	ma-sec
Millihenry	....	mh
Millisecond	....	msec
Millivolt	....	mv

Term or quantity	Letter symbol	Abbreviation
Minute	. . . .	min
Number of series turns of a winding	N, S (ns)	
Oersted	. . . .	oe (ns)
Ohm	Ω	
Permeability	μ	
of free space	μ_v	
Permeance	$\mathcal{P}$	
Pound	. . . .	lb
Power	P, p	
Power factor	. . . .	pf
Radio frequency	. . . .	rf
Reluctance	$\mathcal{R}$	
Resistance	R, r	
Resistivity	ρ	
Revolutions per minute	. . . .	rpm
Root-mean-square	. . . .	rms
Second	. . . .	sec
Sine	. . . .	sin
Square	. . . .	sq
Tangent	. . . .	tan
Temperature	t, θ	
Temperature, absolute	T	
Temperature coefficient of resistance	α	
Time	T, t	
Volt	. . . .	v
Volt-ampere	. . . .	va
Voltage	$V, v: E, e$	
Watt	. . . .	w
Wattsecond	. . . .	wsec
Weber	. . . .	wb (ns)
Work	W, w	

GRAPHICAL SYMBOLS

Alternating voltage source[1]	⊙	Inductor[1]	
		Fixed	⌐⦷⦷⦷⌐
Battery[1] (Long line is positive)	⊣⏐⏐⊢	Iron core	≡⦷⦷⦷
		Mutual	⦷⦷⦷ / ⦷⦷⦷
Capacitor[1]		Variable	⌐⦷⦷⦷⌐
Fixed	⊣⊢	Instrument[1] *Identifying abbreviation	(*) or (*)
Variable	⊬⊢	Receiver[1]	▯⊏
		Rectifier[1]	▶⊢
Circuit breaker[1]	⌒	Resistor[1]	
		Fixed	⌐⋀⋀⋀⌐or⌐▭⌐
Crossing conductors[1]		Variable	⋀⋀⋀ or ⋀⋀⋀ or ▭
Connected	┼	Switch, knife[2]	
Not connected	┼	Single pole	╱
		Double pole	⊐
D-C Generator[2] (See page 25)	(Gen)	Terminal[1]	○ or ●
		Transformer, iron core[1]	⦷⦷⦷ / ⦷⦷⦷
Fuse[1]	⊸⌇⊸	Transmitter[1]	⊐◁
Ground connection[1]	⏚	Tubes	⊥ / ⌐ Anode Cold Indirectly cathode heated cathode
Illuminating lamp[1]	⊕		∩ • - - - Filament Gas- Grid filled

[1] American Standard Graphical Symbols for Telephone, Telegraph, and Radio Use, ASA Z32.5-1944
[2] American Standard Graphical Symbols for Power, Control, and Measurement; ASA Z32.3-1943

CHAPTER 1

SOME FUNDAMENTAL IDEAS ABOUT ELECTRICITY

1.1. Units. Certain units in the various systems used in engineering have been defined and proposed by international congresses and adopted in the United States by acts of Congress. In the centimeter-gram-second (cgs) system, the centimeter (cm), the gram (g), and the second (sec) are the basic units of length, mass, and time, respectively. The meter-kilogram-second (mks) system, proposed in 1901 by Giorgi, an Italian scientist, was based on the meter (m), the kilogram (kg), and the second. It was adopted in 1935 by the International Committee on Weights and Measures and became effective Jan. 1, 1948.

Two systems of mks units, the rationalized and the unrationalized, have been proposed. Most quantities have the same unit in either system. The ones that differ do so by a factor of 4π. In this book the rationalized system will be used.

Units larger and smaller than the basic ones are created by using prefixes, the most common of which are:

$$
\begin{aligned}
\text{deci-} &= \text{one-tenth} \\
\text{centi-} &= \text{one-hundredth} \\
\text{mil- or milli-} &= \text{one-thousandth} \\
\text{micro} &= \text{one-millionth} \\
\text{hecto-} &= \text{one hundred} \\
\text{kil- or kilo-} &= \text{one thousand} \\
\text{meg- or mega-} &= \text{one million}
\end{aligned}
$$

As an example of the use of the factor-label system in computations involving conversion factors, assume that a velocity of 100 mi per hr is to be expressed in centimeters per second. Dimensionally one may convert from miles to feet, from feet to inches, and from inches to centimeters. Next one may convert from hours to minutes and from minutes to seconds. In order that the quantity being considered will not be changed in magnitude, each set of conversion factors introduced must be equal to unity. Thus the factors in the conversion being considered may be written as

1

$$\frac{100 \text{ mi}}{1 \text{ hr}} \times \frac{5,280 \text{ ft}}{1 \text{ mi}} \times \frac{12 \text{ in.}}{1 \text{ ft}} \times \frac{2.54 \text{ cm}}{1 \text{ in.}} \times \frac{1 \text{ hr}}{60 \text{ min}} \times \frac{1 \text{ min}}{60 \text{ sec}}$$
$$= 4,480 \text{ cm per sec}$$

1.2. The Nature of Electricity. The process of determining the composition of matter has been that of division and subdivision. A molecule is the smallest unit quantity of a material that can exist in an independent state and retain the chemical properties of the material. Some molecules can be divided into atoms, the smallest unit quantities of an element that can exist alone or in combination with similar units of any element. Molecules are sometimes atoms but usually they consist of a union of two or more atoms.

The American Standards Association defines electricity as "a physical agent pervading the atomic structure of matter and characterized by being separable, by the expenditure of energy, into two components designated as positive and negative electricity, in which state the electricity possesses recoverable energy." The concept of two kinds of electricity arose from the fact that one can produce small particles of one kind, any two of which exert a force of repulsion on each other, and also particles of a second kind, any two of which also exert a force of repulsion on each other. A particle of the first kind and one of the second kind exert a force of attraction on each other. Hence, the statement, "Like charges repel, unlike charges attract." The decision as to which kind of charge was to be called positive was an arbitrary one made by Benjamin Franklin. The kind of charge that predominates on a glass rod after it has been rubbed with silk is denoted as positive. The kind that predominates on a resin rod after it has been rubbed with wool is denoted as negative.

Certain particles of matter whose existence has been proved experimentally are electrons, neutrons, and protons. Electric charge exists only in integral multiples of that of an electron. A coulomb, the mks unit of charge, is defined by the equation that expresses Coulomb's law.

$$F = \frac{Q_1 Q_2}{4\pi \epsilon \epsilon_v d^2} \qquad \text{newtons} \qquad (1.1)$$

Here F is the force exerted on each of two spherical bodies, one charged with Q_1 and the other with Q_2 coul,* ϵ is a property of the region in which the bodies are located, ϵ_v is a property of free space, and d is the distance in meters from the center of one body to that of the other. Coulomb's law applies if the radii of the bodies are small compared with d. ϵ is the capacitivity, or dielectric constant, of the material compared with that of free space. ϵ_v is the capacitivity of free space and is 8.85×10^{-12} f per m.

* A nonstandard abbreviation for coulomb.

Hence for a vacuum $\epsilon = 1$.   For air at normal atmospheric pressure and 0 C, $\epsilon = 1.00059$, and it may be used as unity for most computations.

A newton is that force which, when applied to a body having a mass of 1 kg, gives it an acceleration of 1 m per sec per sec.   A newton is equal to 0.225 lb.

From (1.1) a coulomb is defined as that charge which, when possessed by each of two bodies separated 1 m in a vacuum, causes them to exert a force of $1/(4\pi \times 8.85 \times 10^{-12}) = 8.99 \times 10^9$ newtons.   Since this force is equivalent to about 1 million tons, in a practical case isolated charges are likely to be much smaller than a coulomb.

An electron has a negative charge of 1.60×10^{-19} coul magnitude. At rest or when moving with low velocities the mass of an electron is 9.1×10^{-31} kg.   The ratio of charge to mass is

$$\frac{1.60 \times 10^{-19}}{9.1 \times 10^{-31}} = 1.76 \times 10^{11} \text{ coul per kg}$$

The high ratio of charge to mass for an electron makes it possible to accelerate or decelerate one at a rapid rate.

The atom of a material has a center portion, the nucleus, that contains the particles possessing most of the mass of the atom.   The nucleus is surrounded by one or more planetary electrons moving in orbits at various distances from it.   The number of electrons is different for each element. Hydrogen has one electron per atom, helium two, and so on up to uranium, which has 92.

An atom is electrically neutral; the total positive charge of the nucleus equals the negative charge of the electrons.

A proton is a positively charged particle that is the nucleus of a hydrogen atom.   Its charge is equal to that of an electron; its size is slightly greater; its mass is 1,837 times as great.

A neutron is an uncharged particle in the nucleus of some elements. Its mass is about 0.14 per cent greater than that of a proton.

The simplest atom, that of hydrogen, contains one electron and one proton.   Atoms have energy levels that can be occupied by electrons. The lowest energy level, nearest the nucleus, may contain not more than two electrons.   The next higher energy level may contain not more than eight electrons.   Normally the electron in a hydrogen atom occupies the lowest energy level.   However, by adding energy to it the electron can be caused to shift to outer levels.   In a normal atom the electrons in the highest energy level determine the chemical properties of the atom and are called the valence electrons.

A metal is composed of crystals of various shapes and sizes.   The atoms are forced by interatomic action into a pattern called a space-lattice.   One of the valence electrons in each atom, called a free electron, moves from atom to atom in a metal body.   Normally the motion is such as to maintain the average charge of the body at zero.   The electrons are not free in the sense that they can leave the body without acquiring energy above that normally possessed.   If an electron attempts to leave a body that was electrically neutral, the body acquires the positive charge of a proton that is no longer neutralized.   Then the body exerts a force tending to pull the electron back into the atoms of the body.   It has been determined experimentally that there are about 10^{23} atoms in a cubic centimeter of metal.   This is also the number of free electrons.

An atom of one material differs from that of another in the structure of the nucleus and in the number and the arrangement of the electrons.   The number of excess positive charges in a nucleus of an atom of an element is the atomic number of the element and determines the position of the element in the periodic table.

When two charged spherical bodies are isolated in space, the force exerted by each upon the other acts along the line joining the body centers. When three or more charged spherical bodies are isolated in space, the total force acting on any one of the bodies is the vector sum of the individual forces exerted on it by the other bodies.

Example 1.   Three small bodies with equal positive charges are located at the respective vertices of a right triangle whose sides are 3, 4, and 5 cm.   Determine the relative magnitudes of the forces acting on the bodies and the direction of each force.

Solution.   Consider the bodies as located at the points A, B, and C in Fig. 1.1. Since all bodies have charges with the same polarity, each will exert a repelling force on the other.   Let F be the magnitude of the force vector* $\mathbf{F}_{A-B}$ exerted on the body at A by the charge on the body at B.   Then the magnitude of the force vector $\mathbf{F}_{A-C}$ exerted on the body at A by the charge on the body at C is $(\frac{5}{4})^2 F$, since the forces exerted by charged bodies on each other vary inversely as the square of the distance from one body to the other.   Now $\mathbf{F}_A$, the total force acting on the body at A is $\mathbf{F}_A = \mathbf{F}_{A-B} + \mathbf{F}_{A-C}$.   The horizontal component of $\mathbf{F}_A$ is $F + (\frac{5}{4})^2 F \cos 36.9° = 2.25F$.   The vertical component of $\mathbf{F}_A$ is $(\frac{5}{4})^2 F \sin 36.9° = 0.938F$.   Then $F_A = \sqrt{(2.25F)^2 + (0.938F)^2} = 2.44F$. $\mathbf{F}_A$ is directed above the horizontal by the angle $\alpha = \tan^{-1}(0.938F/2.25F) = \tan^{-1} 0.417 = 22.6°$.

The magnitude of the force vector $\mathbf{F}_{B-A}$ exerted on the body at B by the charge on the body at A is equal to that of $\mathbf{F}_{A-B}$, or F as shown.   The magnitude of the force vector $\mathbf{F}_{B-C}$ exerted on the body at B by the charge on the body at C is $(\frac{5}{3})^2 F$.   Then $\mathbf{F}_B = \mathbf{F}_{B-A} + \mathbf{F}_{B-C}$.   The horizontal component of $\mathbf{F}_B$ is $F + (\frac{5}{3})^2 F \cos 53.1° = 2.67F$.   The vertical component of $\mathbf{F}_B$ is $(\frac{5}{3})^2 F \sin 53.1° = 2.22F$.   Then $F_B = \sqrt{(2.67F)^2 + (2.22F)^2} = 3.47F$. $\mathbf{F}_B$ is directed above the horizontal by the angle $\beta = \tan^{-1}(2.22F/2.67F) = \tan^{-1} 0.832 = 39.8°$.

* Force is a vector quantity having both magnitude and direction.   A vector quantity is represented by a boldface symbol such as $\mathbf{F}_{A-B}$.   The magnitude of a vector quantity is represented by either the symbol $|\mathbf{F}_{A-B}|$ or F_{A-B}.

The magnitude of the force vector $\mathbf{F}_{C-A}$ exerted on the body at C by the charge on the body at A is equal to that of $\mathbf{F}_{A-C}$, or $(\tfrac{5}{4})^2F$ as shown. The magnitude of the force vector $\mathbf{F}_{C-B}$ exerted on the body at C by the charge on the body at B is equal to that of $\mathbf{F}_{B-C}$, or $(\tfrac{5}{3})^2F$ as shown. Then $\mathbf{F}_C = \mathbf{F}_{C-A} + \mathbf{F}_{C-B}$. Since $\mathbf{F}_{C-A}$ and $\mathbf{F}_{C-B}$ are normal to each other, then

$$F_C = \sqrt{[(\tfrac{5}{4})^2F]^2 + [(\tfrac{5}{3})^2F]^2} = 3.18F$$

$\mathbf{F}_C$ is directed below $\mathbf{F}_{C-A}$ by the angle

$$\gamma = \tan^{-1}[(\tfrac{5}{3})^2F/(\tfrac{5}{4})^2F] = \tan^{-1} 1.78 = 60.7°$$

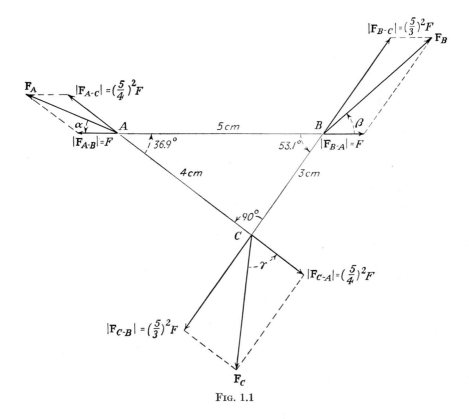

FIG. 1.1

1.3. Electric Current.
An electric current results from the motion of charged particles. In a solution such as copper sulfate, atoms are dissociated when electrons are freed from bonds that formerly held them in the atoms. Then the solution contains free electrons and positively charged ions, where an ion is the portion of an atom that remains after an electron is removed. In the solution the electrons can be made to move, thereby creating an electron current in the direction of the motion.

At the same time the ions move in the opposite direction and create a current of positive charges. In electronic tubes there are cases in which motion of both electrons and positively charged particles occur. In metals only the free electrons move, since the positively charged portions of the atoms are bound in position and cannot move in response to forces that urge them to move in a direction opposite to that in which the free electrons move. The direction of what is called conventional current is that in which positively charged particles either move or are urged to move. In a metal the actual current is that resulting from the motion of the free electrons and is opposite to the conventional current direction.

Since the charge of an electron is 1.60×10^{-19} coul, then

$$\frac{1}{1.60 \times 10^{-19}} = 6.25 \times 10^{18}$$

electrons have a combined charge of 1 coul. When charges are moving through a given conductor at the rate of 1 coul per sec, by definition the resulting current is 1 ampere (amp). Other common units of current are the microampere ($1 \ \mu a = 10^{-6}$ amp) and the milliampere

$$(1 \ ma = 10^{-3} \ amp)$$

In this book most electrical quantities that do not vary with time are represented by capital letters and those that do vary with time by lower-case letters.

In mathematical terms, current i is expressed by

$$i = \frac{dq}{dt} \qquad amp \qquad (1.2)$$

where i is instantaneous current and dq/dt is interpreted as the rate of flow of charges in coulombs per second. In other terms dq coul is the infinitesimal quantity of electricity, passing through the cross section of a given conductor during the infinitesimal time interval dt sec. If a quantity is to be divided into infinitesimal portions, there should be no limit as to how many times the quantity can be divided or subdivided. Since an electron has the smallest known unit of electric charge, then an electric current does not meet exactly the conditions required in (1.2). However, in most electric conductors the number of electrons is so great that (1.2) yields results that agree with experimental data.

If charges are moving through the cross section of a conductor at a constant rate, the current is constant and may be expressed as $I = Q/T$ amp, where Q is the charge in coulombs moving during a time interval of T sec.

1.4. Electric Potential and Electromotive Force. Assume that an electron is held stationary at an isolated point in air and that a second electron is moved toward it. Since the electrons exert repelling forces on each other, and the movement of a force through a distance represents energy, or work, then work is done on the second electron and it acquires potential energy, or energy due to position. The potential energy possessed by the second electron when it is at one point less that possessed when it is at another point is a measure of the difference of electric potential of the points or the voltage between the points. The mks unit of electric potential is the volt and is defined by the equation $V = W/Q$, where W is the work in newton-m done in moving Q coul of charge between two points whose difference in potential is V v.

The property of a physical device that causes charged particles to move or to tend to move is an electromotive force (emf). A source of emf does not produce electrons; it supplies the energy that causes the motion of electrons already present. From some sources only a limited amount of energy is available and the emf decreases as energy is delivered. From other sources the emf can be kept constant by the continuous conversion of energy from another form to the electrical form. When a source of emf is introduced into a closed metallic loop, the charges in the metal are subjected to forces. The positive charges are bound in position but some of the electrons progress along the loop. An electric circuit is a system of conductors through which electric charges can move.

1.5. Computations of Rates of Change. Some quantities are defined in terms of the rate of change of another quantity with respect to a third quantity. For instance, velocity is the rate of change of distance with respect to time. Acceleration is the rate of change of velocity with respect to time. Hence acceleration is the time rate of change of another time rate of change. An electric current is defined as the time rate of flow of electric charges through the cross section of a conductor. A given current might be expressed in mathematical form as an equation, as data recorded from the readings of an indicating instrument, or in graphical form as the record from a curve-drawing instrument.

The instantaneous value of a current is defined by (1.2). It is a measure of the time rate of movement of charges at the instant of time being considered. The rate of movement may vary with time; the instantaneous value will vary accordingly. If (1.2) is to be used directly to determine the equation of the current in a circuit, the equation must be known that relates to time the motion of electric charges through a given cross section of the circuit.

Example 1. The time variation of the charge q passing through a certain conductor is given by the equation $q = 50t^2$ coul, where t is in seconds. Plot the curve showing the time variations of q. Determine the equation of the instantaneous current i, and plot the curve. Compute the value of the current at $t = 2$ sec and that at $t = 3$ sec.

Solution. Substitution of the values $t = 1$, $t = 2$, $t = 3$, $t = 4$, and $t = 5$ sec in the given equation yields the respective values $q = 50$, $q = 200$, $q = 450$, $q = 800$, and $q = 1,250$ coul. From these values the curve q in Fig. 1.2 was plotted. As could have been predicted from the equation, the curve is a parabola.

The current equation is obtained from (1.2). Since $i = dq/dt$ and it is given that $q = 50t^2$, then $i = d(50t^2)/dt = 100t$ amp. Substitution of the values $t = 1$, $t = 2$, $t = 3$, $t = 4$, and $t = 5$ sec yields the respective values $i = 100$, $i = 200$, $i = 300$, $i = 400$, and $i = 500$ amp. From these values the curve i in Fig. 1.2 was plotted. It is a straight line.

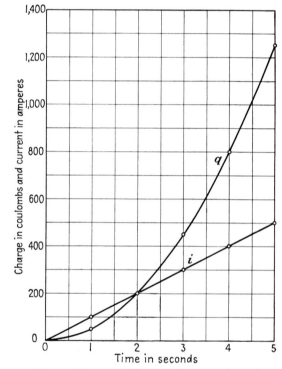

FIG. 1.2 Time variations of charge q and current i in a certain conductor. An ordinate of the current curve is equal to the slope of the charge curve at the same instant.

When the relation between two quantities is shown by a graph whose equation is unknown, the rate of change of one quantity with respect to the other can be computed from a graphical construction.

Example 2. In Fig. 1.3 is the time variation of the charge through the cross section of a certain conductor. Determine the current through the cross section at $t = 2$ milliseconds (msec) and that at $t = 4$ msec.

Solution. Graphically the rate of change of the charge at a given instant with respect to time is equal to the slope of the curve at that instant. The line *ab* was drawn tangent to the curve at $t = 2$ msec. Its slope is ac/bc. ac was scaled as 4.2 coul and bc as 2 msec, or 0.002 sec. Then

$$\frac{ac}{bc} = \frac{4.2 \text{ coul}}{0.002 \text{ sec}} = 2,100 \text{ coul per sec}$$

which, by definition, is 2,100 amp.

The line de was drawn tangent to the curve at $t = 4$ msec. Its slope is $df/ef = 4.7$ coul/0.004 sec $= 1,175$ coul per sec, which, by definition, is 1,175 amp.

In Example 2, if it were desired to plot a curve showing the time variation of the current, other current values could be obtained by the method

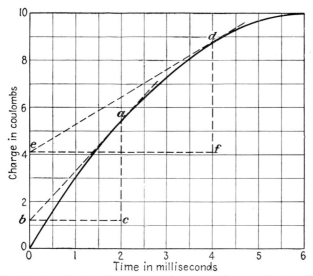

Fig. 1.3   Graphical method for determining the current in a conductor when the time variations of the charge through the conductor are given.   At any instant the current is equal to the slope of the tangent to the charge curve at that instant.

outlined and the curve drawn through the plotted points.   The accuracy of the current values depends upon the scale to which the curve is drawn and the accuracy with which the measurements are made.

1.6. Kinds of Current.   The kind of current is defined in terms of the graph that represents the time variations of the current.

A unidirectional current is one that is always in the same direction.   It may vary in magnitude.   Time variations of three examples of unidirectional currents are shown in Figs. 1.4 and 1.5.   Such a graphical representation is a current wave or a current wave form.   The curves are oscillograms and were obtained with an instrument known as an oscillograph.

A direct current is a unidirectional current that varies little or none in magnitude during a time interval being considered. Current curve *b* of Fig. 1.4 is a direct current (also called a continuous current). Current

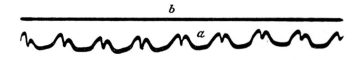

FIG. 1.4   Examples of unidirectional currents: (*a*) Current delivered to a 500-ohm resistor by a small d-c generator; (*b*) current delivered to a 500-ohm resistor by a 60-cell lead-acid storage battery.

curve *a* of Fig. 1.4 would be considered as a direct current for some applications but not for all.

A bidirectional current flows first in one direction and then in the other. When such a current is represented graphically, positive values represent current in one direction and negative values represent current in the opposite direction. Three bidirectional currents are represented in Fig. 1.6.

An oscillating current alternately increases and decreases in magnitude with respect to time according to a definite law (see Fig. 1.7).

A periodic current alternately increases and decreases in magnitude with respect to time in such a manner that any given value recurs at equal time intervals. The interval is the period of the current. Periodic currents are shown in Figs. 1.5 and 1.6.

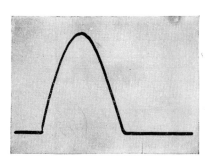

FIG. 1.5   Unidirectional current delivered to a battery by a half-wave tube rectifier.

An alternating current is a periodic current that has an average value of zero over a period. In graphical terms, over the period the current-time curve has an area above the time axis equal to that below the axis.

The definitions of the kinds of emf are similar to those of the kinds of currents. However, a given kind of emf does not always produce the same kind of current.

For direct current in a metal conductor, it is convenient to picture the free electrons as distributed uniformly throughout the volume and moving at a uniform velocity. Let the area of cross section of the conductor of Fig. 1.8 be A sq m and the electron velocity be v m per sec to the right.

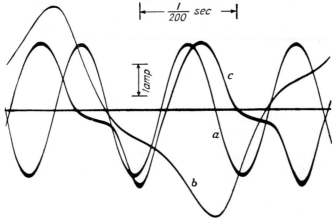

FIG. 1.6   Examples of bidirectional currents: (a) A "sine wave" current delivered to a resistor by an a-c generator; (b) a "nonsinusoidal" current delivered to an unloaded transformer by an a-c generator; (c) input current to a transformer that delivers current to a half-wave tube rectifier.

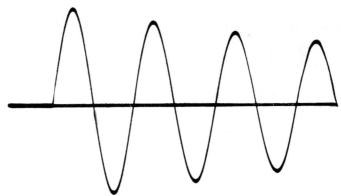

FIG. 1.7   Oscillating current produced in a series circuit of resistance, inductance, and capacitance when a d-c voltage is suddenly impressed.

The electrons passing through the cross section in 1 sec would be those that at the start of the time interval are contained within the volume lA cu m, where l, in meters, is equal numerically to v. If n_f is the number of free electrons per cubic meter, the current is $i = n_f lA$. Since $l = v$ numerically, $i = n_f vA$ electrons per second.

In a metal conductor the electron velocity is usually rather low. A No. 14 copper wire, such as is used in residence lighting circuits, has a cross section of 2.1×10^{-6} sq m and can carry 15 amp of direct current without excessive temperature rise. There are about $n_f = 10^{29}$ free

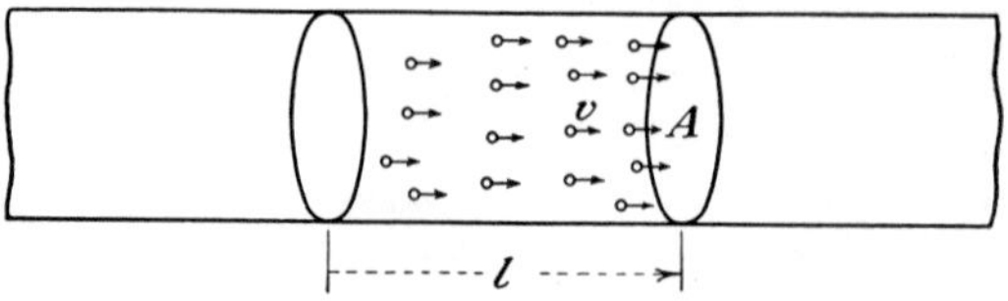

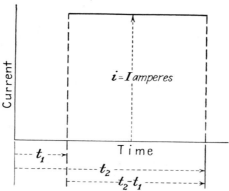

Fig. 1.8   Electrons moving at a uniform velocity v in a conductor.

electrons per cu m in copper and 15 amp is 15 coul per sec. Since 1 coul $= 6.25 \times 10^{18}$ electron charges, in this wire there is a current of $15 \times 6.25 \times 10^{18} = 9.38 \times 10^{19}$ electrons per sec. Then

$$v = \frac{i}{n_f A} = \frac{9.38 \times 10^{19}}{10^{29} \times 2.1 \times 10^{-6}} = 4.5 \times 10^{-4} \text{ m per sec}$$

This corresponds to a movement of 1 ft in about 11 min.

Although the electron velocity in a circuit may be low, this does not mean that an appreciable time must elapse after a switch is closed before electric energy can be delivered at a point some distance from the emf source. On the contrary, when the switch is closed an impulse travels along the circuit with a velocity that may be only slightly less than the velocity of light. As a result in most circuits the motion of all electrons starts almost simultaneously.

Fig. 1.9   Graphical representation of a current that is constant during the time interval $t_2 - t_1$.

1.7. Computation of Areas and Average Values.   Consider Fig. 1.9 which represents a current that was constant at I amp during a time interval $t_2 - t_1$ sec. The area between the curve and the time axis during the interval is $I(t_2 - t_1)$ amp-sec. But an ampere-second is a coulomb; thus the area is equal to the number of coulombs passing, during the interval, through the cross section of a conductor carrying the current. When a constant current I amp exists in a conductor for a time interval T sec, the charge Q passing through a cross section of the conductor is $Q = IT$ coul.

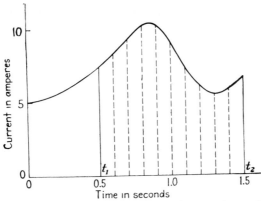

FIG. 1.10   Current in a certain circuit during a time interval $t_2 - t_1$.

The current of Fig. 1.10 varied during a time interval from $t_1 = 0.5$ to $t_2 = 1.5$ sec. To compute the charge in coulombs passing, during the interval, through a cross section of a conductor carrying the current, the area between the curve and the time axis within the limits t_1 and t_2 must be determined. The area can be measured approximately with an instrument called a planimeter. Another method is to divide the figure into a number of approximate trapezoids with equal altitudes, approximate the area of each, and then add the individual areas. In Fig. 1.10 the time interval was divided into 10 equal parts of 0.1 sec each and 11 ordinates erected as shown. Let the first ordinate be i_0, the second i_1, the third i_2, etc. Now the original figure has been divided into 10 figures, each of which is nearly a trapezoid. Since the area of a trapezoid is equal to the product of the altitude and one-half the sum of the bases, the area of the first is approximately $0.1 \times (i_0 + i_1)/2$, the area of the second is $0.1 \times (i_1 + i_2)/2$, etc. The total area is approximately

$$0.1 \times \left(\frac{i_0 + i_1}{2} + \frac{i_1 + i_2}{2} + \frac{i_2 + i_3}{2} + \cdots + \frac{i_8 + i_9}{2} + \frac{i_9 + i_{10}}{2} \right)$$

$$= 0.1 \times \left(\frac{i_0}{2} + i_1 + i_2 + i_3 + \cdots + i_9 + \frac{i_{10}}{2} \right)$$

This relation leads to the following rules for approximating the area of a figure.   (1) Divide the base into a number of equal increments.   (2) Measure the boundary ordinates and those at each of the division points. (3) Add one-half the initial boundary ordinate, each of the ordinates at the division points, and one-half the final boundary ordinate.   Multiply this sum by the increment of the base, and the result is the approximate area of the figure.

In Fig. 1.10 the respective ordinates were scaled as 7.5, 8.3, 9.2, 10.2, 10.1, 9.0, 7.3, 6.0, 5.5, 5.8, and 6.7 amp.   The sum of one-half the first ordinate, the next nine ordinates, and one-half the eleventh ordinate is 78.5 amp.   The area of the figure is approximately

$$78.5 \text{ amp} \times 0.1 \text{ sec} = 7.85 \text{ amp-sec} = 7.85 \text{ coul}$$

The accuracy of the value of an area computed by the above method depends upon the number of ordinates used and the irregularity of the curve.   Enough ordinates should be used that the sections of the curve between successive ordinates are nearly straight lines.

When the equation of a current i is given in terms of the time t, the area A between the curve representing the current and the time axis over a time interval from t_1 to t_2 can be computed by the principles of calculus. The result is $A = \int_{t_1}^{t_2} i \, dt$.   With i in amperes and t in seconds the area is in ampere-seconds or coulombs.   Then the charge Q moving through a cross section of a conductor that carries the current for a time interval $t_2 - t_1$ sec is

$$Q = \int_{t_1}^{t_2} i \, dt \tag{1.3}$$

This result might have been obtained directly from (1.2).   Since

$$i = \frac{dq}{dt}$$

then $dq = i \, dt$.   From   this $\int_0^Q dq = \int_{t_1}^{t_2} i \, dt$.   Here   the   charge   is assumed to be zero at time t_1 and Q coul at time t_2.   Integration of the term on the left-hand side of the equality and substitution of the limits yields $Q = \int_{t_1}^{t_2} i \, dt$.

If a current is constant during a given time interval, the average value of the current during the interval is equal to the instantaneous value. When a current in a circuit varies during a specified time interval, the average current during that interval is the value of the current that, if constant during an equal interval, would move as many coulombs through the circuit as are moved by the varying current.   In equational form the average current is $I_a = Q/T$ amp, where Q coul are moved in T sec.   In Fig. 1.11 is a graphical representation of the average value of a current i

whose time variations are shown. A constant current is represented by the horizontal line whose ordinate is I_a. The area under the curve i is equal to the area under the line over a complete cycle of i.

Since the area under a current-time curve is a measure of the number of coulombs moved in a circuit, when a current-time curve is given whose equation is not known the average current can be computed by a method similar to that used in computing the number of coulombs moved. Consider the current-time curve of Fig. 1.10. In computing the area under

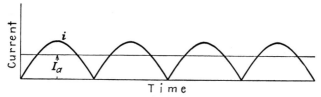

FIG. 1.11   Graphical representation of the average value of a current.   The number of coulombs moved in a circuit during a cycle of the varying current i is equal to the number that would be moved by the constant current I_a during an equal period.

this curve, the time interval $t_2 - t_1$ was divided into 10 equal increments and the ordinates i_0 through i_{10} were scaled. The approximate area was shown to be $0.1 \times (i_0/2 + i_1 + i_2 + \cdots + i_9 + i_{10}/2)$. The average current I_a during the interval is equal to the area divided by the base of $t_2 - t_1 = 1$ sec. Then

$$I_a = \frac{i_0/2 + i_1 + i_2 + \cdots + i_9 + i_{10}/2}{10} = \frac{78.5}{10} = 7.85 \text{ amp}$$

The average value of a current can be computed as follows: (1) Divide the time interval into a convenient number of equal increments, say n. (2) Scale or compute the initial and the final ordinates, and the ordinates at the division points. (3) Add one-half the first ordinate, the ordinates at the division points, and one-half the final ordinate. This sum divided by n is the approximate value of the average current.

When computing the average value of a current that varies cyclically with the time, in general the time interval chosen should be the period of a complete cycle. In some cases the symmetry of the current wave is such that a shorter time interval will yield the same value.

If the positive portion of a bidirectional wave is identical in shape to the negative portion, the net area over a period of one cycle is zero and the average current is zero. The half-period average value of an a-c wave is sometimes computed, using either the positive or the negative portion of the wave.

1.8. Resistance. As electric charges move under the influence of an emf, they may collide with each other and with other portions of atoms.

The collisions impede the progress of the charges and produce heat.   The property of a circuit that causes such an energy conversion is called resistance and represented by the symbol R when constant.   Since the distribution of the drifting free electrons in a metal conductor is not the same for all kinds of currents, the resistance of such a conductor depends upon the kind of current in it.   When the current is direct, the resistance of a conductor may be defined from the relation of the value of the emf acting to that of the current produced.   The resistance depends upon the dimensions of the conductor, the material of which it is composed, and the temperature at which it is operating.

The ohm is one unit of resistance.   The filament of a 115-v 100-w tungsten-filament lamp has about 130 ohms resistance when at its normal operating temperature.

PROBLEMS

1.1. Express 287,000 v in kilovolts, in millivolts, and in microvolts.

1.2. Express 50 ma in amperes and in microamperes.

1.3. In Fig. 1.1 assume that the charges are equal in magnitude but that the charge on the body at B is opposite in sign to that on the others.   Compute the relative magnitude and the direction of the force on each body.

1.4. In Fig. 1.1 assume that the charges have the same sign but that the charge on the body at C is twice that on the others.   Compute the relative magnitude and the direction of the force on each body.

1.5. Two electrons are held 0.01 m apart in air.   How much force does each exert on the other?   What acceleration does each have if the restraining forces are suddenly removed?

1.6. An electron and a proton are held 0.005 m apart in air.   How much force does each exert on the other?   What acceleration does each have if the restraining forces are suddenly removed?

1.7. The quantity of electricity passing through a certain conductor varies according to the equation $q = 40t$ coul, where t is in seconds.   What is the equation of the current in the conductor?   Sketch the curves showing the time variation of the charge and that of the current.

1.8. In a region in a certain circuit, electrons accumulate.   The quantity increases linearly from 10 μcoul at $t = 0$ to 40 μcoul at $t = 5$ msec.   Sketch the curve showing the time variation of the electron current toward the region.

1.9. In Fig. 1.4a scale the values with a ruler and determine what percentage change in the current, in terms of the maximum current, occurs during a cycle.

1.10. Determine the period and the frequency of each current in Fig. 1.6.

1.11. If copper contains 10^{29} free electrons per cu m, how many coulombs of free electrons are there in a United States penny that has a diameter of 0.76 in. and a thickness of 0.05 in.?

1.12. Most of the time electrons are moving from the earth to the surrounding clouds.   Consider the earth as a sphere 8,000 mi in diameter.   If the rate of outward flow of the electrons is 5 μa from each square mile and is uniform over the entire surface, compute the current from the earth.   How much time would be required to remove 500,000 coul from the earth?

1.13. If electrons are leaving the earth at a uniform velocity and the current from each square mile is 5 μa, how many electrons leave each square foot per second?

1.14. The electrons that move slowly from the earth to the clouds are returned quickly by lightning strokes. Measurements show that the average stroke returns 30 coul. If the average rate of outward flow is 5 μa per sq mi, how many times per year must the earth be struck to return all the electrons? How many times per second?

1.15. A certain copper wire has a diameter of 0.02 in. With a direct current of 5 ma in the wire what is the velocity of the electrons?

When the frequency of the current is 10^8 c, assume that the only free electrons that move are those within 0.002 in. of the surface and that all these move with the same velocity. At an instant when the current at this frequency is 5 ma, what is the velocity of the electrons that are moving?

1.16. In a certain conductor the current is 12 amp from $t = 0$ to $t = 3$ sec, 4 amp from $t = 3$ to $t = 5$ sec, and 20 amp from $t = 5$ to $t = 10$ sec. How many coulombs move through the conductor during the 10-sec interval? Compute the average current during the interval.

1.17. In Fig. 1.6c is a current-time curve for a certain circuit. Determine the maximum positive and the maximum negative values of the current.

1.18. In a certain conductor the current varied during a 10-msec interval according to the equation $i = 40 + 3t^2$ amp, where t is in milliseconds. Sketch the current-time curve. Compute the average current during the interval.

1.19. Express 0.08 megohms in ohms.

1.20. Express 32 μohms in ohms.

1.21. For a certain electron tube it is specified that a peak (maximum) current of 15 amp and an average current of 2.5 amp should not be exceeded. From an oscillogram it was found that a 50-c current through the tube was zero during 60 per cent of a cycle and nearly constant at 12 amp during the remainder of the cycle. Was the tube being operated within its ratings?

1.22. The tube of Prob. 1.21 is operated so that the current is constant at 15 amp during the conducting part of a cycle. For what portion of a cycle may the tube conduct if the average current rating is not to be exceeded?

1.23. The emf generated in a coil on a certain d-c generator is 4 v from $t = 0$ to $t = 0.007$ sec, zero from $t = 0.007$ to $t = 0.01$ sec, 4 v from $t = 0.01$ to $t = 0.017$ sec, zero from $t = 0.017$ to $t = 0.02$ sec, etc. The directions of the emf during successive half cycles are opposite in the coil, but by means of a commutator the directions in an external circuit are made to be the same. Consider the relations in the external circuit. Sketch the curve showing the emf-time relations. Compute the average emf.

1.24. Express 1 electron per sec in amperes.

1.25. The following current-time values for a natural lightning discharge were obtained from an oscillogram.

Time, μsec	Current, amp	Time, μsec	Current, amp	Time, μsec	Current, amp
0	21,000	500	680	5,000	120
100	1,700	1,000	570	7,000	100
200	970	1,500	350	15,000	50
300	900	2,000	200	20,000	0
400	780	3,000	125		

Plot the current-time curve. Compute the quantity of electricity represented by the discharge.

CHAPTER 2

APPLICATIONS OF OHM'S LAW AND KIRCHHOFF'S LAWS

2.1. Ohm's Law. Figure 2.1 represents a circuit consisting of a copper wire connected between the terminals of a dry cell. Positive charges in the wire are urged in a counterclockwise direction, as indicated by the arrow representing the instantaneous current i. Electrons in the wire move clockwise. Consider the portion of the wire between the surface of cross section at a and that at b. If the surface areas are equal, an electron arrives at a with a velocity and a kinetic energy equal to those possessed when it left b. However, because of the resistance of the wire between the surfaces, energy is required from the cell to move an electron from one surface to the other. This energy is converted into heat in the wire. The amount of energy per unit of charge moving between the surfaces is the difference of potential or the voltage between the surfaces. Polarity markings ($+$ and $-$) are assigned in pairs to points or surfaces in an electric circuit. In Fig. 2.1 the center cell terminal is positive and at a higher potential than the outer terminal because the cell can deliver the energy required to move electrons clockwise in the circuit. If a conducting element in which positive charges were free to move were connected between the terminals, the cell would cause the charges to proceed from the center terminal through the element to the outer terminal.

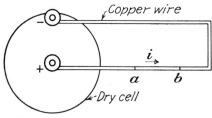

FIG. 2.1 A simple electric circuit.

The polarities of the terminals of a metallic conductor that is carrying a continuous current are fixed by the direction of the current. With the direction of a current taken as that in which positive charges move or are urged to move, the terminal at which the current enters is positive and the one at which it leaves is negative.

In Fig. 2.2 is represented a metallic conductor of resistance R ohms

18

that has a continuous current of I amp entering terminal a and leaving terminal b.   The remainder of the circuit of which the conductor is a part is not represented.   The difference of potential between a and b is related to the current and the resistance by Ohm's law which is now stated as: *The difference of potential in volts required to send a current through the resistance between two surfaces in a conductor is equal to the product of the current in amperes and the resistance in ohms.*   The cause-and-effect relationship between what are now called voltage and current was perceived by Georg Simon Ohm, a German scientist, in 1826 and published in 1827 in a paper, "The Galvanic Chain, Mathematically Treated."* In Ohm's words: "The amount of current in a galvanic chain is directly proportional to the sum of all the tensions and inversely proportional to the total reduced length of the chain."

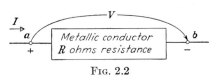

Fig. 2.2

The potential from one point to another is considered as positive when the second point is at the higher potential.   Hence, in Fig. 2.2 the potential from b to a is positive and the potential from a to b is negative.

In Fig. 2.2 the symbol V represents the voltage drop in volts from a to b and is taken as positive since a drop in potential occurs from a to b. Note that the sign of the voltage drop from one point to a second one is opposite to that of the potential from the first to the second.   Application of Ohm's law to Fig. 2.2 yields

$$V = IR \qquad (2.1)$$

In most metallic conductors the voltage drop between two surfaces is directly proportional to the current in the conductor for constant temperature operation.   For these the resistance R in (2.1) is constant.   In conducting gases, in liquids, and in insulating materials the voltage drop is not always proportional to the current.   When it is not, the resistance R in (2.1) is a function of the current and not a constant.

The difference between an emf and a voltage drop is purely a matter of convention.   In Fig. 2.2 an emf E v taken positive from b to a is equivalent mathematically to the voltage drop V taken positive from a to b.

When a varying current of i amp is sent through a conductor of R ohms resistance, the voltage drop v v between conductor terminals, taken positive in the direction of current flow, is given by $v = iR$.   If R is a constant, v is proportional to i.   If R varies as i varies, v is not proportional to i.

---

* See *Weston Engineering Notes*, vol. 7, no. 2, July, 1952.   Published by Weston Electrical Instrument Corporation.

2.2. Kirchhoff's Laws. The term element is applied to each of the physical two-terminal units that comprise an electric circuit. Thus a dry cell, a lamp, a fuse, etc., are elements. Ordinarily a piece of wire used to make a connection is not considered as an element. If one terminal each of two or more elements are connected to a common point, it is a junction point or a junction. A branch of an electric circuit is the series combination of elements that extends from one junction to another.

Kirchhoff's law relative to currents is: *At a junction of branches in an electric circuit the sum of the branch currents directed toward the junction is equal to the sum of the branch currents directed away from the junction.*

Kirchhoff's law relative to voltages is: *Along any continuous path in an electric circuit the algebraic sum of the emfs is equal to the algebraic sum of the voltage drops occurring across the resistances of the elements in the path.* A corollary to this law is: *The potential between any two points in an electric circuit is the same regardless of the path followed in determining the potential.*

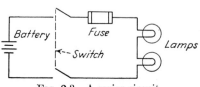

FIG. 2.3   A series circuit.

Ohm's and Kirchhoff's laws may be applied to any circuit regardless of the kind of emf, the kind of current, or the nature of the resistance. When applied in the general form, the instantaneous values of the emfs should be used. The d-c circuit is a special form of electric circuit. Certain relations that exist in it are not true for circuits in general. When a d-c circuit is first energized from a source of constant emf, or when a sudden change is made in the circuit connections, other emfs that exist for a short time (transient emfs) may be produced by certain properties of the circuit. After the transient emfs have died out, usually in a fraction of a second, the currents become constant. The circuit is then in a steady state.

2.3. Series Circuits. Elements that are electrical conductors are in series when they are connected end to end to form a closed circuit. Figure 2.3 is a diagram representing a battery, a fuse, two blades of a switch, and two lamps in series. The amount of detail to be shown in a circuit diagram depends upon the intended use of the diagram. Figure 2.3 would be useful when making connections of the elements in a laboratory. If a diagram is to be used only for making a theoretical analysis of a given circuit, one would probably not take the time to draw the diagram in as much detail as in Fig. 2.3. The switch and the fuse are required in the laboratory circuit for safety and normally are not considered in analyzing the circuit.

When elements are in series, the same current exists in each. In Fig. 2.4, three elements of constant resistance R_1, R_2, and R_3 ohms, respectively, are represented in series across a battery of constant emf E v.   To write the voltage equation of this circuit from Kirchhoff's law of voltages, two trips are made around the circuit.   On the first trip only the emfs are considered in determining their algebraic sum.   If the direction of travel through a source of emf is from the negative to the positive terminal, a positive sign is assigned to the emf.   If the direction of travel through the source is from the positive to the negative terminal, a negative sign is assigned to the emf.   In Fig. 2.4 there is only one source of emf; hence current will leave the positive battery terminal and flow clockwise about the path.   An arrow on the diagram represents the direction of the current.   The symbol I assigned to the arrow represents the magnitude in amperes of the current.   On the second trip around the circuit only the resistance drops are considered in determining their algebraic sum. When the travel is in the direction of the current through an element having resistance, a positive sign is assigned to the resistance drop.

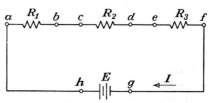

FIG. 2.4   Resistance elements in series across a battery.

When the travel is in the direction opposite to the current, a negative sign is assigned to the resistance drop.

The voltage equation for the circuit of Fig. 2.4 can be written by application of the above principles.   Let the direction of travel about the circuit be clockwise.   On the first trip only the emf of the battery is encountered, and since travel through the battery is from the negative to the positive terminal, the algebraic summation of the emfs is $+E$ v.   It is assumed that all resistance in the circuit is represented by R_1, R_2, and R_3.   On the second trip a resistance drop is encountered in each of the three elements.   Since the travel through each element is in the direction of the current, the sign of each resistance drop is positive.   The algebraic summation of the resistance drops is $+IR_1 + IR_2 + IR_3$.   Equating the algebraic sum of the emfs to the algebraic sum of the resistance drops yields

$$E = IR_1 + IR_2 + IR_3 = I(R_1 + R_2 + R_3) \qquad \text{v} \qquad (2.2)$$

The term $R_1 + R_2 + R_3$ is the equivalent resistance of the series combination of elements.   *When resistance elements are in series, the sum of their resistances is the equivalent resistance.*

By the application of Ohm's law to the individual elements in Fig. 2.4,

$$V_{ab} = IR_1 \qquad \text{v} \qquad (2.3)$$
$$V_{cd} = IR_2 \qquad \text{v} \qquad (2.4)$$

and $V_{ef} = IR_3$ v, where V_{ab}, V_{cd}, and V_{ef} are the respective voltage drops from the points a to b, c to d, and e to f. The voltage from one terminal of an element to the other is called the voltage across the element.

Dividing (2.3) by (2.2) yields $V_{ab}/E = R_1/(R_1 + R_2 + R_3)$. This result shows that *the voltage across one of the resistors in a series combination of resistors is to the voltage across the combination as the resistance of the resistor is to the equivalent resistance of the combination.*

In analyzing the circuit of Fig. 2.4 it was assumed that R_1, R_2, and R_3 were the only resistances present. The resistances of the battery and the connecting wires were assumed to be zero. Any electric conductor has some resistance; thus the current in the circuit is less than computed from (2.2) with E, R_1, R_2, and R_3 given. Reasonable approximations that may be made in the analysis of circuits are based on experience and judgment. An approximation that yields satisfactory results in one circuit may yield grossly incorrect values in another. For example, in Fig. 2.4 assume that the exact values are $E_1 = 120$ v, $R_1 = 200$ ohms, $R_2 = 300$ ohms, and $R_3 = 500$ ohms. Neglecting the resistance of the battery and the connecting leads, the current is

$$\frac{120 \text{ v}}{200 + 300 + 500 \text{ ohms}} = 0.12 \text{ amp}$$

In a circuit such as this, the resistance of the battery and the leads might be of the order of 0.1 ohm or less. Assuming it to be 0.1 ohm, the total resistance of the circuit is 1,000.1 ohm and the current is slightly less than 0.12 amp. The emf and resistance values often are not known to a sufficient number of significant places to justify the consideration of the resistance of the source and the leads.

In Fig. 2.1, assume that the dry cell has an emf of 1.5 v. If the resistance of the cell and the wire is taken as zero, the current is 1.5 v divided by 0 ohms or an infinite value. This result is absurd because it is the resistance of the cell and the wire, however small it may be, that must be divided into the emf to obtain the current.

2.4. Difference of Potential and Polarity Markings. The absolute potential of a point is a measure of the work per unit charge that must be done in moving positive charges to that point from a point of zero potential. Any point, often it is the earth, may be chosen arbitrarily as one of zero potential. In electric-circuit computations one is usually interested in the difference of potential between two points rather than in their absolute potentials. In d-c circuits, polarity markings may be assigned to the terminals of the various elements. The positive terminal is considered as at a higher potential than the negative terminal. The polarities of the terminals of a resistor are fixed by the direction of the current, current enters at the positive terminal and leaves at the negative terminal. The circuit of Fig. 2.4 is redrawn in Fig. 2.5 with the polarities of the various terminals indicated. The marks are associated in pairs. That is, a is positive with respect to b, c is positive with respect to d, etc. Just because e is $+$ and b is $-$, it does not follow that e is positive with respect to b. As a matter of fact, b is positive with respect to e.

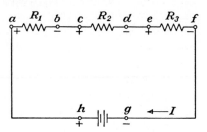

Example 1. In the circuit of Fig. 2.6 determine the potential between points a and d and that between e and b. In each case specify which of the two points is at the higher potential.

FIG. 2.5   Circuit of Fig. 2.4 with polarities of various terminals indicated.

Solution. The current I is computed by applying Kirchhoff's law of voltages. Starting from k and traversing the circuit in a clockwise direction, the summation of the emfs is $+100 - 60 + 40 = +80$ v. The summation of the resistance drops is $+5I + 3I + 2I = +10I$ v. Hence $80 = 10I$, from which $I = 8$ amp.

The circuit of Fig. 2.6 is redrawn in Fig. 2.7 with the current value and the polarities of the resistor terminals indicated. In going from a to d by the path

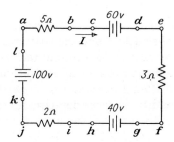

FIG. 2.6   A series circuit containing several emfs and resistances.

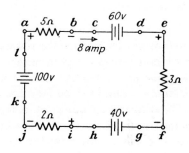

FIG. 2.7

abcd the first potential difference encountered is that from a to b. This has a magnitude of 8 amp $\times$ 5 ohms $= 40$ v. Since a is $+$ and b is $-$, the potential a to b is -40 v. The next potential difference encountered is that from c to d. Its magnitude is 60 v, the emf of the battery there. Since c is $+$ and d is $-$, the potential c to d is -60 v. In equation form

$$\text{Potential } a \text{ to } d = -40 - 60 = -100 \text{ v}$$

The negative value obtained shows that there is a fall of potential from a to d, hence a is at the higher potential.

The potential from a to d by the path *ahd* should also be -100 v; therefore as a check let us write a potential equation following that path.

$$\begin{aligned}\text{Potential } a \text{ to } d &= -100 \text{ v} + 8 \text{ amp} \times 2 \text{ ohms} - 40 \text{ v} + 8 \text{ amp} \times 3 \text{ ohms}\\ &= -100 + 16 - 40 + 24 = -100 \text{ v}\end{aligned}$$

The potential from e to b will be determined along each of the two paths between the points. Along the path edb,

$$\text{Potential } e \text{ to } b = +60 \text{ v}$$

The positive sign shows that b is at a higher potential than e. Along the path ejb,

$$\text{Potential } e \text{ to } b = -8 \text{ amp} \times 3 \text{ ohms} + 40 \text{ v} - 8 \text{ amp} \times 2 \text{ ohms}$$
$$+ 100 \text{ v} - 8 \text{ amp} \times 5 \text{ ohms}$$
$$= -24 + 40 - 16 + 100 - 40 = +60 \text{ v}$$

2.5. Battery Electromotive Force and Internal Resistance. In analyzing circuits, the emf of a cell or a battery is usually assumed to be constant. Such an assumption may be nearly correct in some cases but very much in error in others. The emf of a cell depends upon factors such as the temperature, the condition of the electrolyte, and the direction and magnitude of the current. A standard cell maintains a nearly constant emf only if very little current is drawn. When a battery delivers current for a time, its emf decreases.

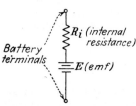

FIG. 2.8 Emf and internal resistance of a battery.

The voltage between the terminals of a battery that is carrying current differs from the emf by the resistance drop. The resistance that causes this voltage drop is the internal resistance. As far as external relations are concerned, a battery may be considered to have its emf and internal resistance separate as in Fig. 2.8.

The direction of a battery current is fixed by the external circuit connected to the battery. When one or more resistive elements form a closed circuit between battery terminals, current leaves the positive terminal and enters the negative terminal. In Fig. 2.9 an element of R ohms resistance is connected to the terminals of a battery. Since the battery is the only source of emf present, the current I amp will leave the positive terminal and traverse the circuit in a clockwise direction. Starting from the negative

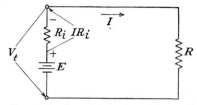

FIG. 2.9 A resistor of resistance R connected to the terminals of a battery.

battery terminal and traversing the circuit in the direction of the current, first there occurs a rise in potential of E v, the emf of the battery. Next there occurs a resistance drop of IR_i v in the internal resistance R_i ohms. The voltage V_t between battery terminals equals the emf less the internal resistance drop.

In Fig. 2.10 a d-c generator whose emf is E v, driven by a prime mover PM, is charging a battery whose emf is E_b v. The resistor of R ohms

resistance is inserted to help limit the current of I amp.   Most d-c generators have one or more field windings that may be represented by
standard symbols.   In most cases considered in this text what happens
in the generator is not studied and, except where necessary, the field
windings are not represented.   In most d-c generators the emf and the
terminal voltage vary with the amount of current drawn.   In most cases
the variation will be neglected and it will be assumed that the generator
maintains constant terminal voltage
regardless of the amount of current
drawn.

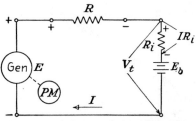

The generator will charge the battery in Fig. 2.10 if the emfs are
opposed as shown and E is greater
than E_b.   Then current is forced into
the positive terminal of the battery
and leaves by the negative terminal.
Following a path through the battery, starting at the negative termi-

Fig. 2.10   A battery being charged by
a generator.   The emf E of the generator
is greater than the emf E_b of the battery.

nal, first there is a rise of potential of E_b v and next a further rise of IR_i v.
Here the voltage V_t between battery terminals is equal to the emf plus the
internal resistance drop.

The internal resistance of a battery is seldom constant.   The resistance
varies with the temperature, the condition of the materials in the battery,
and the current.   In a circuit such as that of Fig. 2.10 it would be found
that the charging current would change with time because of changes in
the generator emf, in the battery emf, and in the internal resistance.

2.6. Voltage and Current Ratings of Electrical Apparatus.   The rated
voltage of a source of emf is that upon which its performance guarantees
are based.   For a battery the rated voltage is about equal to the emf.
The rated current of a battery is specified by the manufacturer as a value
that should not be exceeded if satisfactory life is to be obtained.   The
rated voltage and current of a generator are specified by the manufacturer and listed on the machine name plate.   Of the factors considered in
rating a given machine, temperature rise is usually an important one.
The terminal voltage of most generators can be varied over a wide range
by simple controls.   As all generators have some overload capacity,
either or both rated voltage and current of a machine can be exceeded by
limited amounts for a short time without injuring the machine.

A resistor has a specified resistance and may also have a current rating
that should not be exceeded in continuous operation if the temperature
rise is not to exceed a safe value.

2.7. Parallel Circuits.   In Fig. 2.11 are shown connections between
two lamps and a battery.   The lamps are in parallel with each other.

The parallel combination is in series with the battery. There are three currents, one from junction a to junction b through lamp 1, a second from a to b through lamp 2, and a third from b to a through the battery. According to Kirchhoff's law the third current is the sum of the other two.

Two or more sources of emf may be connected in parallel to supply current to a single load or to two or more loads connected in parallel. A load on an electrical system is any element that draws energy from the system, such as a lamp, a soldering iron, a loud-speaker, a motor, etc. The behavior of a circuit under various conditions of operation depends in

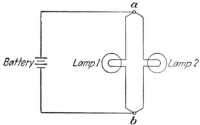

FIG. 2.11 Two lamps in parallel supplied from a battery.

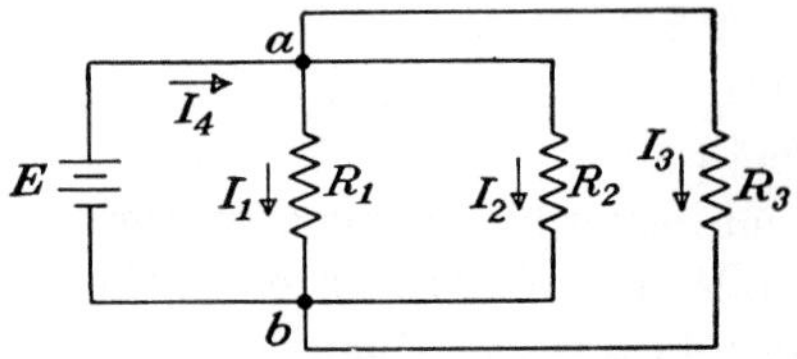

FIG. 2.12 Three loads in parallel supplied from a battery.

part upon the nature of the loads on the circuit. In Fig. 2.12 loads of R_1, R_2, and R_3 ohms resistance, respectively, are supplied in parallel with current from a battery of emf E v. The resistance of each load is assumed to include that of any leads in its respective branch. There are four currents, designated as I_1, I_2, I_3, and I_4 amp, with directions as indicated. The voltage drop V_{ab} v from a to b is the same along any path between the points.

Application of Ohm's law to the paths through the resistors yields $I_1 = V_{ab}/R_1$, $I_2 = V_{ab}/R_2$, and $I_3 = V_{ab}/R_3$.

Application of Kirchhoff's current law at either of the junctions yields $I_4 = I_1 + I_2 + I_3$. Combination of this equation with the preceding ones yields

$$I_4 = \frac{V_{ab}}{R_1} + \frac{V_{ab}}{R_2} + \frac{V_{ab}}{R_3} = V_{ab}\left(\frac{1}{R_1} + \frac{1}{R_2} + \frac{1}{R_3}\right)$$

The quantity $1/R_1$ is the conductance G_1 of branch 1. Its unit is the mho, a word obtained by spelling "ohm" backward. The conductance G mhos of a resistive element is the factor by which the voltage drop V v across it is multiplied to obtain the current in it. In symbols $I = VG$. In Fig. 2.12 the total current drawn by the three loads is I_4 and the common voltage drop across them is V_{ab}. As far as the circuit to the left of a and b is concerned, the three loads could be replaced by a resistive element that drew the current I_4 with the voltage drop V_{ab}. Let R_e

be the resistance and G_e be the conductance of the element. Then $R_e = V_{ab}/I_4$ and $G_e = I_4/V_{ab}$. In Fig. 2.12 the respective conductances of the branches are $G_1 = 1/R_1$, $G_2 = 1/R_2$, and $G_3 = 1/R_3$. *The equivalent conductance of a number of parallel resistance elements is equal to the sum of the individual conductances.* Here $G_e = G_1 + G_2 + G_3$ and $1/R_e = 1/R_1 + 1/R_2 + 1/R_3$. Then $R_e = 1/(1/R_1 + 1/R_2 + 1/R_3)$.

When two units of respective conductance $G_1 = 1/R_1$ and $G_2 = 1/R_2$ are in parallel, the equivalent conductance is

$$G_e = G_1 + G_2 = \frac{1}{R_1} + \frac{1}{R_2}$$

The equivalent resistance is

$$R_e = \frac{1}{G_e} = \frac{1}{1/R_1 + 1/R_2} = \frac{R_1 R_2}{R_1 + R_2}$$

This shows that, *when two resistors are in parallel, their equivalent resistance is equal to the product of the individual resistance values divided by their sum.* From the preceding

$$R_e = \frac{R_1}{R_1/R_2 + 1} \tag{2.5}$$

a relation that is useful for computing with a slide rule the equivalent resistance of two parallel resistors whose individual resistances are such that their product or sum cannot be determined readily by inspection. Let R_1 be the lesser and R_2 the greater of the two resistances. To obtain the equivalent resistance of the two in parallel, divide the lesser by the greater to obtain their ratio R_1/R_2. Then the equivalent resistance is equal to the lesser resistance divided by this ratio plus unity.

Example 1. A 189-ohm resistor is in parallel with a 237-ohm resistor. Compute the equivalent resistance.
Solution. When 189 is divided by 237 on a slide rule, the result is 0.797. Then the equivalent resistance is $189/1.797 = 105$ ohms.

When two resistors are in parallel, their equivalent resistance is less than the resistance of either resistor. If the resistance values differ greatly, the equivalent resistance is only slightly less than that of the resistor of lesser resistance. For example, if 1,000 ohms are in parallel with 5 ohms, the ratio of the resistances is 0.005. The equivalent resistance is

$$\frac{5}{1.005} = 4.975 \text{ ohms}$$

a value that is only 0.5 per cent less than the lesser resistance.

With three or more resistors in parallel, it is possible to derive an equation for the equivalent resistance in terms of the individual resistance values.   However, a simple method for obtaining the equivalent resistance is to compute the individual conductances, add them, and take the reciprocal of the result.

In the circuit of Fig. 2.12, $I_1 = V_{ab}G_1$ and $I_2 = V_{ab}G_2$.   Then

$$\frac{I_1}{I_2} = \frac{G_1}{G_2}$$

Hence *the ratio of the currents in two parallel resistors is equal to the ratio of the conductances.*   In other terms, the ratio of the currents is the inverse of the ratio of the respective resistances.

Further in the circuit of Fig. 2.12, $I_1 = V_{ab}G_1$ and $I_4 = V_{ab}G_e$.   Then $I_1/I_4 = G_1/G_e$.   Hence *the current in one of a number of parallel resistors is to the total current drawn by the combination as the conductance of that resistor is to the conductance of the combination.*

Example 2.   A 2-, a 4-, and a 5-ohm resistor are in parallel across a 6-v source. Compute the individual and the equivalent conductances and the total current.

Solution.   The conductance of the 2-ohm resistor is $G_1 = \frac{1}{2} = 0.5$ mho; that of the 4-ohm resistor is $G_2 = \frac{1}{4} = 0.25$ mho; and that of the 5-ohm resistor is $G_3 = \frac{1}{5} = 0.2$ mho.   The equivalent conductance is

$$G_e = 0.5 + 0.25 + 0.2 = 0.95 \text{ mho}$$

The total current is $I = 6 \text{ v} \times 0.95 \text{ mho} = 5.7$ amp.

Example 3.   The resistors of Example 2 in parallel in a certain circuit draw a total current of 190 ma.   Compute the current in each resistor.

Solution.   The current I_1 in the 2-ohm resistor is to the total current as G_1 is to G_e.   Hence $I_1/190 = 0.5/0.95$, from which $I_1 = 100$ ma.   For the current I_2 in the 4-ohm resistor, $I_2/190 = 0.25/0.95$, from which $I_2 = 50$ ma.   Likewise for the current I_3 in the 5-ohm resistor, $I_3/190 = 0.2/0.95$, from which $I_3 = 40$ ma. As a check the sum of the three currents is $100 + 50 + 40 = 190$ ma.

Two or more sources of emf are operated in parallel to obtain a current capacity greater than that of one source.   The sources should be connected together with like polarities, i.e., plus to plus, and minus to minus. If, by error, the polarity of one source is reversed, there will be an abnormally large current circulating between the sources that may cause damage.   When two or more batteries are in parallel, it is desirable that the emfs be equal so that there will be no current in any battery when no load current is being drawn.   When two or more d-c generators are in parallel, the emfs of the individual generators can be adjusted to cause the total current to divide among the generators in a desired manner.

Example 4.   A battery that has an emf of 120 v and an internal resistance of 0.2 ohm is to be connected in parallel with a second battery that has an emf of 120 v and an internal resistance of 0.4 ohm.

a. If the batteries are properly connected for parallel operation, how much current will flow in each when no load current is being drawn?   Compute the voltage across each battery.

b. If the batteries are connected in parallel with incorrect polarities, how much current will flow in each when no load current is being drawn? Compute the voltage across each battery.

c. The batteries are properly connected for parallel operation. A load having a resistance of 5 ohms is connected across them. Compute the load current, the current in each battery, and the voltage across each battery.

d. The batteries are properly connected for parallel operation. A load drawing 60 amp is connected across them. Compute the load resistance, the current in each battery, and the voltage across each battery.

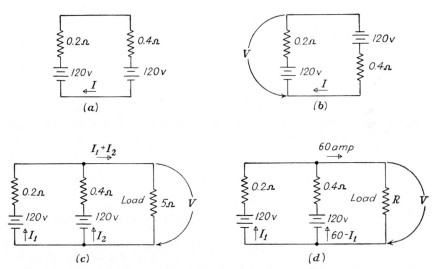

Fig. 2.13

Solution. *a.* The given connections of the batteries are shown in Fig. 2.13*a.* Until a load is connected, the two batteries constitute a series circuit. Assume that a current I flows clockwise as indicated. Tracing the circuit in a clockwise direction and equating the algebraic sum of the emfs to the algebraic sum of the resistance drops yields $120 - 120 = 0.2I + 0.4I$, from which $I = 0$. With no current in either battery the voltage across each will be equal to the emf which is 120 v.

b. The given connections of the batteries are shown in Fig. 2.13*b.* Assume that a current I flows clockwise as indicated. Tracing the circuit in a clockwise direction and equating the algebraic sum of the emfs to the algebraic sum of the resistance drops yields $120 + 120 = 0.2I + 0.4I$, from which $I = 400$ amp.

The potential from the lower terminal of the left-hand battery through that battery to its upper terminal is 120 v $- 400$ amp $\times 0.2$ ohm $= 40$ v. Hence the upper terminal is positive and the lower is negative with $V = +40$ v. Since the batteries are connected directly by leads whose resistance is assumed to be zero, the right-hand battery will also have a terminal voltage of 40 v with the upper terminal positive. Note that this polarity is the reverse of what it would be if it were determined by the emf of the battery alone.

c. The given connections of the batteries are shown in Fig. 2.13*c.* The current in the left-hand battery has been designated as I_1 and assumed to be directed as shown. The current in the right-hand battery has been designated as I_2 and assumed to be directed as shown. According to Kirchhoff's law regarding currents, at the upper terminal of the right-hand battery the current directed to the load is $I_1 + I_2$, since it must equal the sum of the battery currents toward the terminal.

There are three currents in the circuit but they have been designated in terms of two, I_1 and I_2. To compute I_1 and I_2, two voltage equations can be set up by the application of Kirchhoff's law of voltages. The voltage equation for the path through the batteries is

$$120 - 120 = 0.2I_1 - 0.4I_2 \qquad (1)$$

The voltage equation for the path through the load and the right-hand battery is

$$120 = 0.4I_2 + 5(I_1 + I_2) \qquad (2)$$

The simultaneous solution of (1) and (2) yields $I_1 = 15.6$ amp and $I_2 = 7.8$ amp. The load current is $I_1 + I_2 = 23.4$ amp. The voltage across each battery is also the voltage across the load and is $V = 23.4$ amp $\times$ 5 ohms $= 117$ v.

d. The given connections of the batteries are shown in Fig. 2.13d. The load current has been designated as the given value of 60 amp and the current in the left-hand battery as I_1 amp. Then by application of Kirchhoff's law of currents the current in the right-hand battery is $60 - I_1$ amp directed as shown. The resistance of the load has been designated as R ohms. Here there are two unknown quantities, I_1 and R. The voltage equation for the path through the batteries is $120 - 120 = 0.2I_1 - 0.4(60 - I_1)$. From this $I_1 = 40$ amp. Hence $60 - I_1 = 20$ amp. The voltage V can be computed from the voltage equation

$$120 = 0.2I_1 + V = 0.2 \times 40 + V$$

From this $V = 112$ v. Then $R = V/60 = 112/60 = 1.87$ ohms.

2.8. Combinations of Resistors. In Fig. 2.14a, resistors having respective resistances of R_2 and R_3 are in parallel. This parallel combination

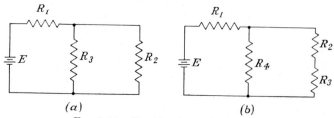

(a)   (b)

Fig. 2.14   Combinations of resistors.

is in series with a resistor of resistance R_1 across the battery. In Fig. 2.14b, resistors having resistances of R_2 and R_3 are in series. This series combination is in parallel with a resistor of resistance R_4. The resultant combination is in series with a resistor of resistance R_1 across the battery.

Example 1. In Fig. 2.15 compute the various currents.

Solution. The equivalent resistance of the three parallel resistors is computed from the relation of the conductances.

$$G_e = \tfrac{1}{80} + \tfrac{1}{50} + \tfrac{1}{40} = 0.0125 + 0.02 + 0.025 = 0.0575 \text{ mho}$$

$$R_e = \frac{1}{G_e} = \frac{1}{0.0575} = 17.4 \text{ ohms}$$

With the parallel resistors replaced by their equivalent, the circuit reduces to

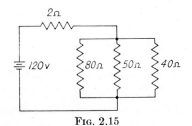

FIG. 2.15

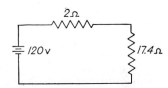

FIG. 2.16   Simplification of the circuit of Fig. 2.15.

that in Fig. 2.16. Since the two resistors here are in series, their equivalent resistance is $17.4 + 2 = 19.4$ ohms. The battery current is

$$\frac{120 \text{ v}}{19.4 \text{ ohms}} = 6.18 \text{ amp}$$

This is the current in the battery and the 2-ohm resistor in the original circuit.

The voltage V across the parallel resistors is the product of the battery current and the equivalent resistance of those resistors, or

$$V = 6.18 \text{ amp} \times 17.4 \text{ ohms} = 107.6 \text{ v}$$

V might have been computed from the fact that it is equal to the battery emf less the voltage drop in the 2-ohm resistor. By this method

$$V = 120 \text{ v} - 6.18 \text{ amp} \times 2 \text{ ohms} = 107.6 \text{ v}$$

which agrees with the value above.

The current in the 40-ohm resistor is $107.6 \text{ v}/40$ ohms $= 2.69$ amp; that in the 50-ohm resistor is $107.6 \text{ v}/50$ ohms $= 2.15$ amp; and that in the 80-ohm resistor is $107.6 \text{ v}/80$ ohms $= 1.35$ amp.

2.9. Rheostats. A rheostat is an element whose resistance can be changed without opening the circuit in which it is connected. Rheostats are constructed in many forms. The size of a rheostat is governed largely by the amount of heat that it must dissipate with a reasonable temperature rise.

The circuit diagram of a lamp rheostat is in Fig. 2.17. This rheostat consists of six incandescent lamps, seven single-pole double-throw switches, and two bus bars. By changing the switch positions the resistance between the rheostat terminals can be varied in steps from a maximum value with all lamps in series to a minimum value with all lamps in parallel. This type of rheostat has these objectionable features:

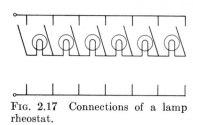

the resistance for any given setting of the switches depends upon the current through the rheostat because the resistance of an incandescent lamp increases as the current in it increases; the resistance can be changed only in steps and the steps are not uniform; and the rheostat does not have much overload capacity because the life of a lamp is

FIG. 2.17   Connections of a lamp rheostat.

short if it operated more than a few per cent above rated voltage. However, a lamp rheostat costs less than most other types and is useful for instructional purposes because the brilliance of a lamp is a rough indication of the amount of current through it.

The field rheostat of Fig. 2.18 is designed to control the current in the field circuit of a motor or a generator. Each of the two current ratings on the name plate of a field rheostat is a maximum rating for a certain setting of the contact arm. If the resistance elements in the rheostat were made of the same material and had the same area of cross section throughout, each element could carry the same maximum current and the rheostat would have only one current rating. However, when the rheostat is used as intended, the current in it will be the greatest when the contact arm is at the "resistance out" position and will decrease as more and more elements are cut in by moving the contact arm. Consequently

FIG. 2.18   Circuit diagram of a field rheostat.

all elements need not have the same current capacity, and a saving in cost and size is made by using elements of smaller cross section in the positions where a smaller current capacity is permissible.

The greater current rating of a field rheostat is that of the unit nearest the "resistance out" end. The resistance of the field winding with which a rheostat is used should be sufficient to limit the current to this rating when the rheostat is set for minimum resistance. The resistance of the field winding plus the total resistance of the rheostat should be sufficient to limit the current to the lesser current rating when the rheostat is set for maximum resistance. If a rheostat is to be used in an application other than that for which it is designed, both current ratings must be known if one is to compute whether or not the rheostat will overheat with any setting of the contact arm.

If the resistances of the various elements in a field rheostat were equal, the current in the circuit would decrease by increasingly smaller steps as each element is inserted in the circuit.   Usually it is desired that the current in a circuit containing a field rheostat be decreased in approximately equal steps as each element of resistance is inserted.   This requires that the resistances of the elements be unequal.

Example 1.   The field winding of a d-c motor has a resistance of 80 ohms and is to be excited from a 250-v source.   A field rheostat with 20 steps of resistance is to vary the voltage applied to the field winding from 100 to 250 v.   What should be the total resistance and the current ratings of the rheostat?   If the current is to be decreased in equal increments as each element of the rheostat is inserted, what should be the resistances of the first and last elements?

Solution.   The maximum current in the circuit will be

$$\frac{250 \text{ v}}{80 \text{ ohms}} = 3.13 \text{ amp}$$

and the minimum will be 100 v/80 ohms = 1.25 amp.   These should be the current ratings of the rheostat.

The maximum resistance in the circuit will be 250 v/1.25 amp = 200 ohms. Since there are 80 ohms in the field winding, the total resistance of the rheostat must be 120 ohms.

The total change in current to be produced by the rheostat is

$$3.13 - 1.25 = 1.88 \text{ amp}$$

The current increment for each step in the rheostat is

$$\frac{1.88 \text{ amp}}{20 \text{ steps}} = 0.094 \text{ amp per step}$$

With the rheostat arm set on the "resistance out" position, the current in and the resistance of the circuit are 3.13 amp and 80 ohms, respectively.   When the first step of resistance is inserted, the current will be decreased to

$$3.13 - 0.094 = 3.04 \text{ amp}$$

and the resistance of the circuit will be increased to 250 v/3.04 amp = 82.3 ohms. The increase of resistance, 82.3 − 80 = 2.3 ohms, is the resistance in the first step.

With the rheostat arm set on the "resistance in" position, the current in and the resistance of the circuit are 1.25 amp and 200 ohms, respectively.   When all but the last step of the rheostat are inserted, the current will be

$$1.25 + 0.094 = 1.34 \text{ amp}$$

and the resistance of the circuit is 250 v/1.34 amp = 186 ohms.   The increase of resistance, 200 − 186 = 14 ohms, is the resistance of the last step.

A common type of slide-wire rheostat has a strip of alloyed wire forming closely spaced turns on a porcelain tube.   One end of the wire is connected as in Fig. 2.19 to terminal A, the other
to B.   By moving the slider a connection can
be made from terminal C to any of the various
turns of wire.   For some applications only
two terminals, say A and C, are used.   The
resistance between those terminals can be
varied from zero to a maximum by moving the slider.

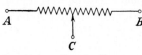

FIG. 2.19   Circuit diagram
of a slide-wire rheostat.

A slide-wire rheostat connected as in Fig. 2.20, is a voltage divider.
The output voltage can be varied from zero up to the input value.   The
load is in parallel with the portion of the rheostat that is included between

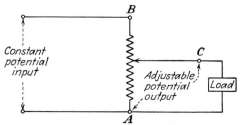

FIG. 2.20   Slide-wire rheostat connected as a voltage divider.

the output terminals.   This parallel combination is in series with the
remainder of the rheostat.

Example 2.   The voltage applied to a 100-ohm load is to be varied from 120
to 1 v using a 125-v source.   If the voltage control is to be obtained by a slide-
wire rheostat in series with the load,
what should be the resistance and the
current rating of the rheostat?

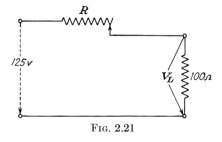

FIG. 2.21

Solution.   The circuit diagram is in
Fig. 2.21.   With the rheostat set for
maximum resistance, V_L is to be the
minimum value of 1 v.   The corresponding voltage across the rheostat is
$125 - 1 = 124$ v.   By the proportion
existing between the voltages across
resistors in series and the resistances of
the resistors, $R/124 = 100/1$, from
which $R = 12{,}400$ ohms as the required rheostat resistance.

The maximum current in the circuit will be 1.2 amp and will occur when 120 v
are applied to the 100-ohm resistor.   If the rheostat is wound of wire of uniform
size, the required current rating is 1.2 amp.

A slide-wire rheostat with the ratings just computed would not be listed as a
standard product of any manufacturer, for it would represent an abnormal
design.

Example 3. A slide-wire rheostat with a maximum resistance of 80 ohms is to be connected as a voltage divider to provide the voltage control required in Example 2. Specify the current rating of the rheostat.

Solution. The current rating will be fixed by the current the rheostat must carry when the slider is set so that 120 v is applied to the 100-ohm load. The diagram for this position is in Fig. 2.22. Since the total resistance of the rheostat

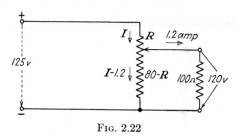

Fig. 2.22

is 80 ohms, if the resistance of the portion of the rheostat in series with the source is called R ohms, the resistance of the remainder of the rheostat is $80 - R$ ohms. For the given setting of the slider, the load current is 1.2 amp. The current in one portion of the rheostat is I amp and that in the other portion is $I - 1.2$ amp. The following voltage equations can be set up

$$125 = IR + 120 \qquad \text{and} \qquad 125 = IR + (I - 1.2)(80 - R)$$

from which I is found to be 2.74 amp as the required current rating of the rheostat.

The cost and size of the rheostat required here are much less than would be required with the arrangement of Example 2.

In some applications of voltage dividers, a negligible current is drawn from the output terminals. If the input voltage is constant, the output voltage is directly proportional to the rheostat resistance included between the output terminals. For such applications high-resistance rheostats are used to keep small the energy required from the source.

The variation of the output voltage of a voltage divider with the slider position depends upon the relative values of the resistance of the rheostat and that of the load.

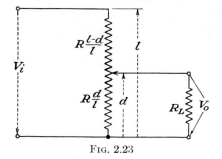

Fig. 2.23

Consider the circuit of Fig. 2.23. Here the input voltage is V_i, the output voltage is V_o, the rheostat resistance is R ohms, and the load resistance is R_L ohms. The total rheostat length is l m and the portion included between the output terminals is d m. If the rheostat resistance is distributed uniformly along the length, the resistance of the portion of the rheostat in parallel with the load is Rd/l ohms and the resistance of the remainder of the rheostat is $R(l - d)/l$ ohms. The equivalent resistance of the parallel branches is

$$\frac{R_L \times Rd/l}{R_L + Rd/l} \quad \text{ohms}$$

The equivalent resistance of the combination of the rheostat and the load, as seen at the input terminals, is

$$\frac{R(l - d)}{l} + \frac{R_L \times Rd/l}{R_L + Rd/l} \quad \text{ohms}$$

The voltage across the parallel branches is the output voltage V_o. This voltage is to the input voltage V_i as the equivalent resistance of the parallel branches is to the equivalent resistance of the entire circuit. From this relation it can be shown that

$$\frac{V_o}{V_i} = \frac{(R_L/R)(d/l)}{R_L/R + d/l - (d/l)^2}$$

From this equation the curves of Fig. 2.24 were plotted. These show how the output voltage of a voltage divider varies with the position of the slider for four ratios of load resistance to rheostat resistance. The curves convey information regarding the proper choice of a rheostat for use as a voltage divider for a specific application. If the load draws no current (i.e., its resistance is infinite), the output voltage is directly proportional to the setting of the slider. If the load resistance is one-half that of the rheostat, the output voltage is no longer directly proportional to the setting of the slider. Instead, when the slider is at the mid-position, the output voltage is only one-third of the input voltage. The output voltage changes twice as much during the movement of the slider from the mid-position to the end where maximum output voltage is obtained as it did during the movement from the end where zero output voltage was obtained to the mid-position. The control of the voltage near the maximum-voltage-output end of the rheostat is not as fine as that near the other end. The slope of a curve is a measure of the fineness of control of the output voltage, the less the slope, the finer the control. Inspection of the curves shows that as the ratio of the resistance of the load to that of the rheostat is reduced, the voltage control near the low-voltage-output end of the rheostat becomes finer, while the control at the other end becomes coarser.

For a given voltage-divider application, the resistance and the current capacity of a rheostat should be such that the rheostat will not be overheated for any slider setting to be used. If the output voltage is to be varied from zero to the value of the input voltage, from Fig. 2.24 it can

be seen that for satisfactory voltage control throughout the entire range
the resistance of the rheostat should not be more than about twice that
of the load. If the output voltage is to be varied from zero to about
10 per cent of the input voltage, the voltage control can be made fine

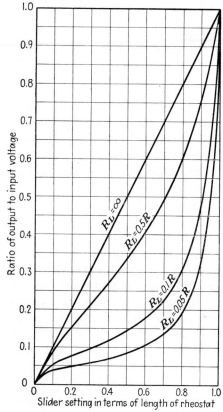

Fig. 2.24　Characteristics of a slide-wire rheostat when connected as a voltage divider.
R is the resistance of the rheostat; R_L is the resistance of the connected load.

throughout most of this range by using a rheostat whose resistance is
about twenty times that of the load.

In the preceding discussion the slide-wire rheostats have been considered to have a constant resistance per unit length. Some step-wound
rheostats are wound with one size of wire throughout one portion of the
length, a second size throughout a second portion of the length, and so on.

The energy delivered at the output terminals of a voltage divider may
be much less than that put in at the input terminals. However, the cost
of the energy loss is often a small price to pay for the range of control
obtained.

In commercial tests and laboratory experiments a load rheostat may be used to absorb electrical energy from a machine being tested. The circuit diagram of one type of load rheostat is in Fig. 2.25. In the upper portion of the diagram are represented six resistors that are cast-iron grids, each having approximately 4 ohms resistance.

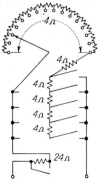

One resistor is tapped at about 20 points with leads connected to contact buttons on the arc through which the movable arm may be swung. By means of the switches and the arm the resistance of this portion of the rheostat can be adjusted in small steps from 24 ohms to 0.8 ohm.

As shown in Fig. 2.25, there is a switch on the rheostat that is in parallel with a 24-ohm resistor. By opening this switch the resistor is put in the circuit and 24 ohms are added to the resistance determined by the setting of the other switches and the movable arm. With 115 v applied to its terminals, the rheostat may be operated at any setting of the switches and the arm without overheating.

Fig. 2.25 Circuit diagram of a Purdue load rheostat.

2.10. Special Rheostat Connections. In Fig. 2.26a is represented a slide-wire rheostat of R ohms resistance with connections made to one end of the resistance wire at A and to the slider at C. This connection may be satisfactory if the resistance range required is not greater than that

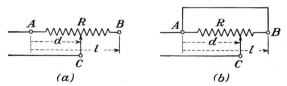

(a)   (b)

Fig. 2.26 Slide-wire rheostat connections. When a maximum resistance not greater than one-fourth of the total resistance of the rheostat is required, the control is finer and the current capacity is greater with the connections of b than with those of a.

of the rheostat and the maximum current to be carried does not exceed the rheostat rating. However, if the maximum resistance required is less than one-fourth that of the rheostat, it may be that the control is coarser than desired. The control can be made finer by connecting a lead between terminals A and B, as in Fig. 2.26b. Here the resistance between A and C is zero with the slider at either end of the rheostat and is a maximum when the slider is at the center of the rheostat. At the latter position the halves of the rheostat are in parallel. Since each has a resistance of $R/2$ ohms, the two in parallel have an equivalent resistance of $R/4$ ohms. The resistance between A and C can be varied from 0 to $R/4$ ohms by moving the slider one-half the length of the rheostat.

Without a connection between A and B, the slider is moved only one-fourth of the length of the rheostat in varying the resistance from 0 to $R/4$ ohms and the control is coarser than that when A and B are connected. The circuits of Fig. 2.26 can be compared by graphical representations of the relations between the resistance and the slider setting. In Fig. 2.26a the rheostat length is l m and the distance of the slider from

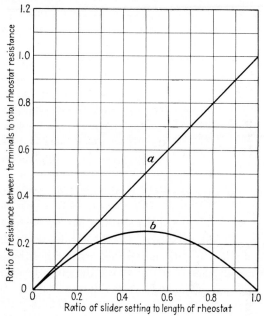

Fig. 2.27   Relation between resistance and slider setting on a slide-wire rheostat: (a) External connections to one end of resistance wire and to the slider; (b) same as a except that an additional lead is used to connect the two ends of the resistance wire.

end A is d m. Since the resistance is uniformly distributed along the length of the rheostat, then by proportion $R_{AC}/R = d/l$, where R_{AC} is the equivalent resistance between terminals A and C. With R and l fixed quantities, the curve showing the relation between the ratio R_{AC}/R and the ratio d/l is the straight line a in Fig. 2.27.

In Fig. 2.26b there are two paths in parallel between the terminals A and C. The resistance of one path is Rd/l ohms and that of the other is $R(l-d)/l$ ohms. The resistance R_{AC} is the product of these resistances divided by their sum. Hence

$$R_{AC} = \frac{Rd/l \times R(l-d)/l}{Rd/l + R(l-d)/l}$$

from which $R_{AC}/R = (d/l) - (d/l)^2$. With R and l fixed quantities, the curve showing the relation between the ratio R_{AC}/R and the ratio d/l is the parabola b in Fig. 2.27. Points on this curve were obtained by assigning various values to the ratio d/l and computing the corresponding values of R_{AC}/R. For example, when $d/l = 0.2$, $R_{AC}/R = 0.2 - (0.2)^2 = 0.16$.

Finer control of resistance than can be obtained with a given slide-wire rheostat is possible if a higher-resistance slide-wire rheostat is connected to the original rheostat as in Fig. 2.28. Since the control with the higher-resistance rheostat is finest when its slider is at the center, the proper method of operating the rheostats is to set first the slider on that rheostat at the center. Then the current is brought near the desired value (slightly less) by moving the slider on the lower-resistance rheostat. Next the slider on the higher-resistance rheo-

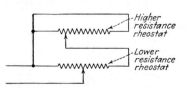

FIG. 2.28 Slide-wire rheostat connections for obtaining fine control of resistance. Coarse control is obtained by moving the slider on the lower-resistance rheostat and fine control by moving the slider on the higher-resistance rheostat.

stat is moved to adjust the current to the desired value.

2.11. Function Voltage Dividers. In Fig. 2.20, with constant input voltage and no connected load, the output voltage was shown to vary linearly with respect to the slider position, i.e., the output voltage is a linear function of the slider position. If the divider is a circular rheostat, the voltage output is proportional to the angular position of the slider. A function voltage divider is one in which the output voltage is proportional to some function of the angular position rather than to the angular position. In a sine voltage divider the output voltage is proportional to the sine of the angular position.

When load current is drawn from a function voltage divider, the output voltage is not the desired function of the slider position. The percentage error present depends upon the relative values of the resistance of the load and that of the divider.

2.12. Galvanometers, Ammeters, and Voltmeters. A galvanometer is an instrument utilizing mechanical motion caused by a current to indicate the presence of or to measure the current. For an observable deflection galvanometers seldom require more than a few milliamperes and often require far less. Most galvanometers for d-c measurements are of the permanent-magnet moving-coil type, as in Fig. 2.29. Here a cylindrical soft-iron core is mounted between soft-iron pole pieces attached to a permanent magnet. About the core is an aluminum frame to which are attached shafts that are pivoted in jewel bearings. The frame can be rotated through less than a half revolution in the magnetic field established by the magnet in the region between the core and the pole pieces.

On the frame is wrapped a coil of fine wire through which is sent current to produce a turning effort. The current is led through a fine coil spring into one end of the coil, through the coil, and then out through a second spring. The springs also produce a turning effort that opposes that produced by the current in the coil. A pointer or mirror is usually attached to the shaft that supports the aluminum frame.

A galvanometer has current, voltage, and power sensitivities. The current sensitivity is the current in microamperes required to produce a standard deflection. For a portable galvanometer with an attached scale the standard deflection is that of the smallest scale division. The voltage sensitivity is the voltage in microvolts required to produce a standard deflection. The power sensitivity is equal to the product of the current and voltage sensitivities.

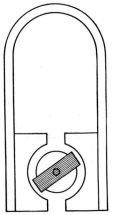

An ammeter is an instrument for measuring an electric current. The terms milliammeter and microammeter are usually applied to instruments whose scales are graduated in milliamperes and microamperes, respectively. Most d-c ammeters contain a permanent-magnet moving-coil movement (a galvanometer). Current in the moving coil moves a pointer over a graduated scale. The pointer stops at a position of equilibrium where the turning effort (torque) of the current is balanced by that of the

Fig. 2.29 A permanent-magnet moving-coil galvanometer.

springs. Usually it is desired that the deflection of the pointer be directly proportional to the current so that the scale graduations will be spaced uniformly.

Introducing an ammeter into a circuit adds resistance to the branch of the circuit in which the instrument is connected. As a result the reading of the ammeter is less than the current in the branch prior to the introduction of the ammeter. In most cases the change of current is negligible. In some cases the change is objectionably great. The voltage sensitivity of an ammeter is a measure of the voltage drop between terminals when the current required for full-scale deflection is flowing. Most d-c ammeters are made so that this voltage drop is 50 mv. Some have other values in the range from 20 to 200 mv.

Few d-c ammeters carry more than 10 ma in the moving coil. In an instrument with a capacity of more than 10 ma, two resistors, one called a shunt, are connected with respect to the moving coil as in Fig. 2.30. The resistances of the two branches are so adjusted that a known proportion of the current I to be measured goes through the moving coil. With

the current in the moving coil limited to 10 ma, the greater the current
to be measured, the greater is the pro-
portion of the total current that flows
through the shunt.

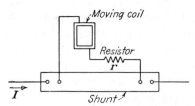

FIG. 2.30   Connections of the moving
coil of an ammeter and a shunt for
measuring currents greater than the
capacity of the moving coil. The
shunt and the resistor are made of a
material whose percentage change of
resistance with a given change of temperature is much less than that of
copper.

Example 1.   In Fig. 2.30 the moving
coil and the resistor of resistance r have
respective resistances of 2 and 3 ohms.
The moving coil produces full-scale deflection with a current of 10 ma.   Compute
the resistance of the shunt if the ammeter
is to have a range of (a) 150 ma and (b)
50 amp.

Solution.   a. The circuit for the 150-ma
instrument is in Fig. 2.31.   With a total
current of 150 ma (0.15 amp) and a current of 10 ma (0.01 amp) in the moving
coil, the current in the shunt is 140 ma
(0.14 amp).   The voltage V_{TT} between the terminals TT on the shunt is equal
to the current in the moving coil times the resistance of that branch.   Hence
$V_{TT} = 0.01$ amp $\times$ 5 ohms $= 0.05$ v (50 mv).   The current in the shunt times

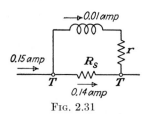

FIG. 2.31

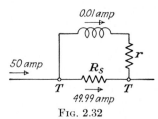

FIG. 2.32

the resistance R_S of the shunt is also V_{TT}.   Hence 0.14 amp $\times R_S = 0.05$ v,
from which $R_S = 0.357$ ohm.

b. The circuit for the 50-amp instrument is in Fig. 2.32.   As before

$$V_{TT} = 0.05 \text{ v}$$

Now $R_S = 0.05$ v$/49.99$ amp $= 0.001$ ohm.

Most ammeters with capacities of 25 amp or less have an enclosed shunt
in the case with the moving coil.   There are two binding posts for external
connections.   Ammeters of higher capacities have an external shunt that
has four binding posts.   Two of these are used to connect the shunt in the
circuit where the current is to be measured.   The moving-coil circuit is
connected to the other two posts by special leads.   A given instrument
and the leads intended for use with it are calibrated as a unit.

A voltmeter is an instrument for measuring voltage (difference of
potential).   Its scale is usually graduated in kilovolts, volts, or millivolts.
A permanent-magnet moving-coil movement is used in most d-c voltmeters.   Current is required in the moving coil to produce a pointer

deflection. With the coil-circuit resistance constant, the voltage applied is directly proportional to the current in the coil and the scale can be graduated in volts rather than in amperes. At one time most d-c voltmeters required about 10 ma in the moving coil to produce full-scale deflection. Later a need for voltmeters with a greater current sensitivity led to the development of ones that require only 1 ma for full-scale deflection. Further improvements have been such that commercial voltmeters now available require only 5 μa for full-scale deflection.

A voltmeter with a capacity greater than about 100 mv has a resistor in series with the moving coil. The resistor resistance is such that the current will produce full-scale deflection when voltage equal to the instrument capacity is applied to its terminals. For example, assume that a 5-ohm 10-ma movement is to be used in a 150-v voltmeter. The total resistance of the voltmeter should be 150 v/0.01 amp = 15,000 ohms. Here the necessary resistance of the resistor is 15,000 − 5 = 14,995 ohms.

The current sensitivity of a voltmeter is often expressed in ohms per volt, a value obtained by dividing the resistance of the voltmeter by its capacity. Thus a 150-v 150,000-ohm voltmeter has a sensitivity of 150,000 ohms/150 v = 1,000 ohms per v.

Although the same type of movement is used in a d-c ammeter as in a d-c voltmeter, identical movements are not necessarily used. In an ammeter high voltage sensitivity (i.e., low voltage drop) is desired. If the capacity is more than 10 ma, it makes little difference whether the full-scale current in the moving coil is 50 μa or 10 ma. In a voltmeter high current sensitivity (i.e., low current) is desired. If the capacity is more than a few volts, it makes little difference whether the resistance of the moving coil is 5 or 500 ohms. An ammeter movement is likely to have fewer turns and larger wire than a voltmeter movement.

The voltage that can be measured with a given voltmeter can be increased by connecting a resistor (multiplier) in series with the instrument across the voltage being measured. The voltage being measured is equal to the voltmeter reading multiplied by the ratio of the sum of the resistances of the voltmeter and the multiplier to the resistance of the voltmeter.

2.13. Ammeter and Voltmeter Connections. In Fig. 2.33 the ammeter A_1 measures the current in the branch containing the resistance R_1. Ammeter A_2 measures the current supplied by the battery. To connect an ammeter in a circuit is to introduce resistance into the circuit. Usually the resistance of an ammeter is so small compared with that of the circuit into which it is introduced that the current in the circuit is nearly the same with as without the ammeter present. Before connecting an ammeter in a circuit, one should take care that its capacity is greater than the expected current value. When experimenting with temporary

circuits, a protecting switch may be connected in parallel with an ammeter, as in Fig. 2.34.   The switch should be opened only when the ammeter
is to be read.   Although the resistance of an ammeter is low, that of the
switch when closed is even lower.   With the switch closed, if there is an

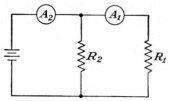

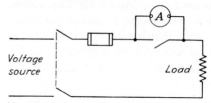

FIG. 2.33   Ammeter connections.
Ammeter A_1 measures the current in the resistor of resistance
R_1. Ammeter A_2 measures the
battery current.

FIG. 2.34   Protecting switch in parallel
with an ammeter.

excessive current after the circuit is energized most of it will go through
the switch and very little through the ammeter.   If the current in the
circuit is greater than the ammeter capacity but not sufficiently great to
cause the circuit to be interrupted by a protective device such as a fuse

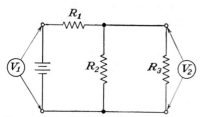

FIG. 2.35   Voltmeter connections.
Voltmeter V_1 measures the difference of
potential between the battery terminals.
Voltmeter V_2 measures that between
the terminals of the resistor of resistance R_3.

or a circuit breaker, there is a possibility that the ammeter will be damaged when the protecting switch is
opened.

In Fig. 2.35 the voltmeter V_1 is
connected to measure the voltage between the battery terminals.   Voltmeter V_2 is connected to measure the
voltage between the terminals of the
resistor of resistance R_3.   Voltmeter
leads are often provided with clips
for making connections to binding
posts or wires.   Such clips are rep-
resented here by arrows.   To connect a voltmeter in a circuit is to connect resistance between the points to which the voltmeter is connected.
In some cases the current required by a voltmeter will be sufficient to
change the circuit relations, and the voltage between two points will not
be the same with the voltmeter connected as without it.

2.14. Measurement of Resistance by the Voltmeter-ammeter Method.
The resistance of an element can be computed by Ohm's law if the voltage
across and the corresponding current through it can be measured.   Two
arrangements of instruments for these measurements are in Fig. 2.36.
Here E is the emf of the voltage source, R_1 is the resistance of a control
rheostat, and R_x is the resistance to be determined.   A control rheostat

is usually required to limit the current in the element to what is considered to be a reasonable value.

The ammeter and the voltmeter cannot be connected so that they will register simultaneously the current through and the voltage across an element. In Fig. 2.36a, the voltmeter registers the voltage across the element but the ammeter registers the sum of the current through the

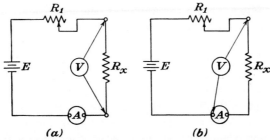

FIG. 2.36 Two possible arrangements of instruments for the measurement of resistance.

element and that through the voltmeter. Since the resistance of a voltmeter is usually given on its calibration card, correction for the current in it can be made and the value of R_x determined. If V is the voltmeter reading in volts, I is the ammeter reading in amperes, and R_v is the voltmeter resistance in ohms, the voltmeter current is V/R_v, and

$$R_x = \frac{V}{I - V/R_v} \qquad \text{ohms}$$

In Fig. 2.36b, the ammeter registers the current in the element. However, the voltmeter registers not the voltage across the element but the voltage across the ammeter, the lead joining the ammeter to the element, and the element. Included also is the voltage caused by the resistance of the contact between a lead and the binding post of the ammeter and that of the contact between the same lead and the binding post of the element. If the ammeter resistance is known, correction for the voltage across it can be made. However, the lead and contact resistances are not known. When a protecting switch is used with an ammeter, additional lead and contact resistances are present. The resistance of a lead or a contact is likely to be of the order of 0.01 to 0.001 ohm or less.

Although the instruments introduce errors in measuring resistances with either of the circuits of Fig. 2.36, it usually happens that with one of the two the error is negligible. For any given element one can determine by experiment which circuit yields the lesser error. Record both instrument readings, first with the voltmeter connected directly across the element and then with the voltmeter connected across the ammeter and

the element.   If it should happen that no observable change occurs in
the reading of either instrument when the voltmeter connection is shifted,
then the presence of the instruments causes a negligible error with either
circuit.   It may be that shifting the voltmeter connection causes an
observable change in the ammeter reading but no change in the voltmeter reading.   Such results show that the current taken by the voltmeter is not negligible compared with the current through the element,
and that the voltage across the ammeter, the leads, and the contacts is
negligible compared with the voltage across the element.   In this case,
the instrument readings taken when the voltmeter is across the ammeter
and the element should be used.   The resistance as computed by dividing
the voltmeter reading by the ammeter reading will be correct to an
accuracy as good as is obtainable with the instruments used.

It may be that shifting the voltmeter connection causes an observable
change in the voltmeter reading but no change in the ammeter reading.
Such results show that the voltage across the ammeter, the leads, and
the contacts is not negligible compared with the voltage across the element and that the voltmeter current is negligible compared with the
current in the element.   In this case the instrument readings taken when
the voltmeter is connected directly across the element should be used.
The resistance as computed by dividing the voltmeter reading by the
ammeter reading will be correct to an accuracy as good as is obtainable
with the instruments used.

It may be that shifting the voltmeter connection causes observable
changes in both the voltmeter and the ammeter readings.   Such results
show that the voltage across the ammeter, the leads, and the contacts is
not negligible compared with the voltage across the element and that the
voltmeter current is not negligible compared with the current in the element.   In this case the instrument readings taken when the voltmeter is
connected across the element only should be used and correction made
for the voltmeter current as outlined previously.

In determining which method of connecting the instruments results in
the lesser error, one should repeat the test until he is certain the change
in instrument readings was caused by shifting the voltmeter connection
and not by a change in the supply voltage.

2.15. Measuring Resistance with a Voltmeter.   Resistance within a
limited range can be measured with the circuit of Fig. 2.37.   The resistance R_x of an element is to be measured.   Two voltmeter readings are
taken, one with it connected from a to b, and another with it connected
from a to c.   With the first connection the reading is the terminal voltage
of the source which, in most cases, is equal to the emf E of the source.
Call the reading V_1.   With the voltmeter connected from a to c, it is
in series with the element.   Call the reading V_2.   The voltage across

the element is equal to the terminal voltage of the source less the volt-meter reading; hence it is equal to $V_1 - V_2$. From the fact that when two elements are in series, the voltages across them are directly proportional to their resistance values, $R_x/R_v = (V_1 - V_2)/V_2$ or

$$R_x = \frac{R_v(V_1 - V_2)}{V_2}$$

where R_v is the resistance of the voltmeter.

The accuracy of this method of measuring resistance depends upon the relative magnitudes of V_1 and V_2 and the accuracy with which each

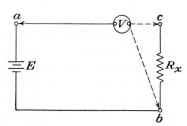

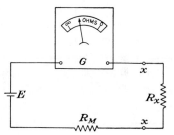

FIG. 2.37   Circuit for measuring the resistance R_x with a voltmeter. One reading is taken with the voltmeter connected from a to b and a second with it connected from a to c.

FIG. 2.38   Circuit of an ohm-meter.

can be read.   The given value of R_v has usually been determined to a high degree of accuracy.   If V_1 and V_2 are nearly equal, a small percentage error in either or both values may cause a much larger percentage error in their difference and a corresponding large percentage error in the computed value of R_x.   If V_2 is a small part of full-scale deflection of the voltmeter, the error in the reading may be a large percentage of the value read. V_1 and V_2 should differ by at least 10 per cent of full-scale deflection and V_2 should be not less than 10 per cent of full-scale deflection if R_x is to be determined with reasonable accuracy.

2.16. Ohmmeters.   A permanent-magnet moving-coil movement may be used in an ohmmeter, an instrument with a scale calibrated in ohms. A small dry cell is a common source of the current to produce movement of the pointer.   In Fig. 2.38 a movement G, a cell of emf E v, and a multiplier of known resistance R_M ohms are in series between the terminals x-x.   When no external connections are made to the terminals, there is no current in the coil and the instrument pointer is at the left-hand end of the scale.   This position may be marked on the scale as ∞ ohms since it corresponds to infinite resistance externally.   When a lead of negligible resistance connects the terminals, the current in the coil depends upon the value of E and the internal resistance in the ohm-meter. Assume that E is 1.5 v and the movement requires 1 ma for full-scale deflection. To use fully the instrument scale, the deflection should be full scale when the external resistance is zero. If R_G ohms is the galvanometer resistance, then $R_G + R_M$ should be

$$\frac{1.5 \text{ v}}{0.001 \text{ amp}} = 1,500 \text{ ohms}$$

for full-scale deflection with the terminals short-circuited. If 1,500 ohms are used, the right-hand end of the scale may be marked 0 ohms.

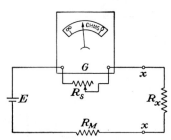

If an external resistance of 1,000 ohms is connected, the current in the coil is 1.5 v/(1,000 + 1,500) ohms = 0.0006 amp, or 0.6 ma. The corresponding pointer deflection is 0.6 of full scale and that point may be marked 1,000 ohms. In a similar manner the percentages of full-scale deflection corresponding to various assumed external resistances can be computed and the scale marked accordingly. Then the resistance of an element of unknown resistance can be read on the scale after the element has been connected to the terminals.

FIG. 2.39 Ohmmeter circuit with a shunt of resistance R_s across the galvanometer. By adjusting R_s some correction can be made for changes in the value of E.

In the above ohmmeter the pointer deflection is one-half of full scale when the external resistance is equal to $R_M + R_G$. The instrument is usually rated in terms of the ohms represented by mid-scale deflection.

The above ohmmeter does not measure ohms by dividing voltage by current. It is a voltmeter calibrated to read in ohms for a given value of E. Since the emf of a cell decreases with age, a means is provided to make adjustments for changes in the emf. One method is to connect an adjustable shunt in parallel with the movement as in Fig. 2.39. In using such an ohmmeter, the terminals x-x are first short-circuited. Then the shunt resistance R_s is adjusted until the pointer deflection is full scale. Next the short circuit is removed. Then the element whose resistance is to be measured is connected between the terminals and its resistance read on the scale. Unfortunately, when the resistance of the shunt is changed, the equivalent resistance of the internal ohmmeter circuit is changed and the scale calibration is changed. The error in a scale reading depends upon how large the movement resistance is with respect to the total resistance of the internal circuit.

Example 1. A movement that has a resistance of 50 ohms and requires 1 ma for full-scale deflection is to be used in the circuit of Fig. 2.39 to make an ohmmeter with a mid-scale reading of 1,200 ohms.   During the useful life of the cell its emf decreases from 1.5 to 1.3 v.

   a. Determine the values of R_M and R_S so that the mid-scale reading will be correct when the emf is 1.4 v.

   b. When the emf is 1.5 v, what value of R_S will give full-scale pointer deflection with the terminals *x-x* short-circuited?   With this value of R_S what is the error in the reading at mid-scale deflection?

   Solution.   *a.* The circuits for the given conditions are in Fig. 2.40.   Since the current in the movement is to be one-half as much with 1,200 ohms connected

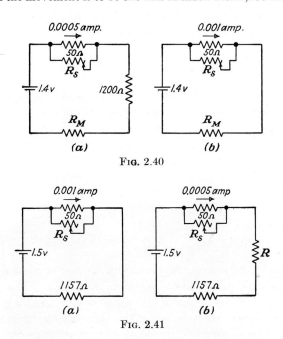

Fig. 2.40

Fig. 2.41

between the terminals *x-x* as with zero resistance between the points, the resist ance of the circuit within the ohmmeter must be 1,200 ohms.   The cell current in Fig. 2.40*b* is 1.4 v/1,200 ohms = 0.00117 amp and the current in R_S is

$$0.00117 - 0.001 = 0.00017 \text{ amp}$$

By proportion, $R_S/50 = 0.001/0.00017$, or $R_S = 300$ ohms.
   The voltage across the movement in Fig. 2.40*b* is

$$50 \text{ ohms} \times 0.001 \text{ amp} = 0.05 \text{ v}$$

The voltage across R_M is 1.4 − 0.05 = 1.35 v.   Then

$$R_M = \frac{1.35 \text{ v}}{0.00117 \text{ amp}} = 1{,}157 \text{ ohms}$$

   b. The circuits for the given conditions are in Fig. 2.41.   In *a* the voltage across the movement and the shunt is 0.05 v; hence the voltage across the 1,157-

ohm resistor is $1.5 - 0.05 = 1.45$ v. The cell current is

$$\frac{1.45 \text{ v}}{1{,}157 \text{ ohms}} = 0.00125 \text{ amp}$$

The current in the shunt is $0.00125 - 0.001 = 0.00025$ amp and

$$R_s = \frac{0.05 \text{ v}}{0.00025 \text{ amp}} = 200 \text{ ohms}$$

In Fig. 2.41b, the pointer deflection is one-half that in circuit a; hence R is equal to the resistance of the remainder of the circuit or

$$1{,}157 + \frac{50 \times 200}{50 + 200} = 1{,}197 \text{ ohms}$$

With an external resistance of 1,197 ohms the ohmmeter reading is 1,200 ohms. The error is 3 ohms or $(3 \times 100)/1{,}197 = 0.25$ per cent.

2.17. Recorders and Oscillographs. A d-c ammeter indicates correctly the instantaneous value of a current only if the current is constant

Fig. 2.42   Parts of a low-frequency recorder.   (*Sanborn Company.*)

or changing slowly. If the current is changing rapidly, the inertia of the moving parts and the damping in the instrument prevent the pointer from indicating correctly the instantaneous values. For use in measuring or recording currents or voltages whose variations contain frequency components less than 60 c, recording instruments have been developed. The galvanometer is combined with a paper drive mechanism, as shown in

Fig. 2.42.   The galvanometer is a moving-coil mechanism in a magnetic
field produced by the permanent mag-
net shown.   A writing arm, at the
end of which is a stylus, is attached
to the coil.   The stylus is a ribbon of
phosphor bronze that can be heated
by sending current through it; 3.5
amp at 1.25 v is required.   The recording paper used is heat sensitive.   It
is pulled over a sharp edge by the
paper drive mechanism.   As the
heated stylus moves over this edge, it
makes a record in rectangular coordinates.   A record specimen is shown
in Fig. 2.43.   The paper speed can
be adjusted in steps from 0.25 to 100
mm per sec.

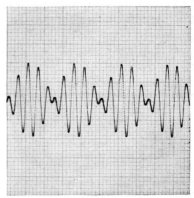

Fig. 2.43   Record obtained with the
recorder of Fig. 2.42.   (*Sanborn Company.*)

The moving coil of a magnetic-type oscillograph has less inertia than

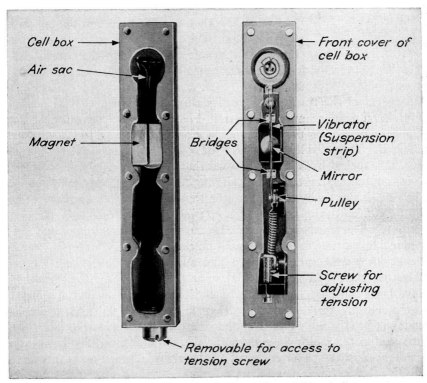

Cell box

Air sac

Magnet

Bridges

Front cover of
cell box

Vibrator
(Suspension
strip)

Mirror

Pulley

Screw for
adjusting
tension

Removable for access to
tension screw

Fig. 2.44   An oscillograph galvanometer.   (*General Electric Company.*)

that of the recorder described above and follows closely the instantaneous current values over a greater range of frequencies than does that of the recorder. The oscillograph vibrator of Fig. 2.44 consists of a strip of phosphor bronze that extends from an insulated terminal over two supporting bridges, around an insulated pulley, then back over the bridges to a second terminal. The tension in the strip can be adjusted. The strip rests in slots on the bridges to keep its outgoing portion parallel to

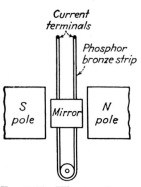

Current
terminals

Phosphor
bronze strip

S
pole

Mirror

N
pole

Fig. 2.45   Vibrator of moving-coil oscillograph between poles of a permanent magnet.

and insulated from the returning portion. Midway between the bridges a small rectangular mirror is cemented to the two portions of the strip. A vibrator is placed between the two poles of a permanent magnet, as in Fig. 2.45. The magnet forms part of the sides of a cell that is filled with a colorless oil to damp out the natural mechanical vibrations of the vibrator. The cell has a lens through which light passes to and from the mirror. When current is sent through the vibrator, one portion of the strip moves slightly in one direction and the other portion moves in the opposite direction. This turns the mirror through an angle that is proportional to the current. A light beam reflected from the mirror also turns through an angle that is proportional to the current.

A record of the time variation of a current obtained with an oscillograph is an oscillogram. As shown in Fig. 2.46, light from an incandescent lamp filament F passes through a triangular prism P to the vibrator mirror E. Reflected light from E is directed upon a long, narrow mirror M. M is rocked by a cam, so shaped that the light beam reflected from M is swept along a ground-glass viewing screen VS at constant velocity. The cam is driven by a small motor that also rotates a shutter. The shutter cuts off the light from the lamp while M is returning to its starting position. The trace of the light beam moves in the direction of line AA' to give a linear time axis. If there is no current in the vibrator, mirror E is stationary and an illuminated line appears on the viewing screen. Changing current in the vibrator causes the trace of the light beam to move back and forth along line BB and the current-time curve appears on the screen. If the vibrator current is cyclic, the light beam can be made to trace the same path each time it traverses the screen by adjusting the speed of the motor that rocks M. To obtain an oscillogram, a film or a light-sensitive paper is placed on the viewing screen and exposed to the light beam for a short time. Then the film is developed and the permanent record obtained.

If the vibrator current is not cyclic, the current-time record is obtained by lifting the mirror M out of the path of the light beam and allowing the beam to enter a drum D through a slit that can be closed by a shutter. Inside the drum, film or paper is rotated on the outside of a cylinder. A time axis is introduced by rotating the cylinder at constant speed. An interlocked system of relays opens the shutter on the drum and makes a desired change in the electric circuit being studied, at the position of the rotating drum where it is desired that exposure of the film be started.

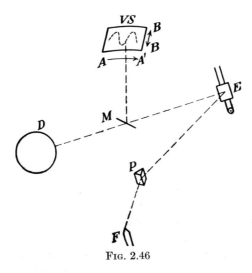

FIG. 2.46

The magnetic type of oscillograph is current actuated, with a vibrator current of the order of 100 ma or less. If the wave form of a voltage is to be studied, a resistor is connected in series with the vibrator across the voltage source.

The cathode-ray type of oscillograph is voltage actuated. A cathode-ray tube contains a heated cathode which is a source of electrons; means for forming the electrons into a concentrated beam; beam-deflecting devices; and a fluorescent viewing screen which is illuminated when struck by the beam. In Fig. 2.47 are represented the cathode, two sets of deflecting plates, and the viewing screen. Through the action of several electrodes in the tube that are not represented, electrons are caused to leave the cathode and travel through the evacuated tube to the viewing screen. The application of voltage between the vertical deflecting plates produces an electric field between them. As an electron passes through this field, its path of flight is deflected toward the plate that is positive. As a result it strikes the viewing screen and produces a light spot there at a different point than does an electron that made the trip

during an interval when no voltage was applied between the plates.   With
an alternating voltage applied between the plates, the spot of light moves
up and down with a deflection at any instant that is proportional to the
voltage at that instant.   In a similar manner the spot of light can be
made to move back and forth in a horizontal plane by applying an alternating voltage to the horizontal deflecting plates.   Electrons are conducted from the viewing screen back to the cathode along a strip of
conducting material painted inside the tube.

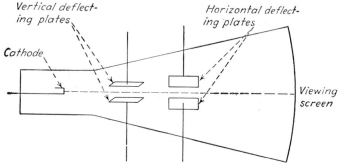

FIG. 2.47   Relative locations of certain parts of a cathode-ray tube.

The cathode-ray oscillograph can be used to show the relations between
any two quantities, if one voltage can be obtained that is proportional at
every instant to one of the quantities and a second voltage can be obtained
that is proportional at every instant to the second quantity.   If the time
variation of a quantity is to be shown, a linear horizontal time axis is
obtained by applying to the horizontal plates a voltage that varies
linearly with time.

Oscillograms can be obtained from a cathode-ray oscillograph by
photographing the pattern that appears on the viewing screen.

2.18. Energy and Power.   Power is the time rate of change of energy.
In an electric circuit the instantaneous power is $p = dw/dt$ w (j per sec),
where w is the energy in joules and t is the time in seconds.

In a branch of an electric circuit the power p is equal to the product
of the voltage v v across the branch and the current i amp in the branch,
or $p = vi$ w.   The value of a watt is fixed by the definitions of the volt
and the ampere.

The preceding equation holds for any circuit or branch of a circuit
regardless of the kind of voltage and of current being considered.   At
any instant the power is equal to the product of the instantaneous voltage
and the instantaneous current.   In Fig. 2.48 both the current and the
voltage are varying with time.   Note that the power also varies with
time and is zero when either the voltage or the current is zero.   Note

further that there are time intervals during which the power is positive and others during which it is negative. If the power is considered as positive when energy is being delivered to a branch of a circuit, the power is negative when energy is being delivered by the branch. Any branch for which the power is bidirectional contains a source of energy. If resistance only is present, the sign of the voltage and that of the current reverse together and their product is always positive.

In a branch of a d-c circuit in which a constant current I amp is produced by the constant voltage V v, the power P is constant and is

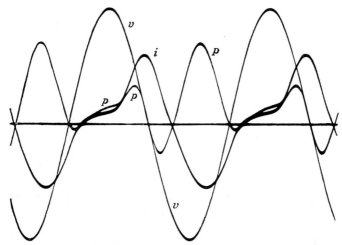

Fig. 2.48　Oscillograms of the voltage v, the current i, and the power p to a half-wave tube rectifier.

$P = VI$ w. If the branch contains resistance R ohms only, then $V = IR$ and $P = I^2R$ w, or $I = V/R$, and $P = V^2/R$ w.

When the rate P w at which energy is put into a branch is constant, the energy W put into the branch during a given time interval is equal to the product of the rate and the interval. Hence $W = P(t_2 - t_1)$ j, where t_1 and t_2 are the respective times in seconds at the beginning and at the end of the interval. The preceding relation may be expressed as $W = PT$ j or as $W = VIT$ j, where T in seconds is the time during which the current, the voltage, and the power are constant.

When the rate p w at which energy is put into a branch of an electric circuit varies during a time interval, the energy W put into the branch during the interval depends upon the manner in which p varies. If the relation between the power and the time is given by an equation or a curve, the energy during an interval from t_1 to t_2 is equal to the area bounded by the curve, the time axis, and the power ordinates at t_1 and t_2.

Example 1. In a certain 8-ohm resistor the current is constant at 10 amp for 2 sec; then it is suddenly changed to 5 amp and kept constant at that value for 3 sec. Next it is suddenly changed to 20 amp and kept constant at that value for 5 sec. How much energy is put into the resistor during the total elapsed time of 10 sec?

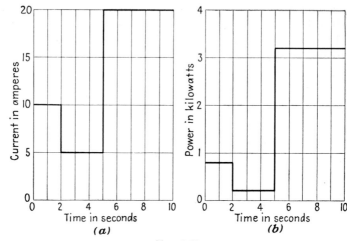

FIG. 2.49

Solution. The current-time curve is in Fig. 2.49a. The power-time curve is in Fig. 2.49b and was obtained as follows: While the current was 10 amp, the power was $10^2 \times 8 = 800$ w. While the current was 5 amp, the power was $5^2 \times 8 = 200$ w. While the current was 20 amp, the power was

$$20^2 \times 8 = 3,200 \text{ w}$$

The energy put into the resistor during the 10-sec interval is equal to the area under the power-time curve. This area is

$$800 \text{ w} \times 2 \text{ sec} + 200 \text{ w} \times 3 \text{ sec} + 3,200 \text{ w} \times 5 \text{ sec} = 18,200 \text{ j}$$

Example 2. The current in an 8-ohm resistor varied linearly from 5 amp at $t = 0$ to 25 amp at $t = 10$ sec. How much energy was put into the resistor during this interval?

Solution. The equation of the current-time curve is $i = 5 + 2t$ amp. The equation of the power-time curve is

$$p = i^2 R = (5 + 2t)^2 \times 8 = 200 + 160t + 32t^2 \text{ w}$$

The area under this curve from $t = 0$ to $t = 10$ sec is the energy W and is

$$W = \int_{t_1}^{t_2} p \, dt = \int_0^{10} (200 + 160t + 32t^2) \, dt = \left[200t + 80t^2 + \frac{32t^3}{3} \right]_0^{10}$$
$$= 20,670 \text{ j}$$

In a branch of a d-c circuit the energy input W during a given time interval T is $W = VIT$. Here the current $I = Q/T$; hence

$$W = V \frac{Q}{T} T = VQ$$

From this $V = W/Q$, with V in volts, W in joules, and Q in coulombs. The voltage between the branch terminals is equal to the work done upon or by each unit charge as it moves from one terminal to the other. The charge of an electron is 1.6×10^{-19} coul. While an electron travels between two points that differ in potential by 1 v, an energy transfer of 1.6×10^{-19} j occurs. This quantity of energy is an electron volt.

Example 3. How much energy is acquired or given up by an electron while traveling through a potential difference of 600 v?

Solution. Assume that the electron enters the negative terminal of a resistor to which 600 v are applied. If it leaves the positive terminal with a velocity equal to that with which it entered the negative terminal, its kinetic energy is unchanged. An energy transfer of 600 electron volts or

$$600 \times 1.6 \times 10^{-19} = 9.6 \times 10^{-17} \text{ j}$$

from a source to the resistor has occurred for each electron passing through.

If the electron moves in a vacuum through a potential of 600 v from negative to positive and starts from rest, its kinetic energy increases from zero to 600 electron volts (9.6×10^{-17} j). If it is assumed that the velocity v attained is small compared with that of light, the velocity may be computed by equating the kinetic energy $\frac{1}{2} m_0 v^2$ to 9.6×10^{-17} j, where m_0, the rest mass, is 9×10^{-31} kg. From this it is found that $v = 1.46 \times 10^7$ m per sec. This velocity is about $\frac{1}{20}$ of 3×10^8 m per sec, the velocity of light, and the assumption of constant mass causes little error.

Electrical and mechanical units of power are related by

$$746 \text{ w} = 1 \text{ hp}$$

The form in which energy exists can be changed. Because the energy put into a resistor in an electric circuit is converted into heat and then is not available in the electrical form, a common expression is that a resistor consumes energy.

One unit of heat energy is the kilogram-calorie, defined as the heat energy required to raise the temperature of 1 kg of water from 15 to 16 C, since that quantity happens to be $\frac{1}{100}$ of the amount of heat required to raise the temperature of 1 kg of water from 0 to 100 C.; 1 kg-cal of heat energy is equal to 4,200 j, from which 1 j = 0.00024 kg-cal.

The specific heat of a material is the ratio of the amount of heat required to raise the temperature of a given mass of the material from 15 to 16 C to that required to raise the temperature of an equal mass of water from 15 to 16 C.

2.19. Power Measurement. In a d-c circuit the power is usually computed as the product of the measured voltage and current. If the voltage is constant the power is directly proportional to the current. If the voltage changes little as the current varies over a wide range, the current is often used as a measure of the power. For example, a 50-kw generator might deliver 400 amp at 125 v. If it were delivering 200 amp, it would be said to be delivering half load even though the voltage might differ from 125 v and the power was not exactly 25 kw.

In some d-c circuits the voltage may vary over such a range that it is desirable to have an instrument, a wattmeter, to measure the power. In an a-c circuit the instantaneous power varies with the time. As in Fig. 2.48, instantaneous power variations can be recorded. However, when these variations are cyclical the average power is the value usually measured. It is equal to the area under the power curve during a given time interval divided by the length of the interval. In a d-c circuit in which the voltage and the current are constant, the average power is equal to the instantaneous power.

Example 1. The power input to a certain circuit was constant at 2 kw for 20 min, then it was constant at 4 kw for 5 min, and next it was constant at 3 kw for 25 min. Compute the energy input and the average power input for the total 50-min interval.

Solution. The energy input was

$$2 \text{ kw} \times 20 \text{ min} + 4 \text{ kw} \times 5 \text{ min} + 3 \text{ kw} \times 25 \text{ min} = 135 \text{ kwmin}$$

The average power was 135 kwmin/50 min = 2.7 kw.

In an a-c circuit the average power may be equal to or it may be less than the product of the voltmeter and the ammeter readings. In a circuit that is in a cyclic state the instantaneous values of voltage and current are multiplied to produce an instantaneous torque on the movement of a wattmeter that is proportional to the instantaneous power. The inertia of the movement is enough that with a frequency of perhaps 15 c or higher the instrument pointer cannot follow the instantaneous power values. Instead the pointer has a steady deflection proportional to the average power. A wattmeter has two electric circuits. Through one is sent the current of the element whose power is being measured. To the other is applied the voltage across the element. The current circuit is made to have a low resistance so that the voltage drop caused by rated current through it is of the order of 0.5 v or less. The voltage circuit is made to have a high resistance so that with rated voltage applied the current in it is of the order of 100 ma or less.

When a wattmeter measures the power taken by a given element, there are I^2R losses in both the current and the voltage circuits. Most wattmeters cannot be so connected that the loss in one of the circuits is not registered on the instrument.

2.20. Root-mean-square Value of a Current.   When a current varies cyclically, its heating effect may be compared with that of a direct current. The rms value of a cyclically varying current is equal to the value of the continuous current that, when sent through a resistor of constant resistance for a period equal to that of one cycle, produces an amount of heat in the resistor equal to that which would be produced during an equal period when the varying current is sent through the resistor.

Example 1.   Consider a resistor of R ohms resistance in which the current is constant at 4 amp for 3 sec, next is constant at 10 amp for the next 2 sec, and then

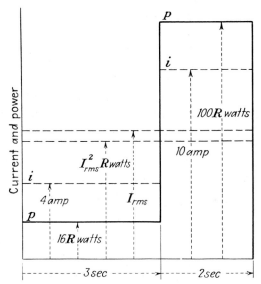

Fig. 2.50   Graphical representation of a certain varying current i, the power p produced by that current in a resistor of constant resistance R, and a constant current I_{rms} that produces the power $I_{rms}^2 R$.   The area under the curve p is equal to that of the rectangle of which $I_{rms}^2 R$ is the altitude.   The constant current I_{rms} would produce the same amount of heat in the resistor during a 5-sec interval as is produced by the varying current i in an equal period.

continues this cycle of values.   The rms current I_{rms} that, if constant during the 5-sec interval, would produce an amount of heat equal to that of the varying current is to be determined.   The heat energy of the varying current is

$$4^2 \times R \times 3 + 10^2 \times R \times 2 = 248R \qquad \text{j}$$

A constant current of I_{rms} amp during a 5-sec interval would produce I_{rms}^2 $\times R \times 5$ j.   Equating the two energy values, $5I_{rms}^2 R = 248R$, from which $I_{rms} = 7.04$ amp.

The above relations are shown graphically in Fig. 2.50.   The time variations of the current are shown by the curve i, the time variations of the power by the curve p, and the rms current by I_{rms}. The area under the power curve is equal to that under the horizontal line $I_{rms}^2 R$.

For a constant resistance the time variation of the power will be similar to that of the square of the current. Because of this the rms value of a current may be computed by determining the area under the current-squared wave during the time interval being considered, dividing this area by the interval, and extracting the square root of the quotient. The area under the current-squared wave divided by the time interval is the mean (or the average) of the squared current values. The square root of the mean of the squared values is the rms value. It is also known as an effective or a virtual value.

When the time variation of a current is given by a graphical record or an equation, the area under the current-squared wave can be determined by the principles of Art. 1.7. From those principles the rms value of a current can be approximated by these rules: (1) Choose a time interval that includes a set of current values that are repeated. If the positive and negative portions of the wave are not similar, an interval of one cycle should be used. If the portions are similar, an interval of one-half cycle may be used. If the portions are similar and each is symmetrical with respect to the maximum current ordinate, an interval of one-quarter cycle that includes all values between the minimum and the maximum may be used. (2) Divide the time interval into a number of equal increments. (3) Scale or compute the initial current value, the current values at the division points, and the final current value. (4) Square each of these values. Add one-half the square of the initial value, the squares of the values at the division points, and one-half the square of the final value. (5) Divide the sum by the number of increments used, to obtain the mean of the squared values. (6) Extract the square root of the quotient to obtain the approximate rms value.

Example 2. The current in a certain circuit varies according to the equation $i = 20 \sin 300t$ amp, where t is in seconds. The quantity 300 is in radians per second in order that $300t$ will be in radians. Compute the rms current.

Solution. This type of equation appears often in a-c circuit computations. The value of a sine function varies from $+1$ to -1. The given current attains a maximum positive value of 20 amp when the sine function is 1. The angle in radians whose sine is 1, is $\pi/2$, $5\pi/2$, $9\pi/2$, etc. The current first attains a maximum positive value when $300t = \pi/2$, or at $t = \pi/600$ sec. It attains the same maximum positive value again when $300t = 5\pi/2$, or at $t = \pi/120$ sec. The current is zero when the sine function is zero. This occurs when $300t$ is 0, π, or any integer multiple of π radians. The current attains a maximum negative value of -20 amp when $300t$ is $3\pi/2$, $7\pi/2$, $11\pi/2$, etc. The current first attains a maximum negative value when $300t = 3\pi/2$, or at $t = \pi/200$ sec. It attains the same maximum negative value again at $300t = 7\pi/2$, or at $t = 7\pi/600$ sec. The current wave (a sine wave) is in Fig. 2.51. By inspection it is seen that one cycle of values occurs in $2\pi/300$ sec. To compute the rms value of the wave, a time interval of one-quarter cycle may be used. If the interval is divided into five equal increments, each is $\pi/10$ radians, or $18°$. Ordinates will be located at

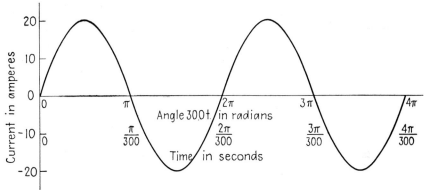

Fig. 2.51　A sine wave of current.

$0°$, $18°$, $36°$, $54°$, $72°$, and $90°$. The remaining steps in the computation are in Table 2.1. The sine values were taken from a table of trigonometric functions.

TABLE 2.1

Angle, degrees	Sine of angle	i amp $20 \times$ sine of angle	i^2 amp squared			
0	0	0	0	$0 \times \frac{1}{2} =$		0
18	0.309	6.18	38	$38 \times 1 =$		38
36	0.588	11.76	138	$138 \times 1 =$		138
54	0.809	16.18	262	$262 \times 1 =$		262
72	0.951	19.02	362	$362 \times 1 =$		362
90	1.00	20.00	400	$400 \times \frac{1}{2} =$		200
Sum of weighted i^2 values	.....	.....	...			1,000

$$\text{Average } i^2 = 1,000/5 = 200$$
$$I_{rms} = \sqrt{200} = 14.14 \text{ amp}$$

The exact rms value of the current $i = 20 \sin 300t$ can be computed by calculus. Since $i^2 = 400 \sin^2 300t$, the area A under the current-squared wave is

$$A = \int_0^{\pi/2} 400 \sin^2 300 \, dt = 400 \left[\frac{300t}{2} - \frac{\sin 600t}{4} \right]_0^{\pi/2} = 100\pi \text{ amp}^2\text{-radians}$$

With a time interval of $\pi/2$ radians, the mean of the squared values, is

$$I^2_{\text{rms}} = \frac{100\pi \text{ amp}^2\text{-radians}}{\pi/2 \text{ radians}} = 200 \text{ amp}^2$$

The rms current is $I_{\text{rms}} = \sqrt{200 \text{ amp}^2} = 14.14$ amp.

It happens that the rms value computed in the table above from selected ordinates is the exact value. The rms value of a sine wave is $14.14/20 = 0.707$

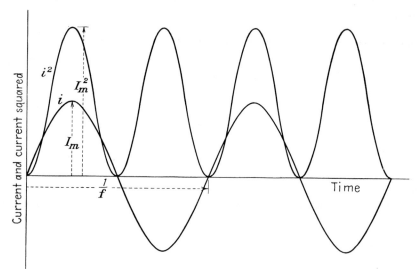

Fig. 2.52   Time variations of the current and of the current squared for a sinusoidal current. The time for 1 cycle is $1/f$ sec, where f is the frequency of the current in cycles per second.

times the maximum ordinate. For a current wave that is not sinusoidal, the ratio of the maximum to the rms value may be, but is not necessarily, equal to $\sqrt{2} = 1.414$. For a current that does not vary with time, the instantaneous, maximum, average, and rms values are equal.

Curves showing how a sinusoidal current and the current-squared values vary with time are in Fig. 2.52.

Most a-c ammeters are so constructed as to read rms current. Although the rms value is defined in terms of the heating effect of a current, most types of a-c ammeters do not utilize heat in producing the deflection of the instrument pointer. Certain magnetic effects of the current that vary as the square of the current are utilized in measuring the rms current. The thermocouple ammeter is the only common type that utilizes the heating effect of a current, and it is seldom used except in high-frequency circuits.

In a d-c circuit the average and the rms current values are equal or nearly so.   In such a circuit an a-c ammeter may be used to measure the current.

The rms value of a cyclically varying voltage is equal to the value of the continuous voltage that, when applied to a resistor of constant resistance for a period equal to that of one cycle, produces an amount of heat in the resistor equal to that which would be produced during an equal period when the varying voltage is applied to the resistor.   The rms value of a voltage can be computed by methods similar to those outlined for computing the rms value of a current.

In determining the rms voltage or current from an oscillogram, it is unnecessary after scaling the ordinates to convert each into terms of volts or amperes.   Instead one may scale the ordinates and compute the rms value in terms of any convenient unit of length, and then apply the conversion factor to express the result in terms of the desired unit.

2.21. Heating and Cooling Curves.   The losses in electric machines and circuits are converted into heat.   Of the heat produced in a given circuit, part is stored in the material comprising the circuit; the remainder is transferred to the surrounding medium, often air.   The amount of heat stored in a given circuit depends upon the volume and the specific heat of the material and the difference between the temperature of the material and that of the surrounding medium.   The amount of heat transferred depends upon the surface area of the circuit and the temperature difference between the surface and the medium.

Assume that a copper wire crosses a room in which the air temperature is maintained at 25 C and that initially the wire is at that temperature. Now assume that in the wire there is suddenly produced a current that causes an I^2R loss of P w.   Further assume that as the resistance of the wire changes the current is changed to keep the loss at P w.   During the first second following the establishment of current, P j of heat energy is produced in the wire and its temperature will start to rise at a certain rate. As soon as its temperature exceeds that of the air, the wire will begin to transfer heat to the air.   As a result, part of the P j are stored in the wire and the remainder are transferred to the air.   During the next second an additional P j is produced in the wire and the temperature will rise still more.   Of this second increment of energy, less than of the first will be stored in the wire and more will be transferred because of the increased temperature difference between the wire and the air.   Since it is the amount of energy stored in the wire that determines its temperature rise, the rise will be greater during the first second than during the next one. As time goes on, during each second more heat is transferred and less is stored than during the preceding one.   As a result the rate of temperature increase becomes less and less as time increases.   The wire will reach a constant temperature when all the heat produced in it is transferred.

The temperature varies with time as shown by the heating curve in Fig. 2.53.

In an actual machine or circuit the conditions seldom duplicate those assumed above. However, if a thermometer is placed on a machine being tested, the load kept constant, and the thermometer readings recorded at frequent intervals, it will be found that the temperature variation agrees in general with the heating curve. At first the temperature rises rapidly, later more slowly, and finally becomes constant after perhaps 2 hr or more.

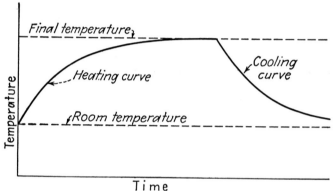

FIG. 2.53   Heating and cooling curves of an electrical machine.

The cooling curve of a machine shows the decrease of temperature with time after heat is no longer generated within the machine. The temperature decreases from the original operating value to that of the surrounding air. At the beginning of the cooling period a certain quantity of heat is stored in the machine. At this time the greatest difference in temperatures exists, so heat is transferred at its most rapid rate and the temperature drops most rapidly. As soon as a decrease of machine temperature occurs, the rate of heat transfer decreases. Continuation of this causes the rate of temperature change to become less and less as time increases, as shown by the cooling curve in Fig. 2.53.

2.22. Efficiency. The ratio of the output to the input of a circuit element—both expressed in the same unit of power or energy—is the efficiency of the element. If a given generator delivering 800 w requires 1,000 w to drive it, the generator efficiency for that load condition is 800/1,000 = 0.8 per unit, or 0.8 per unit × 100 per cent/1 per unit = 80 per cent. If, during a working day, the generator delivered 5 kwhr to a varying load and the energy input during that period was 7 kwhr, the all-day efficiency was 5/7 = 0.714 per unit, or 71.4 per cent.

The difference between the input and the output of a given circuit or

machine represents the loss in it. The efficiency may be expressed by
any one of the following:

$$\text{Per cent efficiency} = \frac{\text{output}}{\text{input}} \times 100$$

$$\text{Per cent efficiency} = \frac{\text{output}}{\text{output} + \text{loss}} \times 100$$

$$\text{Per cent efficiency} = \frac{\text{input} - \text{loss}}{\text{input}} \times 100$$

$$\text{Per cent efficiency} = \left(1 - \frac{\text{loss}}{\text{input}}\right) \times 100$$

$$\text{Per cent efficiency} = \left(1 - \frac{\text{loss}}{\text{output} + \text{loss}}\right) \times 100$$

For computing the efficiency of a given element, one of the preceding
equations may be more convenient to use than another. The full-load

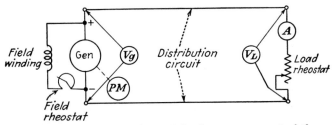

FIG. 2.54 Circuit arrangement for determining by measurement of the output and
the input the efficiency of a distribution circuit.

efficiencies of electric motors range from about 60 per cent for a ¼-hp
motor up to above 90 per cent for 100-hp motors or larger. The full-load
efficiencies of transformers range from about 95 per cent for small sizes
up to 99.5 per cent or more for large sizes.

Example 1. The efficiency of a certain distribution circuit when delivering
50 kw at 220 v is to be determined. Explain how to do this experimentally by
direct measurement of the output and the input.

Solution. The circuit arrangement is shown in Fig. 2.54. A d-c generator
that has a rating of about 50 kw and whose output voltage can be adjusted readily
to values above 220 v is connected across one end of the circuit. For the shunt
generator indicated, the voltage can be adjusted by manipulating the field
rheostat. Across the other end of the circuit is an ammeter in series with a load
rheostat. A voltmeter is connected across each end of the circuit.

For a circuit output of 50 kw the current would be 50,000 w/220 v = 227 amp.
If the two ends of the circuit were some distance apart, operators might be
stationed at the ends with a means of communication between them. Then
one operator could vary the resistance of the load rheostat and the other could
vary the generator voltage until the voltage V_L at the load end of the circuit
was 220 v when the load current was 227 amp. Some time might be required

to arrive at this condition because a change in either the generator voltage or the load rheostat resistance would change both the load voltage and current. After the desired load voltage and current were obtained, the voltage V_g at the generator end of the circuit would be read on the voltmeter there. Assume that the reading is 232 v. The efficiency of the circuit is

$$\frac{\text{Output}}{\text{Input}} \times 100 = \frac{220 \text{ v} \times 227 \text{ amp}}{232 \text{ v} \times 227 \text{ amp}} \times 100 = 94.8 \text{ per cent}$$

In this circuit it happens that the efficiency is the ratio of the output voltage to the input voltage; for circuits in general, the efficiency is not the ratio of voltages.

In the efficiency determination above, disadvantages are that a load rheostat of large capacity is required and that the efficiency was determined for only one load condition.

In the efficiency determination above an error in the ammeter reading does not cause an error in the computed efficiency because that reading cancels in the computations. Of course, if the ammeter is in error the efficiency is not determined for the exact load condition desired. Assume that the voltmeter reading V_L was correct but that the reading V_g was 2 per cent in error. For these conditions the correct value of the efficiency is

$$\frac{220 \times 227}{232(1 \pm 0.02) \times 227} \times 100 = \frac{94.8}{1 \pm 0.02} \text{ per cent}$$

It happens that $1/(1 + 0.02) = 0.98$ (nearly) and $1/(1 - 0.02) = 1.02$ (nearly). Hence the correct value of the efficiency is either 94.8×0.98, or 94.8×1.02 per cent. This means that a 2 per cent error in measuring one voltage resulted in an equal error in the efficiency.

By computations similar to those just made, it can be shown that a 2 per cent error in measuring the output voltage also results in a 2 per cent error in the efficiency. If a 2 per cent error is made in measuring the input voltage and an equal error made in measuring the output voltage, it may happen that the two errors will compensate and the value of the efficiency be correct. However, it may happen that the errors will add and the computed efficiency may be 4 per cent in error.

Example 2. The efficiency of a certain distribution circuit when delivering 50 kw at 220 v is to be determined. Explain how to do this without actually loading the circuit.

Solution. In Example 1 the current for the given load condition was computed as 227 amp. Since the only loss is the I^2R in the wires, it can be computed if their resistance is measured. To measure the resistance, connect the wires together at the load end, and make connections at the generator end as in Fig. 2.55. Any available source of direct voltage could be used with an ammeter and a voltmeter of suitable capacities. Assume that a 6-v battery is used and the rheostat adjusted so that the ammeter reading is 5 amp. Further assume that the corresponding voltmeter reading is 0.27 v. The resistance of the wires is 0.27 v/5 amp = 0.054 ohm.

Now we have the information from which we can compute *what the circuit efficiency would be* if the circuit were loaded to the specified conditions. With

227 amp in the wires, the loss would be $227^2 \times 0.054 = 2{,}780$ w. The efficiency is

$$\eta = \frac{\text{output}}{\text{output} + \text{loss}} \times 100 = \frac{50{,}000}{52{,}780} \times 100 = 94.7 \text{ per cent}$$

In making the above division on a slide rule, one is certain of the 9 and the 4 in the result and is estimating that the third figure is a 7. If the resistance value is exact, then the computed efficiency is correct to two significant figures.

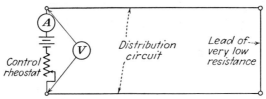

FIG. 2.55　Measuring the resistance of the two wires of a distribution circuit.

The efficiency may be expressed also as

$$\eta = \left(1 - \frac{\text{loss}}{\text{output} + \text{loss}}\right) \times 100 = \left(1 - \frac{2{,}780}{52{,}780}\right) \times 100 = 100 - 5.27$$
$$= 94.73 \text{ per cent}$$

In making the division here on a slide rule, one is certain of the 5 and the 2 and is estimating that the third figure is a 7. If the resistance value is exact, then the computed efficiency is correct to three significant figures, or one more than when the other expression for efficiency was used.

For the preceding cases assume that in the resistance measurements the voltmeter reading was 2 per cent low and that the ammeter reading was 3 per cent high. Then the correct voltage is 0.27×1.02 v and the correct current is 5×0.97 amp. The correct resistance is $(0.27 \times 1.02)/(5 \times 0.97) = 0.0567$ ohm. The correct efficiency is

$$\eta = \left(1 - \frac{227^2 \times 0.0567}{50{,}000 + 227^2 \times 0.0567}\right) \times 100 = 100 - 5.52 = 94.48 \text{ per cent}$$

The efficiency value without making correction for the instrument errors was 94.73 per cent. The percentage error in this value is

$$\frac{(94.73 - 94.48) \times 100}{94.48} = 0.265 \text{ per cent}$$

This means that instrument errors totaling 5 per cent caused an error in the computed efficiency of only about $\frac{1}{4}$ of 1 per cent. This is because the loss was such a small part of the input that a relatively large error in the loss represented a much smaller error in the efficiency. Many electric machines and circuits have high efficiencies and low percentage losses. Their efficiencies are usually determined by measuring the losses rather than by direct measurement of inputs and outputs. In those cases where the losses cannot be measured exactly various approximations are made.

2.23. The Neper; the Bel; and the Decibel. The terms amplification and attenuation are used in connection with certain circuits as a measure of the increase or the decrease of current, voltage, or power that occurs in an element, or combination of elements. If the output current I_o amp is obtained from a circuit element when the input current is I_i amp, the current gain is defined as $\ln (I_o/I_i)^*$ nepers. By this definition if I_o is ϵ times as great as I_i, the current gain is 1 neper; if I_o is ϵ^2 times as great as I_i, the current gain is 2 nepers, etc.

If n_1 is the current gain in nepers in a circuit element having I_2 amp output and I_1 amp input, by the preceding definition $n_1 = \ln (I_2/I_1)$, which may be written as $I_2/I_1 = \epsilon^{n_1}$. If this element delivers the current I_2 to a second one that has an output current I_3 amp, the current gain n_2 of the second element is $n_2 = \ln (I_3/I_2)$ nepers, which may be written as $I_3/I_2 = \epsilon^{n_2}$. The ratio of the output current I_3 of the second unit to the input current I_1 of the first is $I_3/I_1 = I_3/I_2 \times I_2/I_1 = \epsilon^{n_2}\epsilon^{n_1} = \epsilon^{n_1+n_2}$. From this $n_1 + n_2 = \ln (I_3/I_1)$. But $\ln (I_3/I_1)$ is the gain of the combination of the two elements. This result is one of the reasons for the choice of a logarithmic function to define the gain.

If the output voltage V_o v is obtained from a circuit element when the input voltage is V_i v, the voltage gain is defined as $\ln (V_o/V_i)$ nepers. The voltage gain is numerically equal to the current gain only when $V_o/V_i = I_o/I_i$. Many circuit elements are designed to satisfy this condition.

If the output power P_o w is obtained from a circuit element when the input power is P_i w, the power gain is defined as $0.5 \ln (P_o/P_i)$ nepers. The power gain, the voltage gain, and the current gain are numerically equal when $V_o/V_i = I_o/I_i$.

The *bel*, named for Alexander Graham Bell, is a unit of gain defined in terms of logarithms to the base 10. Power gain, corresponding to P_o w output and P_i w input, is defined as $\log (P_o/P_i)$ bels. The decibel (db), one-tenth of a bel, has proved to be a unit of more convenient size than a bel. Hence, in that unit the gain is $10 \log (P_o/P_i)$ db.

If n nepers and d db correspond to the gain represented by the power ratio P_o/P_i, then $n = 0.5 \ln (P_o/P_i)$, from which $P_o/P_i = \epsilon^{2n}$. Also $d = 10 \log (P_o/P_i)$, from which $P_o/P_i = 10^{0.1d}$. Equating the two values of P_o/P_i yields $\epsilon^{2n} = 10^{0.1d}$. Taking the logarithm to the base 10 of each side of the equation yields $2n(0.4343) = 0.1d$, from which $8.686n = d$. Since the number of decibels is greater than the number of nepers, then the neper is a larger unit of gain than the decibel and 1 neper $= 8.686$ db.

If the power output of an element is 10 times the power input, the

---

* ln means $\log_\epsilon$; log means $\log_{10}$.

power gain is 10 log 10 = 10 db. If the power output is 100 times the power input, the power gain is 10 log 100 = 20 db.

If attenuation occurs, the power output is less than the power input and the power gain in decibels is a negative number. When it is known that attenuation occurs, the power loss is a positive number if it is defined by 10 log (P_i/P_o) db.

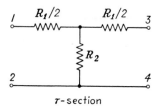

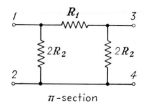

τ-section π-section

FIG. 2.56

2.24. Attenuation Sections. Symmetrical T and π sections, shown in Fig. 2.56, are in common use in networks.

In the circuit of Fig. 2.57 a T section is interposed between a battery of emf E v and a load of resistance R_o ohms. The expression will be derived relating R_o, R_1, and R_2 in order that the resistance R_{12} between terminals 1 and 2 will equal R_o. It can be seen that

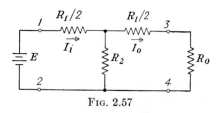

FIG. 2.57

$$R_{12} = \frac{R_1}{2} + \frac{(R_o + R_1/2)R_2}{R_o + R_1/2 + R_2}$$

Equating this to R_o and solving for R_o yields $R_o = \sqrt{R_1^2/4 + R_1R_2}$. Customary procedure is to choose values of R_1 and R_2 that will cause a desired attenuation loss and also satisfy the preceding equation.

Example 1. In the circuit of Fig. 2.57, $R_o = 200$ ohms and the current loss is to be 4 db. Compute the values of R_1 and R_2.

Solution. One condition to be satisfied is that $200 = \sqrt{R_1^2/4 + R_1R_2}$. The other is that $4 = 20 \log (I_i/I_o)$. Since I_i, the total current taken by two parallel resistive branches, is to I_o, the current in one of the branches, as the resistance of the branch is to the equivalent resistance of the two parallel branches, then

$$\frac{I_i}{I_o} = \frac{R_1/2 + 200}{(R_1/2 + 200)R_2/(R_1/2 + R_2 + 200)} = \frac{R_1/2 + R_2 + 200}{R_2}$$

Substitution of this ratio in the preceding equation yields

$$\log \frac{(R_1/2 + R_2 + 200)}{R_2} = 0.2$$

from which $(R_1/2 + R_2 + 200)/R_2 = 10^{0.2} = 1.585$.   Combination of this equation with $200 = \sqrt{R_1^2/4 + R_1R_2}$ yields $R_1 = 90.5$ ohms and $R_2 = 419$ ohms. (A negative value was also obtained for R_1 but was discarded because it has no physical significance.)

In the circuit of Fig. 2.58 a π section is interposed between a battery of emf E v and a load of resistance R_o ohms.   The expression will be derived relating R_o,

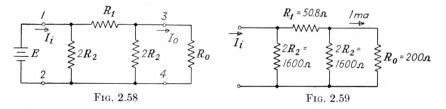

FIG. 2.58   FIG. 2.59

R_1, and R_2 in order that the resistance R_{12} between terminals 1 and 2 will equal R_o.   It can be seen that

$$R_{12} = \frac{2R_2[R_1 + (2R_2R_o)/(2R_2 + R_o)]}{2R_2 + R_1 + (2R_2R_o)/(2R_2 + R_o)}$$
$$= \frac{2R_2(2R_1R_2 + R_1R_o + 2R_2R_o)}{(2R_2 + R_1)(2R_2 + R_o) + 2R_2R_o}$$

Equating this to R_o and solving for R_o yields $R_o = \sqrt{4R_1R_2^2/(R_1 + 4R_2)}$.

Example 2.   In the circuit of Fig. 2.58, $R_o = 200$ ohms and $R_2 = 800$ ohms. Compute the value of R_1 such that $R_{12} = R_o$.   Compute the current loss in the π section.

Solution.   Substitution of the given values of R_o and R_2 in the equation derived yields $200 = \sqrt{4R_1 \times (800)^2/(R_1 + 4 \times 800)}$, from which $R_1 = 50.8$ ohms. In the circuit of Fig. 2.59 the values of R_o, R_1, and R_2 are shown.

Next it is assumed that 1 ma flows in R_o.   The corresponding current in the right-hand 1,600-ohm resistor is $(200/1,600) \times 1 = 0.125$ ma.   Then 1.125 ma flows in R_1 and the voltage across it is 1.125 ma $\times$ 50.8 ohms = 57.3 mv.   The voltage across the left-hand 1,600-ohm resistor is the sum of that across R_1 and R_o; hence it is $57.3 + 200 = 257$ mv.   The current in that resistor is

$$\frac{257 \text{ mv}}{1,600 \text{ ohms}} = 0.161 \text{ ma}$$

Then $I_i = 0.161 + 1.125 = 1.286$ ma.   The current loss is

$$20 \log \frac{1.286}{1} = 20 \times 0.109 = 2.18 \text{ db}$$

2.25. Maximum-power-transfer Theorem.   Assume that a constant voltage source of E v having an internal resistance of R ohms delivers a current I amp to a load of R_l ohms resistance through wires having a total resistance of R_w ohms.   Then $I = E/(R + R_l + R_w)$.   The power P_l delivered to the load is $P_l = I^2R_l = E^2R_l/(R + R_l + R_w)^2$ w.   If R_l is infinite (i.e., an open circuit), the load current is zero, the load voltage is

E v, and the load power is zero. If R_l is zero (i.e., a short circuit), the load current is $E/(R + R_w)$ amp, the load voltage is zero, and the load power is zero. As the load resistance is decreased from an infinite value, the load power at first increases until the load resistance has a value that causes the load power to be a maximum. Then for any further decreases of load resistance, the load power decreases. The value of load resistance for which the load power is a maximum can be obtained by differentiating the preceding equation with respect to R_l, setting the result equal to zero, and solving this new equation for R_l. By this process

$$\frac{d}{dR_l} \frac{E^2 R_l}{(R + R_l + R_w)^2} = E^2 \frac{(R + R_l + R_w)^2 - R_l[2(R + R_l + R_w)]}{(R + R_l + R_w)^4} = 0$$

from which $(R + R_l + R_w)(R + R_w - R_l) = 0$. Setting the first quantity equal to zero yields $R_l = -R - R_w$, a value that may be disregarded because of the physical requirement that R_l be a positive quantity. Setting the second term equal to zero yields $R_l = R + R_w$. Hence the load power is a maximum when the load resistance is equal to the combined resistance of the source and the wires. The load current is $E/2(R + R_w)$ amp, which is one-half of the load current with zero load resistance. The load voltage is $[E/2(R + R_w)](R + R_w) = E/2$ v. The load power is $E/2 \times E/2(R + R_w) = E^2/4(R + R_w)$ w. The power produced in the source is $E \times E/2(R + R_w) = E^2/2(R + R_w)$ w. Since the power delivered is one-half that produced, the efficiency is 50 per cent when the power delivered is a maximum. Power distribution systems are never operated near the condition of maximum power delivered because the cost of the energy lost is too great to be tolerated for economic operation. Communication systems are often operated near the condition of maximum power delivered, since the amount of energy involved is so small that the cost of the energy lost is insignificant.

PROBLEMS

2.1. With 25 amp in a certain conductor the resistance drop is 5 v in a length of 500 ft. Compute the resistance of the conductor.

If the conductor resistance is constant, how much current in the conductor will cause a resistance drop of 1.5 v?

2.2. For a certain carbon-electrode arc lamp the relation between the current through and the voltage across the arc is:

Amperes	Volts	Amperes	Volts
3	75	7	59
4	69	8	57
5	65	9	55
6	62		

Plot curves showing the relation between the voltage and the current and the resistance and the current.

2.3. For a certain vacuum tube the relation between the plate voltage and the plate current is:

Volts	Milliamperes	Volts	Milliamperes
65	10	185	50
100	20	210	60
130	30	245	70
160	40	260	75

Plot curves showing the relation between the current and the voltage and the resistance and the current.

2.4. When a d-c ammeter that has a resistance of 0.01 ohm reads 3 amp, what is the voltage between its terminals?

2.5. When a d-c voltmeter that has a resistance of 15,000 ohms reads 120 v, what is the current in it?

2.6. A certain 150-v d-c voltmeter has a guaranteed accuracy of 0.5 per cent of full-scale deflection. When 10 v is applied to the instrument, it reads 10.7 v. What is the percentage error in the instrument reading? Does the instrument meet its guarantee?

2.7. A 200-ohm resistor is connected to a 24-v source. Compute the current in the resistor. If a 0.5-ohm resistor is inserted in the circuit, compute the voltage across it.

2.8. Several resistors in series draw 30 ma from a 45-v source. If a 3-ohm resistor is inserted in the circuit, compute the voltage across it.

2.9. Two resistors in series draw 5 ma from a 120-v source. The voltage across one resistor is 20 v. Compute the resistance of each resistor.

2.10. A rheostat is in series with a 200-ohm resistor across a 12-v source. The current in the circuit is to be varied from 5 to 25 ma. Through what range should the rheostat resistance be adjustable?

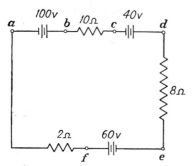

FIG. 2.60

2.11. In Fig. 2.60 compute the voltages V_{cf}, V_{ae}, and V_{bd}. Which point in the circuit is positive with respect to all others? Between which two points is the difference of potential the greatest?

2.12. When a certain automobile storage battery that has an emf of 6.6 v is charged with 25 amp, the voltage between the battery terminals is 7.2 v. Compute the battery internal resistance.

2.13. A certain battery that has an emf of 32 v and an internal resistance of 0.04 ohm is to be charged at 20 amp by connecting it in series with a resistor across a 120-v source. Compute the resistance of the resistor. Near the end of the charging period the battery emf has risen to 38 v. Neglecting the probable change in the internal resistance, what will be the charging current?

2.14. Assume that the emf and the internal resistance of a certain battery are constant at 45 v and 0.25 ohm, respectively. What is the battery terminal voltage when it is being charged with 10 amp? When it is discharging 20 amp?

2.15. When 40 v are applied to the terminals of a battery whose emf is 35 v, the charging current is 20 amp. If 80 v were applied, what would be the charging current? Neglect any change in the internal resistance.

2.16. Two batteries and a resistor are connected as in Fig. 2.61. A voltmeter is to be connected to the terminals A and B to measure the terminal voltage of one

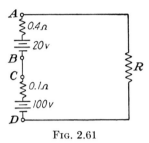

Fig. 2.61

battery. Which voltmeter terminal, positive or negative, should be connected to A if $R = 5.5$ ohms? If $R = 1.5$ ohms? What would the voltmeter read in each case?

2.17. Three dry cells, each having an internal resistance of 0.05 ohm and an emf of 1.5 v, are in series with a 50-ohm receiver and a 35-ohm transmitter to form a simple telephone circuit. The connecting wires have a total resistance of 2 ohms. Compute the receiver voltage.

2.18. Two voltmeters, with respective resistances of 10,000 and 15,000 ohms, are connected in series to measure a voltage greater than the capacity of either. The first voltmeter reads 80 v. Compute the voltage being measured.

2.19. A certain resistor has a conductance of 2,500 micromhos (μmho). Compute its resistance.

2.20. A decade conductance unit is to be adjustable in 0.1-mho steps from 0 to 1 mho using 11 contact points with resistors between points. Compute the resistance values required.

2.21. In Fig. 2.62 compute the currents in the resistors and in the leads joining the resistors.

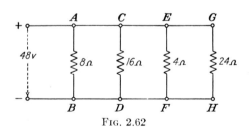

Fig. 2.62

2.22. A 50-, a 200-, and a 500-ohm resistor are in parallel. The current in the 200-ohm resistor is 50 ma. Compute the current in and the voltage across each of the other resistors.

2.23. A 40-, an 80-, and a 100-ohm resistor in parallel draw a total of 3.8 amp. Compute the current in and the voltage across each resistor.

2.24. Compute the equivalent resistance between the points A and B in the circuit of Fig. 2.63.

2.25. In the circuit of Fig. 2.63, 10 amp are entering terminal A. Compute the current in the 12-ohm resistor.

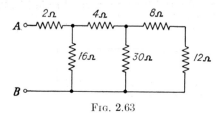

FIG. 2.63

2.26. Compute the equivalent resistance of seven 35-ohm resistors in parallel.

2.27. Three resistors in parallel have respective conductances of 0.2, 0.8, and 0.5 mho. The current in the first resistor is 4 amp. Compute the currents in the other resistors, the total current, and the voltage across the resistors.

2.28. Resistors of 10, 50, and 200 ohms, respectively, are available. How would you connect the resistors to obtain an equivalent resistance slightly less than 10 ohms? Compute the resistance.

2.29. A 20- and a 50-ohm resistor are in parallel. This combination is in series with an 8-ohm resistor across the terminals of a battery. The current in the 50-ohm resistor is 3 amp. Compute the voltages across the other resistors and the battery terminal voltage.

2.30. In Fig. 2.64 all resistances are negligible except those indicated. Compute the currents in the resistors and in the leads, AB, CD, DE, EF, and GH.

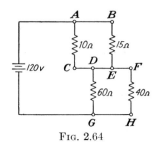

FIG. 2.64

2.31. Two 100-ohm resistors are in series. When a resistor of R ohms resistance is connected in parallel with one of them, the equivalent resistance of the combination of the three resistors is 180 ohms. Compute R.

2.32. A certain amplifier uses three tubes whose heaters are each rated at 6.3 v. Two heaters are rated at 0.8 amp and the third at 0.3 amp. Compute the resistance of each heater.

2.33. A 24-vd-c source is available to supply the heaters of Prob. 2.32.

a. It is suggested that the heaters be connected in series with a rheostat across the source. Would this connection be satisfactory?

b. A second suggestion is that the heaters be connected in parallel and that this combination be connected in series with a rheostat across the source. Compute the resistance and current capacity of the rheostat.

c. Draw a circuit diagram showing how the total current drawn from the source could be limited to 0.8 amp with each heater operating with rated voltage and current. State the disadvantages, if any, of this and the preceding connection.

2.34. A certain battery-operated radio receiver has five tubes whose filaments are rated at 2 v and 60 ma and two tubes whose filaments are rated at 2 v and 130 ma. Two dry cells, each having an emf of 1.5 v and an internal resistance of 0.05 ohm, supply current to the filaments. Draw a circuit diagram in which each filament receives rated voltage. Should a fixed resistor or a rheostat be used?

2.35. Figure 2.65 is a simple two-way telephone circuit containing two 50-ohm receivers and two 35-ohm transmitters. The battery consists of three dry cells in series, each having an emf of 1.5 v and an internal resistance of 0.05 ohm. The total resistance of the wires joining the ends of the system is 2 ohms. Compute the currents in the transmitters and the receivers.

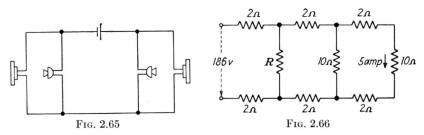

Fig. 2.65   Fig. 2.66

2.36. In Fig. 2.66 compute the value of R.
2.37. In Fig. 2.67 compute the value of I.

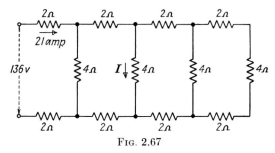

Fig. 2.67

2.38. In Fig. 2.68 compute the currents in and the voltages across the resistors. Compute the magnitudes and the directions of the currents in the leads AC, EB, BG, GD, DI, FH, and HJ.

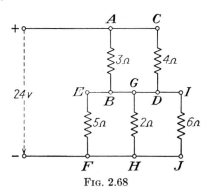

Fig. 2.68

2.39. In Fig. 2.69 compute the voltage between A and B, and specify which is at the higher potential. If a wire of negligible resistance were connected from A to B, how much current would flow in it?

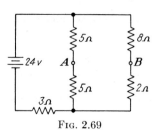

FIG. 2.69

2.40. A 120-v direct current is applied to a series combination of a 4-ohm resistor, a 15-ohm resistor, and an ammeter whose resistance is negligible. Compute the ammeter reading. A 10-ohm resistor is then connected in parallel with the 15-ohm resistor. How much current will flow in the 10-ohm resistor? What change in the ammeter reading occurs when the 10-ohm resistor is connected? Why is the change not equal to the current in the 10-ohm resistor?

2.41. The connection diagram of a shunt motor and a "3-point" starter is in Fig. 2.70. The armature has a resistance of 0.25 ohm and the shunt field winding has

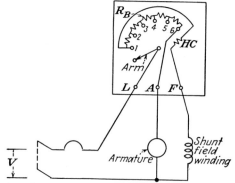

FIG. 2.70 Connection diagram for a shunt motor with a "three-point" starter.

a resistance of 78 ohms. The holding coil HC has a resistance of 2 ohms. The source voltage V is 120 v.

a. With the starter arm held on contact point 1 how much current will flow in the field winding?

b. What should be the resistance R_B to limit the armature current to 60 amp when the arm is first moved to contact point 1?

2.42. The switches on the lamp rheostat of Fig. 2.17 are set as follows: switches 1 and 4 to the upper bus bar; switches 2 and 7 to the lower bus bar; all other switches open. If the resistance of each lamp is 100 ohms, compute the equivalent resistance of the rheostat.

2.43. For the lamp rheostat of Fig. 2.17 determine the sequence of switch positions for varying the resistance from a maximum to a minimum.

2.44. The lamp rheostat of Fig. 2.17 contains 115-v lamps. Determine the sequence of switch positions that could be used safely in varying the current from a maximum to a minimum if the rheostat is used to control the current in a 230-v circuit.

2.45. A certain field rheostat has current ratings of 5 and 2.5 amp and a resistance of 60 ohms.

a. The rheostat is connected in series with a 50-ohm field winding across a 250-v source. Through what range can the winding voltage be varied?

b. Compute the least allowable resistance of a field winding that may be connected in series with the rheostat across a 500-v source.

2.46. A field rheostat that has rated currents of 5 and 2.5 amp and 60 ohms resistance is connected in series with a 90-ohm field winding across a 440-v source. Is the rheostat suitable for the application?

2.47. A field rheostat that is rated 250 v, 100 ohms, 3 amp with all resistance out and 1.5 amp with all resistance in has 25 resistance steps. It is in series with an 85-ohm field winding across a 250-v source.

a. If the resistance of each step were the same, how much would the current in the circuit be changed as the first step is cut in? How much as the last step is cut in?

b. The current is to be changed by an equal increment as each step is cut in. Compute the resistances of the first and last steps.

2.48. There are available four 3-ohm resistors and a rheostat whose resistance can be varied from 40 to 1,000 ohms in steps of 20 ohms. Show how to obtain a desired resistance of 10 ohms.

2.49. A 100-ohm slide-wire rheostat that has a current rating of 2 amp is connected in series with a resistor of R ohms resistance across a 240-v source. Compute the smallest permissible value of R.

2.50. A 100-ohm slide-wire rheostat is connected as a voltage divider with an input voltage of 120 v. With the slider in a certain position the output voltage is 60 v with a load connected and 90 v with no load connected. Compute the resistance of the load.

2.51. A 50,000-ohm slide-wire rheostat is connected as a voltage divider with 120 v input. The slider is set so that 0.6 of the rheostat resistance is included between the output terminals. Compute the voltage across a 20,000-ohm load.

2.52. A 100-ohm slide-wire rheostat that has a current rating of 2 amp is connected as a voltage divider with 120 v input. The slider is set so that 0.75 of the rheostat resistance is included between the output terminals. The output current is 1 amp. Compute the output voltage and the currents in the two sections of the rheostat. Will either section of the rheostat overheat?

2.53. An 80-ohm slide-wire rheostat is connected as a voltage divider to control the voltage across a 100-ohm load. The input voltage is 120 v. For what slider position is the current a minimum in the section of the rheostat that is in parallel with the load? Compute the minimum current.

2.54. A 90-ohm rheostat that has a rating of 2 amp is connected as in Fig. 2.26*b.* If the current in the circuit is 3 amp, through what range can the resistance of the rheostat be varied without overheating it? Through what distance may the slider be moved?

2.55. A 50-mv instrument that has 5 ohms resistance is connected across a 0.1-ohm shunt to form an ammeter. When the instrument reads 30 mv, what is the current that is being measured?

2.56. If a 10-ma d-c instrument that has 5 ohms resistance is used as a voltmeter, what would be its capacity?

a. The above instrument is to be used as a 50-ma milliammeter. Compute the resistance of the shunt required.

b. The above instrument is to be used as a 150-v voltmeter. Compute the resistance of the multiplier required.

2.57. Would a 5-amp d-c ammeter that has 50 mv across its terminals when carrying rated current be satisfactory for use as a millivoltmeter to measure a voltage that is known to be approximately 20 mv?

2.58. A certain 40,000-amp shunt used with a millivoltmeter to measure current in an aluminum plant has a voltage drop of 100 mv when carrying rated current. Compute the resistance of the shunt and the power loss in it at rated current.

2.59. A 15,000-ohm 150-v voltmeter is used with a 10,000-ohm multiplier. What voltage applied to the combination will produce full-scale deflection on the voltmeter? If 200 v is applied to the combination, what will be the voltmeter reading?

2.60. Would a 150-v voltmeter that requires 10 ma to produce full-scale deflection be satisfactory as a milliammeter to measure a current that is known to be approximately 4 ma?

2.61. When a 150-v voltmeter that has a sensitivity of 100 ohms per v reads 90 v, what is the current in it?

2.62. What is the sensitivity in ohms per volt of a 300-v voltmeter that has a resistance of 6 megohms?

2.63. A certain voltmeter has three terminals, one marked +, a second marked 15 v, and the third marked 150 v. The resistance between the + terminal and the 150-v terminal was measured as 15,000 ohms and that between the 15- and the 150-v terminals as 16,500 ohms. Draw a diagram showing the internal connections of the instrument.

2.64. A 40,000-ohm resistor is in series with a 100,000-ohm resistor across 250 v.

a. Compute the voltage across the second resistor.

b. If a 150,000-ohm voltmeter is connected across the second resistor, what will be its reading?

c. If a 15,000-ohm voltmeter is connected across the second resistor, what will be its reading?

2.65. Two resistors are in series across 250 v. When a 15,000-ohm voltmeter is connected across one resistor, the reading is 75 v. When the voltmeter is connected across the other resistor, the reading is 50 v. Compute the resistance of each resistor.

2.66. When instruments are connected as in Fig. 2.36a for measuring resistance, the voltmeter reading divided by the ammeter reading is an approximate value of the unknown resistance. Prove that the error in this value is $100I_v/I$ per cent, where I_v is the voltmeter current and I is the ammeter reading.

2.67. In measuring the resistance of a certain element the connections of Fig. 2.36 were used. With the instruments connected as in *a* the readings were $V = 0.8$ v and $I = 50$ amp. With the instrument connected as in *b* the readings were $V = 1.2$ v and $I = 50$ amp. The voltmeter resistance was 300 ohms and that of the ammeter was 0.001 ohm. Compute the resistance of the winding and the percentage error that would be made in each case if the resistance were assumed to be equal to the voltmeter reading divided by the ammeter reading.

Why is the difference of the two voltmeter readings not equal to the voltage across the ammeter?

2.68. A resistor of exactly 10 ohms resistance is in parallel with a resistor of R ohms resistance. The equivalent resistance of the combination is measured with a voltmeter and an ammeter. The voltmeter reading is 100 v and the ammeter reading is 10.5 amp. Neglect any errors caused by the resistance of the ammeter or by the current drawn by the voltmeter.

a. If the instruments have no calibration error what is the value of R?

b. The voltmeter reading is ¼ per cent too high and the ammeter reading is ½ per cent too low. What is the percentage error in the value of R computed without correction for the calibration errors?

2.69. In Fig. 2.37 a 15,000-ohm voltmeter read 120 v when connected from *a* to *b* and 30 v when connected from *a* to *c*. Neglecting instrument errors, what is the resistance being measured?

2.70. For the ohmmeter of Example 1, Art. 2.16, when the cell emf is 1.3 v what value of R_s will give full-scale galvanometer deflection with terminals x-x short-circuited? With this value of R_s what is the error in the reading when the pointer is at mid-scale?

2.71. A certain resistor draws 80 w at 120 v. How much current and power will 72 v produce in the resistor?

2.72. Determine the current and its direction in the circuit of Fig. 2.71. Compute the power delivered to each resistor, and the power delivered by, or to, each battery. Show that the total power of the elements receiving power is equal to that of the elements delivering power.

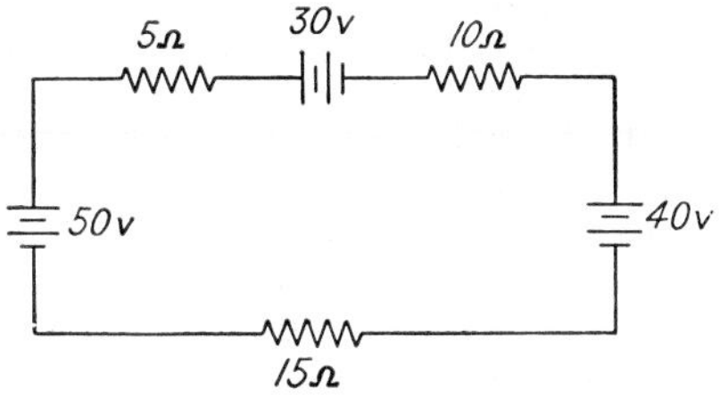

FIG. 2.71

2.73. Three identical resistors draw 300 w when connected in parallel to a 125-v source. How much voltage applied to the resistors in series will cause them to draw an equal value of power?

2.74. A 100- and a 200-ohm resistor are each rated 50 w. What is the maximum voltage that may be applied to the resistors in series without overheating either?

What is the maximum voltage that may be applied to the resistors in parallel without overheating either?

2.75. A 50-ohm 50-w, a 200-ohm 100-w, and a 400-ohm 100-w resistor are in series. Compute the resistance, the current capacity, and the power capacity of the combination.

If the above resistors are in parallel, compute the resistance, the current capacity, and the power capacity of the combination.

2.76. The 50- and the 200-ohm resistors of Prob. 2.75 are in series. This combination is in parallel with the 400-ohm resistor. Compute the resistance, the current capacity, and the power capacity of the entire combination.

2.77. A certain battery-operated short-wave receiver has three tubes, the filaments of which are rated at 1.4 v and 50 ma. The filaments in parallel are supplied from a dry cell that has an emf of 1.5 v and an internal resistance of 0.05 ohm. What current and power does each filament receive?

2.78. A certain radio receiver has three tubes whose heaters are rated at 6.3 v and 300 ma, and two tubes whose heaters are rated at 25 v and 300 ma. A 110-v source supplies the heaters. Draw the diagram of a circuit arrangement whereby each filament receives rated voltage, and specify the resistance and power rating of the rheostat required.

2.79. A 1,000-ohm slide-wire rheostat is connected as a voltage divider. The input voltage is 120 v. The slide is set so that 800 ohms of the rheostat are included between the output terminals.

   a. If no load current is being drawn, compute the power loss in the rheostat.

   b. If the load is drawing 100 ma, compute the power delivered to the load, the power loss in the rheostat, and the ratio of the power delivered to the load to that drawn from the source.

   c. Solve (*b*) if the load is drawing 200 ma.

2.80. A signal lamp that is rated at 5 w and 110 v is in series with a resistor across a 125-v source. Compute the resistance and the power rating of the resistor if the lamp operates at normal brilliancy.

2.81. The current in a 4-ohm resistor was kept constant at 4 amp for 2 sec and then was changed to 6 amp and kept constant at that value for the next 3 sec. How much energy was put into the resistor during the 5-sec interval?

2.82. The monthly energy rates of a certain corporation for residential customers are 6.5¢ per kwhr for the first 30 kwhr, 4.5¢ per kwhr for the next 30 kwhr, and 2.5¢ per kwhr for all additional energy.

a. Compute the monthly bill and the average cost of the energy per kilowatthour for a customer who uses 70 kwhr.

b. Solve *a* for a customer who uses 140 kwhr.

c. How much energy must a customer use for an average energy cost of 3.5¢ per kwhr?

2.83. A 2,000-ohm 10-w resistor is to be replaced by 2,000-ohm 5-w resistors. What is the minimum number of resistors required?

2.84. The monthly energy rates of a certain corporation for an industrial customer are 4¢ per kwhr for the first 100 kwhr, 3¢ per kwhr for the next 100 kwhr, and 2¢ per kwhr for all additional energy. In addition there is a demand charge of $1.50 per kw of maximum demand.

During a month a customer used 500 kwhr and his maximum demand was 15 kw. Compute the bill for the month and the average cost per kilowatt hour.

2.85. The monthly energy rates of a certain corporation for a customer with a connected load greater than $7\frac{1}{2}$ hp are 2.5¢ per kwhr for the first 100 hr use of the maximum kilowatt demand, 1.5¢ per kwhr for the next 100 hr use of the maximum kilowatt demand, and 1¢ per kwhr for all above 200 hr use of the maximum kilowatt demand.

a. During a month a customer used 360 kwhr and his maximum demand was 12 kw. Compute the bill for the month and the average cost per kilowatthour.

b. With a maximum demand of 12 kw how much energy must a customer use for the average cost to be 1.6¢ per kwhr?

2.86. Four kilograms of water are to be heated from 20 to 70 C by an electric heater. If 30 per cent of the heat energy produced is lost by radiation, how much electrical energy is required?

How much current must be drawn from a 120-v source to cause the temperature change in 20 min?

2.87. How long must 20 amp flow through a 6-ohm resistor to produce 350 kg-cal of heat?

2.88. If electrical energy costs 5¢ per kwhr, how long can 1 μa be sent through a 1-ohm resistor for a cost of 1¢?

2.89. A certain 1,000-hp motor operated continuously at full-load for a year. The energy cost 1¢ per kwhr. If the motor had been replaced by one whose losses were 10 hp less, compute the saving in the energy bill for the year. Approximately what percentage improvement in the motor efficiency would be required to cause the above reduction in losses?

2.90. If an 83,000-hp motor has a full-load efficiency of 96 per cent and energy costs $\frac{1}{2}$¢ per kwhr, compute the cost for operating this motor for 5 hr. Compute the cost of the energy converted into losses during this period.

2.91. The tractive effort required to drive a certain truck is 110 lb. Compute the horsepower required to drive it 600 ft in 1 min at constant speed.

The truck is propelled by a d-c motor supplied from a 120-v storage battery. The motor and gearing have an efficiency of 55 per cent. Compute the current and the power delivered by the battery.

2.92. The watthour constant of a watthour meter is the number of watthours required to produce one revolution of the disk. The meter in a certain residence has a constant of $\frac{1}{3}$. At a time when a refrigerator was the only connected load the disk made 25 revolutions in 2 min. How much power did the refrigerator use?

2.93. In calibrating the meter of Prob. 2.92 it was found that with a constant load of 500 w the disk made 20 revolutions in 48.2 sec. Compute the percentage error in the meter registration.

2.94. The current in a 5-ohm resistor was constant at 10 amp for 5 sec, then it was constant at 4 amp for the next 4 sec, and finally it was constant at 16 amp for the next 1 sec.

a. How many coulombs were moved through the resistor during the 10-sec interval? What current, constant during an equal interval, would move an equal number of coulombs?

b. How much energy was delivered to the resistor during the 10-sec interval? What current, constant during an equal interval, would deliver an equal amount of heat to the resistor?

2.95. The current in one branch of a rectifier circuit was nearly constant at 12 amp during one-sixth of a cycle and zero during the remaining part of a cycle. Compute the average and the rms values of the current.

2.96. The current in a telephone transmitter varied with time as follows:

Time, msec	Current, ma	Time, msec	Current, ma	Time, msec	Current, ma
0	20.0	0.7	18.5	1.4	22.1
0.1	19.4	0.8	18.9	1.5	22.2
0.2	18.9	0.9	19.4	1.6	22.1
0.3	18.5	1.0	20.0	1.7	21.8
0.4	18.3	1.1	20.6	1.8	21.2
0.5	18.2	1.2	21.2	1.9	20.6
0.6	18.3	1.3	21.8	2.0	20.0

Plot the current-time curve. Compute the frequency, the average value, and the rms value of the current.

2.97. A certain wire that serves as a common conductor for a d-c and an a-c circuit carries a current whose equation is $i = 40 + 50 \sin 400t$ amp, where t is in seconds. Compute the rms value of the current.

2.98. The voltage is maintained at 240 v at the generator end of a certain distribution circuit, each wire of which has 0.1 ohm resistance. Compute points for and plot the curve that shows the relation between the power delivered to the load and the load current. A tabular form such as the following is suggested:

Load current I_L, amp	Load voltage $240 - 0.2I_L$, v	Load power, $(240 - 0.2I_L)I_L$, w
0	240	0
50	230	11,500

What is the maximum power that the circuit can deliver and what is the efficiency corresponding to the maximum power?

2.99. A certain room cooler with a rating of 10,000 British thermal units (Btu) per hr has a ¾-hp motor to drive the compressor and a ⅙-hp motor to drive the condenser and circulating fans. Assume that each motor when operating delivers its rated output, that the smaller motor has an efficiency of 50 per cent, and that the larger motor has an efficiency of 70 per cent. Compute the cost of operating the cooler 20 hr per day for 30 days if the electrical energy costs 2½¢ per kwhr.

2.100. For the circuit of Fig. 2.72 write the voltage equations using actual currents. Compute the currents.

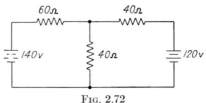

60Ω 40Ω

$140v$ 40Ω $120v$

Fig. 2.72

2.101. For the circuit of Fig. 2.73 write the voltage equations using actual currents. Compute the currents.

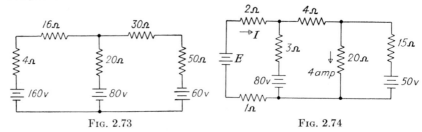

16Ω 30Ω

4Ω 20Ω 50Ω

$160v$ $80v$ $60v$

Fig. 2.73

2Ω 4Ω

I

E 3Ω 15Ω

$80v$ $4amp$ 20Ω $50v$

1Ω

Fig. 2.74

2.102. Compute the emf E and the current I in the circuit of Fig. 2.74.

2.103. A certain circuit element that contains no energy source delivers 2 ma at 20 mv when the input is 5 ma at 30 mv. Compute the current loss, the voltage loss, and the power loss.

2.104. Compute the efficiency of the element of Prob. 2.103.

2.105. In Fig. 2.57, $R_o = 500$ ohms, $R_1 = 80$ ohms, and $R_2 = 2,000$ ohms. Compute the current loss, the voltage loss, and the power loss.

2.106. In Fig. 2.57, $R_o = 500$ ohms. Compute the values of R_1 and R_2 such that the current loss equals the power loss of 5 db.

2.107. In Fig. 2.58, $R_o = 1,000$ ohms, $R_1 = 160$ ohms, and $R_2 = 4,000$ ohms. Compute the current loss, the voltage loss, and the power loss.

2.108. In Fig. 2.58, $R_o = 1,000$ ohms. Compute the values of R_1 and R_2 such that the current loss equals the power loss of 2 db.

2.109. A circuit element that has a power amplification of 5 db delivers energy to a second element that has a power attenuation of 2 db. Compute the over-all gain or loss of the two elements.

2.110. A 100-ohm load is to receive 2 mw from a T section attenuator that has a power loss of 4 db. This attenuator receives its energy from a π section attenuator that has a power loss of 2 db. In each attenuator the ratio of the input voltage to the input current is equal to the ratio of the output voltage to the output current. Compute the resistance values for the attenuators.

2.111. When a certain plane is flying at 300 mi per hr the drag of the external antennas is 80 lb. Compute the horsepower used to overcome the drag.

CHAPTER 3

FURTHER APPLICATIONS OF OHM'S AND KIRCHHOFF'S LAWS

3.1. Networks. An electric network is a system of interconnected conducting elements. A passive network, such as one composed of a group of resistors, contains no source of emf. A passive network is bilateral if the magnitudes of the currents in its branches are independent of the polarity of the voltage applied to it. A passive network is linear if the currents in it are directly proportional to the voltage applied to it. In this text, all passive networks are to be considered as bilateral unless otherwise specified.

In a given network if certain currents, voltages, and resistances are given, some or all of the remaining currents, voltages, and resistances can be computed. What may be called a general method for computing these quantities will be presented first.

Equations obtained by the applications of Ohm's and Kirchhoff's laws are solved simultaneously for the unknown quantities. In applying the laws, the following procedure is suggested:

1. Draw a neat diagram of the circuit of a size that can be read easily. If the original diagram has a number of crossing lines, it may be worthwhile to redraw it if some or all of the crossing lines can be eliminated.

2. On the diagram indicate the polarities and the magnitudes of the given emfs, the directions and the magnitudes of the given currents, and the given resistance values.

3. Assign a symbol such as E_1, E_2, etc., respectively, to each unknown emf. If more than one emf is unknown, it may be that the polarities of each source of emf must be specified if only one set of values is to be obtained.

4. Assign a symbol such as R_1, R_2, etc., respectively, to each unknown resistance.

5. At any junction assign a direction and a symbol such as I_1, I_2, etc., respectively, to all but one of the unknown currents that leave or approach the junction. Apply Kirchhoff's law of currents and express that current

in terms of the symbols assigned to the other currents. If it is not possible to tell by inspection the direction of an unknown current, assume a direction arbitrarily. If the computed value of a current is negative, the direction of the current is opposite to that assumed.

At other junctions assign current symbols and directions until all currents have been assigned symbols and directions.

6. Apply Kirchhoff's voltage law and write as many independent equations as there are unknown quantities to be determined. To ensure that the equations are independent, each path traversed should include some part of the circuit not traversed in writing the other equations.

7. Solve the independent equations for the values of the unknown quantities.

Example 1. In Fig. 3.1, $E_1 = 120$ v, $E_2 = 110$ v, $R_1 = 2$ ohms, $R_2 = 0.5$ ohm, and $R_3 = 10$ ohms. The resistances of the battery and the generator are assumed to be negligible compared with the other resistances in the circuit. Determine the current in each branch of the circuit.

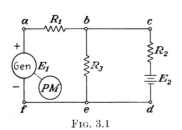

FIG. 3.1

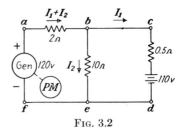

FIG. 3.2

Solution. The circuit is redrawn in Fig. 3.2 with the given numerical quantities indicated. There are three unknown currents. At junction b the current in the branch $bcde$ is denoted as I_1 in the direction b to c. The current in the branch be is denoted as I_2 in the direction b to e. The third current in the branch $efab$ in the direction e to f is equal to $I_1 + I_2$. The three currents have been expressed in terms of two unknowns.

Along the path $abefa$, equating the algebraic summation of the emfs to that of the IR drops yields

$$120 = 2(I_1 + I_2) + 10I_2$$

Along the path $bcdeb$, equating the algebraic summation of the emfs to that of the IR drops yields

$$-110 = 0.5I_1 - 10I_2$$

The simultaneous solution of the above equations yields $I_1 = -4.61$ amp and $I_2 = 10.77$ amp. Then $I_1 + I_2 = 6.16$ amp. The current in the right-hand branch is 4.61 amp in the direction c to b, that in the center branch is 10.77 amp in the direction b to e, and that in the left-hand branch is 6.16 amp in the direction e to f.

As a check on these values, along the path $abcdefa$, equating the algebraic sum of the emfs to that of the IR drops yields

$$120 - 110 = 6.16 \times 2 - 4.61 \times 0.5$$
$$10 = 10$$

Example 2. In Fig. 3.3, loads having resistances of R_1 and R_2 are supplied from a distribution circuit having a generator at each end. $E_1 = 125$ v, $E_2 = 115$ v, $R_3 = 0.2$ ohm, $R_4 = 0.3$ ohm, and $R_5 = 0.4$ ohm. The load of resistance R_1 draws 20 amp and that of resistance R_2 draws 30 amp. Assume all resistances not indicated are negligible. Compute the voltage across each load, the power delivered to each load, and the efficiency of the distribution circuit.

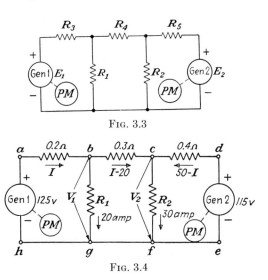

Fig. 3.3

Fig. 3.4

Solution. There are three unknown currents but they can be expressed in terms of one unknown current I as in Fig. 3.4. Since R_1 and R_2 are unknown, there are three unknown quantities. Before setting up three equations for computing the unknowns, let us inspect the circuit. If emfs and drops are summed along the path $abcdefgha$, I is the only unknown encountered. Along that path

$$125 - 115 = 0.2I + 0.3(I - 20) - 0.4(50 - I)$$

from which $I = 40$ amp.

The voltage across R_1 could be determined by computing R_1 and multiplying it by 20 amp. However, if the voltage is called V_1 as in Fig. 3.4, it can be computed from a voltage equation written for a clockwise path along the left-hand loop. Here $125 = 0.2I + V_1$. Since $I = 40$ amp, then

$$V_1 = 125 - 0.2 \times 40 = 117 \text{ v}$$

V_2 can be computed from a voltage equation written for a clockwise path along the right-hand loop. Here

$$-115 = -0.4(50 - I) - V_2$$

Since $I = 40$ amp, then $V_2 = 115 - 0.4 \times 10 = 111$ v.

The values of V_1 and V_2 can be checked by a voltage equation written for a clockwise path along the center loop. Here $0 = 0.3(40 - 20) + 111 - 117$, or $0 = 0$.

When some of the currents are given, as in the above case, it often happens that some of the unknowns can be computed from one equation for each.

The load of resistance R_1 draws 20 amp at 117 v; hence its power is

$$117 \text{ v} \times 20 \text{ amp} = 2{,}340 \text{ w}$$

The load of resistance R_2 draws 30 amp at 111 v; hence its power is

$$111 \text{ v} \times 30 \text{ amp} = 3{,}330 \text{ w}$$

The power output of the circuit is that to the two loads, or

$$2{,}340 + 3{,}330 = 5{,}670 \text{ w}$$

The power input to the circuit is that delivered by the two generators, or

$$125 \text{ v} \times 40 \text{ amp} + 115 \text{ v} \times 10 \text{ amp} = 6{,}150 \text{ w}$$

The efficiency of the circuit with the given loads is 5,670 w/6,150 w = 0.922 per unit, or 92.2 per cent.

Example 3. Four batteries are being charged by a d-c generator as in Fig. 3.5. The emfs of the generator and the batteries and the resistances of the various parts of the circuit are indicated. Compute the current in each battery and in the generator.

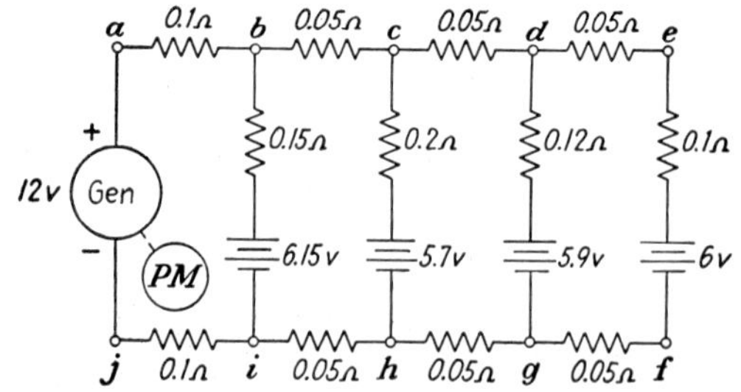

FIG. 3.5

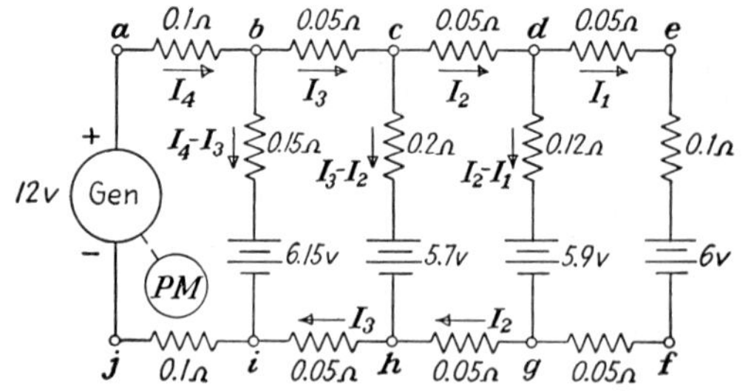

FIG. 3.6

Solution. The currents can be expressed in terms of the quantities I_1, I_2, I_3, and I_4 as in Fig. 3.6. Four independent voltage equations are required. There is no voltage equation in which only one unknown appears. The respective paths *defgd*, *cdghc*, *bchib*, and *abija* will be followed clockwise in writing voltage equations. The equations are

$$5.9 - 6 = 0.2I_1 - 0.12(I_2 - I_1)$$

from which
$$-0.1 = 0.32I_1 - 0.12I_2 \tag{1}$$

$$5.7 - 5.9 = 0.1I_2 + 0.12(I_2 - I_1) - 0.2(I_3 - I_2)$$

from which
$$-0.2 = -0.12I_1 + 0.42I_2 - 0.2I_3 \tag{2}$$

$$6.15 - 5.7 = 0.1I_3 + 0.2(I_3 - I_2) - 0.15(I_4 - I_3)$$

from which
$$0.45 = -0.2I_2 + 0.45I_3 - 0.15I_4 \tag{3}$$

and
$$12 - 6.15 = 0.2I_4 + 0.15(I_4 - I_3)$$

from which
$$5.85 = -0.15I_3 + 0.35I_4 \tag{4}$$

From (1),

$$I_1 = \frac{-0.1 + 0.12I_2}{0.32} = -0.313 + 0.375I_2$$

Substitution of this value of I_1 in (2) yields

$$-0.238 = 0.375I_2 - 0.2I_3 \tag{5}$$

Equations (3), (4), and (5) are independent and contain three unknowns. From (5),

$$I_2 = \frac{-0.238 + 0.2I_3}{0.375} = -0.635 + 0.533I_3$$

Substitution of this value of I_2 in (3) yields

$$0.32 = 0.34I_3 - 0.15I_4 \tag{6}$$

Equations (4) and (6) are independent and contain two unknowns. From (4), $I_3 = (-5.85 + 0.35I_4)/0.15 = -39 + 2.33I_4$. Substitution of this value of I_3 in (6) yields $I_4 = 21.1$ amp.   Then

$$I_3 = -39 + 2.33I_4 = -39 + 2.33(21.1) = 10.2 \text{ amp}$$
$$I_2 = -0.635 + 0.533I_3 = -0.635 + 0.533(10.2) = 4.8 \text{ amp}$$
$$I_1 = -0.313 + 0.375I_2 = -0.313 + 0.375(4.8) = 1.5 \text{ amp}$$

The current in the right-hand battery is $I_1 = 1.5$ amp.   The current in the second battery from the right is $I_2 - I_1 = 3.3$ amp.   The current in the third battery from the right is $I_3 - I_2 = 5.4$ amp.   The current in the left-hand battery is $I_4 - I_3 = 10.9$ amp.   The current values will be checked by a voltage equation for the path *aefja*.   Here

$$12 - 6 = 0.2I_4 + 0.1I_3 + 0.1I_2 + 0.2I_1$$

or
$$6 = 0.2(21.1) + 0.1(10.2) + 0.1(4.8) + 0.2(1.5)$$
$$6 = 6.02$$

3.2. Loop Currents.   Maxwell devised a method of solving circuits by using loop (or mesh) currents.   A loop current is one that exists in all portions of a closed loop in a network.   In Fig. 3.7, three loops exist and three loop currents can be designated.   The loop current I_1 follows the loop *abefa*.   The loop current I_2 follows the loop *bcdeb*.   The third loop is *abcdefa*.   A loop current could be designated for this loop.   However, all relationships in the network involving currents can be expressed in terms of I_1 and I_2; therefore designation of a third loop current would be extraneous.   If desired, that loop current could have been used instead of either I_1 or I_2.   The loop current I_1 is the actual current in the branch *efab*.   It is only one component of the actual current in the branch *be*. The loop current I_2 is the actual current in the branch *bcde*.   It is a component of the actual current in the branch *eb*.

In Fig. 3.7 both loop currents were considered as positive in the clockwise direction.   Either one or both might have been considered as positive in the opposite direction.

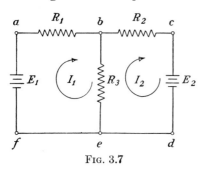

FIG. 3.7

After enough loop currents have been designated that all the branch currents in a network can be expressed in terms of the loop currents, one can write voltage equations for the loops for which currents were designated.   Each voltage equation is an expression of the statement that the algebraic sum of the emfs along the loop is equal to the algebraic sum of the resistance drops caused by the loop currents.

Refer to Fig. 3.7.   Along the loop *abefa*, the algebraic sum of the emfs is $+E_1$.   Along this loop the current I_1 flows through $R_1 + R_3$ ohms and the current I_2 flows through R_3 ohms.   The algebraic sum of the resistance drops is $I_1(R_1 + R_3) - I_2R_3$, since the direction of travel is with I_1 and against I_2.   Then $E_1 = I_1(R_1 + R_3) - I_2R_3$.

Along the loop *bcdeb*, by the above principles,

$$-E_2 = I_2(R_2 + R_3) - I_1R_3$$

By solving the preceding equations simultaneously, I_1 and I_2 can be computed.   Then the actual current in R_3, taken positive from b to e, is $I_1 - I_2$.

By using loop rather than branch currents some saving in time is made in obtaining voltage equations in that coefficients of certain current terms are obtained directly by adding resistances rather than by combining terms of which the current is a common factor.

3.3. Use of Node-pair Voltages.   A terminal of a circuit element, such as a battery or a resistor, is also called a node.   When a terminal of one element is connected to a terminal of a second element, either terminal may be considered as a node common to the two elements.   By choosing one node in a network as a reference of potential, the potential of all other nodes with respect to the first can be expressed.   Next by applying Kirchhoff's current law, equations relating the node potentials can be written and these solved to determine the potentials.   Finally, the current values can be obtained.   If the number of nodes is less than the number of branches, the use of the node-pair method requires the writing and the simultaneous solution of fewer equations than does the general method or the loop-current method.

Example 1. In Fig. 3.8 is a three-branch network with nodes a, b, and c. If node c is chosen as a reference point, node a is seen to be $+120$ v above it. Then b is the only node whose potential with respect to c need be expressed as an unknown. Let V v be the voltage drop from b to c. By inspection it can be seen that the current from b in the 400-ohm resistor is $V/400$ amp and that from b in the 600-ohm resistor is $V/600$ amp. The voltage drop from a to b is $120 - V$; thus the current toward b in the 360-ohm resistor is $(120 - V)/360$ amp. By Kirchhoff's current law it follows that the sum of the first two currents is equal to the third. Hence $V/400 +$ $V/600 = (120 - V)/360$, from which $V = 48$ v. The currents are $48/400 = 0.12$ amp, $48/600 = 0.08$ amp, and $(120 - 48)/360 = 0.2$ amp.

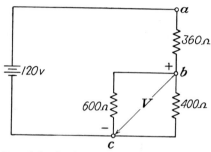

FIG. 3.8   A circuit having nodes at the points a, b, and c.

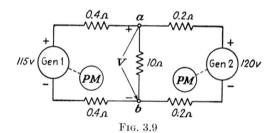

FIG. 3.9

Example 2. In Fig. 3.9 compute the branch currents and the load voltage V.

Solution. Assume that V is less than 115 v. Then a current will leave the positive terminal of each generator. That from Gen 1 is $(115 - V)/(2 \times 0.4)$ amp. That from Gen 2 is $(120 - V)/(2 \times 0.2)$ amp. The load current is $V/10$ amp. Since the sum of the first two currents equals the third,

$$\frac{115 - V}{2 \times 0.4} + \frac{120 - V}{2 \times 0.2} = \frac{V}{10}$$

from which $V = 115.26$ v. Although V is not less than 115 v as was assumed, the preceding relations may be used. The current in Gen 1 is

$$\frac{115 - 115.26}{0.8} = -0.32 \text{ amp}$$

A current of 0.32 amp is entering the positive terminal of Gen 1 rather than leaving it. This means that the machine is not actually operating as a generator and delivering electrical energy. Instead it is operating as a motor and receiving electrical energy. The current leaving the positive terminal of Gen 2 is

$$\frac{120 - 115.26}{0.4} = 11.85 \text{ amp}$$

The current in the 10-ohm resistor is $115.26/10 = 11.53$ amp. As a check on the current values, $-0.32 + 11.85 = 11.53$ amp.

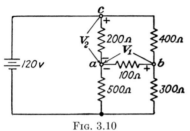

FIG. 3.10

Example 3. In Fig. 3.10 compute the six currents.

Solution. The node-pair voltages V_1 and V_2 v are used with polarities as indicated. The current in the 200-ohm resistor is $V_2/200$ amp directed toward a, and that in the 100-ohm resistor is $V_1/100$ amp directed toward a. The current in the 500-ohm resistor is $(120 - V_2)/500$ amp directed from a. The sum of the first two currents is equal to the third; hence

$$\frac{V_2}{200} + \frac{V_1}{100} = \frac{120 - V_2}{500} \tag{1}$$

Assuming that V_1 is less than V_2, the current in the 400-ohm resistor is $(V_2 - V_1)/400$ amp directed toward b. The current in the 300-ohm resistor is $(120 - V_2 + V_1)/300$ amp directed from b. The first of these is equal to the second plus that in the 100-ohm resistor. Hence

$$\frac{V_2 - V_1}{400} = \frac{120 - V_2 + V_1}{300} + \frac{V_1}{100}$$

from which

$$19V_1 - 7V_2 + 480 = 0 \tag{2}$$

The simultaneous solution of (1) and (2) yields $V_1 = -8.28$ v and $V_2 = 46.11$ v.

Since V_1 is negative, the actual polarities are the reverse of those indicated. However, the preceding expressions are correct if the negative value of V_1 is used. The current in the 200-ohm resistor is $V_2/200 = 46.11/200 = 0.231$ amp, directed toward a. The current in the 500-ohm resistor is

$$\frac{120 - V_2}{500} = \frac{120 - 46.11}{500} = 0.148 \text{ amp}$$

directed from a. The current in the 100-ohm resistor is

$$\frac{V_1}{100} = \frac{-8.28}{100} = -0.083 \text{ amp}$$

or 0.083 amp directed from a to b. The current in the 400-ohm resistor is $(V_2 - V_1)/400 = [46.11 - (-8.28)]/400 = 0.136$ amp, directed toward b. The current in the 300-ohm resistor is

$$\frac{120 - V_2 + V_1}{300} = \frac{120 - 46.11 + (-8.28)}{300} = 0.219 \text{ amp}$$

directed from b. The battery current is the sum of that in the 200- and the 400-ohm resistors, or $0.231 + 0.136 = 0.367$ amp, directed toward c.

3.4. Superposition Theorem. In a linear network containing more than one source of emf the current in any branch is equal to the algebraic sum of the currents that would be produced in the branch by the emfs acting separately. The principles involved in this theorem have been implied in all the methods used previously in solving networks.

Example 1. In Fig. 3.11 are represented two batteries in parallel supplying current to a 10-ohm resistor. Use superposition to compute the various currents.

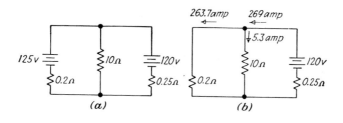

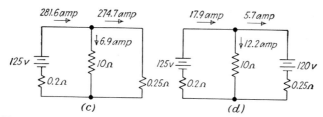

FIG. 3.11   Steps in the application of the superposition theorem.

Solution. First let the emf of the 125-v battery be considered as zero. Here the internal resistance of that battery was 0.2 ohm. A resistor with an equal value of resistance should be shown in the circuit diagram as indicated. Now the 120-v battery is acting alone as in Fig. 3.11b. The magnitudes and the directions of the currents were determined by methods already discussed. Next let the emf of the 120-v battery be considered as zero. Then the 125-v battery is acting alone, as in Fig. 3.11c. The magnitudes and directions of the currents are as indicated. The actual currents in Fig. 3.11d were obtained by superposing the currents in Fig. 3.11b upon those in Fig. 3.11c.

If all currents in a given network are to be determined, the method of superposition is not as advantageous to use as most others. However, there are special cases in which the method of superposition may be useful.

Example 2. The current in the 10-ohm resistor in Fig. 3.11d is to be changed to 10 amp by inserting a battery of negligible internal resistance in series with that resistor. Determine the magnitude and the polarity of the battery emf.

Solution. A change from 12.2 to 10 amp in the 10-ohm resistor is a change of 2.2 amp. Our problem then is to determine what emf inserted in series with the 10-ohm resistor will produce 2.2 amp upward through that resistor with the emfs suppressed in the outside branches. Under that condition the equivalent resistance across the terminals of a battery in series with the 10-ohm resistor is $10 + (0.2 \times 0.25)/(0.2 + 0.25) = 10.11$ ohms. To send 2.2 amp through 10.11 ohms requires $2.2 \times 10.11 = 22.2$ v. This is the required emf of the battery. Its upper terminal should be positive.

3.5. Thévenin's Theorem.

In Fig. 3.12 the elements to the left of terminals a and b comprise a two-terminal linear network. Assume that

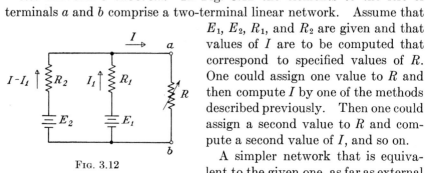

FIG. 3.12

E_1, E_2, R_1, and R_2 are given and that values of I are to be computed that correspond to specified values of R. One could assign one value to R and then compute I by one of the methods described previously. Then one could assign a second value to R and compute a second value of I, and so on.

A simpler network that is equivalent to the given one, as far as external connections to terminals a and b are concerned, will now be derived. For the left- and the right-hand loops the respective voltage equations are

$$E_2 - E_1 = (I - I_1)R_2 - I_1R_1 = IR_2 - I_1(R_1 + R_2)$$
$$E_1 = I_1R_1 + IR$$

The simultaneous solution of these equations yields

$$I = \frac{(E_2 - E_1)R_1 + E_1(R_1 + R_2)}{R_1R_2 + R(R_1 + R_2)} = \frac{(E_2 - E_1)R_1/(R_1 + R_2) + E_1}{R + R_1R_2/(R_1 + R_2)}$$

If R were made infinite, $I = 0$ and $I_1 = (E_1 - E_2)/(R_1 + R_2)$. The voltage appearing between a and b would be

$$E_1 - I_1R_1 = E_1 + \frac{(E_2 - E_1)R_1}{R_1 + R_2}$$

Note that this expression also appears in the numerator of the equation for I.

If the battery emfs were suppressed in Fig. 3.12, the equivalent resistance of the entire circuit to an emf source inserted in series with the resistor of resistance R is $R + R_1R_2/(R_1 + R_2)$. Note that this expression also appears in the denominator of the equation for I and that $R_1R_2/(R_1 + R_2)$ is the equivalent resistance of two elements in parallel.

The above results mean that as far as the relations in an element connected between a and b are concerned, the network to the left of a and b

can be replaced by a source of emf E_e in series with a resistor of resistance R_e.   Here $E_e = (E_2 - E_1)R_1/(R_1 + R_2) + E_1$ and $R_e = R_1R_2/(R_1 + R_2)$.

After the values of E_e and R_e have been computed, in Fig. 3.12 $I = E_e/(R_e + R)$.   Now one can compute the values of I corresponding to various values of R with less labor than was required with the original network.

More extensive analysis than the preceding has established the proof of what is usually called Thévenin's theorem.   *As far as any load connected between the terminals is concerned, a linear two-terminal network may be replaced by a source of emf E in series with a resistor of resistance R.* E is equal to the voltage that appears between the terminals with no external connections between the terminals. R is equal to the resistance measured between the terminals with all emfs in the network made zero.

Example 1.   The network of Fig. 3.13a has two terminals, A and B.   Determine the emf and internal resistance of a source to replace the network between the terminals so that the current in a load connected to the terminals will be the same as if the network were between the terminals.

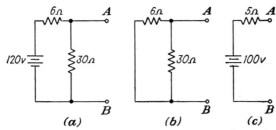

FIG. 3.13   Steps in the application of Thévenin's theorem to determine the two-terminal network of c that is equivalent to the original two-terminal network of a.   The emf in c is equal to the voltage between A and B in a.   The resistance in c is equal to the equivalent resistance between A and B in b.

Solution.   The first step is to determine the voltage V_{AB} that appears between A and B when no load is connected.   Under that condition the 6- and the 30-ohm resistors are in series and V_{AB} is the voltage across the 30-ohm resistor.   Then $V_{AB} = [120/(30 + 6)] \times 30 = 100$ v.   This is the emf to be used in the equivalent circuit in c.

Now consider the emf in the original circuit to be made zero.   The resulting circuit is Fig. 3.13b.   The resistance between A and B is

$$\frac{30 \times 6}{30 + 6} = 5 \text{ ohms}$$

It is the value to be used in the equivalent circuit in c.

Example 2.   In Fig. 3.13a, if a 20-ohm resistor were connected between A and B, how much current would flow in it?

Solution. From the equivalent circuit of Fig. 3.13c it can be seen that if 20 ohms are connected between A and B the resulting current is

$$\frac{100}{5 + 20} = 4 \text{ amp}$$

Example 3. In Fig. 3.13a, compute the maximum power that can be drawn by a load between A and B.

Solution. Again refer to the equivalent circuit of Fig. 3.13c. For this circuit the load will receive maximum power when its resistance is equal to that of the remainder of the circuit. Here the load resistance would be 5 ohms, the load current would be $100/(5 + 5) = 10$ amp, and the maximum load power would be $10^2 \times 5 = 500$ w.

Example 4. Compute the current in the 200-ohm resistor of Fig. 3.14a.

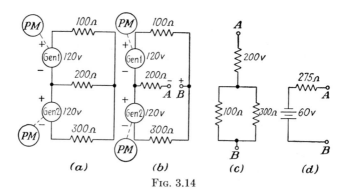

(a)   (b)   (c)   (d)

Fig. 3.14

Solution. Break the branch of the circuit in which the current is to be determined. Let A and B be terminals on the respective sides of the break as in Fig. 3.14b. The 100- and 300-ohm resistors are now in series across 240 v. The current in them is $240/(100 + 300) = 0.6$ amp. Since there is no current in the 200-ohm resistor, the potential from A to B by the path through the upper generator is the rise of 120 v in the generator less the fall of

$$0.6 \text{ amp} \times 100 \text{ ohms} = 60 \text{ v}$$

in the 100-ohm resistor. Then B is at a higher potential than A by

$$120 - 60 = 60 \text{ v}$$

This is the emf in the equivalent circuit of Fig. 3.14d.

In Fig. 3.14c the original circuit has been redrawn with the generator emfs suppressed. The resistance between A and B is

$$200 + \frac{100 \times 300}{100 + 300} = 275 \text{ ohms}$$

It is the value to be used in the equivalent circuit of Fig. 3.14d. If A and B in the equivalent circuit were connected by a lead of zero resistance, the current would be 60 v/275 ohms = 0.22 amp. This is the current that would flow from right to left in the 200-ohm resistor in the original circuit.

Example 5. Compute the current in the 300-ohm resistor of Fig. 3.15*a*.

Solution. Break the 300-ohm branch and locate the terminals *A* and *B* on the respective sides of the break as in Fig. 3.15*b*. The 100- and the 500-ohm resistors are now in series across the battery. The current in them is 6/(100 + 500) = 0.01 amp. The 600- and the 400-ohm resistors are also in series across the

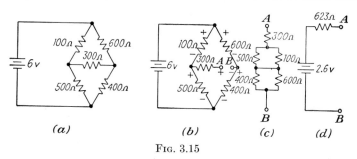

(a)   (b)   (c)   (d)

Fig. 3.15

battery. The current in them is 6/(600 + 400) = 0.006 amp. The potential from *A* to *B* by the path through the 100- and the 600-ohm resistors is a rise of

$$0.01 \text{ amp} \times 100 \text{ ohms} = 1 \text{ v}$$

in the first resistor less a drop of 0.006 amp × 600 ohms = 3.6 v in the latter, or 1 − 3.6 = −2.6 v. Hence *A* is positive with respect to *B* and an emf of 2.6 v is placed in the equivalent circuit of Fig. 3.15*d* to give that polarity.

In Fig. 3.15*c*, circuit *b* is redrawn with the battery emf suppressed. The resistance from *A* to *B* is

$$300 + \frac{500 \times 100}{500 + 100} + \frac{400 \times 600}{400 + 600} = 623 \text{ ohms}$$

It is the value used in the equivalent circuit of Fig. 3.15*d*. If *A* and *B* in the equivalent circuit were connected by a lead of zero resistance, the current would be 2.6 v/623 ohms = 0.0042 amp. This is the current that would flow from left to right in the 300-ohm resistor in the original circuit.

3.6. Norton's Theorem. In Fig. 3.16 the elements to the left of the terminals *a* and *b* comprise a two-terminal network. Assume that E_1 and E_2 in volts and G_1 and G_2 in mhos are given and that the network is to be replaced by a simpler one that is its equivalent as far as an external load of conductance *G* connected to terminals *a* and *b* is concerned. For the left- and the right-hand loops the respective voltage equations are

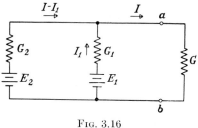

Fig. 3.16

$$E_2 - E_1 = \frac{I - I_1}{G_2} - \frac{I_1}{G_1} = \frac{I}{G_2} - \frac{I_1(G_1 + G_2)}{G_1G_2}$$

$$E_1 = \frac{I_1}{G_1} + \frac{I}{G}$$

The simultaneous solution of these equations yields

$$I = \frac{G(G_2 E_2 + G_1 E_1)}{G + G_1 + G_2}$$

If a short circuit were connected between a and b, it would receive $G_2 E_2$ amp from one battery and $G_1 E_1$ amp from the other. Let $G_2 E_2 + G_1 E_1 = I_e$. Then $I = G I_e / (G + G_1 + G_2)$. When three resistors are in parallel, the current in one of them is equal to the total current of the three multiplied by the ratio of the conductance of the one to the conductance of the three in parallel. Then the source CCS of constant current I_e and the three conductance elements of Fig. 3.17a are equivalent to

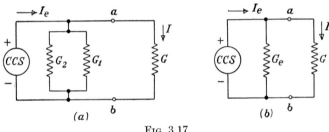

FIG. 3.17

the arrangement of Fig. 3.16. The parallel combination of G_1 and G_2 can be replaced by a resistor of conductance $G_e = G_1 + G_2$, as in Fig. 3.17b.

More extended analysis than the preceding has established the proof of Norton's theorem. *As far as any load connected between the terminals is concerned, a linear two-terminal network may be replaced by a source of constant current I_e amp in parallel with an element of conductance G_e mhos. I_e is the current that would flow in a short circuit between the terminals. G_e is equal to the conductance measured between the terminals with all emfs in the network made zero.*

Example 1. The network of Fig. 3.13a is to be replaced by a source of constant current I_e in parallel with a resistor of conductance G_e. Determine the values of I_e and G_e so that the current in a given load connected to the terminals A and B will be the same as if the original network were connected to the terminals.

Solution. With a lead of zero resistance connected between A and B in the original network, the current in it would be 120 v/6 ohms = 20 amp. This should be the value of I_e.

With the battery emf suppressed in the original network, the conductance between A and B is 1/6 mho + 1/30 mho = 1/5 mho. This should be the value of G_e.

Example 2. If a 20-ohm resistor were connected between A and B in Fig. 3.13a, how much current would flow in it?

Solution. The conductance of the resistor is 1/20 mho. This in parallel with $G_e = $ 1/5 mho computed in Example 1 yields an equivalent conductance of

$\frac{1}{20} + \frac{1}{5} = \frac{1}{4}$ mho. Of the 20 amp delivered by the constant-current source, $(\frac{1}{20}/\frac{1}{4}) \times 20 = 4$ amp will flow in the 20-ohm resistor.

3.7. Special Solution of a Passive Network

Example 1. In Fig. 3.18 determine the various currents.
Solution. As shown in Fig. 3.19, 1 amp is assumed in the 20-ohm resistor between d and h. The voltage across the resistor is 1 amp × 20 ohms = 20 v with polarities as shown. This current also flows through the 2-ohm resistor between c and d, causing a voltage of 2 v with polarities as shown. The voltage from c to g by the path $cdhg$ is 2 + 20 = 22 v, which, as shown, is also the voltage

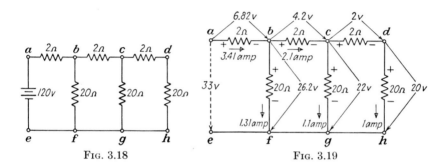

FIG. 3.18   FIG. 3.19

across the 20-ohm resistor between c and g. The current in that resistor is 22 v/20 ohms = 1.1 amp as shown. The current in the 2-ohm resistor between b and c is equal to the 1 amp in the resistor between c and d plus the 1.1 amp in the resistor between c and g, or 2.1 amp as shown. The voltage across the 2-ohm resistor between b and c is 2.1 amp × 2 ohms = 4.2 v with polarities as shown. The voltage from b to f by the path $bcgf$ is 4.2 + 22 = 26.2 v, which, as shown, is also the voltage across the 20-ohm resistor between b and f. The current in that resistor is 26.2 v/20 ohms = 1.31 amp, as shown. The current in the 2-ohm resistor between a and b is equal to the 2.1 amp in the resistor between b and c plus the 1.31 amp in the resistor between b and f, or 3.41 amp, as shown. The voltage across the 2-ohm resistor between a and b is 3.41 amp × 2 ohms = 6.82 v, as shown. The voltage from a to e by the path $abfe$ is 6.82 + 26.2 = 33 v. As shown, this is the applied voltage required to produce the various currents and voltages just computed. The voltage applied in Fig. 3.18 is 120 v; hence the currents there will be greater than in Fig. 3.19 in the ratio 120/33 = 3.64. When the currents in Fig. 3.19 are multiplied by this ratio, the currents in Fig. 3.18 are found to be: in resistor ab, 12.4 amp; in resistor bf, 4.76 amp; in resistor bc, 7.64 amp; in resistor cg, 4 amp; and in resistors cd and dh, 3.64 amp.

Example 2. In Fig. 3.20a determine the various currents with 120 v applied between A and B.
Solution. As in Fig. 3.20b, assume 1 amp directed to the right in the 5-ohm resistor. With directions as shown, the current in the 3-ohm resistor is designated as I_1 and that in the 4-ohm resistor as I_2. The remaining currents are designated as shown. For the path through the 4-, 5-, and 3-ohm resistors the voltage equation is $0 = 4I_2 - 5 - 3I_1$. For the path through the 5-, 6-, and 7-ohm resistors the voltage equation is $0 = 5 + 6(I_2 + 1) - 7(I_1 - 1)$. The simultaneous solution of these equations yields $I_1 = 10.2$ amp and $I_2 = 8.9$ amp.

The other currents are: in the 2-ohm resistor, $I_1 + I_2 = 19.1$ amp; in the 6-ohm resistor, $I_2 + 1 = 9.9$ amp; and in the 7-ohm resistor, $I_1 - 1 = 9.2$ amp. The applied voltage required to produce the currents, as determined by a voltage summation through the 2-, 3-, and 7-ohm resistors is

$$19.1 \times 2 + 10.2 \times 3 + 9.2 \times 7 = 133 \text{ v}$$

The above currents correspond to an applied voltage of 133 v. Since only 120 v are applied, the actual currents will be less in the ratio of 120 to 133 and are: in

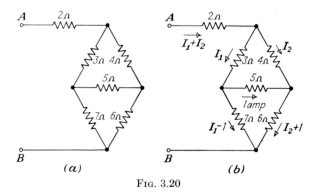

FIG. 3.20

the 2-ohm resistor, 17.2 amp; in the 3-ohm resistor, 9.2 amp; in the 4-ohm resistor, 8 amp; in the 5-ohm resistor, 0.9 amp; in the 6-ohm resistor, 8.9 amp; and in the 7-ohm resistor, 8.3 amp.

3.8. Wheatstone Bridge. In the bridge circuit of Fig. 3.21 currents are produced by a source of emf E and internal resistance R_B. Here a galvanometer G is a detecting device. By adjustment of the resistances R_1, R_2, R_3, and R_4 of the resistors the deflection of G can be made zero. After the adjustment has been made, the positions of the source of emf and the detecting device may be interchanged and the response of the device will again be zero.

The circuit of Fig. 3.21 was devised by Christie and popularized by Wheatstone. When used for measuring resistance, it is a Wheatstone bridge. The circuit is redrawn in Fig. 3.22 with the galvanometer resistance designated as R_G. With a Wheatstone bridge the value of an unknown resistance is determined by comparison. In Fig. 3.22 R_1, R_2, and R_3 are known resistances of three resistors. One of these, say R_3, is adjustable in small steps of resistance. To permit measurement of a wide range of resistance values with reasonable accuracy, R_1 and R_2 are usually adjustable in ratios such as 1 to 10, 1 to 1, 10 to 1, etc. R_x is the resistance of the unit whose resistance is to be measured.

To measure resistance with the bridge of Fig. 3.22, R_3 is varied until the galvanometer reads zero, producing a balanced bridge. With zero galvanometer current there is no voltage between B and D. Then the voltage from A to D is equal to that from A to B and the voltage from D to C is equal to that from B to C. The current I_1 flows from A to D to

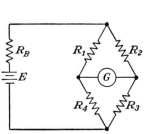

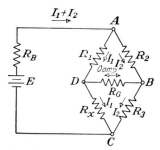

FIG. 3.21   A bridge circuit. By adjustment of the resistances R_1, R_2, R_3, and R_4 the deflection of the galvanometer G can be made zero.

FIG. 3.22   Wheatstone bridge circuit in a balanced condition.

C. The current I_2 flows from A to B to C. From these facts it follows that $I_1R_1 = I_2R_2$ and $I_1R_x = I_2R_3$. From the above equations,

$$\frac{R_x}{R_1} = \frac{R_3}{R_2} \quad \text{or} \quad \frac{R_x}{R_3} = \frac{R_1}{R_2}$$

With R_1, R_2, and R_3 known, R_x can be computed.

The accuracy of a resistance value measured with a Wheatstone bridge depends upon the accuracy of the values of R_1, R_2, and R_3 and upon the sensitivity and the resistance of the detecting device. The accuracy is usually better than that of the voltmeter-ammeter method.

Bridge circuits have applications other than the measurement of resistance. A change in the resistance of one arm produces a change in the galvanometer current. The galvanometer can be calibrated to register the change in any quantity that can be made to change the value of a resistance. Such an application involves relations in an unbalanced bridge as well as in a balanced one. Refer to the unbalanced bridge circuit of Fig. 3.23. Here the galvanometer current I_G is to be expressed in terms of the emf E and the various resistance values. As shown, all currents in the circuit can be expressed in terms of the three currents I_1, I_2, and I_G.

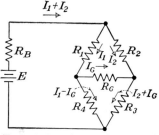

FIG. 3.23   An unbalanced bridge circuit.

To evaluate I_G, a voltage equation can be written for each of three paths. For the path through R_B, R_1, and R_4,

$$E = (I_1 + I_2)R_B + I_1R_1 + (I_1 - I_G)R_4$$

or, rearranging,

$$I_1(R_B + R_1 + R_4) + I_2 R_B - I_G R_4 = E \qquad (3.1)$$

For the path through R_1, R_2, and R_G,

$$-I_1 R_1 + I_2 R_2 - I_G R_G = 0 \qquad (3.2)$$

For the path through R_G, R_3, and R_4,

$$I_G R_G + (I_2 + I_G) R_3 - (I_1 - I_G) R_4 = 0$$

or, rearranging,

$$-I_1 R_4 + I_2 R_3 + I_G(R_G + R_3 + R_4) = 0 \qquad (3.3)$$

Determinants may be used to obtain I_G from (3.1), (3.2), and (3.3). Then

$$I_G = \frac{\begin{vmatrix} (R_B + R_1 + R_4) & R_B & E \\ -R_1 & R_2 & 0 \\ -R_4 & R_3 & 0 \end{vmatrix}}{\begin{vmatrix} (R_B + R_1 + R_4) & R_B & -R_4 \\ -R_1 & R_2 & -R_G \\ -R_4 & R_3 & (R_G + R_3 + R_4) \end{vmatrix}}$$

from which

$$I_G =$$

$$\frac{E(R_2 R_4 - R_1 R_3)}{R_2(R_B + R_1 + R_4)(R_G + R_3 + R_4) + R_B R_G R_4 + R_1 R_3 R_4 - R_2 R_4^2} \\ {} + R_B R_1 (R_G + R_3 + R_4) + R_G R_3 (R_B + R_1 + R_4) \qquad (3.4)$$

Usually R_B is negligibly small compared with the other resistances. If $R_B = 0$ is inserted in (3.4), then

$$I_G =$$

$$\frac{E(R_2 R_4 - R_1 R_3)}{R_2(R_1 + R_4)(R_G + R_3 + R_4) + R_1 R_3 R_4 - R_2 R_4^2 + R_G R_3 (R_1 + R_4)} \qquad (3.5)$$

Example 1. In Fig. 3.23, $E = 1.5$ v, $R_1 = 40$ ohms, $R_2 = 100$ ohms, R_3 is variable, $R_4 = 400$ ohms, $R_G = 250$ ohms, and R_B is negligible. Determine the equation relating I_G and R_3. Plot the curve represented by the equation.

Solution. Substitution of the given values in (3.5) and simplification yields

$$I_G = \frac{1,500 - 1.5 R_3}{4,250 R_3 + 315,000}$$

Inspection of this equation shows that I_G is positive when R_3 is less than 1,000 ohms, that I_G is zero when $R_3 = 1,000$ ohms, and that I_G is negative when R_3 is greater than 1,000 ohms. The galvanometer current reverses in direction as R_3 is varied from a value less than, to a value greater than, that required for a balanced bridge.   For $R_3 = 0$ (that is, a short circuit),

$$I_G = \frac{1,500}{315,000} = 0.00476 \text{ amp} = 4.76 \text{ ma}$$

For $R_3 = \infty$ (that is, an open circuit),

$$I_G = \frac{-1.5}{4,250} = -0.000353 \text{ amp} = -0.353 \text{ ma}$$

Thus three points on the $I_G - R$ curve have been obtained.   By assigning other values to R_3, corresponding values of I_G were obtained.   A plot of the points

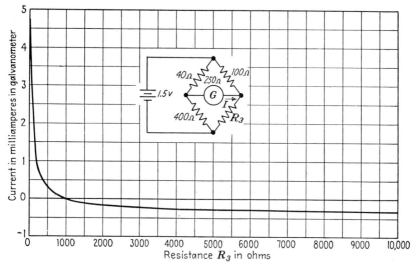

FIG. 3.24   Relation between the galvanometer current and the resistance R_3 in the bridge circuit shown.

yields the curve of Fig. 3.24.   Note that the slope of the curve is greater for R_3 less than 1,000 ohms than it is R_3 greater than 1,000 ohms.   Since the slope is a measure of the sensitivity of the bridge, a given change in R_3 for R_3 less than 1,000 ohms produces a greater change in the galvanometer deflection than an equal change for R_3 greater than 1,000 ohms.

3.9. Equivalent Star and Delta Circuits.

In Fig. 3.25, resistors having respective resistances of R_A, R_B, and R_C ohms are connected in star, or Y. In Fig. 3.26, resistors having respective resistances of R_1, R_2, and R_3 ohms are connected in delta, or mesh.   As far as any external circuits connected to the terminals A, B, and C are concerned one combination may be the equivalent of the other.   A general derivation of the relations that must exist between the resistance values to make the combinations equivalent would require consideration of the case where unequal voltages are applied between the terminals AB, BC, and CA. A simpler derivation that leads to the same result can be obtained from the fact that the resistance between a given pair of terminals, with no connection to the

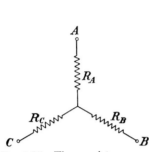

FIG. 3.25 Three resistors connected in star.

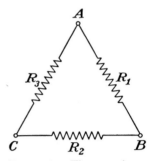

FIG. 3.26 Three resistors connected in delta.

third terminal, is equal in one combination to what it is in the other. In Fig. 3.25 the resistance between A and B is that of two resistors in series, or

$$R_{AB} = R_A + R_B$$

In Fig. 3.26 the resistance R_{AB} between A and B is that of two resistors in series and this combination in parallel with the third resistor, or

$$R_{AB} = \frac{R_1(R_2 + R_3)}{R_1 + R_2 + R_3}$$

Equating the values of R_{AB} yields

$$R_A + R_B = \frac{R_1(R_2 + R_3)}{R_1 + R_2 + R_3} \tag{3.6}$$

Similarly

$$R_{BC} = R_B + R_C \quad \text{and} \quad R_{BC} = \frac{R_2(R_1 + R_3)}{R_1 + R_2 + R_3}$$

from which

$$R_B + R_C = \frac{R_2(R_1 + R_3)}{R_1 + R_2 + R_3} \tag{3.7}$$

Further

$$R_{CA} = R_C + R_A \quad \text{and} \quad R_{CA} = \frac{R_3(R_1 + R_2)}{R_1 + R_2 + R_3}$$

from which

$$R_C + R_A = \frac{R_3(R_1 + R_2)}{R_1 + R_2 + R_3} \tag{3.8}$$

Considering R_A, R_B, and R_C as given quantities, (3.6) to (3.8) when solved simultaneously yield

$$R_1 = R_A + R_B + \frac{R_A R_B}{R_C}$$

$$R_2 = R_B + R_C + \frac{R_B R_C}{R_A}$$

and

$$R_3 = R_A + R_C + \frac{R_A R_C}{R_B}$$

To convert a given delta combination of resistors into an equivalent star combination, the relations may be derived from (3.6) to (3.8). Here R_1, R_2, and R_3 are given quantities and R_A, R_B, and R_C are to be expressed in terms of them. The relations are

$$R_A = \frac{R_1 R_3}{R_1 + R_2 + R_3}$$

$$R_B = \frac{R_1 R_2}{R_1 + R_2 + R_3}$$

$$R_C = \frac{R_2 R_3}{R_1 + R_2 + R_3}$$

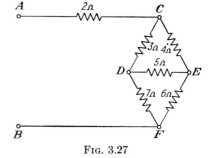

Example 1. Use a delta-to-star transformation to reduce the network of resistors of Fig. 3.27 to a resistor of equivalent resistance.

FIG. 3.27

Solution. The 3-, 4-, and 5-ohm resistors are a delta group that may be replaced by an equivalent star group as in Fig. 3.28a. When this equivalent group has been introduced, the circuit reduces to a combination of series and

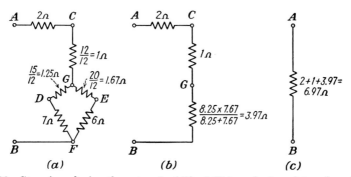

(a)   (b)   (c)

FIG. 3.28   Steps in reducing the network of Fig. 3.27 to a single resistor of equivalent resistance using a delta-to-star transformation.

parallel groups that may be combined as in Fig. 3.28b and c. Hence the equivalent resistance between terminals A and B is 6.97 ohms.

Example 2. Use a star-to-delta transformation to reduce the network of resistors of Fig. 3.27 to a resistor of equivalent resistance.

Solution. The 3-, 5-, and 7-ohm resistors are a star group that may be replaced by an equivalent delta group as in Fig. 3.29a. When this equivalent group has been introduced, the circuit reduces to a combination of series and parallel

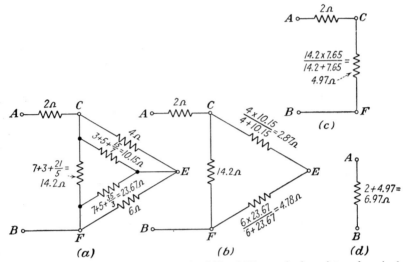

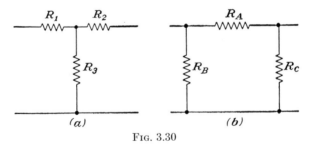

Fig. 3.29   Steps in reducing the network of Fig. 3.27 to a single resistor of equivalent resistance using a star-to-delta transformation.

groups that may be combined as in Fig. 3.29b, c, and d. The equivalent resistance of 6.97 ohms between terminals A and B agrees with the previous result.

If the diagram of a group of star-connected resistors is drawn as in Fig. 3.30a, it resembles the letter T. It is the combination that was called a T circuit in Art. 2.24.

FIG. 3.30

If the diagram of a group of delta-connected resistors is drawn as in Fig. 3.30b, it resembles the Greek letter π. It is the combination that was called a π circuit in Art. 2.24.

3.10. Reciprocity Theorem. Any linear, passive four-terminal network can be reduced to an arrangement of elements such as that of Fig. 3.31. In the reduction it may be necessary to combine resistances in series and resistances in parallel, to transform from delta to star resistances and from star to delta resistances.

Let a conductor of conductance G_7 be connected between terminals a and b and another of conductance G_8 be connected between terminals c and d. We wish to prove that if a source of emf E and negligible resistance is connected in series with the first conductor and produces a current I in the second, then if the source is connected in series with the second conductor it produces a current I in the first.

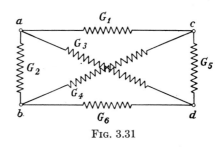

FIG. 3.31

This is the reciprocity theorem. Consider first Fig. 3.32. Terminal b has been chosen as the reference node. Three node-pair voltages, V_1, V_2, and V_3 are sufficient for expressing all currents. The assumed positive directions of the currents are indicated. At the respective nodes a, c,

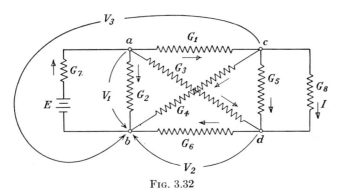

FIG. 3.32

and d, equating the sum of the currents toward a node to the sum of the currents leaving a node yields

$$(E - V_1)G_7 = V_1G_2 + (V_1 - V_2)G_3 + (V_1 - V_3)G_1$$
$$(V_1 - V_3)G_1 = V_3G_4 + (V_3 - V_2)(G_5 + G_8)$$
$$(V_1 - V_2)G_3 + (V_3 - V_2)(G_5 + G_8) = V_2G_6$$

These may be rearranged as

$$(G_1 + G_2 + G_3 + G_7)V_1 - G_3V_2 - G_1V_3 = EG_7$$
$$G_1V_1 + (G_5 + G_8)V_2 - (G_1 + G_4 + G_5 + G_8)V_3 = 0$$
$$G_3V_1 - (G_3 + G_5 + G_6 + G_8)V_2 + (G_5 + G_8)V_3 = 0$$

These may be solved once by determinants to obtain an expression for V_3 in terms of E and the various conductances. They may be solved a second time to obtain an expression for V_2. These expressions have the same denominator. Then an expression for $V_3 - V_2$ can be obtained. From Fig. 3.32 it can be seen that $I = (V_3 - V_2)G_8$. By substitution of the value for $V_3 - V_2$ an expression for I in terms of E and the various conductances can be obtained.

Figure 3.33 differs from that of Fig. 3.32 in that the source of emf E has been moved from the branch containing G_7 to the branch containing G_8. The current in branch 7 is now designated as I. Note that I in Fig. 3.33

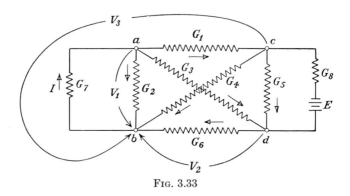

FIG. 3.33

is taken positive in the direction that E establishes current in G_7 in Fig. 3.32. Note also that E in Fig. 3.33, acting alone, would produce current in G_8 in the direction of I in Fig. 3.32.

The same node pair voltages are used in Fig. 3.33 as in Fig. 3.32. The assumed positive directions of the currents are indicated. At the respective nodes a, c, and d, equating the sum of the currents toward a node to the sum of all those leaving a node yields

$$-V_1G_7 = V_1G_2 + (V_1 - V_2)G_3 + (V_1 - V_3)G_1$$
$$(V_1 - V_3)G_1 = V_3G_4 + (V_3 - V_2)G_5 + (V_3 - V_2 + E)G_8$$
$$(V_1 - V_2)G_3 + (V_3 - V_2)G_5 + (V_3 - V_2 + E)G_8 = V_2G_6$$

These may be rearranged as

$$(G_1 + G_2 + G_3 + G_7)V_1 - G_3V_2 - G_1V_3 = 0$$
$$G_1V_1 + (G_5 + G_8)V_2 - (G_1 + G_4 + G_5 + G_8)V_3 = EG_8$$
$$G_3V_1 - (G_3 + G_5 + G_6 + G_8)V_2 + (G_5 + G_8)V_3 = -EG_8$$

These may be solved to obtain an expression for V_1 in terms of E and the various conductances. When this is multiplied by $-G_7$, the result obtained is the same as that for I in Fig. 3.32. But $-G_7V_1$ is also I in Fig. 3.33. Hence I in Fig. 3.33 is equal to I in Fig. 3.32 when E is same in each circuit.

More extended analysis than the preceding shows that the reciprocity theorem holds for any linear passive network.

3.11. Potentiometers and Precise Measurements of Voltage. A potentiometer circuit is composed of two or more sources of emf or electric potential, a detecting device, and other circuit elements. The detecting device is in series with one of the sources and its response can be made zero by adjustment of the elements. In the potentiometer circuit of Fig. 3.34 the emf E of a source having an internal resistance R_i is to be measured. The source is in series with a galvanometer G and a protective resistor of resistance R_p across the output terminals of a voltage divider. A source of emf E_1 is connected to the input terminals of the divider. E_1 must be greater than E. Terminals of the sources

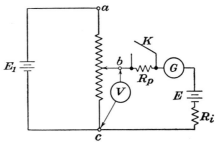

FIG. 3.34   Circuit arrangement for measuring the emf E of a source. The slider on the voltage divider is adjusted until the galvanometer G reads zero. With this setting of the slider the reading of the voltmeter is equal to E. The value of E_1 must be greater than that of E.

having like polarities are connected to point c. A key K is across the protective resistor. A voltmeter is across the output terminals of the divider. R_p should be great enough that, with K open, the current in the right-hand branch will not damage either the galvanometer or the source whose emf is being measured. With K open, the divider slider should be set at c. Then the source of emf E_1 is connected to the divider. Next the slider is moved until the galvanometer reads zero. Now K is closed to short-circuit the protective resistor. This may cause the galvanometer to deflect again. If so, with R_p in the circuit the galvanometer current was too small to cause an observable deflection. If the deflection is not zero with K closed, the slider should be moved until it is. With no galvanometer current there is no resistance drop in the right-hand branch and the voltage read on the voltmeter is equal to E. The accuracy with which E is measured is that of the voltmeter reading and is likely to be not better than 0.1 per cent. In many cases an accuracy almost as good could have been obtained by connecting the voltmeter directly across the source of E. The potentiometer method would be used only when the voltmeter current is greater than the capacity of the source or when the voltage drop in the source internal resistance caused by the voltmeter current is great enough to cause considerable error.

The potentiometer circuit of Fig. 3.35 is used to measure the unknown emf E_x of a cell by comparison with the known emf E_s of a standard cell. A straight wire of uniform cross section is in series with a rheostat of resistance R across a source of emf E_1, where E_1 is greater than either E_s or E_x. The wire is made of a material, such as manganin, whose resistance changes very little with a considerable temperature change. With the double-throw switch S closed to the left, the slider on the wire is moved to a position B such that the deflection of the galvanometer G is zero. The distance BC is then recorded as the position of balance against E_s. A measuring stick is usually mounted near the wire so that the distance BC can be measured readily. Next S is closed to the right and the slider moved to a new position B' such that the galvanometer

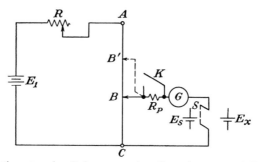

FIG. 3.35   Potentiometer circuit for measuring the unknown emf E_x by comparison with the known emf E_s of a standard cell.

deflection is again zero. Now the balance is against the emf E_x. The distance $B'C$ is then recorded. By proportion $E_x/E_s = B'C/BC$. The accuracy with which E_x is measured depends upon the accuracy with which E_s is known and that with which $B'C$ and BC can be measured.

In the circuit of Fig. 3.35 it is desired that the current through AC be the same when the slider is at B' as it was when the slider was at B. It might happen that the current would change while the slider was being moved. To test this possibility, after a balance at B' is obtained, the slider should be moved back to B to see if it is still a balance point against E_s. If it were not, the rheostat should be adjusted until B is again a balance point. Then a new location for B' would be made. Next another check would be made to see if B were still a balance point.

In Fig. 3.36 is a potentiometer circuit in which known resistance values are used to compare an unknown emf E_x with the known emf E of a standard cell. Here 15 resistors are connected in series between the points O and C. One is connected between the contact points 0 and 0.1, a second between 0.1 and 0.2, etc. The resistances of the resistors should be exactly equal, although it is not necessary that the resistance be any one specified value. In one widely used potentiometer the resistance is about 5 ohms.

In Fig. 3.36 a group of nine resistors are connected between O and L in series with the other resistors.   Each resistor in the second group has one-tenth the resistance of a resistor in the first group.   Of the second group one resistor is connected between points 0 and 0.01, a second between 0.01 and 0.02, etc.

In Fig. 3.36 the rheostat is to be set so that the voltage from C to O is 1.5 v to a high degree of accuracy.   Lead A is connected to the point

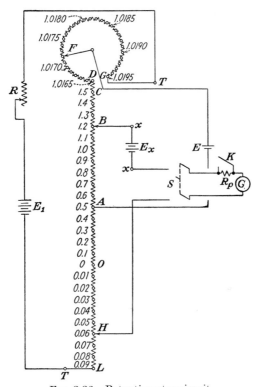

Fig. 3.36   Potentiometer circuit.

marked 0.5, so that the voltage from C to A is 1 v.   The emfs of all standard cells are not equal.   The potentiometer shown may be used with any standard cell whose emf is between 1.0165 and 1.0195 v.   Since the emf of a given cell varies with the temperature, the resistors between C and G are added to permit adjustment for the effect of temperature upon the emf of the cell used.   The resistance of the resistor between C and D is such that the voltage between them is 0.0165 v when the voltage from C to O is 1.5 v.   Each of the individual resistors between D and G has a resistance such that the voltage across it is 0.0001 v when the voltage from C to O is 1.5 v.

To use the potentiometer of Fig. 3.36, the standard cell and the cell whose emf is to be measured are connected as shown. Then the arm F is set at the contact corresponding to the emf of the standard cell at the temperature at which it is then operating. Here F is set for 1.0172 v. Next switch S is closed to the right and the current adjusted by rheostat R until the galvanometer deflection is zero. Final adjustment of R is made with the protective resistor R_p short-circuited by key K. Now the voltages from the various contact points to O correspond to the marked values. Then S is thrown to the left and contact arms B and H are moved until the galvanometer deflection is again zero, K being closed while the final adjustment is made. To check whether the current is still the proper value to make the voltage from F to A equal to the standard cell emf, switch S is thrown to the right again. If the galvanometer reading is zero (with K closed), the current value is correct. If the galvanometer reading is not zero, R should be adjusted to make it zero. Then, with switch S thrown to the left, contact arms B and H should be moved until a zero reading is obtained. Then another check should be made on the current value. The above procedure is repeated until the galvanometer deflection is zero (with K closed) when switch S is closed to either the right or the left. Then the emf being measured is read from the settings of contact arms B and H. In Fig. 3.36 the value is 1.26 v.

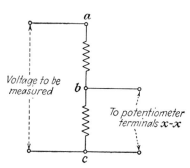

FIG. 3.37 Multiplier arrangement for measuring with a potentiometer a voltage greater than 1.6 v. The output terminals bc are connected in the circuit of Fig. 3.36 in place of the cell whose emf is E_x.

With contact points as indicated in Fig. 3.36, an unknown emf can be measured only to the nearest 0.01 v. With this degree of accuracy it is an unnecessary refinement to provide compensation for changes in the standard cell emf as small as 0.0001 v. In one potentiometer the resistors from O to L are replaced by a long wire of uniform cross section wound in a spiral on a cylinder. As contact arm H is rotated through 10 turns, the point of contact moves from one end of the wire to the other. Thus each revolution of the arm represents 0.01 v. In addition a graduated scale is provided on which it is possible to read to $\frac{1}{100}$ part of a revolution the position of the arm. Then the value of an emf can be measured to the nearest 0.0001 v.

The potentiometer of Fig. 3.36 is designed to measure voltages of 1.6 v or less. To measure greater voltages, a multiplier (also called a volt box) is used, as in Fig. 3.37. The ratio of the resistance from b to c to that from a to c is usually one like 1 to 10 or 1 to 100 or 1 to 1,000.

In Fig. 3.37 current is drawn from the terminals between which the voltage is being measured.   The current can be limited to a low value by using high resistances between a and b, and b and c.   However, the higher these resistances are made, the lower will be the sensitivity of the potentiometer circuit.

The potentiometer of Fig. 3.36 can be adapted for more precise measurements of voltages less than 0.16 v by adding a shunt as in Fig. 3.38. If a tapered contact plug is put in the tapered opening next to contact block 1, the resistor of resistance R_{se} is short-circuited and the circuit is

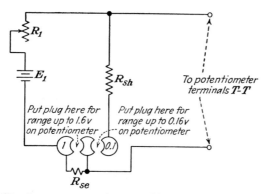

FIG. 3.38   Circuit arrangement for use with the potentiometer of Fig. 3.36.

electrically the same as that of Fig. 3.36.   If the plug is put in the opening next to contact block 0.1, the resistor of resistance R_{sh} is in parallel with the potentiometer.   Also the resistance R_{se} is in series with the above parallel combination. R_{sh} has a value such that, when that resistor is in the circuit, the potentiometer current is 0.1 the current in the battery of emf E_1. R_{se} has a value such that the battery current is the same with the plug in one opening as with it in the other.

When using the circuit of Fig. 3.38 to measure voltages less than 0.16 v, the first step is to standardize the potentiometer against the standard cell. The plug is put in the opening next to contact block 1.   Then the arm F is set at the point corresponding to the emf of the standard cell.   Next the rheostat of resistance R_1 is adjusted until the galvanometer reads zero with the switch S closed to the right.   Now the voltages between the various points on the potentiometer correspond to the marked values. Then terminals of the element whose voltage is to be measured are connected to potentiometer terminals x-x instead of the cell shown in Fig. 3.36.   Next the plug is moved to the opening next to contact block 0.1. This change reduces the potentiometer current to 0.1 of the battery current without changing the battery current.   Then the actual voltages between the various points on the potentiometer are 0.1 of the marked values.   Next switch S is closed to the left and contact arms B and H are moved until a balance is obtained against the voltage being measured. This voltage is 0.1 the value read from the potentiometer at the settings of B and H. After this balance has been obtained, it is advisable to check whether the potentiometer is still in balance against the standard cell.   If not, R_1 should be adjusted until the balance is obtained.   Then new positions of B and H should be obtained and read.

3.12. Distribution Circuits.   Most tungsten-filament lamps are made for operation at voltages in the range from 110 to 125 v.   A 50-w lamp made for 220-v operation would have a more fragile filament than one made for 110-v operation.

As far as economy in the copper volume required is concerned, the use of high voltages is desirable.   However, other factors such as the cost of insulation and safety must also be considered when choosing the voltage for a particular application.   Several types of distribution circuits are in use.   Although only d-c circuits are considered here, similar principles apply to a-c circuits.

3.13. Series Distribution Systems.   In a series distribution system all loads are in series and carry the same current.   This system is suitable for supplying a number of identical loads, such as street lamps.   When a lamp is turned off by short-circuiting it, the current in the remaining lamps momentarily increases.   Then an automatic control device operates to reduce the voltage of the system and thus reduce the current to its original value.   If a lamp burns out, another device operates to short-circuit the lamp terminals and thus permit the other lamps of the system to receive current.

3.14. Constant-voltage Distribution Systems.   In most distribution systems the voltage between the wires that supply the loads is kept nearly constant.   The various loads receive nearly equal voltages, and each load may draw its normal current with little effect upon that drawn by the other loads.   Several loads near each other may be supplied in parallel from a pair of wires as in Fig. 3.39.   When the loads to be supplied from a given generator are some distance apart, systems such as those of Figs. 3.40 and 3.41 are used.   The system of Fig. 3.40 requires the minimum length of conductors.   Here the farther a load is from the generator, the less is the voltage across it.   In the loop system of Fig. 3.41 a load can receive current from either direction.   The load farthest from the generator does not necessarily receive the least voltage.

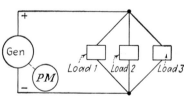

Fig. 3.39   Three loads in parallel supplied from a distribution circuit.

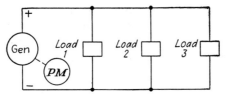

Fig. 3.40   System for supplying distributed loads.

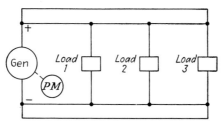

Fig. 3.41   Loop system for supplying distributed loads.

3.15. Three-wire System.   The d-c three-wire distribution system was invented by Thomas A. Edison.   Such a system may receive energy from two d-c generators as in Fig. 3.42.   The wire from a point between the generators is the neutral wire and is usually grounded.   With no loads connected in the system shown, there are 240 v between the outside wires and 120 v between each outside wire and the neutral wire.   Hence, either of two voltages is available.

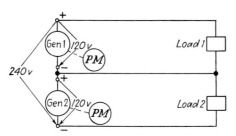

Fig. 3.42   A three-wire system supplied from two generators.

When identical loads at equal distances from the generator are connected to a three-wire system, one load between one outside wire and the neutral wire, and the other between the other outside wire and the neutral wire, the loads are balanced.   Then there is no current in the neutral wire, and the load voltages are equal.   If all loads on a three-wire system were switched on or off in pairs of identical units, the various pairs could be connected in series between the outside wires and no neutral wire would be needed.   However, it is likely that at times greater current will be drawn by loads between one outside wire and the neutral wire than by loads between the other outside wire and the neutral wire. Then at the generators, the neutral wire current is the difference of the sum of the currents in the loads on one side of the system and the sum of the currents in the loads on the other side of the system.

When unequal loads at equal distances from the generators are being supplied, one load between one outside wire and the neutral wire and the other between the other outside wire and the neutral wire, the voltage across the load that is drawing the greater current is less than that across the other load. It is possible for the voltage across the load that is drawing the smaller current to be greater than the voltage between the same two wires at the generator terminals. The IR in the neutral wire is a voltage drop in the side of the circuit containing the load drawing the greater current, but it is a voltage rise in the side containing the other load. When the voltage across one load is higher than that between the same pair of wires at the generator, that load is receiving more power than is being produced by the generator on the same side of the circuit. The additional power received by the load is transmitted to it from the other generator by the effect of the resistance of the neutral wire.

Example 1. In Fig. 3.43 each wire has 0.04 ohm resistance. Load 1 draws 100 amp and load 2 draws 20 amp. Compute the voltage across each load and the efficiency of the circuit.

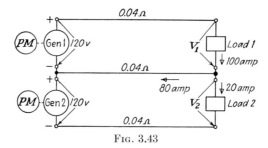

Fig. 3.43

Solution. With the given loads the neutral wire current will be 80 amp to the left as indicated. For the upper loop, the voltage equation is

$$120 = 100 \times 0.04 + V_1 + 80 \times 0.04$$

Hence $V_1 = 120 - 4 - 3.2 = 112.8$ v.
For the lower loop, the voltage equation is

$$120 = -80 \times 0.04 + V_2 + 20 \times 0.04$$

Hence $V_2 = 120 + 3.2 - 0.8 = 122.4$ v.
With the given loads the voltage across load 2 is greater than that across generator 2.
The power delivered by the circuit is the sum of the load powers, or

$$112.8 \text{ v} \times 100 \text{ amp} + 122.4 \text{ v} \times 20 \text{ amp} = 13,728 \text{ w}$$

The power input to the circuit is the sum of the generator powers, or

$$120 \text{ v} \times 100 \text{ amp} + 120 \text{ v} \times 20 \text{ amp} = 14{,}400 \text{ w}$$

The efficiency of the circuit is 13,728 w/14,400 w = 0.953, or 95.3 per cent.

3.16. Voltage Regulation. If the voltage output of a generator that is supplying a distribution circuit is kept constant, the voltage at the load end of the circuit will change when the load current changes because of the effect of the resistances of the wires. The variation of a load voltage as the load current changes is a measure of the voltage regulation of the circuit. The voltage regulation of a circuit is the change in voltage at the load end of the circuit, expressed as a percentage of the rated load voltage, that occurs when the load current is changed from rated value to zero, with the voltage at the input end of the circuit maintained constant at the value required to cause load voltage to be rated value when rated current is delivered.

Example 1. A certain distribution circuit requires 119 v at the input end to deliver rated voltage of 115 v at the load end to a rated load of 50 kw. Compute the voltage regulation.
Solution. With 119 v maintained at the input end, the no-load voltage at the load end will also be 119 v since there is no current in the wires to cause a voltage drop in them. Therefore

$$\text{Voltage regulation} = \frac{119 - 115}{115} \times 100 = 3.5 \text{ per cent}$$

If all the loads at the end of a distribution circuit were connected at one time and all disconnected at another time, the generator voltage could be adjusted to give the desired voltage across the loads, when they were connected, for any value of resistance in the wires. However, all loads are not necessarily connected at one time and it is of interest to know how the load-end voltage varies as the load current is varied. For example, assume that 50 lamps in parallel constitute the rated load on a distribution circuit that required 125 v at the sending end to deliver 115 v to the lamps when all were connected. If the sending-end voltage were maintained at 125 v, when only one lamp is connected the voltage across it would be almost 125 v. As more and more are connected, the voltage across them would decrease from about 125 v with one lamp connected to 115 v with all connected.

A tungsten-filament lamp is sensitive to voltage changes. A 5 per cent change in voltage causes nearly 10 per cent change in the illumination produced. Continued operation at 5 per cent over rated voltage reduces lamp life to about one-half that at rated voltage. Hence, it is desirable that circuits supplying lamps have good (i.e., low) voltage regulation, preferably not more than 3 per cent.

The operating characteristics of a motor are affected by variations in the voltage applied to it. Most motors are so designed that they will operate satisfactorily under normal load conditions if the voltage regulation of the supply circuits does not exceed 10 per cent.

PROBLEMS

3.1. Connections of a fluorescent lamp for operation from a 120-v d-c supply are as

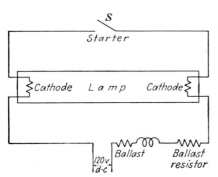

in Fig. 3.44. The first step in starting a lamp is to close the switch S to heat the cathodes. Then, when S is opened, the ballast produces a voltage surge great enough to start a flow of current from one cathode to the other. After current has started, it keeps the cathode temperatures high enough to maintain a current through the lamp. For a certain 20-w lamp the resistance of the ballast, the ballast resistor, and the cathodes is 175 ohms. The operating lamp current is 310 ma.

FIG. 3.44   Circuit diagram of fluorescent lamp for operation from a d-c supply. For operation from an a-c supply the ballast resistor is not required.

    a. How much starting current is drawn by the lamp? Compute the ratio of the starting to the operating current.

    b. In normal operation what are the resistance of the lamp, the power delivered to the lamp, and the power loss in the circuit?

3.2. A certain 30-w fluorescent lamp is intended for operation from a 240-v d-c supply. The ballast resistance is 35 ohms. If the normal lamp current is 300 ma, compute the resistance of the ballast resistor. Neglect the resistance of the cathodes. (Refer to Prob. 3.1 for information regarding the lamp circuit.) Compute the starting current of the lamp with the proper ballast resistor.

3.3. The circuit of Fig. 3.45 is used for certain measurements. With S_2 closed and S_1 open there is a certain current I in the battery and in the 85-ohm resistor. Compute the values of R_1 and R_2 such that with S_1 closed and S_2 open the battery current will be I and the current in the 85-ohm resistor will be $0.1I$. Assume that R is the same in each case.

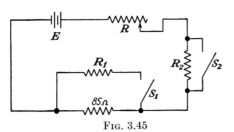

FIG. 3.45

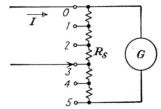

FIG. 3.46   Circuit diagram of an Ayrton shunt.

3.4. In the Ayrton shunt circuit of Fig. 3.46 the resistor has a total resistance $R_S = 0.001$ ohm and is tapped so that the resistances 0-1, 1-2, 2-3, 3-4, and 4-5 are each 0.0002 ohm.   The galvanometer G requires 10 ma to produce full-scale deflection and has a resistance of 4.999 ohms.

   a. What current I fed in at 0 and taken out at tap 3 will produce full-scale galvanometer deflection?

   b. What current I fed in at 0 and taken out at tap 1 will produce full-scale galvanometer deflection?

   c. Prove that for a constant value of I the galvanometer deflection is directly proportional to the resistance in the part of the circuit between 0 and the tap at which the current is taken out.

   3.5. In the Ayrton shunt circuit of Fig. 3.46 the resistor has a total resistance $R_S = 0.001$ ohm and is tapped as indicated.   The galvanometer G requires 10 ma for full-scale deflection and has a resistance of 4.999 ohms.   The taps are to be located so that full-scale galvanometer deflection will occur when currents of 250, 200, 150, 100 and 50 amp are fed in at 0 and taken out at the points 1, 2, 3, 4, and 5, respectively.   Compute the resistances of the various sections of the shunt.

   3.6. The electric circuit of a shunt generator is in Fig. 3.47.   The load is drawing 50 kw at a load voltage $V_L = 250$ v.   Each line wire resistance $R_L = 0.04$ ohm.   The shunt field winding resistance $R_f = 40$ ohms.   The armature resistance R_a varies with the current but for the purpose of this problem may be considered constant at 0.08 ohm.   Compute the generator terminal voltage V_t, the current in the field winding, the current in the armature, the generated emf E_g, and the power developed in the armature.

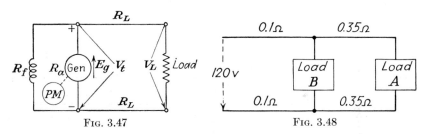

FIG. 3.47	FIG. 3.48

   3.7. In Fig. 3.48 load A consists of two 500-w 115-v lamps in parallel and load B consists of four 200-w 115-v lamps in parallel.   The resistance of a lamp varies with the current in it, but for the purpose of this problem assume that the resistance of each 500-w lamp is constant at 26 ohms and that of each 200-w lamp is constant at 66 ohms.

   a. Compute the voltage across and the current in each lamp.

   b. If two of the 200-w lamps are turned off, determine the voltage across each of the remaining lamps.

   3.8. In Fig. 3.49 the voltage between A and B is 60 v.   Compute the battery terminal voltage.

   3.9. The current supplied to two branches in parallel is 25 amp.   One branch contains 10 ohms resistance.   The other contains 20 ohms resistance and an emf of 50 v.   Compute the current in each branch if energy is being delivered by the source of emf in the one branch.

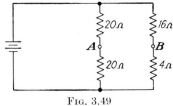

FIG. 3.49

   3.10. In Fig. 3.50, battery A has an emf of 2.6 v and an internal resistance of 0.04 ohm, battery B has an emf of 250 v and an internal resistance of 100 ohms, and battery C has an emf of 45 v and an internal resistance of 5 ohms. Assume that all

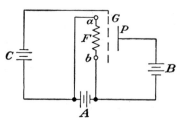

points on the plate P are at a common potential and that all points on the grid G are at another common potential. At a certain time the current in battery A is 2.5 amp, that in battery B is 60 ma, and that in battery C is zero.

a. How much current is entering the filament F at point a?

b. How much current is leaving the filament at point b?

Fɪɢ. 3.50 Circuit containing a three-element vacuum tube.

c. What is the potential between the grid and the mid-point of the filament?

d. What is the potential between the plate and the mid-point of the filament?

3.11. In Fig. 3.51 compute the emf E.

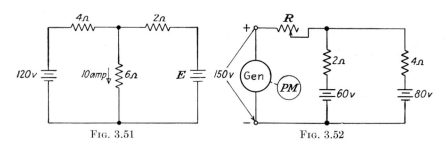

Fɪɢ. 3.51   Fɪɢ. 3.52

3.12. In Fig. 3.52 the battery whose emf is 60 v is being charged with a current of 30 amp. Compute the resistance R of the control rheostat.

3.13. Battery A has an emf of 50 v and an internal resistance of 0.2 ohm. Battery B has an emf of 48 v and an internal resistance of 0.4 ohm. The batteries in parallel supply 20 amp to a load. Compute the load voltage and the current in each battery.

3.14. Solve Prob. 3.13 if each battery has an emf of 50 v.

3.15. A battery that has an emf of 125 v and an internal resistance of 0.4 ohm is in parallel with a second battery that has an emf of 130 v and an internal resistance of 0.2 ohm.

a. Compute the terminal voltage of the batteries when no load is connected.

b. Compute the terminal voltage of the batteries and the current in each when the load current is 60 amp.

c. How much current would be delivered to a short circuit across the battery terminals?

3.16. The terminal voltage of a certain d-c generator decreases linearly from 250 v with zero current output to 200 v with 100 amp output. If a 2.5-ohm resistor is connected across the generator terminals, how much current will it draw?

If a battery that has an emf of 225 v and an internal resistance of 0.25 ohm is connected to the generator, how much charging current will it draw?

3.17. The terminal voltage of a certain d-c generator increases linearly from 125 v with zero current output to 150 v with 100 amp output. If a 2.5-ohm resistor is connected across the generator terminals, how much current will it draw?

If a battery that has an emf of 120 v and an internal resistance of 0.4 ohm is connected to the generator, how much charging current will it draw?

3.18. Two d-c generators, each of which maintains a constant terminal voltage of
120 v, are in series. The positive terminal of one is connected to the negative terminal of the other. A resistor of 20 ohms and another of 40 ohms are connected in
series across the generators. Compute the reading of a 300-v voltmeter if it were
connected between the common junction of the generators and that of the resistors.

Compute the reading of a 25-amp ammeter if it were connected between the junctions instead of the voltmeter.

3.19. In Fig. 3.53 the voltmeter reads 120 v and the ammeter reads 100 ma. Compute the value of R_1 if it is known that R_2 and R_3 are several hundred ohms each.

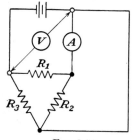

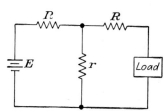

FIG. 3.53   FIG. 3.54   T circuit equivalent of a telephone line.

3.20. The T circuit of Fig. 3.54 is an approximate representation of a telephone
circuit. $R = 400$ ohms represents the resistance of each line wire and $r = 2,000$ ohms
represents the leakage resistance between wires. If $E = 10$ v and the load resistance
is 1,000 ohms, compute the load voltage.

3.21. In Fig. 3.55 the currents $I_1 = 8$, $I_2 = 12$, and $I_3 = 20$ amp are in the indicated directions. Determine E_1 and E_2 and the polarities of the batteries of which
they are the emfs.

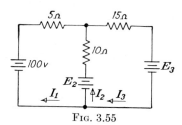

FIG. 3.55

3.22. A d-c generator Gen 1 that has an armature resistance of 0.5 ohm and a generated emf of 240 v is in parallel with another generator Gen 2 that has an armature
resistance of 0.3 ohm and a generated emf of 235 v. The rated current of Gen 1 is
100 amp and that of Gen 2 is 50 amp. Compute the maximum current that can be
drawn by the load without overheating either generator. What is the corresponding
load voltage?

3.23. In Fig. 3.56 the rheostat of resistance R is so adjusted that the galvanometer G
reads zero. The milliammeter has 60 ohms resistance; R_1 is 150 ohms. The milliammeter reading is 8 ma. Compute the current in the rheostat and that in the

resistor.　Note that this is an arrangement whereby the current in a circuit can be measured without introducing a voltage drop in the circuit.

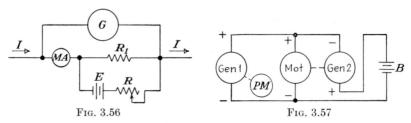

FIG. 3.56　　　　　　　　　　　　　　FIG. 3.57

3.24. In Fig. 3.57, battery B, which has an emf of 120 v and an internal resistance of 0.2 ohm, is being charged with a current of 40 amp.　Generator 2 is a booster generator that is mechanically coupled to and driven by motor (Mot) and has 0.1 ohm resistance.　The main generator Gen 1 maintains a terminal voltage of 110 v and supplies 51 amp.

　　a. Compute the terminal and generated voltages of Gen 2.

　　b. Compute the current in Mot.

　　c. Compute the ratio of the power delivered by Gen 2 to the power input to Mot and the ratio of the power delivered to B to the power output of Gen 1.　Which of these ratios is the efficiency of the motor-generator set?　What efficiency does the other ratio represent?

3.25. For the circuit of Fig. 2.72 compute the power delivered to each resistor and the power delivered by, or to, each battery.　Compare the total power produced with that used.

3.26. For the circuit of Fig. 2.73 compute the power delivered to each resistor and the power delivered by, or to, each battery.　Compare the total power produced with that used.

3.27. For the circuit of Fig. 2.72 write the voltage equations in terms of loop currents.　From these compute the loop currents and the actual currents.

3.28. For the circuit of Fig. 2.73 write the voltage equations in terms of loop currents.　From these compute the loop currents and the actual currents.

3.29. Use the principle of node-pair voltages and compute the currents in the circuit of Fig. 2.72.

3.30. Use the principle of node-pair voltages and compute the currents in the circuit of Fig. 2.73.

3.31. For the circuit of Fig. 2.72 use the superposition theorem and compute the currents.

3.32. For the circuit of Fig. 2.73 use the superposition theorem and compute the currents.

3.33. For the circuit of Fig. 2.72 use Thévenin's theorem and compute the currents.

3.34. For the circuit of Fig. 2.73 use Thévenin's theorem and compute the currents.

3.35. A generator that delivers a constant current of 20 ma is in parallel with a 10^{-4}-mho resistor.

　　a. If a 500-ohm resistor is connected across this combination, how much current will flow in it?

　　b. If a 10^{-3}-mho resistor is connected instead of the 500-ohm resistor, how much current will flow in it?

3.36. Use Norton's theorem and replace the center and right-hand branches of Fig. 2.72 by a constant-current generator in parallel with a resistor,　Compute the generator current and the resistor conductance.

3.37. A battery that has an emf of 24 v and an internal resistance of 0.2 ohm is in parallel with another that has an emf of 27 v and an internal resistance of 0.1 ohm. These are to be replaced by a constant-current generator in parallel with a resistor, Compute the generator current and the resistor conductance.

3.38. Compute the currents in the circuits of Fig. 3.58 by what appears to you to be the method that will require the least time.   Check your results using two other methods.

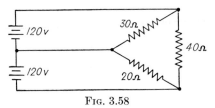

Fig. 3.58

3.39. In Fig. 3.59, 200 v are applied between A and B.   Compute the voltage across each resistor.

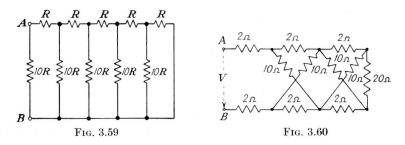

Fig. 3.59   Fig. 3.60

3.40. In Fig. 3.60 compute the voltage V required to produce 4 amp in the 20-ohm resistor.

3.41. In Fig. 3.60 what voltage in series with the 20-ohm resistor would produce 4 amp in a lead of negligible resistance connected between points A and B.

3.42. The current in the 20-ohm resistor in Fig. 3.61 is 5 amp.   Compute E.

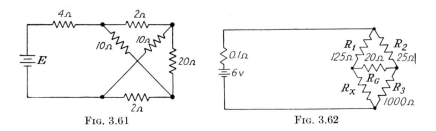

Fig. 3.61   Fig. 3.62

3.43. The Wheatstone bridge of Fig. 3.62 is in balance.   Compute R_x and the currents in the resistors.

3.44. Interchange the positions of the battery and the galvanometer in the Wheatstone bridge of Fig. 3.62.   Then compute R_x and the currents in the resistors.

3.45. In the bridge circuit of Fig. 3.63 compute the current in each of the resistors.*

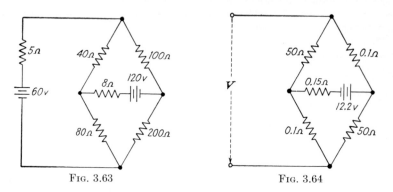

FIG. 3.63   FIG. 3.64

3.46. In Fig. 3.64 the battery is being charged with 10 amp.   Determine the value and the polarity of V.

3.47. The phase windings of a certain three-phase motor are connected in star. The resistance between any pair of terminals measured with direct current is 6 ohms. Compute the resistance of each winding.

3.48. The phase windings of a certain three-phase motor are connected in delta. The resistance between any pair of terminals measured with direct current is 6 ohms. Compute the resistance of each winding.

3.49. Three 60-ohm resistors are connected in star.   Compute the resistance of each of three delta-connected resistors that would have a resistance between terminals equal to that of the star combination.

3.50. Three 30-ohm resistors are connected in delta.   Compute the resistance of each of three star-connected resistors that would have a resistance between terminals equal to that of the delta combination.

3.51. Three resistors are connected in star.   The junction is point O and the terminals are A, B, and C, respectively.   The resistance from A to O equals that from B to O.   With no connection on B, the resistance between A and C was measured as 500 ohms.   With B connected to C, the resistance between A and C was measured as 70 ohms.   Compute each of the resistances.

3.52. The ground resistance of a driven ground rod A was measured by the "three-point method."   Two temporary auxiliary ground rods, B and C, each ½ in. in diameter were driven to a depth of 8 ft at a distance of 25 ft from each other and from A.   The resistances from rod to rod were measured as A-B, 120 ohms; B-C, 140 ohms; and C-A, 160 ohms.   Assume that the ground resistances form a star combination. Compute the ground resistance of A.

3.53. Compute the resistance values for a single star combination of resistors connected to the points A, B, and C that is equivalent to the two sets of resistors of Fig. 3.65.

3.54. The phase windings of a certain transformer are connected in delta as in Fig. 3.66.   Junction points A, B, and C are not readily accessible.   The resistances of the individual windings are to be determined from measurements made at the

---

* For an application of this circuit, see G. A. Caldwell and W. H. Formals, Electrical Drives for Wide Speed Ranges, *Elec. Eng.*, vol. 61, February, 1942.

accessible terminals X, Y, and Z. The resistance between X and Z is 0.1 ohm, that between Y and Z is 0.12 ohm, and that between X and Y is 0.13 ohm. If the resistances of the leads XA, YB, and ZC are negligible, compute the resistances of the phase windings.

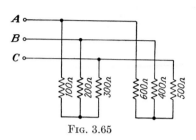

FIG. 3.65

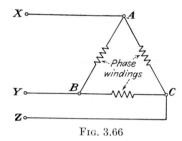

FIG. 3.66

3.55. In Prob. 3.54 the resistances of the leads XA, YB, and ZC are each 0.02 ohm. Compute the resistances of the phase windings.

3.56. In Fig. 3.67 a four-terminal network is inserted between a battery and an adjustable resistor.

a. What is the maximum output voltage of the network and for what value of R does it occur?

b. What is the maximum output current of the network and for what value of R does it occur?

c. What is the maximum output power of the network and for what value of R does it occur?

d. What is the maximum efficiency of the network and for what value of R does it occur?

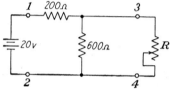

FIG. 3.67 A four-terminal network interposed between a battery and an adjustable load of resistance R.

3.57. Twelve 60-ohm resistors are connected to form the edges of a cube. Compute the resistance between two diagonally opposite vertices and that between two adjacent vertices.

3.58. Six resistors are connected as in Fig. 3.68. Compute the equivalent resistance between points A and N.

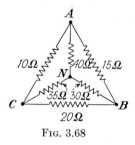

FIG. 3.68

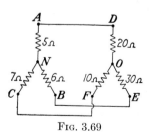

FIG. 3.69

3.59. Six resistors are connected as in Fig. 3.69. A generator that delivers 240 v is connected to points A and C. Compute the generator current and the voltage between points N and O.

3.60. The circuit of a bridge rheostat is in Fig. 3.70.   The resistor between A and B and that between C and D have a resistance of 50 ohms each.   The rheostat between B and C and that between D and A have a resistance of 60 ohms each.   The movable

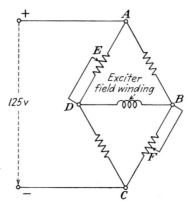

FIG 3.70   Wheatstone-bridge rheostat.

contacts E and F are mechanically coupled so that E is always the same distance from D that F is from B.   The exciter field winding has 120 ohms resistance.

a. When contact E is at point D, what are the direction and the magnitude of the field winding current?

b. What is the position of contact E when the field winding current is zero?

c. When contact E is at point A, what are the direction and the magnitude of the field winding current?

3.61. In a certain series street-lighting circuit the current is kept constant at 6.6 amp and each lamp requires 52 v.   What voltage must be applied when 40 lamps are lighted?   When 12 lamps are lighted?

3.62. In Fig. 3.71 two generators Gen 1 and Gen 2 are supplying the loads L_1 and L_2. L_1 is drawing 200 amp and L_2 is drawing 160 amp.   Compute the load voltages and the efficiency of the circuit.

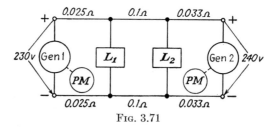

FIG. 3.71

3.63. In Fig. 3.71 the voltage across L_1 is 220 v and that across L_2 is 230 v.   Compute the load currents and the efficiency of the circuit.

3.64. In Fig. 3.71 the resistance of each load is 2 ohms.   Compute the load voltages and the efficiency of the circuit.

3.65. In Fig. 3.72 the generator is supplying 120 amp to load L_1 and 100 amp to load L_2.   Compute the voltage across each load and the efficiency of the circuit.

3.66. In Fig. 3.72 the voltage across L_1 is 118 v and that across L_2 is 120 v.   Compute the load currents and the efficiency of the circuit.

3.67. In Fig. 3.42 each wire has a resistance of 0.1 ohm and each load has a resistance of 5 ohms. Compute the voltage across and the power input to each load.

If a short circuit should occur across the terminals of load 2, how much current would be supplied by each generator and how much voltage will be across load 1?

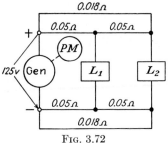

3.68. In a certain three-wire system each outside wire has a resistance of 0.2 ohm and the neutral wire has a resistance of 0.4 ohm. Each of the generators supplying the system maintains a terminal voltage of 250 v. A load between one outside wire and the neutral draws 55 amp. A load between the other outside wire and the neutral draws 15 amp. Compute the voltage across each load and the efficiency of the circuit.

Fig. 3.72

3.69. In the three-wire system of Prob. 3.68 the 15-amp load is disconnected. Compute the voltage across the remaining load.

3.70. A certain three-wire system is supplied by two 125-v generators. Each wire has a resistance of 0.2 ohm. The voltage across a load between one outside wire and the neutral is 128 v and that across a load between the other outside wire and the neutral is 112 v. Compute the current in and the resistance of each load.

3.71. In Fig. 3.73 load 1 draws 40 amp, load 2 draws 15 amp, and load 3 draws 25 amp. Compute the voltage across each load.

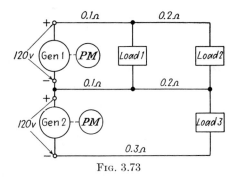

Fig. 3.73

3.72. Two generators, each delivering 250 v, supply a three-wire system in which each wire has 0.2 ohm resistance. The load between one outside wire and the neutral is a 2-ohm resistor and that between the other outside wire and the neutral is a 4-ohm resistor. How much power is delivered to the 2-ohm resistor?

3.73. A certain 100-ohm slide-wire rheostat has its end terminals connected between the outside wires of a 220/110-v three-wire system. Between the slider and the neutral wire of the system a 200-ohm field winding of a generator is connected. Through what range can the field current be varied? What should be the current rating of the rheostat?

3.74. A certain two-wire distribution circuit has a voltage regulation of 10 per cent. With full load on the circuit, what is its efficiency?

CHAPTER 4

PROPERTIES OF CONDUCTORS AND INSULATORS

4.1. Factors Affecting Conductor Resistance. Materials are classified as conducting, semiconducting, and insulating with no clear cut division between one class and another. A material that serves as an insulator for one application might serve as a conductor for another. Metals and carbon are classed as conductors.

Assume that a homogeneous metal conductor that has a uniform cross section A throughout a length l_1 has a resistance R_1. One may think of the conductor as composed of n identical shorter conductors in series, each of length $l_2 = l_1/n$ with a cross section A and resistance R_2. Since the resistance of n identical elements in series is n times that of one, then $nR_2 = R_1$. Thus $R_1/R_2 = l_1/l_2$, proving that the resistance of a conductor is directly proportional to the length.

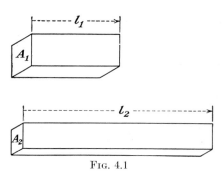

Fig. 4.1

Assume that a homogeneous metal conductor that has a uniform cross section A_1 throughout a length l has a resistance R_1. One may think of the conductor as composed of m identical smaller conductors in parallel, each of cross section $A_2 = A_1/m$ and resistance R_2. Since the resistance of m identical elements in parallel is $1/m$ times that of one, then $R_1 = R_2/m$. Thus $R_1/R_2 = A_2/A_1$, proving that the resistance of a conductor is inversely proportional to the cross section.

The resistance of a given conductor is a function of the kind of current in it; being least for direct current and increasing with increasing frequency of an alternating current. When the resistance of a conductor is given as a certain value, it is the resistance to direct current unless otherwise specified.

The resistance of a given conductor is a function of the temperature. Assume that the conductors of Fig. 4.1 are composed of the same homo-

geneous material and are at the same temperature.   Since the resistances
between ends are directly proportional to the lengths and inversely proportional to the areas, $R_2/R_1 = (l_2/l_1)(A_1/A_2)$, where R_1 and R_2 ohms are
the respective resistances, l_1 and l_2 are the respective lengths, and A_1 and
A_2 are the respective cross sections.   Then

$$R_2 = \frac{R_1 A_1 l_2}{l_1 A_2} \tag{4.1}$$

A unit volume of conductor material may be chosen as a basis for
computing the resistance of a conductor made of the material.   Let a
cube of material, 1 m on each side, be a unit volume.   Then, in (4.1),
$l_1 = 1$ m, $A_1 = 1$ sq m, and R_1 ohms is the resistance between opposite
faces of the cube.   The quantity $R_1 A_1/l_1$ is the resistivity (or specific
resistance) of the material in ohms times square meters divided by
meters, which equals ohm-meters.   Then (4.1) may be written as
$R_2 = \rho l_2/A_2$, where l_2 is in meters and A_2 is in square meters.   Or, dropping subscripts, the resistance R of a conductor of material of resistivity
ρ ohm-m, length l m, and cross section A sq m, is

$$R = \frac{\rho l}{A} \quad \text{ohms} \tag{4.2}$$

The concept of resistivity affords a basis for comparing the conducting
qualities of materials.   A given bar of a given material has a certain
resistance between ends at a given temperature.   If the cross section is
reduced and the length is increased without a change in the bar volume,
in the atomic structure of the material, or in the temperature, the resistance between ends is increased but the resistivity of the material is
unchanged.   The resistivity is a property that is independent of the
dimensions of the sample being considered.

Silver has the lowest resistivity of any known material, but it is only
about 5 per cent lower than that of copper, the most widely used conductor material.   Table 4.1 lists the resistivities of certain conducting
materials.   The annealed copper that has been chosen as the international standard has at 20 C a resistivity of 1.724×10^{-8} ohm-m.

The international ohm was defined from (4.2) as the d-c resistance at
0 C of a mercury column of 14.4521 g mass of uniform cross section and of
106.300 cm length.   The international ohm was discarded as a standard
on Jan. 1, 1948.   Since then the standard is an absolute ohm: 1.000495
absolute ohms = 1 international ohm.   The absolute ohm is specified in
terms of frequency and inductance such that one absolute ohm of inductive reactance will be equal to one absolute ohm of resistance.

Conductor materials are sometimes compared on the basis of the conductance rather than the resistance of a unit conductor.   The conduc-

tivity of a material is numerically equal to the reciprocal of its resistivity. One unit of conductivity is mhos per meter. Commercially conductivity is expressed sometimes as a percentage compared with that of a chosen standard material. The annealed copper that was adopted as the international standard is assumed to have 100 per cent conductivity at 20 C.

TABLE 4.1 RESISTIVITIES OF CONDUCTOR MATERIALS*

Material	ρ ohm-m at 20 C	ρ ohm-cir mils per ft at 20 C
Aluminum	2.83×10^{-8}	17
Antimony	41.7×10^{-8}	251
Bismuth	120×10^{-8}	722
Brass	7×10^{-8}	42
Cadmium	7.5×10^{-8}	45
Cesium, solid	22×10^{-8}	132
Chromium	2.7×10^{-8}	16
Cobalt	9.7×10^{-8}	58
Constantan (40% Ni, 60% Cu)	49×10^{-8}	295
Copper, annealed	1.724×10^{-8}	10.37
Copper, hard-drawn	1.77×10^{-8}	10.65
German silver (18% Ni)	33×10^{-8}	199
Gold, pure drawn	2.4×10^{-8}	14
Iron, cast	9×10^{-8}	54
Lead	22×10^{-8}	132
Magnesium	4.6×10^{-8}	28
Manganin (84% Cu, 12% Mn, 4% Ni)	44×10^{-8}	265
Mercury	96×10^{-8}	577
Molybdenum	5.7×10^{-8}	34
Monel metal	42×10^{-8}	253
Nichrome	100×10^{-8}	602
Nickel	7.8×10^{-8}	47
Platinum	10×10^{-8}	60
Silver (99.98% pure)	1.64×10^{-8}	9.9
Steel, annealed sheet	11×10^{-8} to 50×10^{-8}	66–300
Tin	11.5×10^{-8}	69
Tungsten	5.5×10^{-8}	33
Zinc	6×10^{-8}	36

* Values taken from Smithsonian Physical Tables.

Copper can be produced that has greater than 100 per cent conductivity. The conductivity of hard-drawn copper is usually between 96 and 97 per cent. For certain other materials or alloys the percentage conductivities at 20 C are: aluminum, 61%; brass, 24.7%; nichrome, 1.72%; nickel, 22.1%; and steel 3.5 to 15.7%.

4.2. Circular Mil and Circular Mil-foot. The area A_1 of a circle of diameter d_1 is $\pi d_1^2/4$ square units. The area A_2 of a circle of diameter d_2 is $\pi d_2^2/4$ square units. Then $A_2 = A_1 d_2^2/d_1^2$. If A_1 and d_1 are chosen as the respective units of area and length, A_2 is numerically equal to d_2^2. Then if a circular rather than a square unit of area is used, the irrational factor π does not appear in the expression for the area of a circular conductor. The area of a circle 1 mil (0.001 in.) in diameter has been chosen as the circular unit and is a circular mil (cir mil). The cross section in circular mils of a circular conductor is equal to the square of its diameter in mils.

A circular mil and a square mil are compared in Fig. 4.2. In square units the area of the circle is $(\pi/4)(1 \text{ mil})^2 = \pi/4$ sq mils. That of the square is $(1 \text{ mil})^2 = 1$ sq mil. This means that a circular mil is a smaller unit of area than a square mil, it being $\pi/4 = 0.7854$ as large. In a given cross section there are more circular mils than square mils in the ratio of $4/\pi = 1.273$. If a conductor is not round, one may compute the area first in square mils and then apply the conversion factor 4 cir mils $= \pi$ sq mils to obtain the area in circular mils.

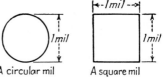

A circular mil   A square mil

Fig. 4.2   A circular mil and a square mil.

For engineering computations of conductor resistances, cross-sectional areas are usually expressed in circular mils and lengths in feet. A conductor 1 mil in diameter and 1 ft long is taken as a unit of volume and called a circular mil-foot.

In (4.2) any unit of length l and any unit of area A may be used if the proper unit of resistivity ρ is used. If l is in feet and A is in circular mils, ρ should be in ohm-circular mils per foot to yield R in ohms. If a circular-mil-foot of a material is considered, the resistance in ohms between the two ends is equal numerically to the resistivity in ohm-circular mils per foot. Because of this equality it is common practice to specify resistivity in ohms per mil-foot although such a unit is incorrect dimensionally.

The resistivity of standard annealed copper at 20 C in ohm-circular mils per foot as computed by conversion is

$$1.724 \times 10^{-8} \text{ ohm-m} \times \frac{39.37 \text{ in.}}{1 \text{ m}} \times \frac{12 \text{ in.}}{1 \text{ ft}} \times \frac{10^6 \text{ sq mils}}{1 \text{ sq in.}} \times \frac{4 \text{ cir mils}}{\pi \text{ sq mils}}$$
$$= 10.37 \text{ ohm-cir mils per ft}$$

For computations involving round conductors, (4.2) is modified to

$$R = \frac{\rho l}{d^2} \qquad \text{ohms} \qquad (4.3)$$

where ρ is the resistivity in ohm-circular mils per foot, l is the length in feet, and d is the diameter in mils. Table 4.1 lists the resistivities of various conductor materials in ohm-circular mils per foot as well as in ohm-meters.

4.3. Current Density. When direct current flows in a straight conductor that is made of a homogeneous material and has a uniform cross section, the assumption that the current is distributed uniformly over the area normal to the flow yields computed values of voltage drops and losses that agree with experimental values. The current in such a conductor divided by the cross section is the current density, commonly expressed in units such as amperes per square inch or amperes per square foot. Where the circular mil is used as the unit of area, it would be logical to express the density in amperes per circular mil. However, in that unit the density in many conductors carrying normal current would be a decimal quantity. For example, a wire of 1,624 cir mils area under certain conditions can carry continuously 3 amp without exceeding a reasonable temperature rise. The corresponding density is

$$\frac{3 \text{ amp}}{1{,}624 \text{ cir mils}} = 0.0018 \text{ amp per cir mil}$$

If the area is divided by the current, the result is

$$\frac{1{,}624 \text{ cir mils}}{3 \text{ amp}} = 541 \text{ cir mils per amp}$$

To permit computations to be made with numbers greater than unity, designers often use the quantity circular mils per ampere and speak of it as the current density.

If the cross section of a conductor that is carrying direct current contains materials of different conductivities, the current density will not be uniform over the cross section. The densities in the materials will be in the same ratios as their respective conductivities.

When an alternating current flows in a straight round conductor that is made of a homogeneous material and has a uniform cross section, the current is not distributed uniformly over the cross section. Instead the current density is least at the center of the conductor and increases with distance from the center to a maximum at the conductor surface. The variation in the density over the cross section depends upon the conductor material, the frequency of the current, and the conductor dimensions. A copper conductor 0.5 in. in diameter carrying a 60-c current has only about 2 per cent greater density at the surface than at the center. If the frequency is increased to 2,000 c, the density at the surface is more than ten times that at the center.

4.4. Voltage Gradient. When the current density is uniform in a conductor of uniform cross section, the voltage drop is the same for each unit length along the conductor in the direction of the current. Here the voltage between any two points along the conductor divided by the distance between the points is the voltage gradient and is represented by the symbol $\mathcal{E}$.

If the current density varies along the path of current flow in a conductor, or if the conductor is composed of nonhomogeneous material, the voltage gradient varies from point to point in the conductor. In general terms the gradient at a point is $\mathcal{E} = dv/dl$, where dv is the infinitesimal voltage drop over an infinitesimal length of conductor dl. In the special case where the gradient is constant at all points in a length l in a conductor the gradient is $\mathcal{E} = v/l$, where v is the voltage drop along the length. The unit in which a voltage gradient is expressed is fixed by the units in which dv (or v) and dl (or l) are expressed. Common units of gradient are millivolts per foot, volts per foot, microvolts per meter, and kilovolts per meter. The gradient at a point is a vector quantity collinear with the vector representing the current density. If the current density in a conductor is constant and the voltage gradient is uniform throughout the length of a conductor, the resistance R ohms of the conductor is $\rho l/A$ and the voltage drop V v along the conductor is IR, where I amp is the current in the conductor. Since $V = IR$, then $V = I\rho l/A$, from which $V/l = \rho I/A$. But $V/l = \mathcal{E}$, the voltage gradient, and $I/A = S$, the current density. Hence

$$\mathcal{E} = S\rho \tag{4.4}$$

where $\mathcal{E}$ is in volts per foot if S is in amperes per circular mil and ρ is in ohm-circular mils per foot.

4.5. Conductors of Nonuniform Cross Section. In Fig. 4.3 is represented a conductor whose cross section is not uniform along its length. The conductor is equivalent to a section cut out of a large washer. A direct current I amp is assumed to be entering at the surface M, the current density being uniform over that surface, and leaving at the surface N, the density also being uniform over that surface. The conductor is assumed to be composed of homogeneous material of resistivity ρ ohm-cir mils per ft and to be of constant thickness 0.1 in.

A surface that contains only points between which there are no differences of potential is an equipotential surface. The trace of such a surface could be determined experimentally for the conductor of Fig. 4.3 by connecting one terminal of a millivoltmeter to a point such as a. A lead from the other millivoltmeter terminal would be moved about on the conductor surface until a zero instrument reading was obtained. The point thus located could be denoted as b. The lead could be moved again and another point such as c located. The process could be continued until enough points had been located to determine the trace. An equipotential surface is everywhere normal to the current direction. In Fig. 4.3 the trace of the equipotential surface is the arc of a circle and the surface is a section of the surface of a cylinder.

In the conductor of Fig. 4.3, the current density is uniform over any one equipotential surface. The voltage gradient is not uniform along the current path. If two equipotential surfaces are chosen that are separated by the infinitesimal distance dl ft, the voltage between the

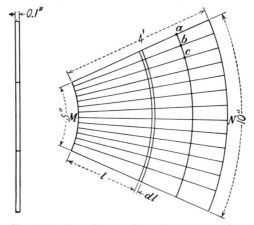

FIG. 4.3   A conductor of varying cross section.

surfaces is dv v. The cross section of A cir mils may be assumed to be constant throughout dl. The resistance between the surfaces is an infinitesimal dR ohm and is equal to $\rho\, dl/A$. Hence $dv = I\, dR = I\rho\, dl/A$, from which $dv/dl = (I/A)\rho$ v per ft. But dv/dl is the voltage gradient $\mathcal{E}$, and I/A is the current gradient S, so that $\mathcal{E} = S\rho$, just as expressed in (4.4).

In the conductor of Fig. 4.3 the greatest current density is normal to the surface M. The area of that surface is

0.1 in. $\times$ 5 in. $\times$ 1.273 $\times$ 10^6 cir mils per sq in. = 6.36 $\times$ 10^5 cir mils

If the current in the conductor were 1,000 amp, the current density at M would be 1,000 amp/6.36 $\times$ 10^5 cir mils = 1.57 $\times$ 10^{-3} amp per cir mil. If the material were standard copper at 20 C, ρ = 10.37 ohm-cir mils per ft and, according to (4.4), $\mathcal{E}$ would be 1.57 $\times$ 10^{-3} $\times$ 10.37 = 0.0163 v per ft, or 16.3 mv per ft. The voltage gradient at the surface N would be one-half of this value since the current density at N is one-half that at M.

4.6. Potential Difference and Line Integrals. Thus far the potential difference between two points in a conductor has been computed by multiplying the resistance between the equipotential surfaces containing the points by the current between the surfaces.   The potential difference can be computed by a more general method.   Consider the section of length $l = 5$ in. of the rectangular conductor of Fig. 4.4.   With the direct current I amp in the conductor the current density S and the voltage gradient $\mathcal{E}$ are uniform throughout the conductor.   Assume that the voltage V_{ab} between the points a and b in the surface of the conductor is to be computed when the voltage V across the 5-in. length of conductor is 2 v.   Here $\mathcal{E} = V/l = 2$ v/5 in. $= 0.4$ v per in.   Since the gradient is constant here and gradient times distance equals voltage, one might expect that V_{ab} could be computed by multiplying the gradient

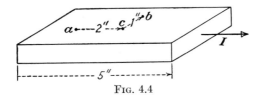

FIG. 4.4

by the distance l_{ab} from a to b.   That procedure would be correct if the direction of travel is always in the direction of the gradient in going from a to b.   Here if one traveled directly from a to b, the path of travel is always at an angle with the direction of the gradient.   The value of V_{ab} is obtained by multiplying l_{ab} by the component of $\mathcal{E}$ that is in the direction of l_{ab}.   That component is $\mathcal{E} \cos \theta$, where θ is the angle from the gradient to the line l_{ab}.   Hence $V_{ab} = \mathcal{E} \cos \theta \, l_{ab}$.   But $l_{ab} \cos \theta = 2$ in. and is the distance from a to c, where c is a point directly along the line of current flow from a and in a line through b normal to the current flow. Hence $V_{ab} = 0.4$ v per in. $\times$ 2 in. $= 0.8$ v.

The potential between a and b in Fig. 4.4 can be computed also as the sum of the potential from a to c and that from b to c.   The path from a to c is collinear with the gradient $\mathcal{E}$.   Hence $V_{ac} = \mathcal{E} l_{ac} = 0.4$ v per in. $\times$ 2 in. $= 0.8$ v.   The path from c to b is normal to the gradient, there is no travel in the direction of the gradient, and no potential from c to b.   Hence $V_{ab} = V_{ac} = 0.8$ v, the value obtained previously along the path directly from a to b.   In fact, the potential from a to b is the same by any path.

It may be that in following a given path from one point to another in a conductor the direction of travel is not always at the same angle with the voltage gradient $\mathcal{E}$.   Also it may be that the magnitude of the gradient varies along the path.   The potential V_{ab} along a path between two points a and b may be expressed as the line integral

$$V_{ab} = \int_{l_1}^{l_2} \mathcal{E} \cos \theta \, dl \qquad (4.5)$$

where θ is the angle from the gradient to the path of integration, l_1 is the distance of point a from an arbitrary reference point, and l_2 is the distance of point b from the reference point. If $\mathcal{E}$ and θ are constant the solution of the above integral is

$$V_{ab} = \mathcal{E} \cos \theta \, (l_2 - l_1)$$

If $\mathcal{E}$ and θ are not constant, the integral can be evaluated if they can be expressed as a function of l.

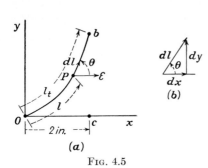

(a)

(b)

Fig. 4.5

Example 1. In Fig. 4.4 prove that $V_{ab} = 0.8$ v along any path from a to b.

Solution. In Fig. 4.5 the origin of a set of coordinate axes has been located at a. The x axis extends from a through c. A point P has been chosen on a curve of length l_t representing any path from a to b. An arc of the curve of length dl from P is indicated. The angle from the gradient $\mathcal{E}$ to this arc is denoted as θ. By (4.5),

$$V_{ab} = \int_0^{l_t} \mathcal{E} \cos \theta \, dl$$

As shown in Fig. 4.5b, $dl \cos \theta = dx$; hence $V_{ab} = \int_0^2 \mathcal{E} \, dx$, where 0 is the x ordinate of the curve at $l = 0$ and 2 is the x ordinate at $l = l_t$. Here $\mathcal{E}$ is a constant of 0.4 v per in. Then $V_{ab} = 0.4x \Big]_0^2 = 0.8$ v.

Example 2. In Fig. 4.3, with a current of 1,000 amp the voltage gradient at M was shown to be 16.3 mv per ft. Compute the voltage from M to a point halfway from M to N and also the voltage from M to N.

Solution. Since the current density decreases along a path from M to N, the voltage gradient decreases proportionally. It can be shown that, along a straight line from M to N, the gradient is expressed by $\mathcal{E} = 65.2/(4 + l)$ mv per ft, where l is the distance in feet from M. For a point halfway from M to N, $l = 2$ ft; hence the voltage V_1 from a to the point is, from (4.5),

$$V_1 = \int_0^2 \frac{65.2 \, dl}{4 + l}$$

In (4.5), $\theta = 0$ and $\cos \theta = 1$ since the path followed is collinear with the gradient. By integration and substitution of the limits

$$V_1 = 65.2 \ln (4 + l) \Big]_0^2 = 65.2(\ln 6 - \ln 4) = 65.2 \ln 1.5$$

$$= 65.2 \times 0.406 = 26.5 \text{ mv}$$

The voltage V_{MN} from M to N is

$$V_{MN} = \int_0^4 \frac{65.2 \, dl}{4 + l}$$

from which

$$V_{MN} = 65.2 \ln (4 + l) \Big]_0^4 = 65.2(\ln 8 - \ln 4) = 65.2 \ln 2$$
$$= 65.2 \times 0.693 = 45.2 \text{ mv}$$

Note that $26.5 \times 100/45.2 = 59$ per cent of the total voltage drop appears along the first one-half of the path.

4.7. Volume Insulation Resistance.   No material has infinite resistivity, but those classed as insulators have far greater resistivities than those classed as conductors.   Within certain limits of voltage gradient, air and certain other gases have such high resistivities that they cannot be measured accurately.   If the voltage applied between two parallel metal plates surrounded by a gas is raised to higher and higher values, the voltage gradient in the gas increases proportionally.   As the gradient increases, free electrons in the gas atoms acquire more and more energy while moving a given distance.   At specified values of pressure and

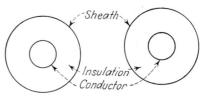

FIG. 4.6   A cable system.

temperature there is for each gas a certain energy level at which the free electrons when striking gas molecules cause additional electrons to be set free, thus dissociating some atoms into positive ions and free electrons. This process is ionization.   Air at 25 C and a barometric pressure of 76 cm of mercury ionizes at a gradient of about 30 kv per cm.   Below that gradient air is a good insulator; at that gradient it suddenly becomes a conductor.   The gradient at which conduction begins is the breakdown gradient or the dielectric strength.   Although air has a higher resistivity than solid or liquid insulating materials, it has a lower breakdown gradient than most.   In a 220-kv power cable the oil-impregnated paper may be only 2.5 in. thick, while in an overhead transmission line operating at the same voltage a spacing of 25 ft or more may be required between bare conductors.   Economy of design of electric apparatus limits the space that may be allotted for insulation; hence the need for materials with high breakdown gradients.   Solid and liquid insulating materials, like gases, suddenly become conductors when their breakdown gradients are reached. In addition to a high resistivity and a high breakdown gradient, an insulating material should have good mechanical properties and good thermal and time stability.   Common insulating materials include cambric, cotton, glass, mica, oil, paper, paraffin, porcelain, rubber, silk, wood, and various synthetic materials.

When two cables, as in Fig. 4.6, transmit electrical energy, there are currents from one conductor to the other through the insulation.   Since these currents do not pass through the load, they are leakage currents. When two cables are buried in the earth, the earth resistance between cable sheaths is negligible compared with the insulation resistance. The resistances R_l of the leakage paths in the insulation may be represented approximately as in Fig. 4.7. Actually there is an infinite number of paths. If the resistances R'_e, R''_e, etc., of the earth paths are negligible compared with the resistance R_l of the insulation paths, the voltage

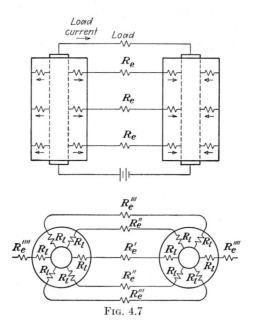

FIG. 4.7

across the leakage paths in each cable is one-half that between conductors. When a metal sheath encloses each cable, each sheath is an equipotential surface. If the insulation is of homogeneous material, the leakage currents follow radial paths between conductor and sheath. With no load connected to a cable system that is supplied from a d-c source, the voltage between conductors at the load end of the system will be the same as that at the sending end if the voltage drop in the conductors caused by the leakage currents is negligible compared with the applied voltage. In most power cables the voltage drop is negligible; in many telephone cables it is not.

The resistance between conductor and sheath in a cable is the volume insulation resistance, or more commonly, the insulation resistance. To measure the insulation resistance of a given cable, one might make connections as in Fig. 4.8. Knowing that the resistance is likely to be high, one might expect that a microammeter would be required to measure the current.   If 110-v direct current were available, that might be used.   If the circuit were connected as shown and then the switch closed, the microammeter pointer might swing violently beyond full-scale and the instrument might be damaged.   If this occurred, one might think that the insulation resistance was much lower than expected.   This might not be the case.   Because of capacitance between the conductor and the sheath, at the instant that voltage is applied and for a short time thereafter, the current may be far greater than the voltage divided by the insulation resistance.   To protect the microammeter from damage a rheostat, of sufficient resistance to limit the current to less than the instrument capacity, may be inserted in series with the voltage source.

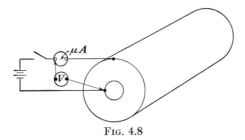

Fig. 4.8

Assume that this is done and that, as the resistance is decreased slowly to zero shortly after the circuit is closed, the microammeter deflection is not offscale.   It would be found that the deflection is not constant but decreases slowly with increasing time.   The continued change of current is not due to the cable capacitance, for the change continues longer than any computed effects of capacitance are measurable.   Dielectric absorption, or soaking up of charge, causes the change and results in an accumulation of charges in the insulating material.   Because of the absorption the current may continue to change for $\frac{1}{2}$ hr or more.   If insulation resistance is to be computed by dividing the voltmeter reading by the microammeter reading, the question arises of when to take the microammeter reading.   The true insulation resistance is considered to be that computed from the reading after it has become constant.   To save time in making insulation resistance measurements, it is standard practice to read the current 1 min after the application of voltage to a specimen.   In some cases the resistance computed from this reading is as low as one-fourth of the true value.

When the voltage used in measuring insulation resistance is increased, the leakage current increases more rapidly than the voltage.   This means that the resistance decreases as the voltage gradient increases.   Most insulating materials have such a characteristic.

The electric circuit of two cables with metallic sheaths and used for the transmission of direct current can be represented as in Fig. 4.9. Here R_C is the conductor resistance per unit length, R_S is the sheath resistance per unit length, and R_L is the leakage resistance per unit length. With load on the system the voltage between conductors will be less at the load end of the system than it is at the sending end.   As a result, the leakage current is greatest in a leakage element at the sending end and least in one at the load end.   However, in a power system the voltage regulation is usually good enough that little error results in assuming that the leakage current per unit length is uniform along the conductor. With this assumption the total leakage current is proportional to the

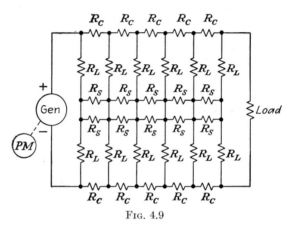

Fig. 4.9

cable length.   Since the leakage resistance is inversely proportional to the leakage current, the leakage resistance of a cable is inversely proportional to its length.   This can be seen also from Fig. 4.9.   If the voltages across the conductor elements of resistance R_C are negligible compared with the voltage between conductors, the leakage paths of one cable can be considered to be in parallel.   The greater the length of the cable, the greater is the number of leakage paths in parallel and the lower is the equivalent resistance of the combination.

As far as the leakage currents are concerned, the cable insulation is a conductor of nonuniform cross section.   The leakage current density is greatest at the conductor surface and least at the inner sheath surface. If the insulation is homogeneous, the voltage gradient in the insulation varies in the same manner as the current density.

The resistivity of an insulating material varies with so many factors and over such a wide range that the insulation resistance of a cable cannot be computed with any degree of accuracy.   The resistivity depends upon the humidity, magnitude of test voltage, pressure, temperature, and thickness of the test specimen.   Table 4.2 lists representative resistivities of certain insulating materials. Values for individual samples may differ greatly from these.

The lowest resistivity of an insulating material listed in Table 4.2 is 1 megohm-m (10^6 ohm-m) for slate. The highest resistivity of a conducting material listed in Table 4.1 is 120×10^{-8} ohm-m for bismuth. Hence the poorest insulating material listed has a resistivity that is $10^6/120 \times 10^{-8} = 0.8 \times 10^{12}$, or nearly a trillion times the resistivity of the poorest conductor material listed. Note further that there are insulating materials that have resistivities a million or a billion times that of slate. As a result in most electric circuits the leakage current is insignificant compared with the useful current.

TABLE 4.2. VOLUME INSULATION RESISTIVITIES OF MATERIALS*

Material	Volume resistivity, megohm-meters
Beeswax	2×10^7
Celluloid	200
Fiber, red	50
Glass, plate	2×10^5
Marble, Italian	1,000
Mica	2×10^9
Paraffin	1×10^8
Porcelain, unglazed	3×10^6
Quartz, fused	5×10^{10}
Sealing wax	8×10^7
Shellac	1×10^8
Slate	1
Wood, paraffined mahogany	4×10^5

* Values taken from Smithsonian Physical Tables.

4.8. Surface Insulation Resistance. When a transmission line wire is supported from a pole by a pin-type porcelain insulator, the film of dirt and moisture on the surface may conduct more leakage current than the volume of the insulator. The resistance of the film is the surface insulation resistance. The resistance between two conductors on opposite sides of a meter square on a surface of an insulating material is the surface resistivity. The resistivity is so greatly affected by humidity that, as stated by the General Radio Company, "merely breathing on the surface of a good insulator like quartz will lower the insulation resistance between terminals spaced ¾ in. apart from above 10 million megohms to below one megohm." Conducting films are seldom uniform and the amount of moisture contained is so variable that a table of surface resistivities has little meaning except for certain specified conditions.

Although surface insulation resistance cannot be computed accurately and varies greatly with humidity, it is by no means of no consequence. In measuring volume resistance, it is necessary to make correction for

the presence of surface resistance. Assume that the volume resistance
of a centimeter cube of an insulating material is to be measured. Metal
plates 1 cm square might be applied to opposite faces of the cube and
electrical connections made to these as in Fig. 4.10. If all the electrons
moved from one plate to the other in parallel lines of travel through the
volume of the cube, the voltmeter reading divided by the ammeter reading would be the resistance of the sample. However, in addition to the
current through the volume of the sample
there are currents from plate to plate in
the film on the four exposed surfaces.
This means that the volume resistance is
in parallel with the surface resistance and
the resistance measured between plates is
the equivalent resistance. If the surface
resistance is large compared with the volume resistance, the equivalent resistance
is slightly less than the volume resistance.

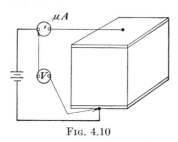

Fig. 4.10

In that case the measured equivalent resistance may be taken as a reasonably accurate value of the volume resistance. However, as is more often the
case, if the surface resistance is small compared with the volume resistance, the equivalent resistance is about equal to the surface resistance
and there is no way to determine from the measured equivalent resistance
what the volume resistance is.

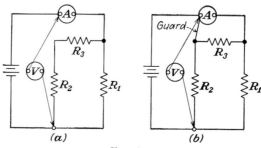

Fig. 4.11

To measure with fair accuracy the volume resistance of an insulating
material, a guard is used. The function of a guard will be explained from
Fig. 4.11. Assume that the three resistors of unknown resistances R_1,
R_2, and R_3 are permanently attached to each other. Assume further
that R_1 is large compared with R_2 and R_3 and that R_1 is to be measured.
If the circuit were connected as in a, most of the current registered on
the ammeter would flow through the branch consisting of R_2 and R_3 in
series and there is no information as to how much current is in R_1.

Now assume that a guard connection with negligible resistance is added as in Fig. 4.11b. Here the ammeter will read the difference of the currents in R_1 and R_3. If the current in R_3 is negligible compared with that in R_1, the ammeter reading is the current in R_1. As the ammeter is in parallel with R_3, the voltage across the two is that across the ammeter and is likely to be of the order of 0.1 v or less. For a typical circuit assume that the test voltage is 500 v. Then the voltage across R_1 is $500/0.1 = 5{,}000$ times that across R_3. If R_3 is not less than one-fiftieth

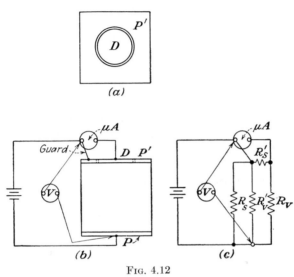

FIG. 4.12

of R_1, the current in R_3 is not more than 1 per cent of that in R_1. Under this condition the voltmeter reading divided by the ammeter reading is within 1 per cent of the value of R_1.

In Fig. 4.10 the surface leakage resistance is in parallel with the volume resistance and the currents in the two paths cannot be separated for measurement. Now consider the centimeter cube of insulating material of Fig. 4.12. Instead of a solid metal plate on each of two opposite faces of the sample, a narrow slot has been cut through one plate, thus leaving a circular disk $\frac{1}{2}$ cm in diameter. The disk is designated as D and the remaining portion of the plate as P'. Electrical connections are made as in Fig. 4.12b. Here there is a surface leakage path, that from D to P', that was not present in Fig. 4.10. The electric circuit is now as shown in Fig. 4.12c. Here R_V is the volume resistance of the portion of the sample directly between D and a surface of equal area on the uncut plate P and is the resistance to be measured. R'_S is the surface leakage resistance between D and P' along the surface of the insulation at the bottom of the slot. R'_V is the volume resistance of the portion of the sample directly between P and P'. R_S is the surface leakage resistance over the four exposed surfaces of the sample.

Note the similarity between the circuit of Fig. 4.12c and that of Fig. 4.11. If R_S and R'_V were combined into an equivalent resistance, the two circuits would correspond with respect to the number of resistors and the location of the instruments. Then in Fig. 4.12c, if R'_S is not too small compared with R_V, the voltmeter reading divided by the ammeter reading is nearly equal to R_V. By connecting a source of emf in series with the ammeter in Fig. 4.12c, the IR of the ammeter can be neutralized and the voltage across R'_S made zero. If this is done, the ammeter reads exactly the current in R_V. This refinement is seldom necessary.

For insulation resistance measurements, metal plates do not always make good contact over their entire surface and inconsistent results may be obtained. Tin foil, applied under pressure, is better than plates but not always satisfactory. Mercury has been used as a contact material, but erratic results may be caused by air bubbles trapped on the insulation surface and by contamination of the insulating material by mercury. A metal-sprayed surface or a coating of a colloidal solution of graphite gives better results than mercury.

4.9. Temperature Coefficient of Resistance. The resistivity of a pure metal increases as the temperature increases. In Fig. 4.13 is shown

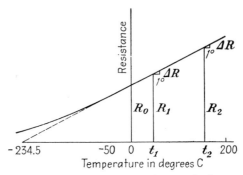

Fig. 4.13   Resistance-temperature curve for standard annealed copper.

the relation between resistance and temperature for a standard annealed copper sample. In the range from -50 to 200 C the curve is nearly a straight line. If it is assumed to be so, the resistance increase ΔR for a 1-degree temperature rise is constant in this range. Although the curve is linear, the resistance is not proportional to the temperature in centigrade degrees because the resistance is not zero at 0 C. The temperature coefficient of resistance of a material at a given temperature is the change in resistance of a sample of the material resulting from a 1-degree change from the given temperature divided by the resistance at the given temperature. The unit of temperature coefficient of resistance is the ohm per centigrade degree per ohm. In Fig. 4.14 the temperature coefficient of resistance α_{t_1} at a temperature t_1 (°C) is

$$\alpha_{t_1} = \frac{\Delta R}{R_1} \tag{4.6}$$

and the coefficient α_{t_2} at a temperature t_2 (°C) is

$$\alpha_{t_2} = \frac{\Delta R}{R_2} \tag{4.7}$$

where ΔR, R_1, and R_2 are expressed in the same unit of resistance.

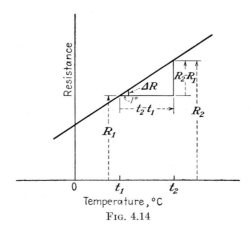

Fig. 4.14

From (4.6) and (4.7), since R_2 is greater than R_1 if t_2 is greater than t_1, the temperature coefficient of resistance decreases as the temperature increases. A conductor of standard copper that has a resistance of 100 ohms at 0 C has a resistance of 100.427 ohms at 1 C. The increase in resistance ΔR for the 1-degree temperature increase is 0.427 ohm and the temperature coefficient at 0 C is $\alpha_0 = 0.427/100 = 0.00427$ ohm per °C per ohm. If the temperature were increased to 20 C, the resistance would increase $20 \times 0.427 = 8.54$ ohms. The resistance at 20 C would be 108.54 ohms. If the temperature were then raised from 20 to 21 C, the increase in resistance would be 0.427 ohm. The temperature coefficient α_{20} at 20 C is $\alpha_{20} = 0.427/108.54 = 0.00393$ ohm per °C per ohm.

From similar triangles in Fig. 4.14, $\Delta R/1 = (R_2 - R_1)/(t_2 - t_1)$. Since $\alpha_{t_1} = \Delta R/R_1$, then

$$\alpha_{t_1} = \frac{R_2 - R_1}{(t_2 - t_1)R_1} \tag{4.8}$$

where α_{t_1} is the temperature coefficient and R_1 is the resistance at t_1, and R_2 is the resistance at t_2, both resistances being expressed in the same unit. From (4.8),

$$R_2 = R_1[1 + \alpha_{t_1}(t_2 - t_1)] \qquad (4.9)$$

a relation that is useful for computing the resistance of a given conductor at one temperature when its resistance and temperature coefficient are known at another temperature.

TABLE 4.3. TEMPERATURE COEFFICIENTS OF RESISTANCE OF
CONDUCTOR MATERIALS*

Material	Temp. coefficient, ohm per °C per ohm at 20 C	Inferred absolute zero, °C
Aluminum..............................	0.0039	−236
Antimony..............................	0.0036	−258
Bismuth...............................	0.004	−230
Brass.................................	0.002	−480
Constantan (60% Cu, 40% Ni).............	0.000008	
Copper, annealed........................	0.00393	−234.5
Copper, hard-drawn.....................	0.00382	−242
German silver.........................	0.0004	−2480
Iron..................................	0.005	−180
Lead.................................	0.0041	−224
Magnesium.............................	0.004	−230
Manganin (84% Cu, 12% Mn, 4% Ni).......	0.000006	
Mercury...............................	0.00089	−1100
Molybdenum...........................	0.0034	−274
Monel metal...........................	0.002	−480
Nichrome..............................	0.0004	−2480
Nickel................................	0.006	−147
Platinum..............................	0.003	−310
Silver (99.98% pure).....................	0.0038	−243
Steel, soft.............................	0.0042	−218
Tin...................................	0.0042	−218
Tungsten..............................	0.0045	−200
Zinc..................................	0.0037	−250

* Values taken from Smithsonian Physical Tables.

Temperature coefficients of resistance of other pure metals range from slightly less than that of copper to about 50 per cent higher. For applications, such as in electrical instruments, where a change in resistance with temperature is undesirable, alloys have been developed whose temperature coefficients are as low as $\frac{1}{600}$ that of standard copper. Coefficients of various conductor materials are listed in Table 4.3.

The temperature coefficient of standard copper is 0.00427 ohm per °C per ohm at 0 C and decreases with increasing temperature to 0.00323 at 75 C. The latter temperature has been chosen by the AIEE as a standard operating temperature for most machines. As an approximation suitable for some computations the coefficient may be taken as 0.004 throughout the usual range of temperatures. In other terms, the resistance of a copper conductor changes about 0.4 per cent for each centigrade degree change in temperature.

Example 1. At room temperature the coil of copper wire in a certain relay had a resistance of 160 ohms. After normal voltage had been applied to the coil for several hours, the resistance was 180 ohms. How much had the coil temperature increased?

Solution. The increase in resistance was $180 - 160 = 20$ ohms. The percentage increase was $(20/160) \times 100 = 12.5$ per cent. Since the resistance of copper changes about 0.4 per cent for each centigrade degree rise in temperature, the temperature rise was about $12.5/0.4 = 30°$.

It is not unusual for the copper temperature in a machine or circuit to rise as much as 50° from one condition of operation to another. Such a rise will cause about $50 \times 0.4 = 20$ per cent resistance increase, an increase that should not be ignored in accurate computations that involve the resistance value.

For accurate computations involving the change of resistance of a conductor with temperature, use of (4.9) requires that the temperature coefficient of resistance of the conductor material be known at the initial or the final temperature. For a standard copper conductor, a relation for computing the resistance at one temperature from its resistance at another temperature, without direct use of the temperature coefficient, can be derived from Fig. 4.13. If the linear portion of the curve is extended, it intersects the temperature axis at -234.5 C. This means that throughout the usual operating temperature range the resistance of a standard copper conductor varies as though it would be zero at -234.5 C. The actual resistance-temperature curve is not a straight line below -50 C, but approaches zero resistance at the true absolute zero temperature near -273 C. The temperature of -234.5 C is the inferred absolute zero temperature for standard copper. In Fig. 4.13 are similar triangles formed by the extension of the linear portion of the curve. Here R_1 and R_2 are the resistances of a standard copper conductor at the respective temperatures of t_1 and t_2. By proportion from the triangles

$$\frac{R_2}{R_1} = \frac{234.5 + t_2}{234.5 + t_1}$$

Resistances are usually measured in the range from 10 to 35 C. In Table 4.4 are listed the factors by which the resistance of a standard copper conductor at various temperatures in this range should be multiplied to obtain the resistance at 75 C, the temperature specified by the American Institute of Electrical Engineers (AIEE) as a standard operating temperature for many machines. For example, for an initial temperature of 10 C, the factor is $(234.5 + 75)/(234.5 + 10) = 1.266$.

TABLE 4.4. FACTORS FOR CORRECTING THE RESISTANCES OF COPPER CONDUCTORS FROM VARIOUS INITIAL TEMPERATURES TO 75 C*

Initial temp., °C	Factor (multiply by)	Initial temp., °C	Factor (multiply by)	Initial temp., °C	Factor (multiply by)
10	1.266	19	1.221	28	1.179
11	1.261	20	1.216	29	1.175
12	1.255	21	1.211	30	1.170
13	1.250	22	1.207	31	1.166
14	1.246	23	1.202	32	1.161
15	1.241	24	1.197	33	1.157
16	1.236	25	1.193	34	1.153
17	1.231	26	1.188	35	1.148
18	1.226	27	1.183		

* Multiply the resistance at a given initial temperature by the corresponding factor to obtain the resistance at 75 C.

The temperature coefficient of resistance of standard copper at a specified temperature can be computed from similar triangles in Fig. 4.13. Thus, at t_1, $\Delta R/R_1 = 1/(234.5 + t_1)$. But $\Delta R/R_1 = \alpha_{t_1}$; hence

$$\alpha_{t_1} = \frac{1}{234.5 + t_1}$$

Then for standard copper the temperature coefficient of resistance at a given temperature t_1 is equal to the reciprocal of $234.5 + t_1$. At 0 C, $\alpha_0 = 1/234.5 = 0.00427$. At 20 C, $\alpha_{20} = 1/(234.5 + 20) = 0.00393$.

The temperature coefficient of resistance of any grade of copper is equal to that of standard copper multiplied by the conductivity (as a decimal) of the grade considered. Thus hard-drawn copper with a conductivity of 97 per cent has a temperature coefficient at 0 C of

$$0.00427 \times 0.97 = 0.00414$$

For a material whose resistance-temperature curve is linear over a given range, a proportion can be set up similar to that for copper. The proportion includes the inferred absolute zero temperature of the material which can be determined from a known temperature coefficient of resistance at a given temperature. In Fig. 4.15, let t_1 be the temperature for which the temperature coefficient α_{t_1} is known, R_1 be the resistance at t_1 of a conductor made of the material, ΔR be the increase in resistance

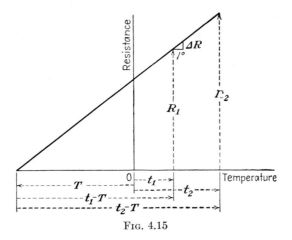

FIG. 4.15

for a one degree rise in temperature above t_1, and T be the inferred absolute zero temperature. By proportion from similar triangles

$$\frac{\Delta R}{R_1} = \frac{1}{t_1 - T}$$

But $\Delta R/R_1 = \alpha_{t_1}$; therefore $\alpha_{t_1} = 1/(t_1 - T)$, from which

$$T = t_1 - \frac{1}{\alpha_{t_1}} \qquad (4.10)$$

In Fig. 4.15, let R_2 be the resistance of the conductor at t_2. By proportion from similar triangles

$$\frac{R_2}{R_1} = \frac{t_2 - T}{t_1 - T} \qquad (4.11)$$

Example 1. A certain conductor that has a resistance of 4 ohms at 40 C has a temperature coefficient of resistance $\alpha_{20} = 0.002$ at 20 C. Compute the resistance at 75 C.

Solution. From (4.10), the inferred absolute zero temperature T for the conductor material is $T = 20 - 1/0.002 = 20 - 500 = -480$ C. From (4.11), $R_2/4 = (75 + 480)/(40 + 480)$, from which $R_2 = 4.27$ ohms.

In Table 4.3 the inferred absolute zero temperatures are listed for various materials.

Figure 4.16 shows resistance-temperature characteristics for manganin. Wire stock is used to make precision resistors whose resistances change very little with age or with the temperature change that occurs in normal use. Stock with the characteristic shown has the same resistance at 15 C and at 30 C. Between those temperatures the maximum resistance occurs at about 22.5 C and is of the order of 0.0015 per cent greater than at 15 C. This stock is well suited for use in apparatus that operates within a temperature range from 15 to 30 C.

Shunt stock manganin is used to make shunts for d-c ammeters. Stock with the characteristic shown has the same resistance at 15 C and at 72 C. Between these temperatures the maximum resistance occurs at about 47 C and is of the order of 0.015 per cent greater than that at 15 C. This stock is well suited for use in shunts that operate within a temperature range from 40 to 60 C.

The curves of Fig. 4.16 are not linear over the range of temperature used; thus the definition of temperature coefficient of resistance used

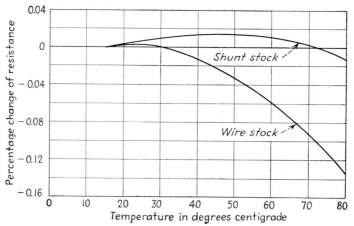

Fig. 4.16   Characteristics of manganin stock.   (*Driver-Harris Company.*)

previously is not directly applicable. The coefficient here is defined sometimes as the slope of the curve and varies from positive values for temperatures less than that at which the resistance is a maximum through zero at that temperature to negative values at greater temperatures.

For manganin the concept of an inferred absolute zero point and proportional relations based on a linear equation would be valid only for a narrow temperature range. A manganin characteristic can be fitted, at least approximately, by a power series of a few terms such as

$$R = R_b[1 + \alpha(t - t_b) + \beta(t - t_b)^2] \qquad \text{ohms}$$

where R is the resistance at a temperature t °C, R_b is the resistance in ohms at a base temperature t_b °C, and α and β are constants that can be evaluated by use of the coordinates of two points on the characteristic.

4.10. Thermistors. A Thermistor is a thermally sensitive resistor made of a semiconducting material. The material has a negative temperature coefficient of resistance and its resistivity varies greatly with temperature.

Figure 4.17 is a characteristic of a material available commercially. Materials with other characteristics are available.

The resistance R of a sample of some Thermistor materials may be expressed, over a limited temperature range, by

$$R = R_1 \epsilon^{\beta(1/t - 1/t_1)} \qquad \text{ohms} \qquad (4.12)$$

where R is the resistance at a temperature t K (temperature in degrees Kelvin $= 273 +$ temperature in degrees centigrade), R_1 is the resistance at a temperature t_1 K, $\epsilon = 2.718$ is the Napierian base of logarithms, and β is a constant over a limited range of temperatures. From a given characteristic values of R and R_1 at the respective temperatures, t and t_1 can be obtained. Then by use of (4.12), β for the material can be computed.

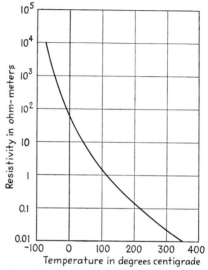

FIG. 4.17   Characteristic of a material that has a negative temperature coefficient of resistance.

Thermistors are used as control units that respond to temperature changes. The change of temperature may be produced by current sent through the Thermistor. If the current is changed, the temperature and the resistance do not change instantly because of the thermal capacity of the Thermistor. If a constant d-c voltage is suddenly applied to a Thermistor in series with a resistor of constant resistance, the initial current is fixed by the cold resistance of the circuit. As the Thermistor warms up, its resistance decreases, slowly at first, thus permitting the current to increase. Increased current causes a rapid decrease of resistance and a more rapid current increase for a time until the Thermistor resistance becomes small compared with the resistance of the remainder of the circuit. Then the current becomes constant at a value that is fixed largely by the circuit resistance. Circuits can be designed for a time delay from the establishment of current to the attainment of steady-state current ranging from a few milliseconds to several minutes.

The temperature of a Thermistor can be varied by temperature changes in a medium, such as a gas or water, that surrounds the Thermistor. With the Thermistor in an electric circuit, the current in that circuit is varied in response to the temperature change.

The temperature of a Thermistor can be varied indirectly by surrounding it by a heating element electrically insulated from it. Then changing the current in the element causes a change in the Thermistor resistance and causes a current change in the circuit in which the Thermistor is connected.

4.11. Thermocouples. Heat energy can be transformed into electrical energy in the thermocouple of Fig. 4.18. Here two iron wires are welded to opposite ends of a constantan wire to form junctions 1 and 2. If the junctions are maintained at different temperatures, an emf appears between the points a

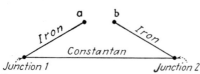

Fig. 4.18 Arrangement of iron and constantan wires to form a thermocouple.

and b. The value of the emf depends upon the difference of the junction temperatures and is usually of the order of millivolts. A thermocouple is most often used to measure temperatures. If one junction, say 1, is maintained at 0 C by placing it in a bath of melting ice, the emf between

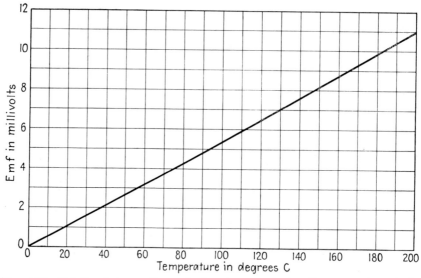

Fig. 4.19 Relation between the emf of an iron-constantan thermocouple and the temperature of one junction with the other junction maintained at 0 C.

a and b varies with the temperature of junction 2 as in Fig. 4.19. Throughout the range of temperatures shown the curve is nearly linear for an iron-constantan thermocouple. When both junctions are at the same temperature, no emf is produced. If the temperatures are unequal, the junction having the higher temperature will be positive with respect to the other.

Since the characteristic of Fig. 4.19 is slightly concave upward, the increase in emf per degree increase in temperature increases with the temperature. However, the quantity is roughly 0.055 mv per °C over the temperature range shown. A millivoltmeter or a potentiometer is used to measure a thermocouple emf. When a millivoltmeter is used, it may be that the circuit resistance is not negligible compared with the instrument resistance. In that case the emf is equal to the instrument reading multiplied by the factor $(R_M + R_C)/R_M$, where R_M is the instrument resistance and R_C is that of the remainder of the circuit.

The characteristic of Fig. 4.19 applies directly to an iron-constantan thermocouple when one junction is maintained at a reference temperature of 0 C. However, the characteristic can be used to determine the emf when the junction is at some other known temperature by taking the difference of the emfs as read from the characteristic for the respective junction temperatures. For example, assume that one junction temperature is 25 C and the other is 160 C. From the characteristic it is found that the corresponding emfs are 1.30 and 8.70 mv. The net emf is $8.70 - 1.30 = 7.40$ mv. As another example, assume that one junction temperature is 25 C and that the measured emf is 6.50 mv. The second junction temperature is that corresponding to $1.30 + 6.50 = 7.80$ mv, and from the characteristic is read as 145 C.

A thermocouple can be used to measure the rms value of a current. One junction is placed near or in contact with a resistor that carries the current to be measured. The resistor and the junction are well insulated thermally so that most of the heat produced is stored in the resistor and causes its temperature to rise. A thermocouple ammeter may be calibrated with direct current for use with alternating currents. Thermocouple ammeters are used chiefly in high-frequency circuits. When a given current is first sent through a thermocouple ammeter, a time delay occurs before the pointer deflection is steady since some time is required for the resistor to attain a constant temperature. A change in the heating element design to decrease the response time decreases the overload capacity. Some thermocouple ammeters will burn out with as little as 150 per cent of rated current.

4.12. Factors Affecting Resistor Sizes and Ratings. In a resistor electrical energy is converted into heat energy. The power input to a resistor depends not only upon its resistance, but also upon the current in it. Most resistors are air-cooled, the heat produced in them being transmitted to the surrounding air. In wire-wound resistors the wire is one having a low temperature coefficient of resistance. One method of construction is to wind the wire on a refractory tube and then bind and solder the wire ends to the terminal connections. After a coating of powdered glassy enamel is applied, the unit is heated at red heat for a time until the enamel is fused and surrounds the wire, the terminals, and the base. After cooling, the enamel is very hard and protects the wire from deterioration by fumes or from mechanical damage. Because the enamel has high heat conductivity, heat is conducted readily from the wire to the surface of the enamel. Thus the surface area from which heat is transmitted to the air is much greater than that of the wire.

Besides the amount of heat to be dissipated the other principal factor that determines the physical characteristics of a resistor is the voltage rating of the resistor. The turns must be spaced far enough apart that the voltage between turns does not break down the insulation between turns. As an example, one manufacturer specifies for one diameter of tube a maximum voltage rating of 400 v for a tube length of 2 in. and a maximum voltage rating of 2,300 v for a tube length of 10 in.

The maximum watt rating of an embedded wire type of resistor is such that the temperature rise above a room temperature of 40 C will not exceed 300 C at the hottest spot on the resistor surface when the resistor is in free air with a clearance of 1 ft or more from the nearest object. When a resistor is mounted near some other object or the circulation of air is restricted, its watt rating should be reduced from the maximum rating specified above. When two or more resistors are operated as a group, the rating of each should be reduced. Grouping is sometimes employed when the voltage or watt rating required is greater than that of the largest unit available.

The size of a resistor depends upon both its watt and its voltage rating. For example, one manufacturer lists a 100-ohm 10-w 315-ma resistor as being $\frac{5}{16}$ in. in diameter and $1\frac{3}{4}$ in. long. A 100-ohm 200-w 1.4-amp resistor is $1\frac{1}{8}$ in. in diameter and $10\frac{1}{2}$ in. long. Here it happens that the rated current squared times the resistance is nearly equal to the watt rating. However, a 20,000-ohm 10-w resistor with dimensions equal to that of the 10-w resistor above is rated at 15 ma. Since

$$0.015^2 \times 20,000 = 4.5 \text{ w}$$

then the 10-w rating is only a nominal one and the resistor should not be used with more than $0.015 \times 20,000 = 300$ v across it.

4.13. Wires and Cables. Copper is the material most widely used for electric conductors because it has high conductivity, its cost is moderate, it is not corroded by the atmosphere, it is very ductile and yet has high tensile strength, it can be brazed, soldered, or spliced readily, and it has a high melting point (1083 C). The conductivity of aluminum is 61 per cent of that of copper. Since its density is 30 per cent of that of copper, for a given weight and length its conductance is about twice that of copper. The larger diameter required for aluminum for a given resistance is advantageous in overhead high-voltage transmission lines where, for a given spacing of conductors, the larger the conductor diameter, the higher the voltage may be before an electric discharge (corona) occurs about the conductors. In regions where ice may form, the larger diameter of an aluminum conductor is a disadvantage. The tensile strength of aluminum is less than that of copper. Steel cores are often used with aluminum to obtain satisfactory over-all conductor strength. Although the steel forms an electrical path in parallel with the aluminum path, the resistance of the steel path is usually so high compared with that of the aluminum that only a small percentage of the current is carried in the steel. The melting point of aluminum is 658 C.

A stranded wire or a cable is a group of wires or a combination of groups of wires. The strands are not insulated from each other in a single conductor cable. Most small conductors composed of strands are called stranded wires although there is no diameter specified as the dividing one between a stranded wire and a cable. Conductors are stranded to increase their flexibility. In a stranded conductor of the same material throughout, the strands are usually of the same diameter. When the strands are to be covered with insulation, it is desirable that the enclosing surface be nearly cylindrical. A single strand forms the core. In the first layer about the core 6 strands are spiraled with each touching the center

Fig. 4.20 Cross section of copper conductor used on Hoover Dam transmission line.

and the adjacent strands. In the second layer are 12 strands, in the third 18, and so on. As a result a single-layer cable contains 7 strands, a double-layer cable 19 strands, a triple-layer cable 37 strands, and so on. Only the center strand has the same length as the complete cable since the strands in a layer are spiraled about the strands underneath. A 19-strand cable 1,000 ft long has a resistance greater than one-nineteenth of that of the center strand because the strands are not in good contact throughout their length. The increase in resistance caused by spiraling depends upon the number of layers but is seldom more than 5 per cent.

Three- and twelve-strand cables, not covered with insulation, are sometimes used for overhead lines. They are less subject to wind vibration than are cables with a cylindrical surface.

In extra-high-voltage overhead lines hollow-core conductors are used to increase the outside conductor diameter and thus reduce the corona loss without increasing the conductor cross section above that needed to carry economically the current in the circuit. The conductor construction of Fig. 4.20 is used on the 287-kv line from Hoover Dam to Los Angeles. Here 10 copper segments are dovetailed to form a conductor of 1.4 in. outside diameter and 0.1 in. wall thickness.

4.14. Wire Sizes. In the United States the most common wire gage for conductors is the American wire gage (AWG). The gage numbers are retrogressive; i.e., the larger the number, the smaller the wire. The ratio of the cross sections of any two successive sizes is constant throughout the range of sizes. The diameter of No. 0000 (four naught) wire was set at 0.460 in. and that of No. 36 at 0.005 in. If a is the ratio of the cross sections of wires with successive numbers,

the area of No. 35 wire = a × area of No. 36 wire

the area of No. 34 wire is a^2 × area of No. 36 wire, and so on. There are 38 sizes between No. 36 and No. 0000, or the factor a is applied 39 times to express the ratio between their areas. Hence

$$a^{39} \times \text{area of No. 36 wire} = \text{area of No. 0000 wire}$$

or $a^{39} \times 5^2 = 460^2$, from which $a = \sqrt[39]{460^2/5^2} = 1.261$.

Since 1.261 is nearly 1.25, then $a = 1.25$ is an approximation accurate enough for most computations. The ratio 1.261 is also nearly equal to 1.2599, the cube root of 2. This leads to another approximation: *The cross section of a wire doubles and the d-c resistance halves for a decrease of three gage numbers.* Since $a^{10} = 1.261^{10} = 10.2$, a reduction of 10 gage numbers approximately multiplies the cross section by 10 and divides the resistance by 10. The properties of standard annealed copper wire are listed in Table 4.5. Cables larger than No. 0000 do not have gage numbers but are specified according to the cross section in circular mils.

Table 4.5 shows that No. 10 wire is approximately $\frac{1}{10}$ in. in diameter, and at 20 C has a resistance of about 1 ohm per 1,000 ft. These relations, plus those given in the preceding paragraph, enable one to compute the cross section or the resistance of a copper wire of any other gage number without reference to the table.

Not enough sizes are listed in Table 4.5 to meet all needs. Consider the case of a motor design where 82 wires are required in each slot to obtain a desired performance characteristic. Assume that the slot area available for copper is 0.1 sq in. = 100,000 sq mils = 127,000 cir mils. The area available for each wire is

$$\frac{127,000 \text{ cir mils}}{82 \text{ wires}} = 1,550 \text{ cir mils per wire}$$

Reference to Table 4.5 shows that No. 18 wire (1,624 cir mils) is too large, so it is necessary to use No. 19 wire (1,288 cir mils), giving a total of $1,288 \times 82 = 105,500$ cir mils in each slot. Then only

$$\frac{105,500}{127,000} = 0.83$$

or 83 per cent of the space available for copper is used. The resistance of the wire, and consequently the I^2R loss for a given current, is $1/0.83 = 1.2$

TABLE 4.5. COMPLETE WIRE TABLE, STANDARD ANNEALED COPPER, AMERICAN WIRE GAGE*

AWG No.	Diameter, mils at 20 C	Area, cir mils	Area, sq in.	Ohms per 1,000 ft, 20 C (= 68 F)	Lb per 1,000 ft
0000	460.0	211,600.0	0.1662	0.04901	640.5
000	409.6	167,800.0	0.1318	0.06180	508.0
00	364.8	133,100.0	0.1045	0.07793	402.8
0	324.9	105,500.0	0.08289	0.09827	319.5
1	289.3	83,690.0	0.06573	0.1239	253.3
2	257.6	66,370.0	0.05213	0.1563	200.9
3	229.4	52,640.0	0.04134	0.1970	159.3
4	204.3	41,740.0	0.03278	0.2485	126.4
5	181.9	33,100.0	0.02600	0.3133	100.2
6	162.0	26,250.0	0.02062	0.3951	79.46
7	144.3	20,820.0	0.01635	0.4982	63.02
8	128.5	16,510.0	0.01297	0.6282	49.98
9	114.4	13,090.0	0.01028	0.7921	39.63
10	101.9	10,380.0	0.008155	0.9989	31.43
11	90.74	8,234.0	0.006467	1.260	24.92
12	80.81	6,530.0	0.005129	1.588	19.77
13	71.96	5,178.0	0.004067	2.003	15.68
14	64.08	4,107.0	0.003225	2.525	12.43
15	57.07	3,257.0	0.002558	3.184	9.858
16	50.82	2,583.0	0.002028	4.016	7.818
17	45.26	2,048.0	0.001609	5.064	6.200
18	40.30	1,624.0	0.001276	6.385	4.917
19	35.89	1,288.0	0.001012	8.051	3.899
20	31.96	1,022.0	0.0008023	10.15	3.092
21	28.46	810.0	0.0006363	12.80	2.452
22	25.35	642.4	0.0005046	16.14	1.945
23	22.57	509.5	0.0004002	20.36	1.542
24	20.10	404.0	0.0003173	25.67	1.223
25	17.90	320.4	0.0002517	32.37	0.9699
26	15.94	254.1	0.0001996	40.81	0.7692
27	14.20	201.5	0.0001583	51.47	0.6100
28	12.64	159.8	0.0001255	64.90	0.4837
29	11.26	126.7	0.00009953	81.83	0.3836
30	10.03	100.5	0.00007894	103.2	0.3049
31	8.928	79.70	0.00006260	130.1	0.2413
32	7.950	63.21	0.0000496	164.1	0.1913
33	7.080	50.13	0.0000394	206.9	0.1517
34	6.305	39.75	0.0000312	260.9	0.1203
35	5.615	31.52	0.0000248	329.0	0.0954
36	5.000	25.00	0.0000196	414.8	0.0757
37	4.453	19.83	0.0000156	523.1	0.0600
38	3.965	15.72	0.0000123	659.6	0.0476
39	3.531	12.47	0.0000098	831.8	0.0377
40	3.145	9.888	0.0000078	1,049.0	0.0299

* Values taken from "Standard Handbook for Electrical Engineers," 8th ed., McGraw-Hill Book Company, Inc., New York.

times what it would have been if all the space available for copper could have been used.   As a result the motor efficiency is reduced and the temperature rise is increased.

Three or more small wires in parallel may make better use of slot space than one larger wire.   In the slot considered above, 1,550 cir mils were available for each wire.   If three No. 23 (510 cir mils) wires were used in parallel, they would occupy 1,530 cir mils, or nearly all the space available.

4.15. Interior Wiring.   Conductors should be large enough to carry the required load current without overheating and without excessive

TABLE 4.6. NATIONAL ELECTRICAL CODE CONDUCTOR CURRENT-CARRYING
CAPACITIES IN AMPERES (BASED ON 30 C AMBIENT TEMPERATURE)*

Wire size, AWG	A†	B‡	Wire size, thousands of cir mils	A†	B‡
14	20	15	250	280	177
12	26	20	300	310	198
10	35	25	350	350	216
8	48	35	400	380	233
6	65	45	500	430	265
5	76	52	600	480	293
4	87	60	700	525	320
3	101	69	750	545	330
2	118	80	800	565	340
1	136	91	900	605	360
0	160	105	1,000	650	377
00	185	120	1,250	740	409
000	215	138	1,500	815	434
0000	248	160	2,000	960	463

* Values taken from "Standard Handbook for Electrical Engineers," 8th ed., McGraw-Hill Book Company, Inc., New York.
† A: Rubber-insulated conductor in open wiring.
‡ B: One to three rubber-insulated conductors in raceway or cable.

voltage regulation.   For interior wiring the allowable current is based upon National Electrical Code specifications.   The maximum current that a given size of wire can carry without creating a fire hazard depends upon the quality of the insulation and upon the type of wiring used. Rubber insulation is commonly used when the conductor temperature does not exceed 65 C.   For higher temperatures, special grades of rubber, solid synthetics, synthetic and felted asbestos, varnished cambric, glass, and paper are among the materials used.   The Code specifies current-carrying capacities of conductors for a variety of insulating materials and types of wiring and should be consulted for complete information. The Code current-carrying capacities for rubber-covered wires used in open wiring, such as with knobs and cleats, and for one to three rubber-covered wires used in one raceway or cable are listed in Table 4.6.

In determining the proper wire size for an interior wiring installation, one should compute the size required so that the allowable voltage regulation will not be exceeded and also determine from the Code the size required to carry the given load current. If the two sizes are not the same, the larger should be used. When the length of wire in a given installation is relatively great, the allowable voltage regulation generally governs the size. When the length is short, the Code current-carrying capacity generally governs the size.

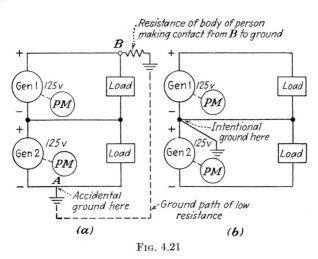

Fig. 4.21

4.16. Grounding. One or more points in an electric circuit may be intentionally connected to the earth (grounded). A good contact between the ground conductor and the earth is required to reduce the resistance of the ground path to a useful value. Pipes, rods, wires, or plates of metal are embedded to provide contact with the earth. Often an electrolyte or a salt is mixed with the earth to increase the conductivity. In regions where the soil is dry or rocky, long, buried copper wires are used to ground transmission line towers.

Power circuits are grounded as a safety precaution. Consider the three-wire system of Fig. 4.21a that has no intentional ground but by chance becomes grounded at A. If someone standing on the earth were to touch the system at B, his body would be in series with the ground path of low resistance across nearly 250 v and a dangerous shock might be received. Now consider the three-wire system of Fig. 4.21b that has the neutral wire intentionally grounded. Here there are not more than 125 v between any point in the system and the earth, or one-half as much as is possible in Fig. 4.21a. As a safeguard to personnel and equipment, frames of motors, generators, transformers, and other electric equipment should be grounded.

PROBLEMS

4.1. A certain copper wire has a resistance of 2 ohms per mi. Compute the resistance of 1,000 ft of this wire.

4.2. Two copper wires of the same length have respective diameters of 0.02 and 0.05 in. The first wire has a resistance of 0.25 ohm. Compute the resistance of the second.

4.3. For a given length and the same material, how does the resistance of a conductor whose diameter is 0.05 in. compare with that of one that is 0.05 in. square?

4.4. How does the resistance of a copper wire that is 2 mm in diameter and 400 m long compare with that of another copper wire that is 5 mm in diameter and 64 m long? How do the volumes of the wires compare?

4.5. Compute the resistance at 20 C between opposite faces of a copper United States penny that is 1.92 cm in diameter and 1.27 mm thick.

4.6. Compute the resistance at 20 C between opposite faces of a silver United States half dollar that is 3 cm in diameter and 2 mm thick.

4.7. Compute the percentage conductivity of mercury.

4.8. Number 6 wire has a diameter of 162 mils. Compute the cross section in circular mils.

4.9. Number 30 wire has a cross section of 100 cir mils. Compute the diameter in mils.

4.10. Compute the cross section in square mils and in circular mils of a rectangular conductor that is 0.04 by 0.12 in.

4.11. The fusing current of a wire varies as the $\frac{3}{2}$ power of the diameter. If 5 amp will fuse a copper wire 6.3 mils in diameter, compute the fusing current of a copper wire 45 mils in diameter. Compute the fusing current density of each wire.

4.12. A certain overhead conductor of diameter d_1 that consists of aluminum surrounding a steel core has a resistance per mile equal to that of a smaller copper conductor of diameter d_2. Assume that a storm surrounds each conductor with an ice coating of thickness t. Prove that the ratio of the ice loads on the conductors is $(d_1 + t)/(d_2 + t)$.

4.13. If a certain carbon rod $\frac{1}{2}$ in. in diameter has 0.015 ohm resistance per linear inch, compute the resistivity of the carbon.

4.14. If an iron wire 0.12 in. in diameter has 23.5 ohms resistance per mile, compute the resistivity of the iron.

4.15. Express a resistivity of 300 ohm-circular mils per ft in ohm-meters.

4.16. A permanent-magnet moving-coil instrument that has a resistance of 5 ohms and requires 10 ma for full-scale deflection is to be used with a manganin shunt to form a 50-amp ammeter. If the shunt is 3 in. long and $\frac{1}{2}$ in. wide, how thick should it be?

4.17. A copper wire that was originally 100 mils in diameter and had 0.2 ohm resistance was passed through a die that reduced its diameter to 50 mils. Compute the new value of resistance at the original temperature.

4.18. Forty 60-w lamps are located 150 ft from a source. The lamp voltage is to be 115 v and the circuit voltage regulation is to be 4 per cent. Compute the diameter of the copper wires for the circuit.

4.19. When a certain 10-hp 230-v d-c motor delivers full load with rated voltage applied its efficiency is 88 per cent. The motor is 150 ft from a 250-v source. What diameter of copper wire should be used?

4.20. Compute the resistance of an aluminum bar that is 500 by 2,000 mils in cross section and 10 ft long.

4.21. In Fig. 4.22 load 1 draws 40 amp and load 2 draws 60 amp. The voltage of load 2 is to be not less than 115 v. Determine the cross sections of the conductors such that the least amount of copper is required. Specify wires of standard sizes for the circuit.

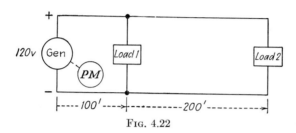

Fig. 4.22

4.22. A rectangular bus bar for connections on a switchboard is to be five times as wide as it is thick. Assuming that the amount of heat that can be transferred to the air is directly proportional to the surface area of a bar, how would the dimensions of an aluminum bar compare with those of a copper bar? Equal currents are to be carried with equal temperature rises. How would the bars compare in weight?

4.23. In a certain plant the bus bars that supply electric furnaces are seamless copper tubes 11 in. square and ½ in. thick. Each bar has a continuous rating of 16,000 amp rms.

  a. Compute the cross section in circular mils of a bar.

  b. Compute the resistance at 20 C of a 10-ft length of a bar.

  c. Assuming a sinusoidal current and a uniform current density, compute the maximum current density in a bar when carrying rated current.

4.24. Number 6 copper wire has a resistance of about 0.4 ohm per 1,000 ft at 20 C. How long a piece of the wire would be required as a shunt across a 10-amp ammeter in order that the combination would form a 50-amp ammeter? Why is this not a desirable method for changing the range of an ammeter?

4.25. A certain copper bus bar is ¼ in. thick and 1½ in. wide. Compute the cross section in circular mils and the resistance at 20 C of a 40-ft length of the bar. For a current of 600 amp, compute the current density in amperes per square inch and the voltage gradient in millivolts per foot.

4.26. A copper conductor that is 80 by 50 mils is at 20 C and carrying 5 amp. Compute the current density in milliamperes per circular mil and the voltage gradient in volts per foot.

4.27. A copper conductor 200 mils in diameter is carrying 40 amp distributed in such a manner that the current density varies as the square of the distance from the conductor center. Compute the current density midway between the conductor center and surface.

4.28. Compute the power used in a 200-ft length of the conductor of Prob. 4.27 at 20 C.

4.29. In a certain conductor the voltage gradient is uniform at 2 mv per m and directed along a straight line from a point *a* to a point *b*. If the points are 4 m apart, what is the voltage between them?

4.30. In a certain conductor the voltage gradient varies according to the equation $\varepsilon = 2 + 5l$ mv per m where l is in meters and is directed along a straight line from a point a at which $l = 0$ to a point b at which $l = 4$ m.   Compute the voltage between a and b and that between a and a point midway from a to b.

4.31. Two identical parallel underground cables are 500 ft long.   Compute the insulation resistance of each per foot of length if the leakage current is 250 μa with 500 v applied between conductors.

4.32. For 2,400 v applied between the conductor and the sheath of a cable that has an insulation resistance of 200 megohms per ft, compute the leakage current per mile of cable.

4.33. A certain cable that is 2,000 ft long has an insulation resistance of 300 megohms per ft.   A 15,000-ohm voltmeter and a 120-v battery are connected in series between the conductor and the sheath.   Compute the voltmeter reading.

4.34. The volume insulation of a certain insulator was 4 megohms.   With 5,000 v applied, the leakage current was 4 ma.   Compute the surface insulation resistance.

4.35. The resistance of a certain iron sample varies linearly from 24 ohms at 20 C to 38.4 ohms at 140 C.   Compute the temperature coefficient of resistance at 20 and at 140 C.

4.36. The resistance of a certain conductor increases 20 per cent as the temperature increases from 30 to 80 C.   Compute the temperature coefficient of resistance at each of the given temperatures.

4.37. The resistance of a certain mercury column varies linearly from 20 ohms at 20 C to 23.2 ohms at 200 C.   Compute (a) the increase in resistance per centigrade degree rise in temperature and (b) the temperature coefficient of resistance at 20 C and that at 200 C.

4.38. The resistance of a certain nickel sample varies linearly from 40 ohms at 0 C to 60 ohms at 80 C.   Compute (a) the increase in resistance for a temperature increase from 0 to 1 C and (b) the temperature coefficient of resistance at 0 C, at 40 C, and at 80 C.

4.39. For the sample of Prob. 4.38 compute the inferred temperature of zero resistance.   Set up the proportion from which the resistance at one temperature can be computed if the resistance at another temperature is known.

4.40. A certain sample of material has a temperature coefficient of resistance of 0.005 at 20 C and a linear resistance-temperature curve.   Compute the inferred temperature of zero resistance, and set up the proportion from which the resistance at one temperature can be computed if the resistance at another temperature is known. Compute the temperature coefficient of resistance of the sample at 100 C.

4.41. A 1-ohm resistance standard manufactured by the Leeds and Northrup Company is an alloy of copper, nickel, and manganese.   Its resistance varies with temperature according to the equation

$$R_t = R_{25}[1 + 0.0000059(t - 25) - 0.00000056(t - 25)^2]$$

where R_t is the resistance in ohms at a temperature t (°C), and R_{25} is the resistance in ohms at 25 C.

a. By how many parts in 10,000 does the resistance increase as the temperature increases from 25 to 50 C?

b. What temperature increase above 25 C would increase the resistance 0.01 per cent?

c. At what temperature will the resistance be a maximum?

d. At what temperature will the resistance be equal to that at 25 C?

4.42. At what temperature does standard copper have a resistivity of 12 ohm-cir mils per ft?

4.43. A certain copper nickel alloy known as $IAIA$ has at 68 F a resistivity of 48×10^{-8} ohm-m and a temperature coefficient of resistance per degree Fahrenheit of 2.75×10^{-6}. Compute the resistivity in ohm-circular mils per foot and compare with that of copper. Compute the temperature coefficient of resistance in terms of centigrade degrees and compare with that of copper.

4.44. Two wires in parallel carry 20 amp total. At 20 C the temperature coefficients of resistance of the wires are 0.002 and 0.004 per degree C, respectively, and the wires carry equal currents. How much current will each wire carry at 100 C? At 0 C?

4.45. The moving coil of a certain d-c ammeter is wound of copper wire. It has 2 ohms resistance at 20 C and requires 10 ma to produce full-scale deflection. The coil is connected across a manganin shunt. If the instrument capacity is 5 amp, what should be the resistance of the shunt at 20 C?

If the instrument reads correctly at 20 C, how much current will go through the moving coil at 40 C when the current being measured is 5 amp? Assume that the resistance of the shunt does not change with temperature.

4.46. A 3-ohm manganin resistor is connected in series with the moving coil of Prob. 4.45 as shown in Fig. 2.30.

a. If the instrument capacity is 5 amp, what should be the resistance of the shunt at 20 C?

b. If the instrument reads correctly at 20 C, how much current will go through the moving coil at 40 C when the current being measured is 5 amp? Assume that the resistances of the shunt and the resistor do not change with temperature.

4.47. If a coil of copper wire has 60 ohms resistance at 30 C, compute its resistance at 90 C.

4.48. If a transformer coil of copper wire has 12 ohms resistance at 10 C and 14.4 ohms at the normal operating temperature, compute the operating temperature.

4.49. A copper coil on a certain transformer has 0.005 ohm at 15 C. When the transformer is delivering its rated load, the coil carries 87 amp rms and has a temperature of 75 C. For rated load, compute the power loss in the coil.

4.50. At 25 C the copper field winding of a certain motor draws 2.4 amp from a 120-v source. Compute the temperature at which the coil draws 2 amp.

4.51. The tungsten filament of a certain radio tube is 2 in. long and 4 mils in diameter and has a normal operating temperature of 2,200 C. Compute the filament resistance at 20 C. Assume that the resistance-temperature curve for the filament is linear up to the operating temperature and compute the resistance at that temperature.

4.52. Compute the surface area of the filament of Prob. 4.51.

If electrons leave the surface at such a rate as to produce a current density of 300 ma per sq cm, compute the current.

4.53. The Keystone Carbon Company manufactures a negative temperature coefficient resistor with the following test data:

Resistance, ohms	Temperature, °C	Resistance, ohms	Temperature, °C
1,140	20	340	100
830	40	270	120
600	60	215	140
450	80	175	160

Plot the resistance-temperature characteristic.

The resistor has a maximum power capacity of 2 w at 150 C. Compute the safe operating current at this temperature.

4.54. The resistor of Prob. 4.53 is in parallel with a coil of copper wire that has 200 ohms resistance at 20 C. Plot the curve showing how the equivalent resistance of the combination varies with the temperature through the range from 20 to 150 C.

4.55. Solve Prob. 4.54 if the coil resistance is 2,000 ohms at 20 C.

4.56. A certain Thermistor has 200 ohms resistance at −20 C and 2 ohms resistance at 115 C. For it compute the value of β in (4.12).

4.57. For a certain Thermistor, β in (4.12) is 2,500. How does the resistance of the element at 100 C compare with that at 20 C?

4.58. The resistance of a certain Thermistor decreases from 100 ohms at 30 C to 50 ohms at 50 C. For this element compute β in (4.12).

4.59. The Thermistor of Prob. 4.56 is in series with a coil of copper wire that has a resistance of 80 ohms at −20 C. Through what range will the resistance of the combination vary as the temperature varies from −20 to 115 C?

4.60. The Thermistor of Prob. 4.56 is in parallel with a coil of copper wire that has a resistance of 80 ohms at −20 C. Through what range will the resistance of the combination vary as the temperature varies from −20 to 115 C?

4.61. For the thermocouple whose characteristic is given in Fig. 4.19, how many millivolts would be produced if one junction were at 0 C and the other at 100 C? If one junction were at 100 C and the other at 200 C?

4.62. One junction of the thermocouple whose characteristic is given in Fig. 4.19 is at 40 C. The thermocouple emf is 8 mv. Determine the temperature of the other junction.

4.63. A certain steel-core aluminum cable has six aluminum strands each 0.211 in. in diameter and seven steel strands each 0.071 in. in diameter. The resistivity of the aluminum is 17 ohm-cir mils per ft and that of the steel is 65 ohm-cir mils per ft, both at 20 C. Neglect the increase in resistance caused by the spiral in the strands, and determine the size of the conductor of standard copper to which this cable is most nearly equivalent.

4.64. A certain cable is composed of 19 strands, each 0.1225 in. in diameter. The material of 7 strands has a resistivity of 35 ohm-cir mils per ft at 20 C. The material of 12 strands has a resistivity of 10.7 ohm-cir mils per ft at 20 C. Neglect the increase of resistance caused by the spiral in the strands and compute the resistance per 1,000 ft of cable.

4.65. Given the resistance of No. 10 copper wire as 1 ohm per 1,000 ft at 20 C and the diameter as 100 mils, solve the following problems without reference to the wire table.

  a. Compute the cross section of No. 21 wire.

  b. Compute the diameter of No. 00 wire.

  c. Compute the resistance per mile of No. 2 copper wire.

  d. Compute the resistance per 1,000 ft of No. 0 copper wire.

4.66. A 20-ft copper bar has a cross section that varies linearly from 0.1 in. square at one end to 0.5 in. square at the other. For 20 C compute the resistance between the ends of the bar.

4.67. A 50-ft copper rod has a diameter that varies linearly from 0.1 in. at one end to 0.4 in. at the other. For 20 C compute the resistance between the ends of the rod.

CHAPTER 5

NONLINEAR RESISTANCE CIRCUITS

5.1. Nonlinear Elements. If the current in a resistive element is not directly proportional to the applied voltage, the element is nonlinear. This designation is a loose one because there is a distinction between linearity and proportionality. If the curve showing the relation between

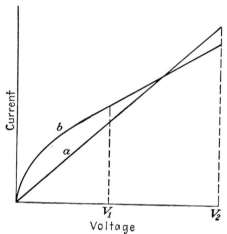

Fig. 5.1 Two curves that are linear over the range of voltages from V_1 to V_2. For curve a the current is directly proportional to the voltage. For curve b the current is not directly proportional to the voltage.

two quantities is a straight line through the point $(0,0)$, the relation is linear and one quantity is directly proportional to the other. Such a curve is a in Fig. 5.1 and would be obtained for a resistor of constant resistance. An element whose resistance increased as the current increased might have a current-voltage characteristic such as b in Fig. 5.1. This curve is nearly linear in the range from V_1 to V_2. However, the current is not directly proportional to the voltage in that range.

The resistance of a conductor varies as its temperature varies. If the temperature of a conductor varies with the current, the resistance of the conductor varies with the current. In many circuits the percentage resistance change over the normal range of current change is so small that little error results in assuming that the resistance is constant. However, for conductors in which the resistance changes appreciably with a change of current, considerable error may result in computations if the voltage and current are assumed to be proportional.

Current-voltage characteristics plotted from experimental data are used when considering nonlinear resistive circuits. In Fig. 5.2 are characteristics of two 115-v tungsten-filament lamps, one rated at 100 w and

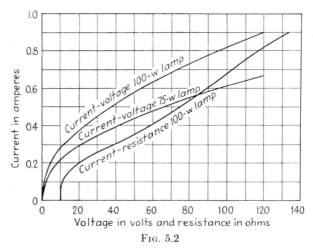

Fig. 5.2

the other at 75 w. For such lamps a short time elapses after the application of a given voltage before the current becomes constant. In taking the data for Fig. 5.2, the voltage was kept constant at a given value until the current became constant. Then the current and voltage values were recorded.

For the 100-w lamp the current-resistance characteristic is also plotted in Fig. 5.2. Points on this were obtained from the data taken for the current-voltage characteristic. Each voltage value was divided by the corresponding current to obtain the resistance corresponding to the current. With rated voltage of 115 applied, the current was 0.87 amp. The resistance was 115 v/0.87 amp = 132 ohms. For currents of 50 ma or less, the resistance was nearly constant at 10 ohms. Over the current range from zero to rated value, the resistance of the lamp varies through a ratio of 1 to 13.

The current-voltage characteristic of the 100-w lamp in Fig. 5.2 was obtained while using a d-c supply. If an alternating voltage were applied to the lamp, the relation between the instantaneous values of current and voltages is not that of the characteristic. When an alternating current of constant rms value flows in a filament, the rate at which electric energy is being converted into heat varies from zero at the current zero to a maximum at the current maximum.   As a result, the filament temperature varies in a cyclic manner between certain minimum and maximum values.   For a current frequency of 60 c or higher, the filament temperature varies so little throughout a cycle that the characteristics of Fig. 5.2 show the relations between rms current and rms voltage.

5.2. Transient Lamp Currents. The resistance of a 100-w 115-v tungsten-filament lamp is 132 ohms at a normal operating temperature of

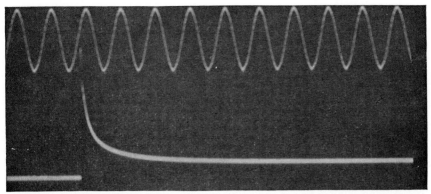

Fig. 5.3   Oscillogram of the transient current in a 100-w 115-v tungsten-filament incandescent lamp when a d-c voltage of rated value was suddenly applied.   The frequency of the timing wave is 60 c.

about 2500 C and 10 ohms at a room temperature of 20 C.   The latter is the cold resistance of the lamp.   If a cold lamp of this rating were connected suddenly to a 115-v d-c circuit, the current would rise instantly to 11.5 amp if in the circuit there is nothing to limit the current but the resistance of the lamp.   At the first instant the lamp would draw 115 v × 11.5 amp = 1,320 w.   This abnormal power quickly heats the filament and increases its resistance rapidly enough to reduce the current to the normal value of 0.87 amp in a fraction of a second.   In the oscillogram of Fig. 5.3 for this circuit, the initial current was about 6.5 amp. The current decreased to the normal value of 0.87 amp within 0.05 sec. The discrepancy between the experimental maximum of 6.5 amp and the predicted maximum of 11.5 amp was caused by inductance in the circuit and by the inertia of the oscillograph vibrator.

5.3. Use of Current-Voltage Characteristics. When the resistance of a conductor is constant, a direct proportion exists between the voltage between two points on the conductor and the current in it.   This proportion is generally used in circuit computations and the current-voltage characteristic is not drawn.   When the resistance of a conductor varies with the current in it, computations can be based upon the characteristic.

Example 1.   Three 100-w 115-v tungsten-filament lamps are in series across 240 v.   Determine the current in, the voltage across, and the power used by each lamp.

Solution.   Since the lamps are in series the same current flows in each lamp. The voltage across each lamp will be 240 v/3 lamps = 80 v.   From the characteristic of Fig. 5.2, for 80 v the current is 0.73 amp.   The power used by each lamp is 80 v × 0.73 amp = 58.4 w.

Example 2.   A 75-w 115-v and a 100-w 115-v tungsten-filament lamp are in series across 115 v.   Determine the current in, the voltage across, and the power used by each lamp.

Solution.   The known facts are that the same current flows in each lamp and the sum of the lamp voltages is 115 v.   Since we do not have an equation relating the current in a lamp to the voltage across it, the problem can be solved by trial and error, using the characteristics of Fig. 5.2.

Assume that the current is 0.4 amp.   For this current, from the characteristic it is found that the voltage across the 75-w lamp is 42 v and that across the 100-w lamp is 24 v.   Since the sum of these voltages is 66 v and not 115 v, the assumed current is too small.   The next step is to assume a greater current and find the corresponding voltages.   If the sum of these is not 115 v, a different current is assumed until the one is found for which the voltages do add to 115. That current is found to be 0.52 amp.   The voltage across the 75-w lamp is 73 v and that across the 100-w lamp is 42 v.

The power used by the 75-w lamp is 73 v × 0.52 amp = 38 w and that used by the 100-w lamp is 42 v × 0.52 amp = 22 w.

Note that neither lamp receives its rated power and that the lamp with the lower watt rating receives more power than the other.

After constructing a current-voltage characteristic for the lamp combination of Example 2, the current corresponding to any given applied voltage can be determined graphically.   In Fig. 5.4 the characteristics of the 100- and the 75-w lamps from Fig. 5.2 have been redrawn as curves A and B, respectively.   To construct the characteristic for the lamps in series, choose a current, say 0.35 amp.   For this current, in Fig. 5.4, the voltage across the 100-w lamp is represented by the distance ab and that across the 75-w lamp by the distance ac.   Then ad is made equal to $ab + ac$, and d is a point on the desired characteristic.   The addition can be made with a pair of dividers.   In a similar manner other points can be located and C, the desired characteristic, drawn.   Now, to solve the problem of Example 2, erect a vertical line at 115 v.   Through the point of intersection of this line with C draw a horizontal line.   The ordinate of the horizontal line, 0.52 amp, is the current in the circuit. The abscissa of the point of intersection of the horizontal line with B is 73 v, the voltage across the 75-w lamp.   The abscissa of the point of intersection of the horizontal line with A is 42 v, the voltage across the 100-w lamp.

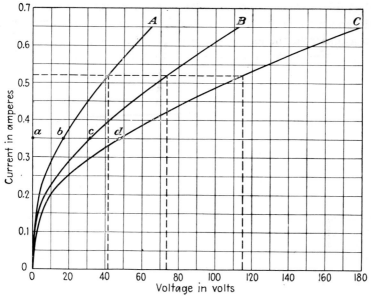

FIG. 5.4 Lamp characteristics. *A*, 100-w tungsten-filament lamp; *B*, 75-w tungsten-filament lamp; *C*, 100- and 75-w tungsten-filament lamps in series.

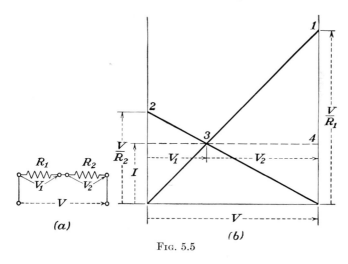

FIG. 5.5

Another graphical method for solving resistance circuits will be explained by considering first its application to a linear circuit. In Fig. 5.5 a resistor of resistance R_1 ohms and one of resistance R_2 ohms are in series across V v. The current in and the voltage across each resistor are to be determined. As in Fig. 5.5*b*, choose any convenient scale and lay off a horizontal line representing V v. At each end of this line erect a vertical line.   Choose any convenient scale for current and on the right-hand line locate point 1 at a distance V/R_1 amp above the horizontal line. Draw a line from the left-hand end of the horizontal line to 1.   This line represents the current-voltage characteristic of the first resistor.   On the left-hand line locate point 2 at a distance V/R_2 amp above the horizontal line, using the same current scale as before.   Draw a line from the right-hand end of the horizontal line to 2.   This line represents the current-voltage characteristic of the second resistor if voltages are measured horizontally from the characteristic to the right-hand line.   Point 3, at the intersection of the oblique lines, determines the current I through the resistors and the respective voltages.   By projecting horizontally from 3 to the right-hand line point 4 is located.   It is a point on the current-voltage characteristic of the series combination of resistors.   The complete characteristic can be obtained by drawing a line through the left-hand end of the horizontal line and 4.

Example 3.   A 100- and a 400-ohm resistor are in series across 48 v.   By the preceding graphical method determine the current in and the voltage across each resistor.   Also determine the current if the voltage were increased to 70 v.

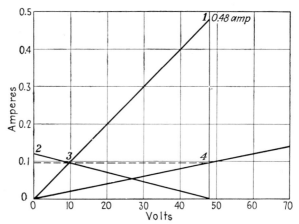

Fig. 5.6   Graphical method for determining the current in and the voltages across a 100- and a 400-ohm resistor in series across 48 v.

Solution.   In Fig. 5.6 a horizontal line is graduated in volts.   At 0 and 48 v vertical lines were erected.   Then a current scale was chosen and values marked as shown.   Point 1 corresponded to 48 v/100 ohms = 0.48 amp.   The line joining the origin and 1 was drawn.   Point 2 corresponded to 48 v/400 ohms = 0.12 amp.   The line joining (48,0) and 2 was drawn.   The oblique lines intersected at point 3.   The current in the resistors is the ordinate of 3 or 0.095 amp.   The voltage across the 100-ohm resistor is the abscissa of 3 or 9.5 v.   The voltage across the 400-ohm resistor is 48 − 9.5 = 38.5 v.

By projecting horizontally from 3 to the vertical line at 48 v, point 4 on the total characteristic is obtained. This characteristic was drawn as a line from the origin extending through 4. The current corresponding to 70 v is read from the characteristic as 0.14 amp.

Example 4. A 75-w 115-v tungsten-filament lamp is in series with a 100-ohm resistor. Determine the current in the combination and the lamp voltage for an applied voltage of 135 v. Construct the current-voltage characteristic of the combination.

Solution. In Fig. 5.7 the 75-w lamp characteristic of Fig. 5.2 has been redrawn. A reversed resistor characteristic is a straight line. Any number of the reversed

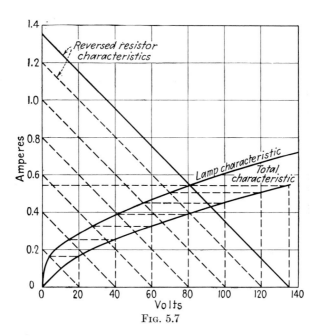

Fig. 5.7

characteristics can be drawn, each corresponding to a given applied voltage. With 135 v applied, the reversed characteristic is drawn from 1.35 amp (135 v/100 ohms) on the current axis to 135 v on the voltage axis. In a similar manner, reversed characteristics corresponding to 120, 100, 80, 60, 40, and 20 v, respectively, were drawn. The intersections of these characteristics and the lamp characteristic determine the operating points on the lamp characteristic corresponding to each of the voltages for which the reversed characteristics were drawn. For example, with 135 v applied, the intersection point shows that the current is 0.545 amp and the lamp voltage is 80.5 v.

Points on the total characteristic are obtained by projecting horizontally to the right from each intersection point on the lamp characteristic until intersection occurs with a vertical line erected at the voltage value corresponding to that for which each resistor characteristic was drawn. The total characteristic was drawn through the points thus determined.

5.4. Fitting an Equation to an Experimental Curve. To determine an equation that will fit a curve plotted from experimental data, start by assuming a form of equation that will yield a curve similar to the one to be fitted. The equation $i = cv^d$, where i is the current in amperes, v is the voltage in volts, and c and d are constants, might fit the 100-w lamp characteristic of Fig. 5.2. To test the choice of equation, it should be rearranged, if possible, to plot in linear form. Consider the equation

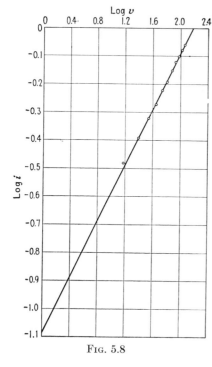

Fig. 5.8

$$i = cv^d \qquad (5.1)$$

Taking the logarithm to the base 10 of each side of the equality

$$\log i = \log c + d \log v \qquad (5.2)$$

Let $\log i$ be considered as one new variable and $\log v$ as another. Then, since $\log c$ is a constant, (5.2) is in the slope-intercept form $y = mx + b$ of a straight line. Various values of v and the corresponding values of i were read from the 100-w lamp characteristic of Fig. 5.2 and tabulated in Table 5.1 in columns 1 and 3. Then the logarithms of v and i were obtained from a table and entered in columns 2 and 4. Next the values of $\log i$ were plotted against the values of $\log v$ in Fig. 5.8. Then it was found possible to draw the straight line shown through most of the points. For the range for $\log v$ from 1.4 to 2.06 (for voltages from 25 to 115 v), the line passes through the points. Throughout this range the given lamp characteristic has an equation of the form assumed. The line extended intersects the vertical axis at -1.085. Then, in (5.2), $\log c = -1.085$, from which $c = $ antilog $(-1.085) = 0.082$.

In (5.2) d represents the slope of the line in Fig. 5.8. The line intersects the horizontal axis at 2.18 and the vertical axis at -1.085. Its slope $d = 1.085/2.18 = 0.5$. Then the 100-w lamp characteristic has the equation

$$i = 0.082v^{0.5}$$

for voltages between 25 and 115 v.

5.5. Ballast Tubes. A ballast tube is a device in which, within a certain range of voltages, the increase of resistance with increase of tem-

TABLE 5.1

(1)	(2)	(3)	(4)
v	$\log v$	i	$\log i$
5	0.70	0.24	−0.62
15	1.18	0.33	−0.48
25	1.40	0.41	−0.39
35	1.54	0.48	−0.32
45	1.65	0.54	−0.27
55	1.74	0.60	−0.22
65	1.81	0.65	−0.19
75	1.88	0.70	−0.15
85	1.93	0.79	−0.10
105	2.02	0.83	−0.08
115	2.06	0.87	−0.06

perature is such as to keep the current nearly constant. The tube may be used with either direct or alternating current. One type of tube has an iron wire filament and is filled with hydrogen. As the tube voltage is increased from zero to the lower values in the operating range, the filament glows near the center. With further increase in the voltage, more and more of the filament glows. The accompanying increase in resistance prevents much of an increase in current. At the upper end of the operating range, the entire length of filament is glowing.

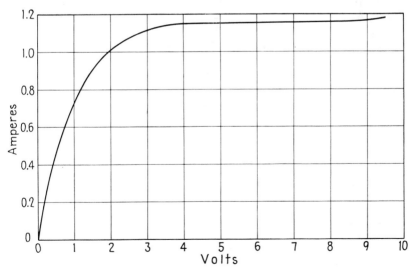

FIG. 5.9   Current-voltage characteristic of a ballast tube that is rated 1.15 amp for a voltage range from 3 to 9.5 v.

A ballast tube may be used in series with a load in which it is desired to maintain constant current even though the supply voltage fluctuates. Since the tube depends upon a temperature change for its operation, following a sudden change of voltage a short time elapses before the current is restored to the desired value.

In Fig. 5.9 is a current-voltage characteristic of a tube rated at 1.15 amp over a range from 3 to 9.5 v. This range is an increase of

$$\frac{100(9.5 - 3)}{3} = 217 \text{ per cent}$$

in the voltage above 3 v. The accompanying increase in current is only

$$\frac{100(1.18 - 1.10)}{1.10} = 7 \text{ per cent}$$

PROBLEMS

5.1. In a conductivity test of a certain liquid the following data were taken after the sudden application of voltage to two plates immersed in the liquid:

Time, μsec	Voltage, kv	Current, ma
0	0	0
40	11	0.1
80	18	0.5
120	23	1.3
160	28	2.1

Plot the curves showing the time variations of the voltage, the current, and the resistance. Plot the curve that shows the variation of the resistance with the current.

5.2. The resistance of a certain circuit varies cyclically with time as follows:

Time, msec	Resistance, ohms	Time, msec	Resistance, ohms
0	10.00	1.1	9.69
0.1	10.31	1.2	9.41
0.2	10.59	1.3	9.19
0.3	10.81	1.4	9.05
0.4	10.95	1.5	9.00
0.5	11.00	1.6	9.05
0.6	10.95	1.7	9.19
0.7	10.81	1.8	9.41
0.8	10.59	1.9	9.69
0.9	10.31	2.0	10.00
1.0	10.00		

A continuous voltage of 20 v is applied. Plot the curves showing the time variations of the resistance and the current in the circuit. Use a resistance scale extending from 9 to 11 ohms and a current scale extending from 1.8 to 2.3 amp. What is the frequency of the current variation?

5.3. A 75- and a 100-w 115-v tungsten-filament lamp are in series. For 0.5 amp what is the resistance of the combination?

5.4. With 100 v applied to the combination of Prob. 5.3, determine the voltage across each lamp.

5.5. How much power would a 100-w 115-v tungsten-filament lamp draw with 90 v applied if the resistance of the lamp did not vary as the applied voltage is varied? Use the characteristic of Fig. 5.2 and determine what the actual power would be with 90 v applied.

5.6. A 100-w 115-v tungsten-filament lamp is in series with a 100-ohm resistor across 120 v. How much power does the lamp receive?

5.7. A variable resistor is in series with a 100-w 115-v tungsten-filament lamp across 200 v. Determine the maximum power the resistor can receive as its resistance is varied.

5.8. Explain why a 75-w 115-v lamp and a 100-w 115-v lamp will not operate satisfactorily in series across a 230-v source. Determine the highest voltage that may be applied to the combination without overheating either lamp.

5.9. Determine the resistance of a resistor to be connected in parallel with a 75-w 115-v lamp such that when this combination is in series with a 100-w 115-v lamp across a 230-v source each lamp operates at its normal brilliance.

5.10. A 100-ohm resistor is in parallel with a 75-w 115-v tungsten-filament lamp. If the combination draws 1.5 amp, determine the current in each branch.

5.11. Construct the current-voltage characteristic for the combination of Prob. 5.10.

5.12. A 100-w 115-v tungsten-filament lamp is in parallel with a 50-ohm resistor. This combination is in series with a second 100-w lamp across a source of voltage V. Determine V if the current in the resistor is 0.4 amp.

5.13. If V in Prob. 5.12 is 145 v determine the current in each lamp.

5.14. A 75- and a 100-w 115-v tungsten-filament lamp are in parallel. This combination is in series with a second 100-w 115-v lamp across 120 v. Determine the current in and the voltage across each lamp.

5.15. Construct the current-voltage characteristic for the entire combination of Prob. 5.14.

5.16. Two 100-w 115-v tungsten-filament lamps are in parallel. This combination is in series with a third 100-w 115-v lamp across 120 v. Determine the current in and the voltage across each lamp.

5.17. Construct the current-voltage characteristic for the entire combination of Prob. 5.16.

5.18. A 75- and a 100-w 115-v tungsten-filament lamp are in parallel. This combination is in series with a 60-ohm resistor. If there is 0.6 amp in the 75-w lamp, compute the voltage applied to the entire combination.

5.19. Two 75-w 115-v tungsten-filament lamps are in parallel. This combination is in series with a 100-w 115-v tungsten-filament lamp. Determine the highest voltage that can be applied to the entire combination without overheating any of the lamps.

5.20. The life of a tungsten-filament lamp varies approximately inversely with the thirteenth power of the ratio of the operating voltage to rated voltage. A certain lamp that is rated at 120 v has an expected life of 1,000 hr at rated voltage. To increase its light output for photographic purposes, the lamp is operated at a voltage that reduces the expected life to 4 hr. Compute the operating voltage.

5.21. The lamp rheostat of Fig. 2.17 contains six 100-w 115-v tungsten-filament lamps. The first and third switches are closed to the upper position and the second and seventh switches are closed to the lower position. With 120 v applied to the rheostat, determine the currents in the various lamps and the equivalent resistance of the rheostat.

5.22. The lamp rheostat of Fig. 2.17 contains six 75-w 115-v tungsten-filament lamps. Determine the maximum and the minimum resistance of the rheostat with 115 v applied.

5.23. The following data were taken on a 15-w fluorescent lamp when operated from a d-c source:

Current, ma	Voltage, v	Current, ma	Voltage, v
10	88	150	64
20	81	200	62
30	75	300	59
50	72	400	57
100	68		

Plot the current-voltage characteristic. Determine the normal operating current of the lamp. How much resistance should be used in series with the lamp across a 120-v source in order that it will receive rated power?

5.24. Thyrite is the trade name of a material whose resistance decreases as the voltage applied to it increases. For a certain sample of this material, the current is related to the voltage by the equation $i = 3.2 \times 10^{-8}v^{3.57}$ amp, where v is in volts.

a. Plot the current-voltage characteristic for voltages up to 1,000 v.

b. If the sample is in series with a 120-ohm resistor across 800 v, determine the voltage across it.

5.25. Two identical Thyrite resistors are in series across a 12-v source and draw 5 ma. The current in each varies as the fourth power of the voltage. Compute the percentage decrease in the voltage across one of the resistors caused by connecting a 400-ohm resistor across it.

5.26. Solve Prob. 5.25 if the Thyrite resistors are replaced by two 1,200-ohm resistors.

5.27. For measuring lightning currents with a cathode-ray oscillograph it is desirable to have a shunt that will produce a high sensitivity for low current values and a greatly reduced sensitivity for high current values. Such a nonlinear shunt can be made by using a Thyrite resistor in parallel with a resistor of constant resistance. A Thyrite resistor used for such an application has a current-voltage characteristic whose equation is $i = 1.2 \times 10^{-4}v^4$ amp, where v is in volts. This resistor is used in parallel with a second resistor of constant 0.2 ohm resistance.

a. Compute the voltage across the shunt when the current is 100 amp.

b. Compute the voltage across the shunt when the current is 25,000 amp.

c. Compare the ratio of the two currents with the ratio of the two voltages.

5.28. A certain bridge circuit consists of three resistors of constant resistance and two Thyrite resistors as in Fig. 5.10. The Thyrite resistors have a current-voltage characteristic whose equation is $i = 3.2 \times 10^{-8}v^4$ amp, where v is in volts. For what values of V will there be no current in the 400-ohm resistor? Compute the points for and plot a curve showing the relation between the current in the 400-ohm resistor and the value of V.

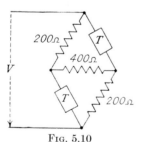

FIG. 5.10

CHAPTER 6

ELECTRONICS

6.1. Thermionic Emission. In an uncharged metallic conductor the free, or unbound, electrons are moving in random paths throughout the conductor volume. Some of the electrons travel beyond the conductor surface. As an electron leaves a conductor, the conductor acquires a positive charge. Since unlike charges attract, the conductor then exerts an attractive force upon the electron that may bring it to rest and then pull it back into the conductor. At usual room temperatures few electrons acquire sufficient energy to cause them to break free from a conductor. If a conductor is heated, more electrons are given the kinetic energy required to carry them from the conductor. The discovery of the escape of electrons from a heated conductor at a rate great enough to be measured was made by Edison about 1883. The phenomenon is called the Edison effect and can be demonstrated with the circuit of Fig. 6.1. Here a conductor called a filament and an electrode called a plate are sealed in an evacuated

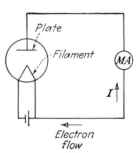

Fig. 6.1 Circuit for demonstrating the Edison effect.

bulb. The battery shown sends current through the filament and heats it. Although there is no metallic connection from the plate to the filament within the bulb, a deflection occurs on the milliammeter MA. Electrons leave the filament, travel through the evacuated space to the plate, and from there through the milliammeter back to the filament. If the filament temperature is increased by increasing the current through it, the plate current increases also but not in a linear relation with the temperature.

In the circuit of Fig. 6.1 the energy required to drive the electrons from the filament to the plate and that to heat the filament are both supplied from the battery. The current entering the right-hand terminal of the filament is less than that leaving the left-hand terminal by the amount of the current registered on the milliammeter.

When a force f newtons acts through an infinitesimal distance ds m, the work done is an infinitesimal $dw = f\, ds$ j. (By definition a newton-meter is a joule.) The work W done as a force f newtons acts along a straight line from a point S_1 m from a given reference point on the line to a point S_2 m from the same reference point is $W = \int_{S_1}^{S_2} f\, ds$ j. This integral can be evaluated if the force is a constant or if the equation is known that expresses f as a function of the distance s from the reference point. If the force is a constant F newtons, then

$$W = \int_{S_1}^{S_2} F\, ds = Fs\, \Big]_{S_1}^{S_2} = F(S_2 - S_1) \qquad j$$

Denoting $S_2 - S_1$, the distance through which the force acts, as S, then $W = FS$ j.

When a force f newtons acts on a body of constant mass M kg, the acceleration a in meters per second per second is such that $f = Ma$. The work done on the body as it moves from point S_1 to point S_2 specified above is $W = \int_{S_1}^{S_2} Ma\, ds$ j. By definition $a = dv/dt$, where v is the velocity in meters per second. Then $a\, ds = (dv/dt)\, ds$. This is equivalent to $dv(ds/dt)$. But $ds/dt = v$; therefore $a\, ds = v\, dv$. Then

$$W = \int_{V_1}^{V_2} Mv\, dv = \tfrac{1}{2} Mv^2 \Big]_{V_1}^{V_2} = \tfrac{1}{2} M (V_2^2 - V_1^2) \qquad j$$

where V_1 is the velocity of the body at point S_1 and V_2 is its velocity at point S_2. If the body was initially at rest, $V_1 = 0$ and $W = \tfrac{1}{2} M V_2^2$ j. If there are no frictional forces opposing the motion of the body, all the work done on it is converted into kinetic energy, the usual expression for which is $\tfrac{1}{2} M V^2$. Note that in the preceding derivation it was not necessary that the relation between force and distance be known. This fact means that when a body of constant mass has reached a given velocity its kinetic energy is a unique value that is independent of how the velocity was attained.

The mass of a body is not a constant but a function of the velocity as expressed by $m = M_0/\sqrt{1 - (v/c)^2}$ kg, where M_0 kg is the mass at zero velocity, v is the velocity in meters per second, and $c = 3 \times 10^8$ m per sec (the velocity of light). When the mass of a body is a function of its velocity

$$f = \frac{d(mv)}{dt} = \frac{d}{dt}\left(\frac{M_0 v}{\sqrt{1 - (v/c)^2}}\right)$$

which, after differentiation and simplification, yields

$$f = \frac{M_0}{[1 - (v/c)^2]^{3/2}} \frac{dv}{dt}$$

The work done on the body as it moves from point S_1 to point S_2 is

$$W = \int_{S_1}^{S_2} f \, ds = \int_{S_1}^{S_2} \frac{M_0}{[1 - (v/c)^2]^{3/2}} \frac{dv}{dt} \, ds$$

As before $(dv/dt) \, ds = v \, dv$; therefore

$$W = \int_{V_1}^{V_2} \frac{M_0 v \, dv}{[1 - (v/c)^2]^{3/2}} = \frac{M_0 c^2}{\sqrt{1 - (v/c)^2}} \Bigg]_{V_1}^{V_2}$$

$$= M_0 c^2 \left[\frac{1}{\sqrt{1 - (V_2/c)^2}} - \frac{1}{\sqrt{1 - (V_1/c)^2}} \right] \quad \text{j}$$

When a body starts from rest, $V_1 = 0$ and the kinetic energy possessed when it reaches a velocity v m per sec is

$$W = M_0 c^2 \left[\frac{1}{\sqrt{1 - (v/c)^2}} - 1 \right] \quad \text{j}$$

When $v/c = 0.1$ or less, $\sqrt{1 - (v/c)^2}$ is nearly equal to $1 - (v/c)^2/2$ and $1/[1 - (v/c)^2/2]$ is nearly equal to $1 + (v/c)^2/2$. Then

$$W = M_0 c^2 \left[1 + \frac{(v/c)^2}{2} - 1 \right] = \tfrac{1}{2} M_0 v^2 \quad \text{j (nearly)}$$

This result means that when an electron is moving with a velocity less than 0.1 that of light its kinetic energy is nearly directly proportional to the square of its velocity.

The amount of energy required to remove an electron from a metal is the work function of the metal and is expressed in volts. When an electron moves through a difference of potential, it either acquires or gives up energy. If an electron leaves the surface of a metal object that originally was uncharged because of an equality of positive charges and electrons, it experiences a force attracting it toward the object. If an electron moving from within an object to its surface is to have its velocity reduced to zero as it reaches the surface, the kinetic energy initially possessed must be given up. Equating the energy given up to the initial kinetic energy and neglecting any change of mass with velocity yields $\phi_0 \times 1.60 \times 10^{-19} = \tfrac{1}{2} M_0 v^2$, where ϕ_0 is the work function in volts, 1.60×10^{-19} j is the energy given up by an electron in traveling through a fall of potential of 1 v, $M_0 = 9 \times 10^{-31}$ kg is the rest mass of an electron, and v is the initial electron velocity in meters per second. Substitution of the value of M_0 in the preceding equation yields

$$\phi_0 = 2.8 \times 10^{-12} v^2 \qquad (6.1)$$

The work function of an electron-emitting substance varies from 1.04 for barium-strontium oxides to 6.27 v for platinum; for tungsten, it is

4.52 v.   For a substance whose work function is known, the velocity that an electron must possess to just reach the surface can be computed from (6.1).   For tungsten it is 1.26×10^6 m per sec, or 780 mi per sec.   An electron with an initial velocity greater than this could leave a tungsten filament.

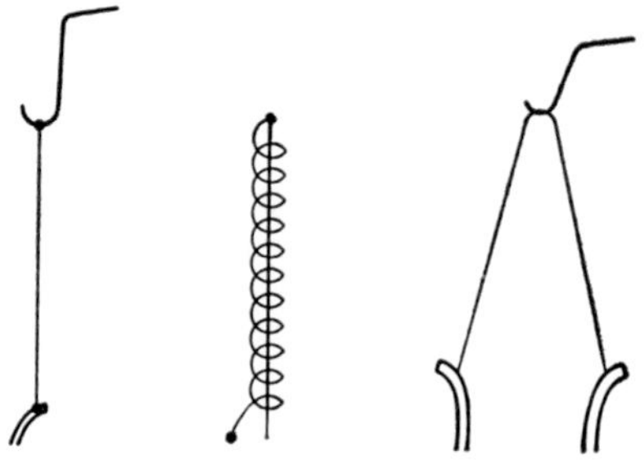

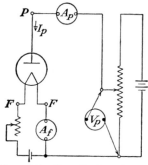

Tube filaments are made in a variety of forms of which some examples are shown in Fig. 6.2.   When alternating current heats a filament, the current variation during a cycle causes a filament temperature variation that may in turn cause an objectionable hum in a communication circuit.

FIG. 6.2 Typical vacuum-tube filaments.

In some tubes the electron emitter, a cathode, is not heated directly by current sent through it.   Instead the current is sent through a heater that is made of tungsten and coated with an insulating material.   The heater is surrounded by the cathode, a thin cylinder of sheet nickel coated with a material having a low work function.

6.2. Diodes.   A diode is a two-electrode tube in which one of the electrodes (the cathode) emits electrons and the other (the anode) collects

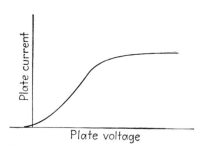

FIG. 6.3 Circuit for determining the characteristics of a high-vacuum diode.

FIG. 6.4 Relation between plate current and plate voltage for a diode operated with constant filament current.

electrons.   In the vacuum tube represented in Fig. 6.3 the filament is the cathode and the plate is the anode.   If the plate were connected externally to the filament, electrons would move from the filament to the plate in the tube.   The flow of electrons can be increased by making the plate positive with respect to the filament.   Here the potential of the plate with respect to the filament can be controlled with the voltage

divider.   With the filament current held constant, the relation between
the plate current as read on the ammeter A_P and the plate voltage as
read on the voltmeter V_P is shown in Fig. 6.4.   With zero plate voltage
some plate current flows.   To stop the flow of electrons to the plate, the
plate must be made negative with respect to the filament.   For low
positive values of plate voltage, the plate current increases more rapidly
than the first power of the plate voltage.   Beyond this region there is
another in which the current increases very little with a considerable
increase in the voltage.   Here the current has reached a saturation value
and most of the electrons emitted by
the filament reach the plate.

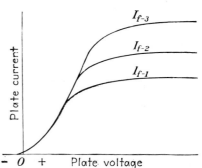

If the filament temperature is increased by increasing the filament
current, the rate at which electrons
can be emitted is increased and a
higher plate current can be produced
before saturation occurs.   The effects
of changes in the filament current
upon the plate-voltage–plate-current
characteristic are shown in Fig. 6.5.
For each filament current I_{f-1}, I_{f-2},
and I_{f-3} the saturation current is
different.

Fig.   6.5   Plate-voltage–plate-current
characteristics of a high-vacuum diode
for three values of filament current.

With a constant filament temperature, within the lower region of the
plate-voltage–plate-current characteristic the current increases about
as the three-halves power of the voltage.   In equational form

$$I_p = K_1 V_p^{3/2} \qquad (6.2)$$

where I_p is the plate current, K_1 is a proportionality constant, and V_p is
the plate voltage.   The statement represented by (6.2) is Child's law.
Since the plate current is not zero at zero plate voltage, (6.2) is not
exact for low values of plate voltage.

The saturation current of a diode depends upon the nature of the
cathode emitting surface as well as upon the cathode temperature.
Cathode temperatures are often expressed in degrees Kelvin (degrees K),
where degrees Kelvin equal 273 plus degrees centigrade.   The saturation
current density and the cathode temperature are related by Richardson's
equation,

$$S = A T^2 \epsilon^{-\varphi_0/kT} \qquad \text{amp per sq cm} \qquad (6.3)$$

an empirical equation that has been found to fit experimental curves
with fair accuracy.   Here A is a factor dependent on the cathode material, T is the temperature in degrees Kelvin, ϕ_0 is the work function in

volts of the cathode material, $k = 8.63 \times 10^{-5}$ electron volt per degree K (Boltzmann's constant), and ϵ is the base of natural logarithms.

How the saturation current density of a given surface increases with the temperature can be computed by (6.3). The first of two terms involving the temperature is T^2; hence doubling the temperature causes this term to quadruple. The second term is the exponential one. Here a small change in the temperature can make an enormous change in the value of the term.

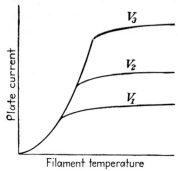

Fig. 6.6 Plate current in a high-vacuum diode as a function of filament temperature for different plate voltages.

Effects of filament temperature changes upon diode characteristics are shown in Fig. 6.6. For a plate voltage V_1, the plate voltage increases more rapidly than the first power of the temperature until a saturation point is reached. Beyond this point the current increases but little with further temperature increases. With higher plate voltages V_2 and V_3, saturation also occurs but at higher plate currents.

It is not possible to maintain all parts of a diode filament at the same temperature. For one thing, when plate current flows, the current is

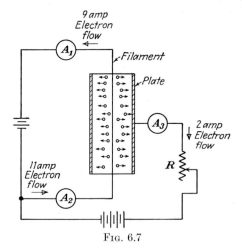

Fig. 6.7

not the same in all portions of a filament. Results obtained with one diode are shown in Fig. 6.7. With the plate circuit open, ammeters A_1 and A_2 had equal readings of 10 amp. Then the plate circuit was closed and the rheostat R so adjusted that a plate current of 2 amp was read

on ammeter A_3.   Then A_1 read 9 amp and A_2 read 11 amp.   The portion
of the filament nearest A_1 carried the least current.   The current increased
in some manner along the filament to a maximum in the portion nearest
A_2.   After a diode has started to conduct plate current, it may be that
current will continue even if the filament circuit is opened at a terminal.
If this occurs, the flow of plate current through part of the filament maintains a filament temperature sufficiently high to cause electron emission
to be maintained.   Such operation of a diode may damage the filament
and should be avoided.

6.3. Incremental and Differential Resistance.   For a diode having the
characteristic of Fig. 6.8, the resistance at a point P_1 can be represented

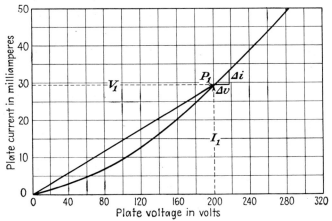

Fig. 6.8   Current-voltage characteristic of a diode.

graphically from a line from the origin to the point.   The slope of this
line is I_1/V_1, the reciprocal of the plate resistance of the diode for the
current I_1.   In certain applications of tubes, one is more interested in
the change of current produced by a given change of voltage than in the
current produced by a given voltage.   If the voltage increase Δv produces
the current increase Δi, then $\Delta v/\Delta i$ is the incremental resistance.   As the
voltage and current increments are made infinitesimally small, the ratio
becomes dv/di, the differential resistance.   Since di/dv is the slope of the
curve, then the differential resistance at any point on the curve is equal
to the reciprocal of the slope of the curve at the point.   If the equation
of the characteristic of a diode is known in terms of v and i, the differential
resistance at a point on the characteristic can be computed analytically.
In general, the characteristic is obtained by experiment.   From data
thus obtained the incremental resistance can be computed and used as
an approximate value for the differential resistance.

Most applications of the concept of differential resistance occur in applications of electronic tubes in which changes in the plate current are produced by a small alternating voltage superimposed on the continuous plate voltage. In Fig. 6.9 a battery, whose emf $E_b = 200$ v, is in series with a source whose sinusoidal emf e varies from $+20$ to -20 v. These emf sources are between the plate and the filament of a tube whose characteristic is in Fig. 6.8. At an instant when the alternating voltage is zero, the battery emf E_b acts alone to produce the plate current i_p. The point P_1 thus determined is the operating point on the characteristic. The operating point can be shifted to other positions by changing E_b. As the alternating emf increases with polarities such that it adds to E_b, the voltage from plate to filament increases and the plate current i_p increases as determined by the tube characteristic. The time variation of i_p can be determined graphically point by point as in Fig. 6.10. The maximum and minimum values of i_p can be determined from the characteristic without plotting

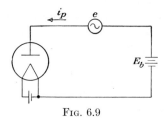

FIG. 6.9

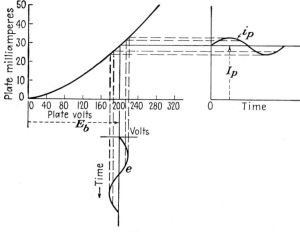

FIG. 6.10

the time variations. For example, maximum i_p will occur when the plate voltage is $200 + 20 = 220$ v. From the characteristic the corresponding plate current is 33 ma. Minimum i_p will occur when the plate voltage is $200 - 20 = 180$ v. From the characteristic the corresponding plate current is 24 ma. The 40-v change in the plate voltage produces a plate current change of

$$33 - 24 = 9 \text{ ma} = 0.009 \text{ amp}$$

The incremental resistance at the operating point is

$$\frac{40 \text{ v}}{0.009 \text{ amp}} = 4{,}400 \text{ ohms}$$

In Fig. 6.10 the maximum increase in the plate current above I_p will equal the maximum decrease below I_p only when the tube characteristic is linear over the given range of plate voltage variation. For some tube applications the operating point is made to occur on a nearly linear portion of the characteristic. Then the alternating component of the plate current will equal approximately the alternating component of the plate voltage divided by the incremental resistance at the operating point. In the previous paragraph it was determined that with 200-v d-c plate voltage the incremental resistance was 4,400 ohms. Then an alternating component of 5 v in the plate voltage would produce an alternating component of plate current of about 5 v/4,400 ohms = 0.0011 amp = 1.1 ma. Conversely, with the incremental resistance known, one can compute the alternating component of plate voltage required to produce a desired alternating component of plate current.

An important distinction between the behavior in a circuit of a non-linear resistor such as an electronic tube and that of a tungsten-filament lamp is that in the tube the voltage and current values as given by the characteristic occur almost instantaneously, while in the lamp there is a time lag after the application of a given voltage. To illustrate this point, the characteristic of a 100-w tungsten-filament lamp of Fig. 5.2 shows that at 50 v the current is 0.57 amp and that at 100 v the current is 0.83 amp. If the lamp voltage were suddenly increased from 50 to 100 v, the current would momentarily double to 1.14 amp, and then quickly decrease to 0.83 amp.

Some conducting elements, e.g., a carbon-arc lamp and a fluorescent lamp, have voltage-current characteristics such that an increase of current causes a decrease of voltage. Curve a in Fig. 6.11 is a characteristic of this type. When such an element is connected to an emf source, there is some resistance in the source and in the connecting leads. Assuming this resistance constant, the corresponding characteristic is the straight line b in Fig. 6.11. For the complete circuit the characteristic is curve c. It was obtained by adding the ordinates of the other two. Now let a voltage V_1 be applied to the circuit. There are two currents, I_1 and I_2, on the total characteristic that correspond to V_1. The current I_1 is an unstable value. A machine or circuit is stable if, following a disturbance and its disappearance, the original operating condition is resumed. A circuit is stable when operating at a point on the total characteristic where an increase of voltage is required to produce an increase of current. In Fig. 6.11 stable values occur only for current values to the right of the minimum point of curve *c*. In an arc, changes in the arc resistance are occurring constantly and the circuit will not remain long at an unstable operating point. In Fig. 6.11, I_2 is the stable operating current corresponding to the voltage V_1. For most applications of arcs, the point of stable operation fixed by the resistance of the leads and the source is at a current far beyond the value desired. To make the circuit stable at a smaller current, a ballast resistor is connected in series with the arc unit. In a fluorescent lamp drawing normal current from a d-c supply,

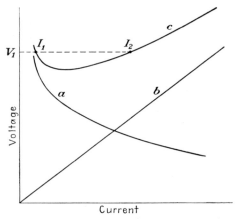

Fɪɢ. 6.11   Characteristics of a series circuit containing a nonlinear resistor such as a fluorescent lamp and a resistor of constant resistance. (*a*) Characteristic of the lamp, (*b*) characteristic of the resistor of constant resistance, and (*c*) characteristic of the entire circuit.

the ballast resistor voltage is about equal to the lamp voltage. The energy lost in the resistor is about equal to that delivered to the lamp, an undesirably high proportion.

When the voltage across an element decreases for an increase of current, the differential resistance is negative.

6.4. Rectification with Electronic Tubes. When the plate of a diode is made negative with respect to the filament, at low values of plate voltage electrons continue to flow from the filament to the plate. If the plate is made more negative, the electron flow can be stopped. If the plate is made still more negative, an electron flow from the plate to the filament can be produced. However, the plate is made of a material that does not readily emit electrons. The reverse flow of electrons is so small that it is usually assumed that the current is zero when the plate is negative with respect to the filament. There is a limit to the reverse voltage that a given tube can withstand. At some voltage the tube suddenly becomes a good conductor and an arc back occurs. The permissible reverse voltage that may be applied to the tube is the peak inverse voltage rating.

A diode can be used as a rectifier since a voltage of a given magnitude moves many electrons readily from the filament to the plate with one polarity and moves very few in the reverse direction when the polarity is reversed.

A typical diode rectifier circuit is in Fig. 6.12. Here one section of the transformer winding supplies current to heat the filament and another supplies voltage in the plate circuit. When alternating current heats a filament, the filament temperature varies during a cycle of current. This variation may be objectionable in a communication circuit but not in an application such as charging a battery. The circuit of Fig. 6.12 produces half-wave rectification. Diodes

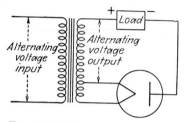

Fig. 6.12 Rectification with a diode.

are made that will supply as much as 1 amp at 100,000-v direct current.

For rectification in low-voltage circuits, a gas-filled tube may be used. Gases such as argon, mercury vapor, or neon are used with a pressure of the order of 10^{-3} mm of mercury. With gas in a tube the voltage drop from the plate to the cathode for a given current is much less than in the

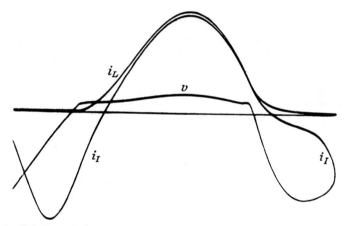

Fig. 6.13 Relations in an argon-filled diode rectifier. i_1 = input current to the transformer; i_L = load current; v = voltage from plate to filament.

same tube when highly evacuated. The voltage drop does not vary much with a considerable change in the current. As a result a gas-tube rectifier has better voltage regulation than it would if the voltage drop were proportional to the current.

In Fig. 6.13 are oscillograms of the transformer input current, the load current, and the voltage from plate to filament in an argon-filled tube in a circuit similar to Fig. 6.12.   Note how little the tube drop v varies as the tube current increases from zero to a maximum.

6.5. Detection or Demodulation.   The process of detection or demodulation is one of rectification, by which a low-frequency component or components can be strained out of a voltage wave containing both low- and high-frequency components.   An incoming radio signal voltage might contain components in the audio-frequency range (from 10 to 20,000 c)

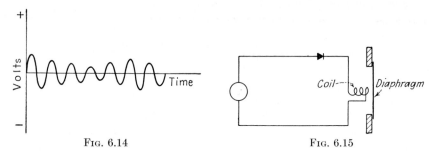

Fig. 6.14   Fig. 6.15

superimposed upon a single radio-frequency component of perhaps 2 Mc. The wave might have a form such as that of Fig. 6.14.   If a current of this wave form were sent through a loud-speaker, no audible response would occur.   The inertia of the speaker diaphragm is great enough that it would vibrate only slightly.   In the circuit of Fig. 6.15 a source of emf e is in series with a rectifier and a loud-speaker coil.   Assume that e varies as in Fig. 6.14 and that the rectifier permits no reverse current.   If only the circuit resistance is considered, the current will vary as in Fig. 6.16a.

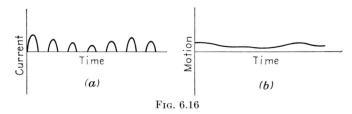

(a)   (b)

Fig. 6.16

If the pull on the diaphragm is proportional to the current, the pull will be pulsating.   Because of the inertia of the diaphragm, its movement does not correspond to the instantaneous current but will more nearly correspond to the average current.   The diaphragm motion will be about as in Fig. 6.16b and corresponds to the audio-frequency components in the original signal.

Crystal detectors offer more resistance to current in one direction than in the other.   The rectification obtained is imperfect, but the motion of the receiver diaphragm is sufficiently like the incoming signal variations to be satisfactory for many applications.

6.6. Triodes. In addition to a heated filament (or cathode) and a plate (or anode), a triode contains a third electrode that is placed between the others. This electrode is a latticework of small wires and is called a grid. The flow of electrons from the filament to the plate through the spaces between the grid wires is controlled by varying the potential of the grid with respect to the filament.

The action of the grid in controlling the plate current can be demonstrated by the circuit of Fig. 6.17. With the plate voltage as read on the voltmeter V_p kept constant, the plate current can be made zero by making the grid sufficiently negative with respect to the filament. If the grid voltage as read on the voltmeter V_g is made zero, there will be some plate current. If the grid voltage is increased with the grid positive with respect to the filament, the plate current is increased. A family of curves can be

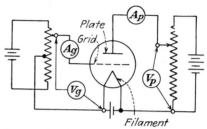

Fig. 6.17 Circuit for obtaining the characteristics of a triode.

obtained, each showing the grid voltage for a given plate voltage. A typical family of curves for a high-vacuum tube is shown in Fig. 6.18.

With the circuit of Fig. 6.17 it can be shown that the grid current as read on the ammeter A_g is usually negligible compared with the plate current when the grid is negative with respect to the filament.

In a triode, the change in grid voltage required to produce a given change in plate current with constant plate voltage is less than the change in plate voltage required to produce an equal change in plate current with constant grid voltage. This property is used to obtain amplification of a voltage.

6.7. Amplification with a Triode. For a triode with the characteristics of Fig. 6.18, with a constant grid voltage of -50 v, an increase in the plate voltage from 200 to 300 v increases the plate current from 5 to 90 ma. If the plate voltage were kept constant at 200 v, a change in grid voltage from -50 to -26 v would have varied the plate current through the same range. Hence a change of 24 v in the grid voltage produces the same change in the plate current as a change of 100 v in the plate voltage. The amplification factor of the triode at the given operating point is $100/24 = 4.2$. In equational form the amplification factor μ of a triode is

$$\mu = -\left.\frac{\Delta V_p}{\Delta V_g}\right|_{I_p = \text{constant}}$$

where ΔV_p is the plate-voltage change required to bring the plate current back to the value I_p that it had before the change ΔV_g in the grid voltage was made. The negative sign is used so that μ will be positive, since with a positive increase in plate voltage ΔV_p is positive and ΔV_g is negative to bring the plate current back to the original value.

The amplification factor of a given tube is not constant but depends upon the operating point on the characteristic. The factor is nearly

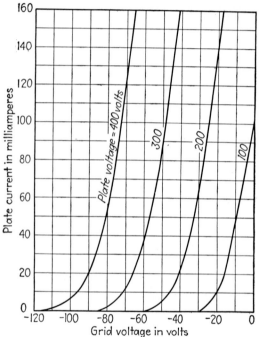

Fig. 6.18   Characteristic curves of a high-vacuum triode with constant filament current. (*Ken-Rad Corp.*)

constant when the tube is being operated on a portion of the characteristic that is nearly linear.

To amplify an emf e, it can be introduced in the grid circuit of a triode. A tube characteristic and an assumed time variation of e are in Fig. 6.19. The operating point P on the characteristic is fixed by the plate and the grid battery voltages. The manner in which e in the grid circuit produces an alternating component of current with a somewhat similar waveform is illustrated in Fig. 6.19. By keeping the grid negative with respect to the filament, very little current flows in the grid circuit and very little energy is drawn from the source that produces e. With a triode it is possible to measure a voltage while drawing a negligible current, a principle used in a vacuum-tube voltmeter.

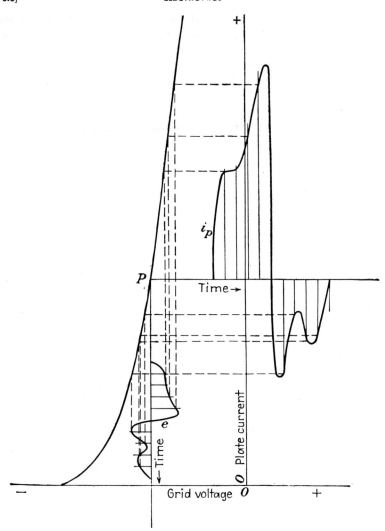

Fɪɢ. 6.19 Alternations in the plate current of a triode produced by an alternating emf introduced in the grid circuit.

6.8. Mercury-vapor Triodes. In a high-vacuum triode the plate current can be controlled by varying the grid voltage. In one type of mercury-vapor triode, the grid serves as a trigger and controls only the starting point of the plate current. With a given grid voltage, conduction of the plate current does not begin until the plate voltage reaches a certain critical value. After conduction starts, a change in the grid potential has little effect upon the magnitude of the plate current. The grid can regain control of the plate current (i.e., the trigger can be reset) only if the plate voltage is reduced to zero. The plate current must remain at zero for a short time (the deionization time) before the grid regains control. The deionization time of mercury-vapor triodes ranges from a few microseconds to about 1,000 μsec. Most tubes of this type are used in a-c circuits where the grid can regain control during the half cycle when the plate voltage is negative.

The value of plate voltage required to start conduction in a mercury-vapor triode depends upon the temperature of the condensed mercury as well as upon the value of the grid voltage. For example, in one such triode with a mercury temperature of 90 C, a plate voltage of 110 v was required to start conduction with a grid voltage of -2 v, and a plate voltage of 550 v was required with a grid voltage of -4 v. With a mercury temperature of 30 C, a plate voltage of 240 v was required to start conduction with a grid voltage of -2 v, and a plate voltage of 900 v was required with a grid voltage of -4 v.

For a mercury-vapor triode at constant temperature and with a given d-c voltage applied, plate current starts at a given point on the alternating plate-voltage wave and stops when the plate voltage becomes zero. The average plate current can be varied by varying the grid voltage. With an alternating grid voltage the plate current can be made to start at any point over most of the positive half cycle of the plate voltage. The average plate current can be varied by shifting the grid-voltage wave with respect to the plate-voltage wave.

6.9. Tetrodes. A tetrode, also called a screen-grid tube, contains a cathode and a plate as does a diode, a fine control grid closely surrounding

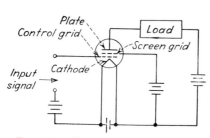

FIG. 6.20   Connections of a tetrode.

the cathode and serving the same functions as the grid in a triode, and a coarse screen grid surrounding the control grid. The plate surrounds the screen grid. A typical circuit in which a tetrode is used is shown in Fig. 6.20. The amplification factor of a given tube can be increased by making the grid of finer mesh and locating it nearer the cathode. However, an increase in the amplification factor means that for a given change in the control grid voltage a greater plate current is produced. This causes a greater voltage across the load and, with a fixed plate battery voltage, a lower voltage between the plate and the cathode. This reduction in voltage reduces the ability of the plate to attract electrons from the cathode. The screen grid is maintained at a nearly constant positive potential with respect to the cathode and causes an accelerating force on the electrons that is nearly independent of the voltage between the plate and the cathode. Some electrons are attracted to the screen grid, but usually of the order of perhaps 80 per cent of them acquire enough kinetic energy to carry them through the screen openings to the anode if it is always more positive with respect to the cathode than the screen grid is.

A tetrode has plate-current–control-grid characteristics that are nearly the same as if the screen grid and the plate were connected together and the tube tested as a triode. With this connection the plate current is of the order of four times the screen-grid current.

When a tetrode is operated with the screen grid at a fixed positive and the control grid at a fixed negative potential with respect to the cathode, the plate current increases very little as the positive potential of the plate with respect to the cathode is increased from a value equal to that of the screen grid to higher values. However, with fixed screen-grid and plate potentials, a small variation in the control-grid potential makes a large change in the plate current. For example, in a certain tetrode with the control grid potential at -2 v and the screen-grid potential at 100 v a change in the plate potential from 350 to 160 v reduced the plate current from 5.3 to 5 ma. With the screen-grid potential at 100 v and the plate potential at 350 v, a change in the control-grid potential from -2 to -2.15 v caused the plate current to change from 5.3 to 5 ma. Here the amplification factor was

$$\frac{-(350 - 160)}{-2 - (-2.15)} = 1,270$$

a much greater value than is obtained in a triode.

Assume that a tetrode is operated with the screen grid at a fixed positive and the control grid at a fixed negative potential with respect to the cathode. With the plate at the same potential as the cathode, the plate current is zero. As the plate potential is made positive, the plate current at first increases rapidly. Then there is a region in which the current decreases as the plate potential increases. Beyond this region the current increases at first rapidly and then at a decreasing rate with further increases in the plate potential. For example, in one tetrode the current increased from 0 to 4.6 ma as the potential was increased from 0 to 10 v, the current then decreased to 3.4 ma at a potential of 60 v, next it increased to 9 ma at a potential of 135 v, and finally increased further to 9.8 ma at a potential of 350 v.

The region in which a decreasing plate current is produced by an increasing plate potential is one of negative plate resistance. Tetrodes are sometimes operated in this region as a negative resistance device. The reduction in plate current occurs because of secondary electron emission. As an electron, a primary one, from the cathode strikes the plate with an appreciable velocity it may knock one or more electrons, secondary ones, out of the plate material and impart a velocity, usually low, to them. When the screen grid is more positive with respect to the cathode than the plate is, some of these electrons are attracted to the grid and thus reduce the net plate current.

6.10. Pentodes. In addition to the four electrodes of a tetrode, a pentode contains a suppressor grid that is a coarse-mesh grid located between the plate and the screen grid and is usually connected to the cathode. With the suppressor grid at cathode potential, both the screen grid and the plate can be positive with respect to it, even though the plate potential may be lower than that of the screen grid. As a result the voltage gradient that exists at the surface of the plate and that at the surface of the screen grid are such that secondary electron emission is prevented. As a result a dip in the plate-circuit–plate-voltage characteristic is prevented in the region where the plate potential is less than the screen-grid potential.

In a pentode the plate current is changed most by a given percentage change in the control-grid potential, a lesser amount by a corresponding change in the screen-grid potential, and very little by a corresponding change in the plate potential. The plate-current–control-grid characteristic has the same general shape as that of a triode.

6.11. Photoelectric Tubes. A photoelectric tube makes use of the principle that certain materials emit electrons when light strikes them. A simple form of the tube has two electrodes, one of which is a silver-coated cathode in the form of a half cylinder on which a thin layer of light-sensitive material is coated. The material chosen depends upon the radiation wavelength to which the tube is to have a good response. Cesium oxide has a fair sensitivity to wavelengths throughout the visible spectrum, but is most sensitive just above this spectrum in the infrared region. This material responds well to the infrared and red rays emitted by an incandescent filament lamp. A combination of cesium oxide and antimony can be made to have good sensitivity to near ultraviolet and blue light. Potassium and sodium are sensitive to ultraviolet light, but are not as satisfactory as the materials mentioned above.

The electron collector, or anode, may be a straight wire located on the cathode axis. Since the output current of a photoelectric tube is usually of the order of 10 μa or less, the leakage resistance between the electrodes should be high. To help achieve this, the leads to the electrodes are sometimes brought out at opposite ends of the tube.

The envelope of a photoelectric tube is made of special glass, the type chosen being such as to permit the ready passage of light rays in the spectrum to which the tube is to respond and to serve as a filter to prevent the passage of light rays outside this spectrum.

A photoelectric tube responds very quickly to the application, removal, or change in the magnitude of the illumination, less than 0.01 μsec being required for a new steady-state condition to be reached. The magnitude of the current produced in a given vacuum photoelectric tube is directly proportional to the intensity of the illumination applied and nearly independent of the magnitude of the anode potential, whenever the anode is at the same or a higher positive potential than the cathode. If the anode potential is made negative with respect to the cathode, for a given tube there is a value of potential at which the current becomes zero, regardless of what the illumination intensity may be.

Gas photoelectric tubes contain a small amount of an inert gas such as argon, helium, krypton, neon, and xenon at a pressure of the order of 0.2 mm of mercury. In such a tube, an electron emitted by the cathode may strike a gas molecule and separate it into a free electron and a positive gas ion. As the original electron and the freed electron progress further toward the plate they may strike other gas molecules and produce still other free electrons and positive gas ions. The ions moving toward the cathode represent a component of current nearly equal to that of the moving electrons, an effect that causes the net current to be nearly twice that represented by electron motion alone. Further current results because the impact of the ions on the cathode causes secondary electron emission there. The combination of the effects described make it possible for the current in a given tube to be of the order of ten times as great as it would have been without the gas.

In a given gas photoelectric tube operated at a given anode potential the anode current is nearly directly proportional to the illumination intensity just as in one of the vacuum type. However, the response of the two types to a change in the anode potential with a fixed illumination intensity is quite different. For example, in one typical vacuum tube with a light flux of 0.1 lumen an increase in anode potential from 30 to 240 v, a 700 per cent increase, caused an increase in the tube current from 4 to 4.5 μa, a 12.5 per cent increase. In a typical gas tube with an equal light flux an increase in the anode potential from 10 to 80 v, a 700 per cent increase, caused an increase in the tube current from 1.7 to 8.5 μa, a 400 per cent increase. Gas tubes are usually operated at less than one-half the voltage used with vacuum tubes.

A photoelectric tube is usually operated with a battery and a load resistor in series between the electrodes, the battery polarity being such that the anode is positive. The resistor resistance is of the order of 1 megohm or more. The power delivered to the resistor is insufficient to operate directly a relay or other similar device. The tube output is amplified by other types of electronic tubes to provide indirect control of the relay.

6.12. Transistors.* A transistor is a device that has certain properties similar to those of certain electronic tubes. A transistor requires no energy to heat a cathode and has a much longer life than a tube. Transistors utilize semiconductors, materials whose conductivities are less than those of metals but greater than those of insulating materials. Germanium and silicon are two semiconductor materials that are widely used.

An atom of germanium contains four valence electrons in its outer shell, electrons that can react with the electrons of neighboring atoms. When germanium solidifies, after having been melted, it assumes a crystalline structure with each atom equidistant from four neighboring atoms. Because of this structure each valence electron is shared with a different atom. A pair of electrons shared by two atoms forms a bond between the atoms, a bond that can be broken by the application of energy exceeding a critical value. Germanium requires 0.75 electron volt of energy, silicon 1.12.

In a germanium sample at normal room temperature, thermal energy causes random agitation of the electrons and may impart enough energy to one of the valence electrons to free it from the bond and cause it to move at random through the crystal structure. When a source of emf establishes an electric field in the material, the electrons acquire a drift motion toward the positive source terminal. This drift represents an electron current like that in a metal conductor.

When an electron is driven from its normal position in the bond between atoms, the position it has vacated is termed a hole. The hole has properties like those of an electron with a positive charge. In time, thermal agitation will bring an electron from an adjacent pair near enough to the hole that the bond between the pair will be broken and the electron moves into the hole. Now a new hole appears in the neighboring atom. Continuation of the above processes causes the hole to move about the material in a random manner. When a source of emf establishes an electric field in the material, the holes drift toward the negative source terminal. This creates a current flow that is in addition to that represented by the motion of the electrons.

In a given semiconductor material the random motion of a free electron usually continues for only a fraction of a second until it enters a hole and is again under bonds. When this recombination occurs, heat energy is released equal in amount to the energy originally expended in freeing the electron. The freeing of electrons and the recombination of electrons and holes is taking place continuously.

The drift conductivity of a pure semiconductor material depends upon

---

* This article is based upon material presented in "Electronic and Radio Engineering," 4th ed., pp. 733–798, Terman, and is used with the permission of the publisher, McGraw-Hill Book Company, Inc., New York, 1955.

the concentration of holes and electrons present. Germanium has a conductivity of 2.13 mho per m at 20 C.   About two-thirds of the current flow results from electron movement, the remainder from hole movement.

The concentrations of the electron and hole current carriers in a semiconductor material can be changed greatly by introducing a small amount of certain other materials, called impurities.

A common impurity used is one having five valence electrons in the outer shell of its atom, such as antimony, arsenic, and phosphorus.   An impurity atom is of about the same size as a germanium atom and can occupy a position normally occupied by one of the latter.   By keeping the number of impurity atoms small compared with the number of germanium atoms present, each impurity atom can be surrounded by germanium atoms.   Then bonds are established between four of the valence electrons of the impurity atom and one valence electron of each of the nearest germanium atoms.   Considerable energy is required to break these bonds.   The fifth valence electron can be removed from an impurity atom by only 0.01 electron volt of energy compared with 0.75 for a germanium atom.   The fifth electron, after being freed, moves about in the crystal either at random under thermal agitation or with a drift under the influence of an applied electric field.

The positively charged ion that remains after an impurity atom has lost an electron is rendered immobile by its bonds to the adjacent germanium atoms and does not contribute to the movement of electricity.

Semiconductors containing donors, impurity atoms that "donate" (under duress) electrons, are called n-type semiconductors because negative charges are supplied by the impurities.

A different type of semiconductor is produced by using an impurity having three valence electrons in the outer shell of its atom, such as aluminum, boron, gallium, and indium.   When an impurity atom is surrounded by germanium atoms, one electron of each of these forms a bond with one each of the impurity electrons.   The impurity atom needs one more electron to complete a bond with the fourth germanium atom and captures one that is driven near by thermal agitation.   Only 0.01 electron volt of energy is needed to make the capture.   After the impurity atom has established bonds with four neighboring germanium atoms, it is a negative ion bonded into the crystalline structure.   The removal of an electron from a nearby germanium atom leaves a hole that moves at random under the influence of thermal agitation, or with a drift under the influence of an applied electric field.

Semiconductors containing acceptors, impurity atoms that accept electrons, are called p-type semiconductors because the holes produced are equivalent to the movement of positive charges.

A junction diode transistor having the rectifying property of a diode

tube is produced by forming a junction of relatively large area between an
n-type material and a p-type material. The current flow is large when
the p-type material is made positive with respect to the n-type material.
Reversal of the polarity of the voltage causes a very small reverse current,
unless the voltage is increased to a magnitude that causes breakdown
similar to that which occurs in an insulating material.

A junction triode transistor having most of the properties of a triode
tube is produced by the sandwichlike arrangement of n-, p-, and n-type
(or p-, n-, and p-type) materials. One outer section is an emitter, the
other is a collector, while the center section is the base. In an n-p-n
transistor the emitter is made negative with respect to the base while
the collector is made positive with respect to it.

6.13. Piezoelectric Effect. This name is applied to the property that
certain crystals possess whereby the application of mechanical vibrations
between points on a certain axis cause an alternating emf to appear
between points on another axis. Conversely, the application of an
alternating voltage between points on one axis will cause the crystal to
vibrate. The vibration will be intense if the frequency of the voltage is
near a natural mechanical frequency of the crystal.

Rochelle salt, quartz, and tourmaline are natural crystal substances
that possess sufficient piezoelectric properties to be useful. Rochelle
salt possesses the strongest properties. It is used in loud-speakers and
in microphones. Quartz and tourmaline have vibration frequencies that
are less affected by changes in temperature than is that of a rochelle salt
and are used where little variation in frequency is permissible. Quartz
is more widely used than tourmaline because it is cheaper.

The vibration of a crystal is not one of simple harmonic motion.
Instead a given crystal may have different resonant frequencies. A
resonant frequency is one for which the amplitude of vibration is much
greater than it is for slightly greater or lower frequencies. Crystals have
resonant frequencies ranging from a few hundred cycles per second to
about one hundred megacycles per second.

PROBLEMS

6.1. At what velocity is the mass of an electron twice as great as it is at rest?

6.2. Through what difference of potential must an electron move in order that its
velocity will increase from zero to 0.1 that of light?

6.3. What velocity is acquired by an electron as it moves from rest through a
potential of 1,000 v?

6.4. A Pliotron tube is said to be able to measure a current of 10^{-17} amp. Express
this current in electrons per second.

6.5. Air at standard atmospheric temperature, humidity, and pressure ionizes and
becomes a conductor at a voltage gradient of about 3,000 kv per m. If an electron
velocity of 2×10^6 m per sec is required to produce ionization in air, how far must an

electron travel in a uniform electric field with the above gradient to acquire this velocity? (This distance is the mean free path of the electron.)

6.6. The ionization potential of a gas is that through which an electron starting from rest must pass to acquire a velocity sufficient to ionize a neutral molecule of the gas. Argon has an ionization potential of about 15 v. Compute the minimum velocity which an electron can possess and ionize an argon molecule. Compute the energy required to ionize the molecule.

6.7. A certain diode had a plate current of 30 μa with 70-v plate voltage and 40 μa with 83 v plate voltage. Compute the d-c resistance of the plate circuit for each of these currents. Compute the a-c resistance of the plate circuit for the region on the tube characteristic between the two current values.

6.8. A certain diode has a plate current of 2.8 ma with 200 v plate voltage. Assuming that the characteristic follows the three-halves power law, compute (a) the plate current that would be produced by 400 v plate voltage; (b) the a-c resistance of the plate circuit at 400 v plate voltage.

6.9. A certain argon-filled diode is connected as in Fig. 6.12 to charge a battery that has an emf of 6.3 v and an internal resistance of 0.12 ohm. Assume that the tube drop is constant at 9 v during the conducting period. Determine the maximum transformer voltage required to produce a maximum charging current of 15 amp.

6.10. From the oscillogram of Fig. 6.13 determine the ratio of the maximum inverse voltage to the maximum voltage drop during the conducting period.

6.11. A triode with the characteristics of Fig. 6.18 is operated with 200 v plate voltage and −30 v grid voltage. For this operating point determine the alternating component of plate current produced by an alternating voltage of 5 v maximum in the grid circuit.

6.12. A triode with the characteristics of Fig. 6.18 is operated with 300 v plate voltage and −45 v grid voltage. A resistive load is in series with the plate battery.

a. Determine the load resistance for which the load voltage is 120 v.

b. With a load resistance as computed in *a*, how much grid voltage is required to cause the load voltage to be 240 v?

6.13. A certain triode had 20 ma plate current with 120 v plate voltage and −5 v grid voltage. When the grid voltage was changed to −4 v, the plate current increased to 25 ma. To bring the plate current back to the original value, it was necessary to reduce the plate voltage to 115 v. Compute the amplification factor at the given operating point.

6.14. The deionization time of a certain mercury-vapor tube is 800 μsec. What is the highest frequency of alternating plate voltage that may be used if the grid is to regain control during each cycle?

CHAPTER 7

MAGNETIC CIRCUITS

7.1. Magnetism. Iron filings sprinkled on a sheet of cardboard over a magnet are arranged in distinct lines extending from one magnet pole to the other. The term *lines of flux* describes the lines of flow in the invisible medium pictured as extending from one pole to the other. If iron filings are sprinkled on a horizontal sheet of cardboard through which a round conductor passes vertically, establishment of current in the conductor causes the filings to become arranged in a circular path about the conductor. From the concept of lines of flux certain computations of magnetic effects are analogous to those for electric circuits.

FIG. 7.1 Positions assumed by a pivoted magnetic needle when placed at various points near a current-carrying conductor.

Magnetic flux is produced by electric charges in motion. The lines produced by a given current constitute the magnetic field produced by the current. At a point in a magnetic field the direction of the field is that of the flux through the point. The direction of the flux is taken arbitrarily as the direction in which the north pole of a magnetic compass would be urged if placed at the point. Such a compass may be used to determine the direction of the flux at various points in space near a current-carrying conductor. In Fig. 7.1 is represented a conductor that is normal to the plane of the paper and is carrying current into the paper. Positions that will be taken by a compass at various points near the conductor are shown. In each case the compass position is such that its length is perpendicular to the line from its center to that of the conductor. This shows that the flux lines about a circular current-carrying conductor are circles. The relation between the flux direction and the current direction is given by a "right-hand" rule. *Grasp a current-carrying conductor by the right hand with the thumb extended parallel to the direction of the current. Then the fingers encircle the conductor in the direction of the flux.*

When the magnetic relations in a definite volume of space are being considered, that region may be called a magnetic circuit or a branch of one. Since there is no material in which magnetic flux may not exist, any magnetic circuit is an element of volume in a magnetic field.

Magnetically, materials are classified as either paramagnetic or diamagnetic. If a sample of a paramagnetic material is placed in a magnetic field, it will be attracted toward the most dense part of that field. All diamagnetic and most paramagnetic materials are designated usually as nonmagnetic since the force exerted on a given sample is so small that it can be detected only by a sensitive measuring device.

In an atom the free electrons revolve about the nucleus. At the same time each electron is spinning about an axis through it. The magnetic properties of a given atom depend upon the number of electrons involved and the locations of the respective orbits. A magnetic field equivalent to that of a tiny magnet is produced by every moving electron. In an atom of some materials the magnetic effects of some electrons are balanced by those of others and no resultant magnetic effect appears externally. In an atom of other materials an external magnetic effect appears. However, in a group of the atoms the individual magnetic effects are so located with respect to each other that they neutralize each other and no magnetic effects appear external to the group. If an external magnetic field is applied to the group, the normal orbits of the electrons and their rates of spin will be changed.

A magnetic dipole, similar to a tiny bar magnet, is formed by any atom that shows external magnetic effects. When a substance containing such atoms is subjected to an external magnetic field, a torque is exerted on each atom tending to align its magnetic field with the external one. At the same time thermal agitation of the atoms is tending to keep them in disalignment.

In a paramagnetic substance such as aluminum, each atom is a dipole but the forces tending to cause alignment with an external magnetic field are very weak compared with the forces resulting from thermal action. As a result the flux in a given sample is only of the order of 0.1 per cent greater than if complete disalignment existed.

In a diamagnetic substance such as copper, each atom has no external magnetic effect. Establishment by an external source of a magnetic field through such an atom, through the medium of induced emf, causes a change in the electron velocity and orbit such as to produce a magnetic action opposed to that of the external source. As a result the flux in a given sample is of the order of 0.01 per cent, or less, smaller than it would be in the same region if the substance were replaced by a vacuum.

A few paramagnetic materials possess greatly different magnetic properties than the others. They are cobalt, iron, nickel, their alloys and compounds, and certain alloys containing manganese. They are called magnetic materials. The iron atom has four more electrons spinning in one direction than in the other. Individual iron atoms react strongly on each other to tend to align adjacent atoms so that the magnetic effects aid. If this tendency existed uniformly throughout any sample, that sample would in a normal state be highly magnetized. However, it happens that each sample is divided into extremely small regions or domains in which this high degree of magnetization does occur. The domains can be arranged in an infinite variety of positions with respect to each other. In what is called a demagnetized sample of iron, the arrangement is such that the magnetic effects are zero external to the sample. A domain contains of the order of 10^{15} atoms. An iron crystal is a cube lattice about 3×10^{-8} cm on each side with an atom at the center and at each corner. Each domain contains crystals that are highly magnetized along one of the cube edges.

When a weak external magnetic field is applied to a demagnetized iron sample, those domains that are magnetized parallel to or at a small angle with the field grow in size by transferring to themselves crystals from neighboring domains.

With further increases in the field strength, sudden shifts, in an interval of the order of 100 μsec, in the direction of the magnetization from one cube edge to another occur in domains that were magnetized at a large angle to the direction of the field. The magnetization shifts to an edge parallel to and in the direction of the field. This sudden shift is known as the Barkhausen effect. The strength of the field required to cause the shift depends upon what impurities are present and whether internal stresses occur. A reduction in the amount of impurities and in the internal stresses reduces the field strength required to cause the magnetization shifts.

With still further increases in the external field strength, a condition is reached where the shift in the direction of magnetization occurs slowly and not suddenly. Then considerable increase in the field strength causes little increase in the number of magnetic lines in the material, which is said to be approaching saturation.

7.2. Development of Magnetic Circuit Relations. In Fig. 7.2 is represented a portion of a long, straight conductor that is carrying I amp. The region of space about the conductor that is enclosed between the cylinders of length l m whose respective radii are r_1 and r_2 m constitutes a magnetic circuit. In this region magnetic flux is produced by the current in the conductor. With air surrounding the conductor the value of the flux is directly proportional to the instantaneous current. If the current is alternating, the flux is zero when the current is zero and the flux is a maximum when the current is a maximum. When the current reverses in direction, the flux reverses in direction.

The current in Fig. 7.2 is said to produce a magnetomotive force (mmf). The value of the mmf acting on a magnetic circuit that encircles a current-carrying conductor is proportional to the value of the current encircled. If N turns of wire carrying I amp were wrapped in a coil, a

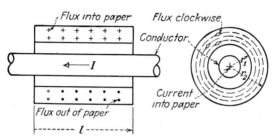

FIG. 7.2   A magnetic circuit surrounding a current-carrying conductor. The circuit consists of the portion of space between two cylinders of length l and respective radii of r_1 and r_2.

closed path that passes once through the coil encircles NI amp. The product of amperes and turns, called ampere-turns, is taken as the unit of mmf in the mks system.

The weber (wb) is the mks unit of flux. For most practical applications the amount of flux involved is small enough that the microweber (μwb) is a more convenient size of unit to use than the weber. Early magnetic computations were made using the cgs system in which the line (also called the maxwell) was the unit of flux. There are 10^8 lines in 1 wb. Since $10^6\ \mu$wb $= 1$ wb, then $1\ \mu$wb $= 100$ lines.

In Fig. 7.3 is represented a steel bar about which is wrapped a current-carrying coil. That the flux is directed upward within the turns can be determined by the right-hand rule previously stated. Another version of the rule is: *Grasp the core with the right hand with the fingers coiled about it in the direction of the current and the thumb extended parallel to it. Then the thumb points parallel to the direction of the flux in the core.* Here the flux passes upward through the bar and returns downward in the air about the turns. The bar is then said to be an electromagnet. The flux leaves the bar at the north pole (N) and enters it at the south pole (S).

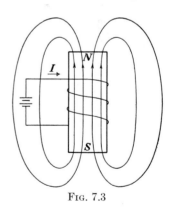

FIG. 7.3

7.3. Reluctance. The ratio of the value of the mmf applied to a magnetic circuit to the value of the flux produced is called the reluctance $\Re$ of the circuit. In the mks system the unit of reluctance is the ampere-turn per weber. The reluctance of a circuit depends upon its length, its cross section, and the material of which it is composed. In addition for certain materials the reluctance is a function of the value of the flux. For a magnetic circuit in homogeneous material in which the cross section A sq m is uniform throughout a length l m the reluctance is

$$\Re = \frac{l}{\mu\mu_v A} \qquad \text{amp-turns per wb} \qquad (7.1)$$

where μ is the permeability of the material and $\mu_v = 4\pi \times 10^{-7}$ (approximately 1.25×10^{-6}) is the space permeability of a vacuum. Comparison of (7.1) with the expression $R = \rho l/A$ for resistance shows that reluctance in a magnetic circuit is analogous to resistance in an electric circuit. The terms $\mu\mu_v$ in (7.1) correspond to $1/\rho$ in the expression for resistance. Since conductivity is the reciprocal of resistivity, the terms $\mu\mu_v$ are a measure of what is inaccurately called magnetic conductivity. The inaccuracy results because there is no conduction of anything physical in a magnetic circuit. Two terms, μ and μ_v, are used in (7.1) because so many materials have about the same magnetic properties as free space that it is convenient to use the properties of free space as a reference. Similar relations might have been used for resistance if the resistivities of other materials were to be compared with that of copper. If this were done, the expression for resistance could be written as $R = \rho\rho_c l/A$, where, at 20 C, ρ_c would be 10.37 ohm-cir mils per ft and ρ would be 1 for copper. For a material with a resistivity twice that of copper, ρ would be 2, etc.

A vacuum has been arbitrarily assigned a permeability of unity. For most engineering computations, the permeability of air is also taken as unity, since only precise measurements can detect a difference between the permeability of air and that of a vacuum. Only a few materials, iron, cobalt, nickel, and certain alloys have permeabilities that may exceed greatly that of air. These are called "magnetic materials" to distinguish them from the "nonmagnetic materials" that have a permeability near unity.

Reluctances in a magnetic circuit are combined in the same manner as resistances are combined in an electric circuit. *When two, or more, magnetic elements are in series, the equivalent reluctance is equal to the sum of the individual reluctances. When two or more magnetic elements are in parallel, the equivalent reluctance is equal to the reciprocal of the sum of the reciprocals of the individual reluctances.*

The reluctance of the magnetic circuit of Fig. 7.2 cannot be computed directly by (7.1) because the length of the paths followed by the flux lines varies from $2\pi r_1$ at the inner surface to $2\pi r_2$ at the outer surface. If the length is used as that midway between the surfaces and this average length denoted as l_a, then $l_a = 2\pi(r_1 + r_2)/2 = \pi(r_1 + r_2)$ m. The area normal to the flux is $l(r_2 - r_1)$ sq m. Now by (7.1) an approximate expression for the reluctance is

$$\mathcal{R} = \frac{l_a}{\mu\mu_v A} = \frac{\pi(r_1 + r_2)}{1 \times (4\pi \times 10^{-7}) \times [l(r_2 - r_1)]}$$
$$= \frac{2.5 \times 10^6(r_1 + r_2)}{l\,(r_2 - r_1)} \qquad \text{amp-turns per wb} \qquad (7.2)$$

7.4. Permeance. The permeance $\mathcal{P}$ of a magnetic element is the reciprocal of the reluctance of the element, or $\mathcal{P} = \mu\mu_v A/l$ wb per amp-turn, where μ, μ_v, A, and l are as in (7.1). Permeances in a magnetic circuit are combined in the same manner as conductances are combined in an electric circuit. *The equivalent permeance of two, or more, magnetic elements in parallel is equal to the sum of the permeances of the individual elements.* The equivalent reluctance of the combination is equal to the reciprocal of the equivalent permeance.

An exact expression for the permeance of the magnetic circuit of Fig. 7.2 can be derived by the use of calculus. Consider two concentric cylindrical surfaces of length l m and respective radii of r and $r + dr$ m. Here dr is an infinitesimal. The area between the surfaces normal to the flux is an infinitesimal $l\,dr$ sq m. The length of the magnetic circuit in the direction of the flux is $2\pi r$ m. The permeance of the magnetic circuit between the surfaces is an infinitesimal $d\mathcal{P}$, where

$$d\mathcal{P} = \frac{\mu\mu_v(l\,dr)}{2\pi r}$$

The permeance $\mathcal{P}$ of the entire magnetic circuit is obtained by integrating with limits on r of r_1 and r_2. Hence

$$\mathcal{P} = \frac{\mu\mu_v l}{2\pi} \int_{r_1}^{r_2} \frac{dr}{r} = \frac{\mu\mu_v l}{2\pi} \left[\ln r \right]_{r_1}^{r_2} = \frac{\mu\mu_v l}{2\pi} \ln \frac{r_2}{r_1}$$

The exact expression for the reluctance $\mathcal{R}$ of the magnetic circuit is

$$\mathcal{R} = \frac{1}{\mathcal{P}} = \frac{2\pi}{\mu\mu_v l \ln (r_2/r_1)} = \frac{2\pi}{1 \times (4\pi \times 10^{-7})l \ln (r_2/r_1)}$$
$$= \frac{5 \times 10^6}{l \ln (r_2/r_1)} \qquad \text{amp-turns per wb} \qquad (7.3)$$

The amount by which the approximate value of the reluctance of a given magnetic circuit as computed from (7.2), differs from the exact value depends upon the relative values of r_1 and r_2. If $r_2 - r_1$ is small compared with r_1, the error will be small.

Example 1. In Fig. 7.2, $r_2 = 1.2r_1$. Compute the reluctance of the magnetic circuit by (7.2) and also by (7.3), and determine the percentage error in the first value.

Solution. By (7.2),

$$\mathcal{R} = 2.5 \times 10^6 \frac{r_1 + 1.2r_1}{l(1.2r_1 - r_1)} = \frac{2.75 \times 10^7}{l} \text{ amp turns per wb}$$

By (7.3),

$$\mathcal{R} = \frac{5 \times 10^6}{l \ln (1.2r_1/r_1)} = \frac{5 \times 10^6}{l(0.1823)} = 2.743 \times \frac{10^7}{l} \text{ amp turns per wb}$$

The error in the previous value is $(2.75 - 2.743) \times 100/2.743 = 0.26$ per cent.

Equation (7.1) is useful for computations for a magnetic circuit in which the permeability, and hence the reluctance, is constant. However, iron does not have a constant permeability, and it is the material most often used in magnetic circuits because it is the cheapest material with a high permeability. The permeability of a given sample of iron varies as the flux in the sample varies but not in a direct proportion. A circuit containing a material whose permeability varies with the value of the flux is usually analyzed by the use of a curve showing the magnetic properties of the material rather than by a direct application of (7.1).

The difference of magnetic potential required to force a flux through the reluctance of all or any portion of a magnetic circuit is called a reluctance drop and is expressed in ampere-turns.

The magnetic relations that correspond to Kirchhoff's laws for the electric circuit are: (1) *The sum of the fluxes coming toward a junction in a magnetic circuit is equal to the sum of the fluxes leaving the junction.* (2) *Around any closed magnetic path the algebraic sum of the mmfs is equal to the algebraic sum of the reluctance drops.*

Example 1. In Fig. 7.2, $I = 20$ amp, $l = 2$ m, $r_1 = 0.01$ m, and $r_2 = 0.02$ m. Compute the flux in the magnetic circuit.

Solution. By (7.3), the reluctance of the circuit is

$$\mathcal{R} = \frac{5 \times 10^6}{l \ln (r_2/r_1)} = \frac{5 \times 10^6}{2 \times \ln (0.02/0.01)} = \frac{5 \times 10^6}{2 \times 0.693}$$
$$= 3.6 \times 10^6 \qquad \text{amp-turns per wb}$$

The mmf acting on the circuit is 20 amp-turns, corresponding to the encircled current of 20 amp. Then the flux is

$$\Phi = \frac{\text{mmf}}{\mathcal{R}} = \frac{20 \text{ amp-turns}}{3.6 \times 10^6 \text{ amp-turns per wb}} = 5.56 \times 10^{-6} \text{ wb} = 5.56 \ \mu\text{wb}$$

Example 2. A flux of 800 μwb may be assumed to be distributed uniformly over a cross section of 2.5×10^{-3} sq m in an air gap 1.25×10^{-3} m long in a magnetic circuit. Compute the reluctance of the gap and the reluctance drop across the gap.

Solution. By (7.1) the reluctance of the gap is

$$\mathcal{R} = \frac{l}{\mu\mu_v A} = \frac{1.25 \times 10^{-3}}{1(4\pi \times 10^{-7})2.5 \times 10^{-3}} = 3.98 \times 10^5 \text{ amp-turns per wb}$$

The reluctance drop is

$$\Phi\mathcal{R} = \left(800 \ \mu\text{wb} \times \frac{1 \text{ wb}}{10^6 \ \mu\text{wb}}\right)(3.98 \times 10^5 \text{ amp-turns per wb}) = 318 \text{ amp-turns.}$$

Example 3. In a certain cast-steel magnetic circuit the flux is distributed uniformly over a cross section of 1.2 sq in. throughout the length of 8 in. For a flux of 480 μwb, the reluctance drop is 105 amp-turns. For a flux of 960 μwb, the reluctance drop is 320 amp-turns. Compute the permeability of the steel for each value of flux.

Solution. The length $l = 8$ in. $\times 1$ m/39.37 in. $= 0.203$ m. The area $A = 1.2$ sq in. $\times 1$ sq m/(39.37)^2 sq in. $= 7.75 \times 10^{-4}$ sq m. The reluctance $\mathcal{R} = l/(\mu\mu_v A) = 0.203/(\mu \times 4\pi \times 10^{-7} \times 7.75 \times 10^{-4}) = 2.08 \times 10^8/\mu$ amp-turns per wb. The flux $\Phi = 480 \ \mu$wb $\times 1$ wb/$10^6 \ \mu$wb $= 4.8 \times 10^{-4}$ wb. Then, since reluctance drop $=$ flux $\times$ reluctance,

$$105 \text{ amp-turns} = 4.8 \times 10^{-4} \text{ wb} \times \frac{2.08 \times 10^8}{\mu} \text{ amp-turns per wb}$$

From this $\mu = (4.8 \times 10^{-4}) \times (2.08 \times 10^8)/105 = 950$ for a flux of 480 μwb.

The permeability for a flux of 960 μwb could be computed in a manner similar to that used above. However, the computation can also be made by the use of proportions. Since 960 is twice 480, if the permeability had been the same for both flux values the reluctance drop in the second case would have been twice that in the first case, or $2 \times 105 = 210$ amp-turns. Since the reluctance drop was 320 amp-turns, the permeability must have decreased in the ratio of 210 to 320. Hence the permeability corresponding to a flux of 960 μwb was

$$\frac{210}{320} \ 950 = 623$$

7.5. Magnetic Potential Gradient. In the toroid of Fig. 7.4 the mmf of the coil is distributed uniformly along the length of the magnetic circuit. The reluctance drop is also distributed uniformly along the circuit. Here the magnetic potential gradient, the reluctance drop per unit length, can be computed by dividing the total reluctance drop by the length of the circuit. The length of the flux path varies from $2\pi r_1$ at the inner surface to $2\pi r_2$ at the outer surface. Consequently, the magnetic potential gradient also varies from the inner surface to the outer one. If r_1 and r_2 are large compared with their difference, $r_2 - r_1$, in many cases it is sufficiently accurate to use the average radius r in computing an average magnetic potential gradient in the circuit.

Magnetic potential gradient is designated by the symbol H and is analogous to voltage gradient in the electric circuit. When the mmf applied to a magnetic circuit varies with time, the magnetic potential gradient in the circuit also varies with time. The symbol H is in common use to represent either a constant gradient or one that varies with time. In the special case where the reluctance drop is distributed uniformly along the length l of a circuit, the gradient H is

$$H = \frac{\text{reluctance drop}}{l}$$

In the toroid of Fig. 7.4 the reluctance drop is equal to the mmf of the coil and the average length of the circuit is $2\pi r$. In mks units the reluctance drop is NI amp-turns; hence

$$H = \frac{NI \text{ amp-turns}}{2\pi r \text{ m}}$$

$$= \frac{NI}{2\pi r} \text{ amp-turns per m}$$

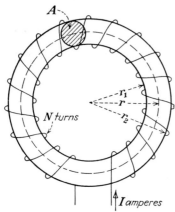

FIG. 7.4 A toroid magnetic circuit.

where r is in meters.

When the reluctance drop is distributed uniformly along a magnetic circuit, the drop is equal to the magnetic potential gradient H in ampere-turns per meter multiplied by the length l m, or

$$\text{Reluctance drop} = Hl \qquad \text{amp-turns}$$

Example 1. In a certain magnetic circuit a reluctance drop of 500 amp-turns is distributed uniformly along a length of 20 in. Compute the magnetic potential gradient in the circuit.

Solution.

$$H = \frac{\text{reluctance drop}}{\text{length}} = \frac{500 \text{ amp-turns}}{20 \text{ in.} \times 1 \text{ m}/39.37 \text{ in.}} = 984 \text{ amp-turns per m}$$

7.6. Flux Density. If the flux is distributed uniformly over the cross section of a magnetic conductor, the flux density is equal to the flux divided by the area. The symbol B is generally used to denote a flux density that may be either constant or a function of time. Hence

$$B = \frac{\text{flux}}{\text{area}} = \frac{\Phi}{A} \qquad \text{wb per sq m}$$

where Φ is the flux in webers and A is the area in square meters.

For magnetic conductors in general, the flux is not necessarily distributed uniformly over a cross section and the flux density may vary from point to point. At a point the flux density is

$$B = \frac{d\Phi}{dA} \qquad \text{wb per sq m}$$

where $d\Phi$ wb is the infinitesimal amount of flux normal to and distributed over an infinitesimal area dA sq m. For many types of magnetic circuits, computations that yield approximate results are based on an average flux density obtained by dividing the total flux by the area.

7.7. Relations between Magnetic Potential Gradient and Flux Density. Since reluctance drop $= \Phi \mathcal{R}$ and $\mathcal{R} = l/\mu\mu_v A$, then

$$\text{Reluctance drop} = \frac{\Phi l}{\mu\mu_v A} \qquad \text{amp-turns}$$

Rearranging,

$$\mu \frac{\text{reluctance drop}}{l} = \frac{1}{\mu_v} \frac{\Phi}{A}$$

But reluctance drop$/l = H$, $1/\mu_v = 1/(4\pi \times 10^{-7}) = 7.96 \times 10^5$, and $\Phi/A = B$. Hence $\mu H = 7.96 \times 10^5 B$, or

$$B = 4\pi \times 10^{-7}\, \mu H \qquad (7.4)$$

where μ is the permeability of the material in a magnetic element, H is

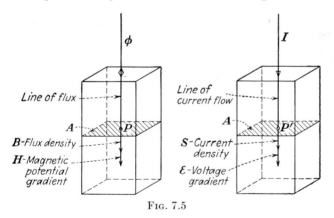

Fig. 7.5

the magnetic potential gradient in ampere-turns per meter, and B is the flux density in webers per square meter.

In Fig. 7.5 relations in a magnetic circuit are compared with those in an electric conductor. In the electric conductor the current density at the point P' is represented by the vector **S** that is directed along the line of current flow through the point. The magnitude of the vector is I/A, where I is the total current distributed uniformly over the area A. The voltage gradient vector $\mathbf{\varepsilon}$ at P' is collinear with $\mathbf{S}$.

In the magnetic element the flux density at the point P is represented by the vector $\mathbf{B}$ that is collinear with the line of flux through the point. The magnitude of this vector is Φ/A, where Φ is the total flux distributed uniformly over the area A. The magnetic potential gradient vector $\mathbf{H}$ at P is collinear with $\mathbf{B}$. The relation between the magnitudes of the $\mathbf{B}$ and $\mathbf{H}$ vectors depends upon the permeability of the material as expressed by (7.4).

Example 1. In Fig. 7.6 is represented a wooden toroid core on which are wound 125 closely spaced turns carrying a current of 12 amp. Compute the flux in the core.

Solution. In mks units the coil mmf is 12 amp $\times$ 125 turns = 1,500 amp-turns. This is also the reluctance drop in the core. At the inner periphery of the core this drop is distributed along the circumference there of 2π in., while at the outer periphery the drop is distributed along a circumference of 3π in. Hence the magnetic potential gradient is not the same at all points in the core.

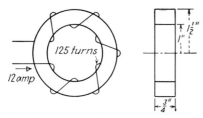

FIG. 7.6 A toroid with rectangular cross section.

Solve the problem first by an approximate method. Take the average length of the flux path as 2.5π in., which is 0.2 m. The magnetic potential gradient along this path is $H = 1,500$ amp-turns/0.2 m = 7,500 amp-turns per m. The core is nonmagnetic and its permeability μ is 1. Hence, by (7.4), the flux density B is

$$B = 4\pi \times 10^{-7} \times 1 \times 7,500 \text{ amp-turns per m} = 9.42 \times 10^{-3} \text{ wb per sq m}$$

The core area is $\frac{3}{4}$ in. $\times$ $\frac{1}{2}$ in. $\times$ 1 sq m/39.37^2 sq in. = 2.42×10^{-4} sq m. The flux Φ in the core is

$$\Phi = BA = 9.42 \times 10^{-3} \text{ wb per sq m} \times 2.42 \times 10^{-4} \text{ sq m} = 2.29 \times 10^{-6} \text{ wb}$$
$$= 2.29 \ \mu\text{wb}$$

With the exciting turns closely spaced, almost all the flux produced will be confined to the core. Assuming that all the flux is confined to the core, the value of the flux can be computed by calculus. Think of two cylindrical surfaces within the toroid, each $\frac{3}{4}$ in. long, one with a radius r and the other with a radius $r + dr$ m. Here dr is an infinitesimal. The magnetic potential gradient tangent to the inner surface is $H = 12$ amp $\times$ 125 turns/$2\pi r$ = $750/\pi r$ amp-turns per m. Since the core has a permeability of 1, the flux density tangent to the inner surface is $B = \mu\mu_v H = 1 \times 4\pi \times 10^{-7} \times (750/\pi r) = 3 \times 10^{-4}/r$ wb per sq m. The flux between the cylindrical surfaces is an infinitesimal $d\Phi$ and is normal to an infinitesimal area dA, where

$$dA = \frac{3}{4} \text{ in.} \times \frac{1 \text{ m}}{39.37 \text{ in.}} \times dr \text{ m} = 0.019 \ dr \text{ sq m}$$

Then $d\Phi = B\,dA = (3 \times 10^{-4}/r) \times 0.019\,dr = 5.7 \times 10^{-6}\,dr/r$ wb. The total flux Φ in the core is obtained by integrating $d\Phi$ between the limits r_1 m, the inner radius of the core, and r_2 m, the outer radius of the core. Then

$$\Phi = 5.7 \times 10^{-6} \int_{r_1}^{r_2} \frac{dr}{r} = 5.7 \times 10^{-6}[\ln r]_{r_1}^{r_2} = 5.7 \times 10^{-6} \ln \frac{r_2}{r_1}$$

Since the ratio r_2/r_1 is equal to 1.5 in./1 in., then

$$\Phi = 5.7 \times 10^{-6} \ln 1.5 = 5.7 \times 10^{-6} \times 0.406 = 2.31 \times 10^{-6} \text{ wb}$$

Note that the approximate value obtained above using an average length differs from this more accurate value by less than 1 per cent.

The reluctance drop over a path of length l m is Hl amp-turns, if the magnetic potential gradient $\mathbf{H}$ is directed along the path and has a constant magnitude of H amp-turns per m at any point in the path. The reluctance drop is $Hl \cos \theta$ if the gradient makes a constant angle θ radians with the path and has a constant magnitude of H amp-turns per m at any point in the path. The reluctance drop is $\int_0^l H \cos \theta\,dl$ if the magnitude and/or the direction of the gradient vary along the path. To evaluate the integral analytically, it is necessary that the equation that relates H to l and the one that relates θ to l be known.

An extension of the above principle leads to Ampère's circuital law which states that the result of integration over a closed curve is equal to the net current in amperes passing through the area bounded by the curve. The net current is the algebraic sum of the individual currents in any number of conductors passing through the area, a current in one direction being assigned a positive sign and one in the opposite direction being assigned a negative sign.

7.8. Air Gaps. In many magnetic circuits an air gap is necessary in order that a desired magnetic effect can be obtained. Even where a closed metal path is desirable, an air gap is often present so that the exciting coils can be form-wound and then slipped over the magnetic circuit. In some transformers the core is made of a long strip of sheet steel wound through the formed coils, a construction that minimizes the effect of the air gap in the magnetic circuit.

The effect of an air gap in a magnetic circuit is seldom negligible. In most cases most of the mmf of the exciting coil is required to send the flux across the air gap. An air gap 0.01 in. long may have a greater reluctance drop than several feet of steel in the same magnetic circuit.

Since the permeability of air is constant, a direct proportion exists between the flux density and the magnetic potential gradient in an air gap, provided that the relative distribution of the lines is the same for all values of the flux. The relations between B and H can be obtained by inserting the value $\mu = 1$ in (7.4). Hence *for an air gap,*

$$B \text{ (wb per sq m)} = 4\pi \times 10^{-7}H \text{ (amp-turns per m)}$$

or $$H \text{ (amp-turns per m)} = 7.96 \times 10^5 B \text{ (wb per sq m)}$$

Example 1. The air gap in a certain magnetic circuit is $\frac{1}{64}$ in. long and 4 sq in. in cross section. How many ampere-turns are required to establish a flux of 2,000 μwb in the gap?

Solution. The flux density is

$$B = \frac{2,000 \ \mu\text{wb} \times 1 \text{ wb}/10^6 \ \mu\text{wb}}{4 \text{ sq in.} \times 1 \text{ sq m}/39.37^2 \text{ sq in.}} = 0.775 \text{ wb per sq m}$$

Since $H = 7.96 \times 10^5 \ B$, then $H = 7.96 \times 10^5 \times 0.775 = 617,000$ amp-turns per m. Since reluctance drop $= Hl$, then reluctance drop $= 617,000$ amp-turns per m $\times \frac{1}{64}$ in. $\times 1$ m/39.37 in. $= 245$ amp-turns.

Example 2. The air gap in a certain magnetic circuit is 0.02 m long and 0.5 sq m in cross section. How much flux is crossing the gap when the reluctance drop is 8,000 amp-turns?

Solution. The magnetic potential gradient is

$$H = \frac{8,000 \text{ amp-turns}}{0.02 \text{ m}} = 400,000 \text{ amp-turns per m}$$

Since $B = 4\pi \times 10^{-7} \ H$, then $B = 4\pi \times 10^{-7} \times 400,000 = 0.503$ wb per sq m. The flux is $\Phi = BA = 0.503$ wb per sq m $\times 0.5$ sq m $= 0.25$ wb.

7.9. Magnetization Curves. In magnetic materials such as iron, steel, cobalt, nickel, and certain alloys, the flux density B is not directly proportional to the magnetic potential gradient H. A curve showing the relations between B and H is not linear except perhaps over a limited range. In considering nonlinear resistance circuits, use was made of current-voltage characteristics that had been determined by experiment. In a similar manner characteristics of magnetic materials are used to solve problems relative to magnetic circuits containing these materials. The magnetic characteristics are called magnetization curves, B-H curves, and saturation curves.

A magnetization curve of a given material is usually plotted in terms of the flux density B and the magnetic potential gradient H. For a complete circuit or device containing one or more magnetic materials, the magnetization curve may show the relation between the total flux and the current in an exciting winding, or that between a quantity that is directly proportional to the total flux and one that is directly proportional to the current.

Typical magnetization curves for cast iron, cast steel, and annealed sheet steel are given in Fig. 7.7. These curves were obtained from tests made on samples of the materials. Other samples may have characteristics that differ considerably from the ones shown. An electrical designer uses magnetization curves furnished by the manufacturer of the magnetic materials to be used. The magnetization curve of a given sample of material does not tell the complete story of the relation between the flux density and the magnetic potential gradient as the gradient varies in magnitude and in direction. However, the curve gives sufficient information for certain magnetic circuit computations.

7.10. Determination of a Magnetization Curve. The magnetization curve of a ring sample of a material can be determined with the circuit of Fig. 7.8. The sample has a circular cross section of A sq m throughout. The average circumference of l m will be used as the length of the

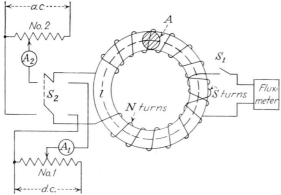

F_IG_. 7.8   Circuit for obtaining magnetization curve for a ring sample of material.

circuit. An exciting coil of N turns is distributed uniformly about the ring. The turns should be closely spaced in order that most of the flux produced will be confined to the magnetic material. The coil may have several layers of turns.

In Fig. 7.8, a search coil of S turns is wound about the exciting coil and connected in series with a switch S_1 across a fluxmeter. It is not necessary that the search coil turns be distributed uniformly about the ring or that the turns be wrapped tightly about the exciting coil.

The fluxmeter in Fig. 7.8 is of the type that measures the change in the flux through the search coil rather than the flux directly. The instrument pointer has no restoring torque acting on it and remains deflected from its initial position after a change in flux is produced. If the initial or the final value of the flux is zero, then the change in the flux is equal to the final or to the initial value of the flux.

In Fig. 7.8 consider that with S_1 closed a direct current of, say 1 amp, is suddenly established in the exciting coil by throwing switch S_2 to the right with the slider on rheostat 1 set some distance from the left-hand end. The sudden change in the exciting current from 0 to 1 amp causes

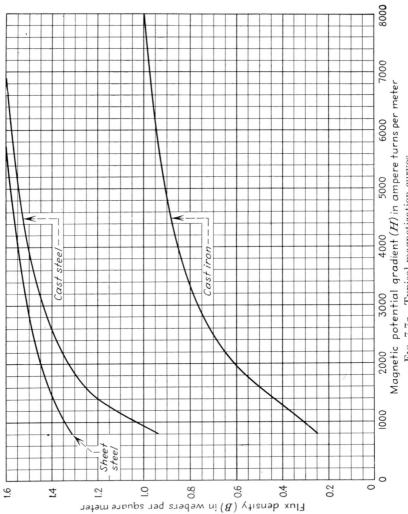

FIG. 7.7a Typical magnetization curves.

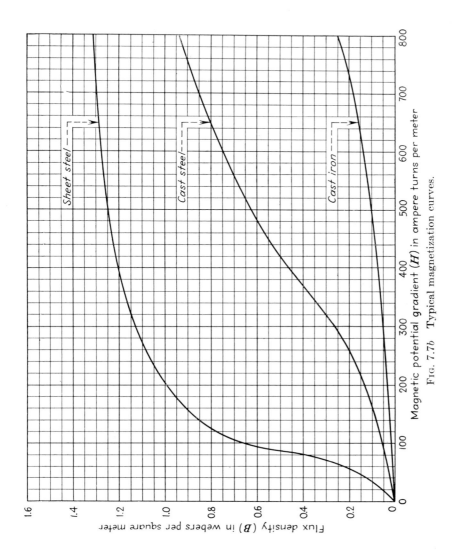

Fig. 7.7b Typical magnetization curves.

a change in the flux. In turn the change of flux induces an emf in the search coil. This emf causes a current in the search coil and the fluxmeter that causes the fluxmeter pointer to move from an initial to a final position. The difference in the fluxmeter readings is directly proportional to the change of flux.

If one were next to open S_2, thereby suddenly decreasing the exciting current from 1 to 0 amp, usually he would find that the fluxmeter pointer did not deflect enough to return to the reading it had originally when the current was zero. If the flux had been zero initially, some flux must remain after the current is varied from 0 to 1 and back to 0 amp. This type of fluxmeter gives no direct information as to how much flux is passing through the search coil if the flux is not changing.

The flux that remains in a magnetic circuit after the current in an exciting coil about the circuit is reduced to zero is residual flux. In some cases the presence of residual flux is desired, but in this case it is not. It is necessary to remove the residual flux each time before establishing a new value of current. One method for removing the residual flux is to send an alternating current through an exciting coil about the circuit and slowly reduce the current to zero. This method is used in Fig. 7.8. The exciting coil can be connected to an a-c source by closing S_2 to the left. The rms value of the current can be controlled by moving the slider on rheostat 2. After the residual flux has been removed, a magnetic material is said to be demagnetized.

If residual flux can be removed by the use of alternating current, what frequency should be used and how much current is required? In many cases only a frequency of 60 c is available and this must be used if possible. It has been found that the residual flux can be removed with a wide range of frequencies but that the initial slope of the magnetization curve obtained following demagnetization varies with the frequency used. One investigator (Burrows) recommends that a frequency of 1 c or less be used. This low frequency can be produced from a d-c source by using a reversing switch that is reversed slowly while the current is being reduced to zero.

In general, the current value required to remove the residual flux from a magnetic material must equal or exceed that used previously in magnetizing the material. Since one may not be certain how much current may have been sent through a given exciting coil previously, it is well to determine by test how much alternating current is required to demagnetize a given magnetic circuit. In Fig. 7.8 the test can be made as follows. Assume that magnetization-curve data are to be taken for exciting currents from 0.1 to 4 amp. Close S_2 to the right and then move the slider on rheostat 1 to the right until the d-c ammeter A_1 reads 4 amp. Next move the slider to the left until A_1 reads 0.1 amp and then open S_2. These adjustments leave the residual flux in the magnetic circuit at the same value that it would have had if the current had been decreased in one step from 4 to 0 amp; at the same time the slider is set so that the direct current will be 0.1 amp the next time S_2 is closed to the right.

Next close S_2 to the left and move the slider on rheostat 2 to the right until the a-c ammeter reads 3 amp. Since the a-c ammeter reads the rms value of the current, a reading of 3 amp corresponds to a maximum value greater than 4 amp. Then slowly move the slider on rheostat 2 to the extreme left and thus reduce the alternating current to zero. Next open S_2. Now close S_1 and then record the fluxmeter deflection as S_2 is closed to the right and the exciting current changes from 0 to 0.1 amp.

If all the residual flux is not removed from the magnetic circuit, the change of flux that occurs as the current is changed from 0 to 0.1 will differ from the change of flux that occurs as the current is changed from 0 to 0.1 amp in the opposite direction. This fact may be utilized to test the completeness of the removal of the residual flux. In the previous manipulation of the circuit, S_2 had been closed to the right and the exciting current had increased from 0 to 0.1 amp. Let that be the positive direction of the current. Next open S_1 and then move the slider on rheostat 1 to the right until the direct current is again 4 amp in the positive direction. Then move the slider to the left until the current is again 0.1 amp in the positive direction. Then open S_2. Next close S_2 to the left, increase the alternating current to 3 amp, and then decrease it slowly to zero. Then open S_2. Now interchange the leads from S_2 to the exciting coil. Next close S_1. Then record the fluxmeter deflection as S_2 is closed to the right and the exciting direct current changes from 0 to 0.1 amp in the negative direction. If the fluxmeter deflection is equal to that obtained when the current was changed from 0 to 0.1 amp in the positive direction, then the residual flux is being removed by the alternating current used.

In magnetic testing in which all the residual flux is to be removed from a sample, tests should be made to be certain that the flux removal has been complete. The maximum value of the alternating current required to remove the residual flux does not always need to be as great as the value of the direct current that established the flux, but only by experiment can one determine how much alternating current should be used in a given circuit.

In Fig. 7.8 the fluxmeter circuit should be kept open by S_1 while the sample is being demagnetized. If S_1 were left closed during the demagnetizing process, the fluxmeter would likely be damaged. It is desirable that S_1 close against a spring so that it will be open at all times except when it is held closed while a fluxmeter reading is being taken.

To obtain data for a magnetization curve with the circuit of Fig. 7.8:

Connect the exciting coil to the d-c source by closing S_2 to the right. Then adjust rheostat 1 until the exciting current has the value desired for the first set of readings. Then open S_2 and next close it to the left. By rheostat 2 increase the alternating current to a value adequate for demagnetizing. Then reduce this current slowly to zero. Next open S_2. Now note the fluxmeter reading. Then, while holding S_1 closed, close S_2 to the right to cause the direct current to change from zero to the value for which it had been set previously. Note the final fluxmeter reading. Since the flux was initially zero, the difference of the fluxmeter readings is proportional to the value of flux corresponding to the exciting direct current.

S_1 is then opened. Next the direct current is increased to the second value desired. The above procedure is repeated to determine the values of flux corresponding to as many other exciting currents as may be desired.

The calibration of a fluxmeter is stated in terms of the flux change through a one-turn search coil required to produce a deflection of one division. With more than one turn in the search coil, the fluxmeter reading equals the product of the change of flux and the number of search coil turns; i.e., the reading is in weber-turns or line-turns. To obtain the flux change in webers, the number of divisions of deflection is multiplied by the calibration in webers per division with a one-turn search coil and the product is divided by the number of search coil turns. In Fig. 7.8, after the flux corresponding to a given set of readings has been computed, the flux is divided by the area A of the sample to obtain the flux density. This computation is based on the assumption that the flux is distributed uniformly over the area, which is not exactly true.

In Fig. 7.8 the magnetic potential gradient corresponding to a given set of readings is computed by dividing the mmf of the exciting coil by the mean length of the sample. This is based on the assumption that all parts of the circuit are subjected to the same gradient. This is not exactly true. A curve plotted from data taken in the manner just described is a virgin magnetization curve.

Example 1. A cast-iron toroid that had a cross section of 0.69 sq in. and a mean length of 20 in. was wound with an exciting coil of 1,300 turns. The toroid was connected as in Fig. 7.8. The fluxmeter calibration was 10,000 lines per division with a one-turn search coil. The magnetization data are recorded in columns 1, 2, and 3 in Table 7.1. The direct current was set first at 0.1 amp and then the magnetic circuit was demagnetized. Next the fluxmeter switch was held closed while the direct current of 0.1 amp was suddenly established in the coil. The fluxmeter deflection of three divisions was recorded in column 2 and the number of search coil turns in column 3. The coil mmf, entered in column 4, was equal to the exciting coil turns (1,300) times the exciting current (0.1 amp), or 130 amp-turns. The magnetic potential gradient H, entered in column 5, was equal to the mmf (130 amp-turns) divided by the length (20 in. $\times$ 1 m/39.37 in. = 0.508 m), or 256 amp-turns per m.   The flux Φ, entered in column 6, was equal to the flux-meter reading in divisions (Φ') multiplied by the calibration (10,000 lines per division with a one-turn search coil), and this product divided by the number of search coil turns (20) to give 1,500 lines.   The flux density B, entered in column 7 was equal to the flux (1,500 lines $\times$ 1 wb/10^8 lines = 1.5×10^{-5} wb) divided by the area (0.69 sq in. $\times$ 1 sq m/39.37^2 sq in. = 4.45×10^{-4} sq m) to give 0.0337 wb per sq m.   The permeability μ, entered in column 8, was computed from (7.3) as $7.96 \times 10^5 \times 0.0337$ wb per sq m/256 amp-turns per m = 105.

The magnetization curve plotted from the tabulated values of B and H is the one for cast iron in Fig. 7.7.

TABLE 7.1

(1)	(2)	(3)	(4)	(5)	(6)	(7)	(8)
I exciting current, amp	Φ' flux-meter reading, divisions	S search coil turns, number	NI mmf, amp-turns $1,300I$	H magnetic potential gradient, amp-turns per m $\dfrac{1,300I}{0.508}$	Φ flux, lines $\dfrac{\Phi' \times 10,000}{S}$	B flux density, wb per sq m $\dfrac{\Phi \times 10^{-8}}{0.000445}$	μ permeability $\dfrac{7.96 \times 10^5 B}{H}$
0.10	3.0	20	130	256	1,500	0.0337	105
0.20	9.1	20	260	512	4,550	0.102	159
0.25	15.0	20	325	640	7,500	0.168	214
0.50	12.9	7	650	1,280	18,400	0.413	257
0.75	17.9	7	975	1,925	25,500	0.573	237
1.00	21.0	7	1,300	2,560	30,000	0.673	209
1.25	24.0	7	1,625	3,200	34,300	0.770	191
1.50	25.8	7	1,950	3,840	36,800	0.827	171
1.75	27.2	7	2,275	4,480	38,900	0.873	155
2.00	28.3	7	2,600	5,120	40,300	0.906	141
2.25	28.8	7	2,925	5,760	41,200	0.925	128
2.50	29.2	7	3,250	6,400	41,700	0.936	116
2.75	30.1	7	3,575	7,045	43,000	0.965	109
3.00	22.2	5	3,900	7,680	44,400	0.997	103
3.25	22.8	5	4,225	8,320	45,600	1.020	94
3.50	23.0	5	4,550	8,950	46,000	1.030	86
3.75	23.5	5	4,875	9,600	47,000	1.060	78
4.00	24.0	5	5,200	10,200	48,000	1.080	72

7.11. Saturation.

A typical magnetization curve for sheet steel is in Fig. 7.9.   At low flux densities the curve is concave upward.   In this region a given percentage increase in the magnetic potential gradient causes a greater percentage increase in the flux density.   At medium flux densities the curve is nearly a straight line. In this region a given percentage increase in the magnetic potential gradient produces about the same percentage increase in the flux density. At high flux densities the curve is concave downward. In this region a given percentage increase in the magnetic potential gradient produces a much smaller percentage increase in the flux density.

The region in which the magnetization curve is departing from a

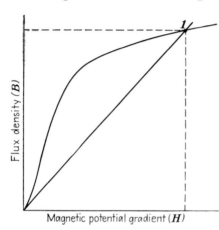

straight line and becoming concave downward is the knee of the saturation curve. No exact boundary points can be specified for the knee because the change in the radius of curvature is gradual in that region. If a given magnetization curve were replotted with a change in the relative scales of B and H, the knee on the second curve would probably appear to lie between points different from those on the original curve.

Fig. 7.9 A graphical representation of normal permeability. The normal permeability at the point 1 is proportional to the slope of the line from the origin to the point.

When the flux density in a magnetic material is above the knee of the magnetization curve, the material is said to be saturated. Saturation is a relative term only and no definite point on the curve can be specified as the one at which saturation begins.

7.12. Normal and Differential Permeabilities. The permeability of a magnetic material may be defined in graphical terms from a magnetization curve. From (7.4),

$$\mu = 7.96 \times 10^5 \frac{B \text{ (wb per sq m)}}{H \text{ (amp-turns per m)}}$$

In Fig. 7.9 consider the point 1 on the magnetization curve and the line drawn from the origin to the point. The slope of the line is B/H; hence the slope is directly proportional to the permeability at the point. This permeability is denoted as relative permeability, normal permeability, or most often by the term permeability.

The normal permeability of a cast-iron sample varies with the flux density as in Fig. 7.10. The normal permeability at zero flux density is proportional to the initial slope of the magnetization curve. As a point whose ordinate is the flux density moves up the magnetization curve,

the slope of a line from the origin to the point at first increases, reaches
a maximum when the line is tangent to the curve, and then decreases for
a further increase in the flux density.   The normal permeability then
varies in an identical manner.   This result is consistent with the permeability values tabulated in column 8 in Table 7.1.

Certain magnetic circuit relations depend not upon the flux density
produced by a given magnetic potential gradient but upon the change in

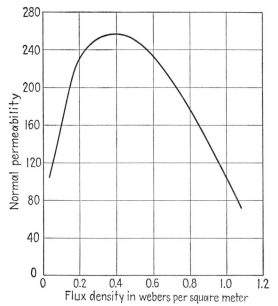

Fig. 7.10   Relation between the permeability and the flux density in a cast-iron
sample.

the density produced by a given change in the gradient.   The rate of
change of the density with respect to the gradient is dB/dH.   The
differential permeability μ_d is expressed by

$$\mu_d = 7.96 \times 10^5 \, \frac{dB \ (\text{wb per sq m})}{dH \ (\text{amp-turns per m})}$$

The value of dB/dH at a given point on a magnetization curve can be
computed analytically if the equation of the curve is known in terms of
B and H.   Since a magnetization curve is determined by experiment, its
equation is not known.   The value of dB/dH at a given point on a magnetization curve can be approximated by drawing a tangent to the curve
and measuring its slope.   The differential permeability of a given sample
of material is equal to the normal permeability only at a point on the
magnetization curve from which a line to the origin is tangent to the

curve. The differential permeability of a given sample varies with the flux density in much the same manner that the normal permeability does but not through the same range of values. Hereafter, when the term permeability is used without a qualifying adjective, it is to be understood that the normal permeability is meant.

Example 1. For the cast-iron sample whose magnetization data are given in Table 7.1 compute the differential permeability at a flux density of 0.75 wb per sq m.

Solution. An approximate incremental method will be used. In the table it happens that one flux density value is 0.77 wb per sq m. The differential permeability will be computed for that density. The result will be about the same as that at the specified density. From the table, at $H = 2,560$ amp-turns per m, $B = 0.673$ wb per sq m, and at $H = 3,840$ amp-turns per m, $B = 0.827$ wb per sq m. Then a change of flux density of $0.827 - 0.673 = 0.154$ wb per sq m is produced by a change of gradient of $3,840 - 2,560 = 1,280$ amp-turns per m. Hence

$$\mu_d = 7.96 \times 10^5 \times \frac{0.154}{1,280} = 96$$

Note that the normal permeability at the same flux density is 191, or about twice the differential permeability.

Permeabilities at the operating flux densities likely to be used range from 100 to 400 for cast iron, from 500 to 2,000 for cast steel, and from 1,000 to 9,000 for sheet steel.

7.13. Magnetic Computations in CGS and English Units. The method to be used in solving a given magnetic circuit problem does not depend upon the system of units used. Many persons prefer to use the cgs system. Many engineering offices use the English system.

The cgs unit of mmf or reluctance drop is the gilbert (gb). The gilbert is about 20 per cent smaller than the ampere-turn, the relation between them being 0.4π gb $= 1$ amp-turn, or 1 gb $= 0.796$ amp-turn.

The cgs unit of flux is the maxwell (mx) or line, where 10^8 mx $= 1$ wb. The cgs unit of flux density is the maxwell per square centimeter. It is also called a gauss (gs).

Reluctance $\Re$ in the cgs system is expressed by $\Re = l/\mu A$ gb per mx, where l is the length in centimeters, μ is the permeability of the material, and A is the cross section in square centimeters. For a given material under given conditions μ has the same value in the cgs system as it has in the mks system. The term oersted has been used in the United States as the name of the cgs unit of reluctance, but the term was not used internationally.

The cgs unit of magnetic potential gradient is the gilbert per centimeter. It is also called an oersted (oe).

In cgs units, the magnetic potential gradient H in gilberts per centimeter (or oersteds), the flux density B in maxwells per square centimeter (or gausses), and the permeability μ are related by $\mu H = B$. For air, or other nonmagnetic material, $\mu = 1$. For such a material H is numerically equal to B.

For a magnetic material a magnetization curve in cgs units shows the relation between the flux density in lines per square centimeter and the magnetic potential gradient in gilberts per centimeter.

The English unit of mmf or reluctance drop is the ampere-turn, the same as the mks unit.

The English unit of flux is the line (or maxwell), the same as the cgs unit. The English unit of flux density is the line per square inch.

Reluctance $\Re$ in the English system is expressed by

$$\Re = \frac{0.313l}{\mu A} \text{ amp-turns per line}$$

where l is the length in inches, μ is the permeability of the material, and A is the cross section in square inches. For a given material under given conditions, μ has the same value as in the mks and the cgs systems.

The English unit of magnetic potential gradient is the ampere-turn per inch.

In English units, the magnetic potential gradient H in ampere-turns per inch, the flux density B in lines per square inch, and the permeability μ are related by $\mu H = 0.313B$. For air, or other nonmagnetic material, $\mu = 1$ and $H = 0.313B$.

For a magnetic material a magnetization curve in English units shows the relation between the flux density in lines per square inch and the magnetic potential gradient in ampere-turns per inch.

A flux density of 1 wb per sq m is equivalent to 10,000 lines per sq cm and to 64,500 lines per sq in. To produce this density in air requires 796,000 amp-turns per m, 10,000 gb per cm, or 20,200 amp-turns per in.

7.14. Series Magnetic Circuits

Example 1.   A flux of 3,200 μwb is to be established in the cast-steel toroid of Fig. 7.11. Compute the flux density, the magnetic potential gradient, and the ampere-turns required in the exciting coil.

Solution.   The flux density is

$$B = \frac{\Phi}{A} = \frac{3,200 \ \mu\text{wb} \times 1 \ \text{wb}/10^6 \ \mu\text{wb}}{4 \ \text{sq in.} \times 1 \ \text{sq m}/39.37^2 \ \text{sq in.}} = 1.24 \ \text{wb per sq m}$$

From the cast-steel magnetization curve of Fig. 7.7a it is found that for $B = 1.24$ wb per sq m, $H = 1,560$ amp-turns per m. The reluctance drop in the circuit is

$$Hl = 1{,}560 \text{ amp-turns per m} \times \frac{60 \text{ in.} \times 1 \text{ m}}{39.37 \text{ in.}} = 2{,}380 \text{ amp-turns}$$

The coil mmf will equal this value.

Example 2. For the magnetic circuit of Fig. 7.11 compute the flux that would be established if the exciting coil has 2,000 turns and carries 2 amp.

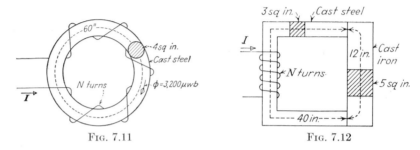

FIG. 7.11   FIG. 7.12

Solution. The reluctance drop is equal to the coil mmf, or

$$2 \text{ amp} \times 2{,}000 \text{ turns} = 4{,}000 \text{ amp-turns}$$

Since this drop is uniformly distributed along the circuit,

$$H = \frac{\text{reluctance drop}}{l} = \frac{4{,}000 \text{ amp-turns}}{60 \text{ in.} \times 1 \text{ m}/39.37 \text{ in.}} = 2{,}670 \text{ amp-turns per m}$$

From the cast-steel magnetization curve of Fig. 7.7a it is found that, for this value of H, the corresponding value of B is 1.42 wb per sq m. Then

$$\Phi = BA = 1.42 \text{ wb per sq m} \times \frac{4 \text{ sq in.} \times 1 \text{ sq m}}{39.37^2 \text{ sq in.}} = 3.66 \times 10^{-3} \text{ wb}$$

Example 3. In the magnetic circuit of Fig. 7.12 compute the mmf required in the exciting coil to establish a flux of 1,500 μwb.

Solution. Approximations will be made in the solution. The exciting coil is represented as concentrated about one portion of the circuit rather than being distributed uniformly along the length of the circuit, as was assumed when the relations in a toroid were studied. With a concentrated coil the flux will not be the same throughout the length of the circuit. The distribution of the flux will depend upon where the coil is placed about the circuit. The flux is not distributed uniformly over any cross section in the circuit. Also one cannot say with certainty what value should be used for the mean length of the magnetic path in each of the two sections of the circuit. The flux lines will not turn through 90° at the corners but will follow a curved path and crowd toward the inside corner.

It will be assumed that: (1) The flux is the same throughout the circuit. (2) The flux density is uniform over any cross section. (3) The mean lengths of the respective paths are 40 and 12 in.

The length l_{cs} and the area A_{cs} of the path in the cast steel are $l_{cs} = 40$ in. $\times$ 1 m/39.37 in. = 1.02 m, and $A_{cs} = 3$ sq in. $\times$ 1 sq m/39.37² sq in. = 1.94 $\times$ 10⁻³ sq m. The length l_{ci} and the area A_{ci} of the path in the cast iron are $l_{ci} =$

12 in. $\times$ 1 m/39.37 in. = 0.305 m, and A_{ci} = 5 sq in. $\times$ 1 sq m/39.37^2 sq in. = 3.23 $\times$ 10^{-3} sq m.

The flux density B_{cs} in the cast steel is

$$B_{cs} = \frac{\Phi}{A_{cs}} = \frac{1{,}500 \ \mu\text{wb} \times 1 \ \text{wb}/10^6 \ \mu\text{wb}}{1.94 \times 10^{-3} \ \text{sq m}} = 0.773 \ \text{wb per sq m}$$

From the cast-steel magnetization curve in Fig. 7.7b it is found that to produce this density a magnetic potential gradient H_{cs} = 620 amp-turns per m is required. The reluctance drop in the cast steel is

$$H_{cs}l_{cs} = 620 \ \text{amp-turns per m} \times 1.02 \ \text{m} = 630 \ \text{amp-turns}$$

The flux density B_{ci} in the cast iron is

$$B_{ci} = \frac{\Phi}{A_{ci}} = \frac{1{,}500 \ \mu\text{wb} \times 1 \ \text{wb}/10^6 \ \mu\text{wb}}{3.23 \times 10^{-3} \ \text{sq m}} = 0.464 \ \text{wb per sq m}$$

From the cast-iron magnetization curve in Fig. 7.7a it is found that for this density a magnetic potential gradient H_{ci} = 1,500 amp-turns per m is required. The reluctance drop in the cast iron is

$$H_{ci}l_{ci} = 1{,}500 \ \text{amp-turns per m} \times 0.305 \ \text{m} = 460 \ \text{amp-turns}$$

The exciting coil mmf is equal to the sum of the two reluctance drops or 630 + 460 = 1,090 amp-turns. Because of the approximations involved there is no justification for three significant figures in the result. The correct result probably lies between 1,000 and 1,200 amp-turns.

Example 4. For the magnetic circuit of Fig. 7.12 determine the flux that would be produced by 2,500 amp-turns in the exciting coil.

Solution. Here the permeabilities of the two portions of the circuit depend upon the flux and it is unknown. The problem can be solved by trial, starting with an assumed value of flux. As a guide for a starting value, note that in Example 3 a flux of 1.5 $\times$ 10^{-3} wb was produced by an mmf of 1,090 amp-turns. An mmf of 2,500 amp-turns will not produce 2,500/1,090 times as much flux because the permeabilities will decrease as the flux increases. Let us choose 2.2 $\times$ 10^{-3} wb for the first trial. The corresponding flux densities are 1.13 wb per sq m in the cast steel and 0.68 wb per sq m in the cast iron. From the respective magnetization curves it is found that the corresponding magnetic potential gradients are H_{cs} = 1,200 amp-turns per m and H_{ci} = 2,320 amp-turns per m. The coil mmf required is 1,200 amp-turns per m $\times$ 1.02 m + 2,320 amp-turns per m $\times$ 0.305 m = 1,930 amp-turns. Since the assumed flux of 2.2 $\times$ 10^{-3} wb requires only 1,930 amp-turns while the given coil mmf is 2,500 amp-turns, the actual flux is greater than 2.2 $\times$ 10^{-3} wb. By repeating the trial process it is found that a flux of about 2.4 $\times$ 10^{-3} wb is produced by a coil mmf of 2,500 amp-turns.

The problem of this example can be solved directly by a graphical method similar to one that would be used in solving nonlinear resistance circuits. As a first step the flux–reluctance-drop characteristic of the cast-steel portion of the circuit is drawn as curve A in Fig. 7.13. This was obtained directly from the magnetization curve of sheet steel of Fig. 7.7 by multiplying each ordinate by 1.94 $\times$ 10^{-3} sq m (A_{cs}) and each abscissa of the curve by 1.02 m (l_{cs}). Next the flux–reluctance-drop characteristic of the cast-iron portion of the circuit was drawn as curve B in Fig. 7.13 by multiplying each ordinate of the cast-iron magnetization curve of Fig. 7.7 by 3.23×10^{-3} (A_{ci}) and each abscissa of the curve by 0.305 m (l_{ci}). The flux–reluctance-drop characteristic C of the entire circuit was obtained by adding the abscissa values of the other curves. Now to determine the flux that would be produced by a coil mmf of 2,500 amp-turns,

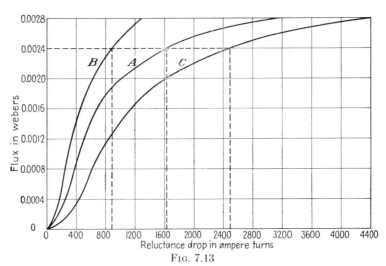

Fig. 7.13

at this abscissa value project vertically to the total characteristic. Then project horizontally to read the flux as 0.0024 wb. If the values of the reluctance drops across the two portions of the circuit are desired, they can be read on the abscissa at the respective points of intersection of the horizontal line at 0.0024 wb with the individual characteristics. The reluctance drop in the cast steel is 1,630 amp-turns and that in the cast iron is 870 amp-turns.

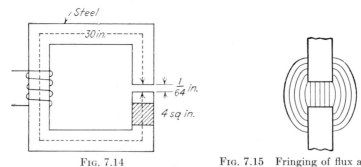

Fig. 7.14   Fig. 7.15   Fringing of flux at an air gap.

Example 5. In the magnetic circuit of Fig. 7.14 compute the coil mmf required to establish a flux of 2,000 μwb. The steel portion of the circuit is cast steel.

Solution. In addition to the factors that introduced inexactness in the solution of magnetic circuits previously considered, the air gap makes necessary other approximations. At the gap the flux will fringe in a manner approximating that in Fig. 7.15. Because of fringing the effective cross section of the gap is greater than the 4 sq in. of the steel facing the gap and the flux density is not uniform in the gap. For the purpose of this example the effect of fringing will be neglected and the density will be assumed to be uniform in the gap as well as in the steel. With these approximations the flux in the gap is 2,000 μwb (0.002 wb) and the area of the gap is equal to 4 sq in. (0.00258 sq m). The flux density B_g in the gap is

$$B_g = \frac{0.002 \text{ wb}}{0.00258 \text{ sq m}} = 0.775 \text{ wb per sq m}$$

In an air gap $H = 7.96 \times 10^5 B$; hence the magnetic potential gradient H_g in the gap is $H_g = 7.96 \times 10^5 \times 0.775 = 617,000$ amp-turns per m. The reluctance drop in the gap is $H_g l_g$. Since $l_g = \frac{1}{64}$ in. $\times$ 1 m/39.37 in. $= 0.0004$ m, then $H_g l_g = 617,000$ amp-turns per m $\times$ 0.0004 m $= 247$ amp-turns.

The flux density in the steel equals that in the air gap, or 0.775 wb per sq m. For this density, from the sheet-steel magnetization curve in Fig. 7.7, the magnetic potential gradient H_s in the steel is 125 amp-turns per m. The reluctance drop in the steel is $H_s l_s$. Since $l_s = 30$ in. $\times$ 1 m/39.37 in. $= 0.762$ m, then $H_s l_s = 125$ amp-turns per m $\times$ 0.762 m $= 95$ amp-turns. The exciting coil mmf is equal to the sum of the reluctance drops in the air gap and the steel, or coil mmf $= 247 + 95 = 342$ amp-turns.

Because of the approximations made in solving this problem, the actual mmf may differ by perhaps 10 per cent from the value just obtained.

Example 6. In the magnetic circuit of Fig. 7.14 compute the flux that would be produced by an exciting coil mmf of 600 amp-turns. The steel portion of the circuit is sheet steel. Neglect the effects of fringing.

Solution. The permeability of the steel portion of the circuit is a function of the flux and the flux is not known. Hence it is not possible to determine by inspection how the total reluctance drop will be divided between the two portions of the circuit. The problem can be solved by trial, first assuming a value of flux and then making computations as in Example 5 to determine the required mmf. The process can be repeated until the value of flux is found that requires 600 amp-turns to produce it. The problem can be solved graphically by the method of Example 4. The problem is analogous to that of determining the current in an electric circuit of lamps in series with a resistor of constant resistance across a given value of voltage. A graphical solution of the magnetic circuit problem will be used.

The flux–reluctance-drop characteristic of the steel portion of the circuit of Fig. 7.14 is curve S in Fig. 7.16. It was obtained by multiplying the ordinates of the sheet-steel magnetization curve of Fig. 7.7b by the steel cross section of 0.00258 sq m and multiplying the abscissas of the magnetization curve by 0.762 m, the mean length of the steel path.

The reversed flux–reluctance-drop characteristic of the air gap in Fig. 7.14 is curve A in Fig. 7.16. The characteristic is a straight line because the gap reluctance is constant. The abscissa intercept is at 600 amp-turns, the mmf applied. The ordinate intercept is the flux that would be produced if all 600 amp-turns were used by the air gap. That flux is computed as follows: Since

$$H = 7.96 \times 10^5 B \text{ in air}$$

then $$\frac{600 \text{ amp-turns}}{4 \times 10^{-4} \text{ m}} = 7.96 \times 10^5 \times \frac{\Phi}{0.00258 \text{ sq m}}$$

from which $\Phi = 0.00487$ wb.

The flux produced by an exciting coil mmf of 600 amp-turns in Fig. 7.14 is determined as the ordinate of the point of intersection of the two curves in Fig. 7.16 and is 0.00295 wb, or 2,950 μwb.

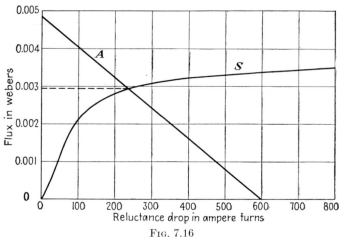

FIG. 7.16

7.15. Branched Magnetic Circuits

Example 1. The dimensions of a certain sheet-steel magnetic circuit are given in Fig. 7.17. The flux in branch A is 1,000 μwb. Determine the fluxes in branches B and C and the mmf of the exciting coil.

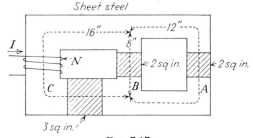

FIG. 7.17

Solution. Approximations made will be to take the mean lengths of the paths as indicated and to consider the given area in a path as extending throughout the mean length of the path. In metric units the length l_A of path A is 0.305 m, the length l_B of path B is 0.203 m, the length l_C of path C is 0.407 m, and the area A_A of path A and the area A_B of path B are each 1.29×10^{-3} sq m, and the area A_C of path C is 1.94×10^{-3} sq m.

The flux Φ_A in branch A is 1,000 μwb, or 0.001 wb. The flux density B_A in branch A is

$$B_A = \frac{\Phi_A}{A_A} = \frac{0.001 \text{ wb}}{1.29 \times 10^{-3} \text{ sq m}} = 0.775 \text{ wb per sq m}$$

For this density, from the sheet-steel magnetization curve of Fig. 7.7, the magnetic potential gradient H_A in branch A is 124 amp-turns per m.   The reluctance drop $H_A l_A$ in branch A is $H_A l_A = 124$ amp-turns per m $\times$ 0.305 m $= 38$ amp-turns.

Since branch B is in parallel with branch A and there is no source of mmf in either branch, the reluctance drop $H_B l_B$ in branch B equals that in branch A, or

$$H_B l_B = H_A l_A \text{ from which } H_B = \frac{H_A l_A}{l_B} = \frac{38 \text{ amp-turns}}{0.203 \text{ m}} = 186 \text{ amp-turns per m.}$$

From the sheet-steel magnetization curve, for this value of H_B the flux density B_B in branch B is 0.96 wb per sq m.   The flux Φ_B in branch B is

$$\Phi_B = B_B A_B = 0.96 \text{ wb per sq m} \times 1.29 \times 10^{-3} \text{ sq m} = 0.00124 \text{ wb}$$

The flux Φ_C in branch C is $\Phi_C = \Phi_A + \Phi_B = 0.001 + 0.00124 = 0.00224$ **wb.** The flux density B_C in branch C is

$$B_C = \frac{\Phi_C}{A_C} = \frac{0.00224 \text{ wb}}{1.94 \times 10^{-3} \text{ sq m}} = 1.15 \text{ wb per sq m}$$

From the sheet-steel magnetization curve, for this value of B_C the magnetic potential gradient H_C in branch C is 325 amp-turns per m.   The reluctance drop $H_C l_C$ in branch C is $H_C l_C = 325$ amp-turns per m $\times$ 0.407 m $= 132$ amp-turns.   The exciting coil mmf is equal to the sum of the reluctance drops along either the path through C and A or that through C and B.   Hence

$$\text{Coil mmf} = H_C l_C + H_A l_A = 132 + 38 = 170 \text{ amp-turns}$$

Example 2.   In the circuit of Fig. 7.17 the exciting coil mmf is 800 amp-turns. Compute the flux in each branch of the circuit.

Solution.   The problem must be solved by trial or graphically because it is not possible to determine directly how the coil mmf will be used up along the circuit.   One method of solution is to assume a flux in branch A and then solve for the required coil mmf as in Example 1.   If the computed mmf differed from the given value, a second estimate of the flux in A would be made and computations made to obtain another value of coil mmf.   The process can be repeated until the flux in branch A is found that requires approximately the given coil mmf. For the circuit of Fig. 7.17 it is found that with a flux of 0.00129 wb in branch A, the flux in branch B is 0.00146 wb, the flux in branch C is 0.00275 wb, and 790 amp-turns are required in the exciting coil.   Since the given coil mmf was 800 amp-turns, the above values of flux are approximately correct.

7.16. Froelich's Equation.   Froelich, a German scientist, found that a magnetization curve for ferromagnetic materials can be fitted approximately by an equation of the form

$$B = \frac{C_1 H}{C_2 + H} \tag{7.5}$$

where B is the flux density, H is the magnetic potential gradient, and C_1 and C_2 are constants to be determined for a given curve.

To determine C_1 and C_2, two equations in which they are the unknowns may be obtained by substituting in (7.5) the corresponding values of B and H at each of two points on the curve. Then C_1 and C_2 are obtained by the simultaneous solution of the equations. One point is usually chosen below the knee of the curve and the other is chosen above it.

After the constants in the Froelich equation have been determined from a given magnetization curve, a curve can be plotted from the equation on a sheet with the magnetization curve. Then one can see how nearly the two curves coincide. Both will pass through the points that were selected in determining the constants. Usually the curves separate most at extremely low and extremely high flux densities.

Example 1. Determine the Froelich equation for the sheet-steel magnetization curve of Fig. 7.7.
Solution. At $B = 0.5$ wb per sq m, $H = 87$ amp-turns per m and at

$$B = 1.3 \text{ wb per sq m}$$

$H = 700$ amp-turns per m. Substitution of these values in (7.5) yields

$$0.5 = \frac{C_1 \times 87}{C_2 + 87} \quad \text{and} \quad 1.3 = \frac{C_1 \times 700}{C_2 + 700}$$

from which $C_1 = 1.68$ and $C_2 = 206$. The Froelich equation of the magnetization curve is $B = 1.68H/(206 + H)$.

This equation will be tested by computing values of B for certain assumed values of H and comparing the results with values read from the magnetization curve. At $H = 40$ amp-turns per m, $B = 1.68 \times 40/(206 + 40) = 0.27$ wb per sq m by the Froelich equation and 0.125 wb per sq m from the magnetization curve. The equation yields a result that is $[(0.27 - 0.125)/0.125] \times 100 = 116$ per cent high. At $H = 5,000$ amp-turns per m,

$$B = \frac{1.68 \times 5,000}{206 + 5,000} = 1.61 \text{ wb per sq m}$$

by the Froelich equation and 1.58 wb per sq m from the magnetization curve. The equation yields a result that is $[(1.61 - 1.58)/1.58] \times 100 = 2$ per cent high.

Example 2. A certain series magnetic circuit consists of a sheet-steel portion 0.4 m long and an air gap 0.0025 m long. Assume that the cross section of the circuit is 0.013 sq m throughout. How much flux will be produced by an mmf of 2,000 amp-turns?
Solution. The Froelich equation of sheet steel that was determined in Example 1 will be used. Let H_S be the magnetic potential gradient in the steel and H_A be that in the air. The flux density B in the steel is equal to that in the air. For the steel, $B = 1.68H_S/(206 + H_S)$ and for the air, $B = 4\pi \times 10^{-7}H_A$. Equating the two values of B,

$$\frac{1.68H_S}{206 + H_S} = 4\pi \times 10^{-7}H_A \tag{1}$$

The reluctance drop $H_S l_S$ in the steel plus the reluctance drop $H_A l_A$ in the air equals the mmf acting on the circuit; hence

$$H_S \times 0.4 \text{ m} + H_A \times 0.0025 \text{ m} = 2,000 \text{ amp-turns} \tag{2}$$

Solving (1) and (2) simultaneously yields $H_S = -3,820$, or 265 amp-turns per m. The negative value has no physical significance and may be discarded. For $H_S = 265$ amp-turns per m, the corresponding value of B is 0.945 wb per sq m. The flux in the circuit is 0.945 wb per sq m $\times$ 0.013 sq m $= 0.0123$ wb.

7.17. Hysteresis. If a material has a constant permeability, a given current in an exciting coil about a magnetic circuit consisting of the material produces a single value of flux. If the material has a permeability that varies as the flux density varies, a given mmf produces a flux whose value may vary over a considerable range.

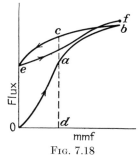

In Fig. 7.18 are typical relations for a magnetic circuit containing a ferromagnetic material. If the circuit initially has no magnetism, the virgin magnetization curve oab shows the variation of the flux with increasing mmf. If the mmf is then decreased, the descending curve bce is above the ascending curve. That is, the mmf od produced the flux da on the ascending curve and a greater flux dc on the

FIG. 7.18

descending curve. The effect that causes the curves to be separated is hysteresis.

In Fig. 7.18, after the mmf is reduced to zero, the flux remains at the value oe, which is the residual flux. If the mmf is increased again, the second ascending curve is ef and does not coincide with either of the other curves. Because of hysteresis, the value of the flux produced in a given magnetic circuit containing a ferromagnetic material depends upon the magnetic history of the circuit.

7.18. Hysteresis Loops. Unless there is a reason for doing so, the magnetic circuit of an electric machine or apparatus is seldom, if ever, demagnetized. If the magnetic circuit is excited by direct current, the electric circuit is probably closed and the current adjusted to a value that gives the desired amount of flux in the magnetic circuit. After a time the electric circuit is opened, the current decreases to zero, and the flux decreases to a residual value. When the electric circuit is again energized, the flux builds up along an ascending curve to a value that may differ from that produced by an equal current the first time the circuit was energized. If the flux density is low, the two values of flux may differ considerably. If the flux density is high it may be difficult to measure any difference between the two values. In any case, after the electric circuit has been closed and opened a number of times (perhaps 10 or more), it is found that the values of the flux and the current become cyclic and follow one curve as the current increases from zero to a given value, and another curve as the current decreases from the given value to zero. The plot of such a cycle of values is a hysteresis loop. In Fig. 7.19 is a hysteresis loop for a certain cast-iron magnetic circuit as the exciting current was varied from 0 to 1 amp and back again to 0.

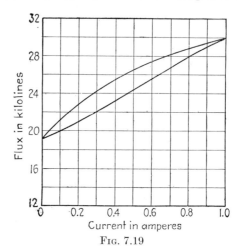

FIG. 7.19

This is called a displaced hysteresis loop to distinguish it from one that is symmetrical to the flux and the current axes.

The magnetic relations in a closed core of uniform cross section and homogeneous ferromagnetic material corresponding to certain variations in the exciting current in a coil about the core are shown in Figs. 7.20 to 7.22. In Fig. 7.20, starting with the core demagnetized, the virgin magnetization curve oa is followed as the current is first increased. As the current is reduced to zero, the curve ab is followed to a residual flux ob. When the direction of the current is reversed and its value again increased, a curve that is a continuation of ab is followed. By "continuation of ab" is meant that there is no abrupt change in the slope of the curves at the point b. There is some value of the reversed current,

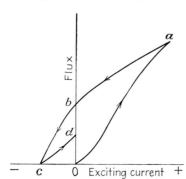

FIG. 7.20 Relation of flux to exciting current for a ferromagnetic circuit starting with the circuit demagnetized.

represented by the distance oc, for which the flux will be zero. The magnetic potential gradient corresponding to the current oc is the coercive force, a factor of importance in the choice of materials for permanent magnets. As soon as the current in Fig. 7.20 is reduced from oc to zero, the flux does not remain zero but follows a curve such as cd and the residual flux is now od.

For a given ferromagnetic material there are no singular values of the residual flux density and the coercive force. The values of these quantities depend upon the maximum value of the magnetic potential gradient

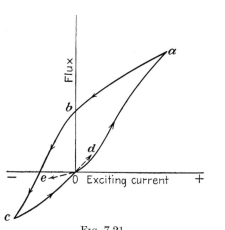

Fig. 7.21

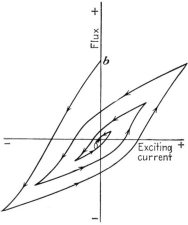

Fig. 7.22 Removing residual magnetism from a ferromagnetic circuit by using a current whose value is being decreased as its direction is reversed.

that was used to magnetize the material. The value of the residual flux density does not increase in direct proportion to the maximum magnetic potential gradient that established it. As saturation is reached, a con-

TABLE 7.2 RELATION BETWEEN RESIDUAL FLUX DENSITY AND MAXIMUM POTENTIAL GRADIENT THAT PRODUCED IT IN A SHEET-METAL SAMPLE

Maximum magnetic potential gradient, amp-turns per m	Maximum flux density, wb per sq m	Residual flux density, wb per sq m
24	0.20	0.10
41	0.40	0.20
64	0.60	0.30
94	0.80	0.36
155	1.00	0.41
210	1.10	0.44
320	1.20	0.46

siderable increase in the maximum gradient produces only a small increase in the residual flux density. In Table 7.2 are values that were obtained by experiment on a sheet-steel core.

A possibility in a ferromagnetic circuit is represented in Fig. 7.21. Starting with the circuit in an demagnetized condition, as the exciting current is increased the flux increases along the virgin magnetization curve oa. As the current is reduced to zero, the curve ab is followed and the residual flux ob remains. As the direction of the exciting current is reversed and its value again increased, the curve bc is followed. c is a point such that when the current is again made zero the flux is zero. It might be said that the circuit is now demagnetized. However, it can be shown experimentally that the material is in a magnetic state such that it responds in a different manner to an increase of current in the positive direction than it does to one in the negative direction. For an increase in the positive direction, a curve od that is a continuation of the curve co is followed. For an increase in the negative direction, a curve oe that has a slope less than that of the curve od is followed.

7.19. Demagnetizing Methods. We shall consider a ferromagnetic material to be demagnetized only when it is in such a state that the flux in it is zero when the magnetic potential gradient applied to it is zero, and any increase of the gradient in one direction produces an increase in the flux density equal in magnitude but opposite in sign to that produced by an equal increase of the gradient in the opposite direction. In a closed ferromagnetic circuit, it is not possible to determine directly when the material is in the state just described. To test a demagnetizing method, it is necessary to apply the method to a given circuit and then compare the values of flux produced by certain values of the current in one direction with the fluxes produced by equal values of the current in the opposite direction.

The demagnetizing method most often used will be explained by reference to Fig. 7.22. Here it is assumed that the residual flux ob remains after the establishment and the interruption of an exciting current in the positive direction. An exciting current is then established in the negative direction. Just how much current must be used can be determined only by experiment. If a magnetization curve is available for the kind of material being tested, one might try first a current value that will produce saturation in the material. The direction of the current is then reversed periodically; at the same time its value is decreased to zero. As indicated in Fig. 7.22, the material is carried in magnetic paths about the origin and ends up in a demagnetized condition. In practice, it is usually necessary to reduce the current in smaller steps and thus make many more trips about the origin than are shown in Fig. 7.22. When direct current is used to demagnetize a magnetic circuit, a reversing switch is used to change the current direction and a voltage divider is used to reduce the current magnitude gradually to zero.

Whenever possible, alternating current is used to demagnetize a magnetic circuit because it is more convenient to have the current direction reversed automatically than to reverse it manually. A voltage divider is used to reduce the magnitude of the alternating current to zero. It is only by trial that one can tell what initial maximum value of alternating current is required to demagnetize a given magnetic circuit. If the magnetic circuit consists of a solid core of large cross section, currents induced in the core by the changing magnetic field may prevent demagnetization if a frequency as high as 60 c is used. However, it may happen that this is the only frequency available. A given rms value of alternating voltage will send less current through an exciting coil about a magnetic circuit than an equal value of direct voltage. Even if a magnetic circuit is laminated, it may be that the value of alternating voltage required to force enough current through the exciting coil to demagnetize the circuit is undesirably high. For example, 2,300 v rms at 60 c may be required to send as much current through an exciting coil as can be produced by 0.5-v direct current.

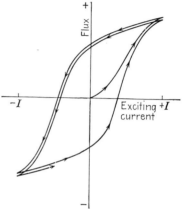

7.20. The Symmetrical Hysteresis Loop. In testing ferromagnetic materials the hysteresis loops most often desired are the symmetrical ones. Since this is the type of loop most frequently pictured, one may get the mistaken idea that magnetic circuits automatically operate on such loops. If the current in an exciting coil about a ferromagnetic circuit is alternated

FIG. 7.23 Magnetic paths followed as a ferromagnetic circuit settles into a symmetrical hysteresis loop. The circuit was first demagnetized and then the exciting current was alternated between $+I$ and $-I$.

ten times or so between positive and negative values of equal magnitude, the magnetic relations will settle into a hysteresis loop but not necessarily one that is symmetrical with respect to the origin. If the maximum current is sufficient to produce saturation, the loop is likely to be nearly symmetrical. To be certain that a loop is symmetrical, one should first demagnetize the circuit, next increase the current to the desired value, and then alternate the current slowly between that and an equal negative value. The magnetic paths traversed would be somewhat as in Fig. 7.23. As the current is first increased from zero to $+I$, the flux increases along a virgin magnetization curve to a certain positive value. When the current is changed next to $-I$, the negative value of flux produced is less than the positive value previously produced by $+I$. When the current is again changed to $+I$, the flux produced is less than that produced initially by the equal initial positive current. The next time the current is made $-I$, the negative flux produced is greater than that produced initially by the equal initial negative current. As the alternations of the current between $+I$ and $-I$ are continued, the maximum positive values of flux decrease slightly and the maximum negative values increase slightly. After perhaps a dozen reversals, the loop becomes symmetrical with equal positive and negative maximum values of flux. To keep the material in the magnetic circuit operating on the given symmetrical hysteresis loop, after a current in either direction is established its value should not be reduced until $+I$ or $-I$ is reached. Also, after a maximum current in either direction has been reached, the

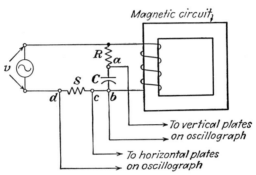

FIG. 7.24   Circuit for showing a symmetrical hysteresis loop on a cathode-ray oscillograph. v is an alternating voltage. S is a low-resistance shunt. C is a capacitor. R is a high-resistance resistor. The leads from b and c should be connected to the grounded terminals on the oscillograph.

current must be decreased only until zero current is reached and then current must be established in a direction opposite to that previously existing. In other words, the current in the exciting coil about the circuit must be varied in such a fashion as to assume in succession the same values of current each time it is varied from a positive maximum to a negative maximum, or vice versa.

Hysteresis loops can be shown on a cathode-ray oscillograph with the circuit of Fig. 7.24. An alternating voltage v is applied to a coil about a magnetic circuit. A coil of a transformer is suitable. The shunt S should have only enough resistance to cause a voltage drop of about 0.5 v when it is carrying the exciting current of the coil. With constant shunt resistance, the voltage across the shunt is at every instant directly proportional to the coil current. This voltage is applied to the horizontal deflecting plates of the oscillograph to produce horizontal deflections directly proportional to the instantaneous exciting currents. A resistor of resistance R is connected in series with a capacitor of capacitance C. The voltage across the capacitor is applied to the vertical deflecting plates of the oscillograph. The voltage across the capacitor will vary with time approximately in the same manner as the flux in the core does if the quantity RCf is equal to or greater than about 3×10^6. Here R is in ohms, C is in microfarads, and f is the frequency of the voltage in cycles per second. Thus, if $C = 10$, and $f = 60$, R should be 5,000 ohms or more.

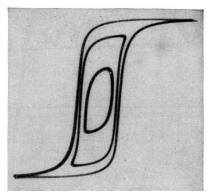

Fig. **7.25**   Hysteresis loops of a magnetic circuit as shown on a cathode-ray oscillograph by means of the circuit of Fig. 7.24.

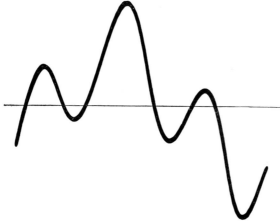

Fig. **7.26**   Waveform of voltage applied to a circuit similar to that of Fig. 7.24.

If the maximum value of v is varied in the circuit of Fig. 7.24 the effect of saturation upon the shape of the hysteresis loop can be seen on the oscillograph (see Fig. 7.25).

The circuit of Fig. 7.24 will show with fair accuracy the hysteresis loop of a magnetic circuit for any waveform of the applied voltage. When the voltage wave of Fig. 7.26 was applied to an exciting coil. the flux-time wave was that of Fig. 7.27. Note that the flux increases from zero to a certain value, decreases slightly, again increases for a time, and then decreases to zero. The resulting hysteresis loop (Fig. 7.28) has two small loops within the larger loop.

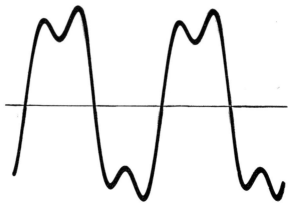

FIG. 7.27 Waveform of flux in a circuit similar to that of Fig. 7.24 when the applied voltage has the waveform shown in Fig. 7.26.

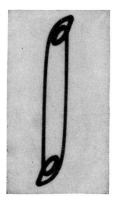

FIG. 7.28 Hysteresis loop that contains two smaller loops.

FIG. 7.29 An unsymmetrical hysteresis loop as shown on a cathode-ray oscillograph. The loop was produced when the exciting mmf consisted of an a-c component superimposed on a d-c component.

An unsymmetrical hysteresis loop from an oscillograph is in Fig. 7.29. Here the positive and the negative values of the exciting mmf were unequal. Saturation is evident at one end of the loop but not at the other.

7.21. Determination of a Symmetrical Hysteresis Loop.

Data for the symmetrical hysteresis loop of a ring sample of ferromagnetic material can be obtained with the circuit of Fig. 7.30.

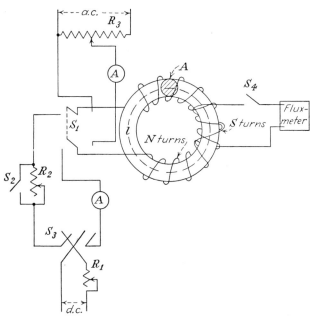

Fɪɢ. 7.30   Circuit for determining hysteresis loop of a ring sample of iron.

Example 1.   A sheet-steel sample that had a cross section A of 7.73×10^{-4} sq m (1.2 sq in.) and an average length of 0.36 m (14.2 in.) was used in the circuit of Fig. 7.30.   The exciting coil had 450 turns.   The fluxmeter calibration was 10,000 lines per division with a one-turn search coil.   The hysteresis loop for a maximum current of 0.5 amp was determined.   The steps followed are:

1. Demagnetize the material.   This was done by closing S_1 to the right to connect the exciting coil to the a-c supply.   The slider on rheostat R_3 was moved to the right until the a-c ammeter read 3 amp.   Then the current was reduced to zero by moving the slider slowly to the left.   The value of 3 amp was chosen as follows: By reference to the magnetization curve for sheet steel in Fig. 7.7, 4,000 amp-turns per m produces a flux density well above the knee of the curve. The sample to be tested here may be expected to have similar properties.   In the sample there would be required 4,000 amp-turns per m $\times$ 0.36 m = 1,440 amp-turns.   To produce this mmf would require 1,440 amp-turns/450 turns = 3.2 amp. Since the a-c ammeter reads the rms value of the current, a reading of 3 amp means that a maximum current of more than 3.2 amp is attained.   For the sample being tested it was found later that an rms current of 0.3 amp was sufficient for demagnetizing even when d-c exciting currents as large as 10 amp had been used.

2. Set the exciting direct current for the maximum value desired for the loop. This was done by first setting rheostat R_1 for maximum resistance, next closing S_2, then closing S_1 to the left, and next closing S_3 to the lower position.   Then the slider on rheostat R_1 was moved until the d-c ammeter read 0.5 amp.

3. Get the magnetic material in a cyclic state. This was done by reversing S_3 about ten times. After the reversals the switch was left closed in the lower position, the one chosen to produce positive current in the coil.

4. Locate points in the first quadrant of the hysteresis loop with respect to the tip of the loop, taking care that the electric circuit is so manipulated that the magnetic material is always carried through the same cycle of values.

Here, after the current is decreased from 0.5 amp to a lower value, it should be decreased only to lower values until zero current is reached. From zero the current should be increased only in the negative direction until −0.5 amp is reached. Further changes should be to smaller currents only from −0.5 to 0 and then to larger currents only from 0 to +0.5 amp. If the current were decreased from +0.5 to +0.4 and then increased to +0.5 amp, hysteresis would carry the material off the original loop. If this error were made, the only certain method for getting back on the original loop would be to demagnetize and start again.

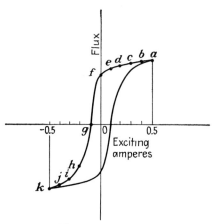

FIG. 7.31   Hysteresis loop for the circuit of Fig. 7.30.

Refer to the hysteresis loop of Fig. 7.31. With the exciting current at +0.5 amp the flux was that at the point a. This flux value was at first unknown, but is determined later by an indirect method. The points b, c, d, e, and f are spaced at 0.1-amp intervals and were first located with respect to point a. To measure the flux change from a to b, it was necessary to change the current quickly from +0.5 to +0.4 amp and observe the corresponding fluxmeter reading. Rheostat R_2 was set for zero resistance. S_2 was then opened, and next resistance was cut in slowly in R_2 until the current had been reduced to +0.4 amp. The desired current change was produced, but the change was made too slowly for an accurate reading to be obtained on the flux meter if its pointer had a tendency to drift. Now that R_2 was set so that the current was 0.4 amp when R_2 was in the circuit, it was necessary to get back to the point a so that the current change could be made quickly. This was done by opening S_3 (thus moving on the loop to f), closing S_2, and then closing S_3 to the upper position (causing negative current and moving on the loop to k). Then S_3 was reversed (thus moving on the under side of the loop from k to a). The fluxmeter switch S_4 was then held closed and a fluxmeter reading taken as R_2 was suddenly inserted in the circuit by opening S_2. The corresponding change of current, the fluxmeter reading produced, and the number of search coil turns are recorded in Table 7.3 under Experimental Values.

Next S_4 was opened. Then the current was adjusted to 0.3 amp at the point c by cutting in further resistance in R_2. The magnetic material was then carried around the loop and back to the point a by manipulations similar to those described previously. The fluxmeter reading for a current change from a to c was then taken. In a similar manner the fluxmeter reading for a current change from a to d and that from a to e were measured. The fluxmeter reading for a current change from a to f was taken as the current was changed from +0.5 to

0 amp by opening S_3. The data taken in these cases are also recorded in the table.

5. Locate points in the second and third quadrants on the upper side of the hysteresis loop with respect to the point f representing the residual flux in Fig. 7.31. The last time in step 4 that R_2 was adjusted, it was so set that when it was in the circuit the current was $+0.1$ amp. That was the setting that was needed next in measuring the flux change for a current change from 0 to -0.1 amp. In taking the last fluxmeter reading in step 4, S_3 had been opened from the positive side. Now S_2 was opened, S_4 closed, and then the fluxmeter reading

TABLE 7.3

Experimental values					Computed values			
I_1 initial current, amp	I_2 final current, amp	D fluxmeter reading, divisions	S search coil turns	$\Delta\Phi$ flux change, lines	I current, amp	Φ flux, lines	H magnetic potential gradient, amp-turns per m	B flux density, wb per sq m
....	....	....	...	....	0.5	107,600	625	1.39
$+0.5$	$+0.4$	2.7	20	1,350	0.4	106,250	500	1.37
$+0.5$	$+0.3$	6.4	20	3,200	0.3	104,400	375	1.35
$+0.5$	$+0.2$	12.0	20	6,000	0.2	101,600	250	1.31
$+0.5$	$+0.1$	23.0	20	11,500	0.1	96,100	125	1.24
$+0.5$	0	23.2	10	23,200	0	84,400	0	1.09
0	-0.1	21.2	3	71,000	-0.1	13,400	-125	0.18
0	-0.2	14.7	1	147,000	-0.2	$-62,600$	-250	-0.81
0	-0.3	17.3	1	173,000	-0.3	$-88,600$	-375	-1.14
0	-0.4	18.3	1	183,000	-0.4	$-98,600$	-500	-1.27
0	-0.5	19.2	1	192,000	-0.5	$-107,800$	-625	-1.39

taken as S_3 was closed to the upper position (producing negative current). The reading is recorded in the table opposite the corresponding current change.

Then S_4 was opened. Next the current was adjusted to the point h (-0.2 amp) by cutting out resistance in R_2. The magnetic material was then carried from h to k by closing S_2; from k to a by reversing S_3; and then to f by opening S_3. Next the flux change from f to h, that from f to i, and that from f to j were measured by manipulating the circuit in a manner similar to that used in measuring the change from f to g. The fluxmeter reading for a current change from f to k was taken as the current was changed from 0 to -0.5 amp by closing S_3 in the negative direction with S_2 closed. The data taken in these cases are also recorded in the table.

The flux changes entered in the fifth column of Table 7.3 were computed by multiplying the fluxmeter readings in divisions by the instrument calibration in lines per division and dividing by the corresponding number of search coil turns used.

After the flux changes were computed, the flux at a and that at k could be computed. The total change from a to k was that from a to f plus that from f

to k. Since the loop is symmetrical, the flux at a was one-half the change from a to k, and that at k was equal to the value at a but of opposite sign. These flux values were entered in Table 7.3 in column 7 opposite the respective current values of $+0.5$ and -0.5 amp. Now that the flux at a was determined, the flux at b, at c, at d, at e, and at f were computed by subtracting the respective flux changes from the flux at a. After the flux at f had been computed, that at g, at h, at i, at j, and at k were obtained by subtracting the respective flux changes from the flux at f. Thus the other values in column 7 were obtained.

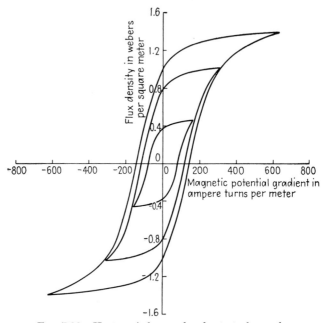

FIG. 7.32   Hysteresis loops of a sheet-steel sample.

Next the various magnetic potential gradients were computed by multiplying the respective current values by the number of turns in the exciting coil and dividing by the mean length of the sample. The various flux densities were computed by dividing the respective flux values by the area of the sample.

Data were taken only for points on the upper side of the loop. The under side was drawn by assuming symmetry. The loop is the largest one in Fig. 7.32.

Any number of symmetrical hysteresis loops can be obtained for a given magnetic circuit, each corresponding to a certain maximum exciting current.

A curve through the maximum ordinates of a group of symmetrical hysteresis loops is a mean magnetization curve, which does not necessarily coincide with the virgin magnetization curve. Usually the two curves are not far apart. For a magnetic circuit that is to be excited with alternating current, the mean magnetization curve should be used.

If one wishes to obtain the mean magnetization curve of a sample with the circuit of Fig. 7.30, one would locate only the end points on a number of hysteresis loops. One would first demagnetize the sample, then increase the exciting current to a desired value, and next reverse the current about ten times to get the sample operating on the hysteresis loop whose end points are to be located. Then the total flux change from one end of the loop to the other can be measured by holding S_4 closed and then recording the flux-meter reading produced by suddenly reversing S_3. One-half of the flux change is the value of flux on the mean magnetization curve corresponding to the current used.

7.22. Residual Flux in Air Gaps

Example 1. The data for the upper half of a hysteresis loop of a certain grade of sheet steel are:

B_S, wb per sq m	0	0.1	0.2	0.3	0.4	0.5	0.6	0.665	0.8	0.9	1.0
H_S, amp-turns per m	47.8	51.7	57.7	63.5	71.5	81.5	95.2	103	137	171	220
	−47.8	−41.8	−37.7	−31.8	−27.8	−19.8	−9.92	0	33.7	87.2	

The steel portion of the circuit of Fig. 7.33 has these characteristics. An alternating current is established in the exciting coil with a maximum value sufficient to cause the steel to operate on the above hysteresis loop. Assume that the cross section of the air gap equals that of the steel. Determine points for and plot the curve showing the relation between the flux in the core and the exciting coil mmf.

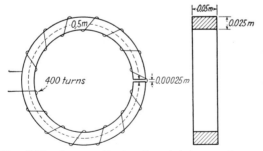

FIG. 7.33   A magnetic circuit containing an air gap.

If the exciting circuit is opened at the instant when the current is a maximum, what will be the residual flux density in the air gap?

Solution. In Fig. 7.34, the hysteresis loop showing the relation between the flux in the core and the reluctance drop in the steel was obtained from the above B_S-H_S loop data. Each value of B_S was multiplied by the cross section of the steel (0.05 m × 0.025 m = 1.25 × 10⁻³ sq m) to obtain the corresponding flux values. Each value of H_S was multiplied by the length of the steel path (0.5 m) to obtain the corresponding reluctance drop values.

In Fig. 7.34, one point on the straight line showing the relation between the flux in the air gap and the reluctance drop across it was computed for the maximum flux density of 1 wb per sq m, since the density in the gap is assumed to be equal to that in the steel. For this density air requires a magnetic potential gradient of $7.96 \times 10^5 \times 1 = 7.96 \times 10^5$ amp-turns per m. The corresponding reluctance drop in the gap is

$$7.96 \times 10^5 \text{ amp-turns per m} \times 0.00025 \text{ m} = 199 \text{ amp-turns}$$

The flux–reluctance-drop curve for the air gap was drawn through this point and the origin.

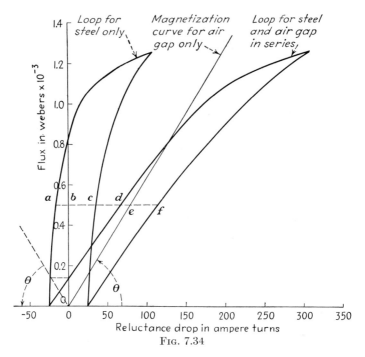

FIG. 7.34

In Fig. 7.34 the loop for the circuit of Fig. 7.33 was obtained as follows: For a value of flux such as that at point b on the vertical axis the reluctance drop in the steel with an increasing flux is bc. The corresponding reluctance drop in the air gap is be. The total reluctance drop in both is $bf = bc + be$. For an equal flux, but decreasing, the reluctance drop in the steel is the negative quantity ba. Physically the steel is now the source of an mmf so that the external mmf required is bd, which is less than the reluctance drop be in the air gap by the magnitude of ba.

By continuing the process of combining the reluctance drop of the steel with that of the air gap for various values of flux, additional points on the total characteristic were determined and the loop drawn as shown.

The residual flux in the air gap can be read directly as 0.14×10^{-3} wb, the intercept of the total characteristic on the flux axis. The value could have been obtained graphically without drawing the total characteristic. A line in the second quadrant passing through the origin and making the same angle θ with the horizontal that the magnetization curve for the air gap does, intersects the second quadrant portion of the hysteresis loop at the ordinate corresponding to the residual flux.

Note that the residual flux in the gap is only about one-sixth of the value that would have existed if the air gap had not been present and the applied mmf had been reduced to zero from the value corresponding to the maximum point on the hysteresis loop.

In Fig. 7.33 assume that the residual flux is at the value of 0.14×10^{-3} wb obtained by applying and then removing an external mmf. Now if the air gap were eliminated by compressing the core, the flux in the core would increase along a hysteresis path to a residual value less than that where the loop for the steel intersects the flux axis. Now if the original air gap were to be reintroduced in the circuit, the residual flux in the gap will be less than before. These results can be demonstrated in another way. If two pieces of soft iron are magnetized while in contact and then the magnetizing agent is removed, more pull is required to separate the pieces the first time than for a subsequent time. Also, if two nails are magnetized by a permanent magnet while in contact, there may be enough residual magnetism for one nail to support the other after the magnet is removed. Then, if the nails are separated once, it may be that there will not be sufficient residual magnetism for one nail to support the other when they are again placed in contact.

To determine the residual flux that will exist in an air gap in a ferromagnetic core, one does not need the complete hysteresis loop of the core material but only the second quadrant portion of it, as in Fig. 7.37.

7.23. Permanent Magnets. Hysteresis causes an undesired energy loss in a ferromagnetic material subjected to a varying mmf. However, hysteresis makes possible self-excited generators and permanent magnets. The second quadrant portion of a hysteresis loop is a demagnetization curve. The residual flux density B_r and the coercive force H_c in a magnetic material depend upon the kind of material and the maximum value of the magnetizing potential gradient. A permanent-magnet material should have a high value of both B_r and H_c. Typical demagnetization curves for four permanent-magnet steels are in Fig. 7.35. These correspond to initial magnetizing gradients of 160,000 amp-turns per m or more.

Example 1. In the magnetic circuit of Fig. 7.36 a residual flux density of 0.3 wb per sq m is to be produced in the air gap. Determine the length l_m of the magnet portion (a) if cobalt-chrome steel is used and (b) if Alnico III is used. Use the demagnetization curves of Fig. 7.35.

Solution. It will be assumed that there is no reluctance drop in the soft-iron pole pieces, that there is no magnetic leakage, that the flux is distributed uniformly in the gap, and that there is no fringing at the gap. If H_m and H_g are the respective magnetic potential gradients in the magnet and in the gap, and l_m and l_g are the respective lengths of the magnet and the gap, then the reluctance drop in the magnet is $H_m l_m$ and that in the gap is $H_g l_g$.   Then,

$$\text{external mmf} = 0 = H_m l_m + H_g l_g$$

from which

$$l_m = -\frac{H_g l_g}{H_m} \tag{1}$$

In this circuit the gap cross section is twice that of the magnet; hence for a gap density $B_g = 0.3$ wb per sq m, the magnet flux density $B_m = 0.6$ wb per sq m. For a gap density of 0.3 wb per sq m, $H_g = 7.96 \times 10^5 \times 0.3 = 240,000$ amp-turns per m.

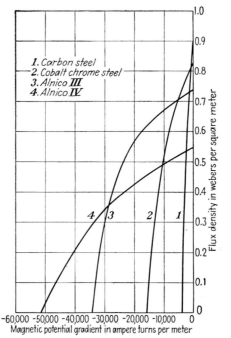

FIG. 7.35   Demagnetization curves of permanent-magnet materials.

a. For cobalt-chrome steel, from Fig. 7.35, at $B_m = 0.6$ wb per sq m,

$$H_m = -8,300 \text{ amp-turns per m}$$

From (1),

$$l_m = -\frac{240,000 \text{ amp-turns per m} \times 0.004 \text{ m}}{-8,300 \text{ amp-turns per m}} = 0.116 \text{ m}$$

b. For Alnico III, from Fig. 7.35, at $B_m = 0.6$ wb per sq m,

$$H_m = -17,500 \text{ amp-turns per m}$$

From (1),

$$l_m = -\frac{240,000 \text{ amp-turns per m} \times 0.004 \text{ m}}{-17,500 \text{ amp-turns per m}} = 0.055 \text{ m}$$

The preceding results show that about one-half as much Alnico III as cobalt steel is required.

When the function of a permanent magnet is to establish flux in an air

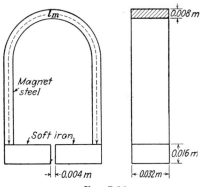

FIG. 7.36

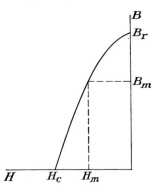

FIG. 7.37   A demagnetization curve of a permanent-magnet material.

gap, an economical design would produce the desired flux with the least amount of material. From Example 1,

$$H_m l_m = -H_g l_g \qquad (7.6)$$

Neglecting leakage, the flux in the magnet equals that in the gap or

$$B_m A_m = B_g A_g \qquad (7.7)$$

where B_m is the magnet flux density, A_m is the magnet cross section, B_g is the gap flux density, and A_g is the gap cross section. Multiplying (7.6) by (7.7) yields $B_m A_m H_m l_m = -B_g A_g H_g l_g$, from which

$$A_m l_m = -\frac{B_g A_g H_g l_g}{B_m H_m}$$

But $A_m l_m$ is the volume of the magnet and H_g is directly proportional to B_g. Then for given gap dimensions and flux density, the minimum magnet volume is obtained when the product of B_m and the corresponding value of H_m is a maximum. The product $B_m H_m$ has the dimension of energy. In Fig. 7.38 are curves that show the relation between $B_m H_m$ and H_m for the materials of Fig. 7.35. These curves show a magnet designer what value of B_m should be chosen to require a minimum of magnetic material.

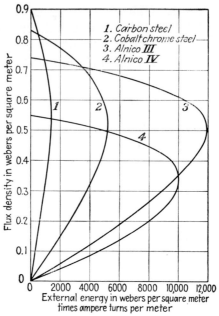

FIG. 7.38 External energy relations in the permanent-magnet materials of Fig. 7.35.

7.24. Leakage Flux. In most cases when current is sent through an exciting coil about a magnetic material, there is flux in the air about the coil and the material as well as in the material. The useful flux is that which produces a desired magnetic effect. The leakage flux is the remainder that does not produce the desired effect.

Usually most of the reluctance offered to the establishment of leakage flux is that of air. Although air has a constant permeability, the reluctance of a leakage path seldom can be computed exactly. The leakage path usually has such an irregular outline that an approximate computation of the reluctance must be used.

For a given magnetic circuit the ratio of the leakage flux to the useful flux usually depends upon the location of the exciting coil. Consider the ferromagnetic circuit of Fig. 7.39 in which three locations of the exciting turns are shown. The points a, b, c, etc., are spaced at 0.05-m intervals along the inner surface of the circuit. In each case the exciting mmf is 3.2 amp × 500 turns = 1,600 amp-turns. The length of the path along the inner surface is taken as 0.8 m. If, in each case, the flux were confined to the metal, the reluctance drop would be distributed uniformly along the length of the circuit. The drop per unit length would be 1,600 amp-turns/0.8 m = 2,000 amp-turns per m. The differences of magnetic potential between various points along the circuit are to be

computed.   Consider first the three analogous electric circuits of Fig.
7.40.   Here the total emf of the batteries is 1,600 v and the total resistance of each circuit is $16R$ ohms, so that the voltage drop across each
resistor is 100 v.   In each circuit there is no voltage between the points
p and h, since the algebraic sum of the emfs in either of the two paths
between the points is equal to the algebraic sum of the resistance drops.

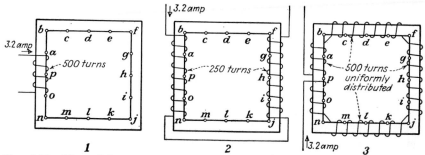

FIG. 7.39   Three different locations for the exciting turns on a certain magnetic
circuit.   The points a, b, c, etc., are spaced at intervals of 0.05 m along the inner
surface of the circuit.

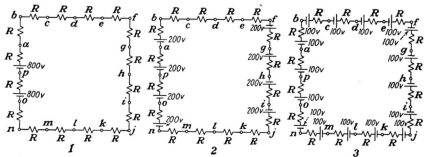

FIG. 7.40   Electric circuits analogous to the magnetic circuits in Fig. 7.39 if it is
assumed that all the flux is confined to the metal portion of the circuit.

In Fig. 7.40 the voltage between points g and i is 200 v in 1, 200 v in 2,
and zero in 3.   The voltage between points d and l is 800 v in 1, zero in 2,
and zero in 3.

If it is assumed in Fig. 7.39 that all the flux is confined to the metallic
path, the magnetic potential between the various points can be computed
in a manner similar to that used for computing voltages between points in
Fig. 7.40.   The magnetic potential between two points in the magnetic
circuit is equal to the rise in magnetic potential resulting from passage
through the exciting turns between those points less the sum of the
reluctance drops in the material between the points.   In each case in
Fig. 7.39 the magnetic potential between p and h is zero, since in going

from one point to the other one-half of the exciting turns and one-half of the material are passed through.

In case 1, Fig. 7.39, the magnetic potential between points g and i is the reluctance drop in a length of 0.1 m and is

$$2,000 \text{ amp-turns per m} \times 0.1 \text{ m} = 200 \text{ amp-turns}$$

In case 2, the exciting turns between g and i produce 400 amp-turns. The reluctance drop in the material between the points is 200 amp-turns. Hence, the magnetic potential between the points is

$$400 - 200 = 200 \text{ amp-turns}$$

In case 3 there is no magnetic potential between points g and i because one-eighth of the exciting turns are between them and one-eighth of the total reluctance drop in the material occurs between them.

By computations similar to the preceding, the magnetic potentials between various pairs of points for each case in Fig. 7.39 were obtained. They are given in Table 7.4.

TABLE 7.4

Points	Ampere-turns of exciting turns between points			Ampere-turns reluctance drop between points			Ampere-turns magnetic potential between points		
	Case 1	Case 2	Case 3	Case 1	Case 2	Case 3	Case 1	Case 2	Case 3
g and i	0	400	200	200	200	200	200	200	0
f and j	0	800	400	400	400	400	400	400	0
e and k	0	800	600	600	600	600	600	200	0
d and l	0	800	800	800	800	800	800	0	0
c and m	0	800	1,000	1,000	1,000	1,000	1,000	−200	0
b and n	0	800	1,200	1,200	1,200	1,200	1,200	−400	0
a and o	0	1,200	1,400	1,400	1,400	1,400	1,400	−200	0

From Table 7.4 it can be seen that the greatest magnetic potentials between points occur in case 1 where the exciting coil is concentrated on a small portion of the circuit.

The air surrounding the metal in the circuits of Fig. 7.39 will carry flux when subjected to a magnetic potential. The reluctance of the air paths is represented by analogy by the resistors of resistance R_1, R_2, R_3, etc., in Fig. 7.41. In the electric circuits the presence of these resistors causes the voltages between various points and the currents in the resistors of resistance R to differ from what they were in Fig. 7.40. In similar manner, in the magnetic circuits of Fig. 7.39 the presence of the air paths causes the magnetic potentials between various points to differ from what they were computed to be with the effects of the air paths neglected, except in case 3. In that case, there was no magnetic potential between any of the points and there will be no flux in the air about the core. The greatest amount of flux in the air about the core will occur in case 1 because the greatest magnetic potentials occur between points along the core.

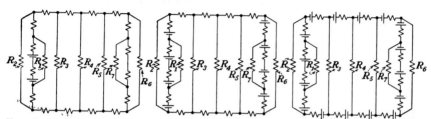

Fig. 7.41   Electric circuits analogous to the magnetic circuits in Fig. 7.39. The reluctance of the air surrounding the metal core in the magnetic circuits is represented by the resistors R_1, R_2, R_3, etc.

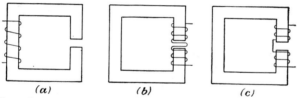

(a)   (b)   (c)

Fig. 7.42   Three different positions for the exciting coil on a given magnetic circuit.

The preceding examples show that leakage flux can be reduced to a minimum by distributing the exciting mmf along a magnetic circuit in the same manner as the reluctance drop is distributed. In case 3 of Fig. 7.39 there is no magnetic potential between the various points selected. At the corners there are points between which magnetic potentials exist; thus there will be some leakage flux. A close approach to the condition of no leakage flux can be made if a toroid is wound with rectangular wire such that adjacent turns almost touch along the inner circumference.

Consider the magnetic circuit of Fig. 7.42. The function of the exciting coil is to establish flux in the air gap. The reluctance drop in the gap is likely to be only slightly less than the coil mmf. Assume, in Fig. 7.42a, that the drop is 1,000 amp-turns and the mmf is 1,200 amp-turns. For this location of the exciting coil, the magnetic potential will vary from 1,000 amp-turns between points on opposite sides of the gap to slightly less than 1,200 amp-turns between points on opposite sides of the coil. All leakage paths are subjected to a magnetic potential nearly equal to that of the coil.

In Fig. 7.42*b* the exciting coil has been placed about the air gap in the circuit. For a coil mmf of 1,200 amp-turns, the reluctance drop in the gap might be 1,100 amp-turns. The magnetic potential between points along the metal portion of the circuit will vary from about 100 amp-turns between points on opposite sides of coil to nearly zero between

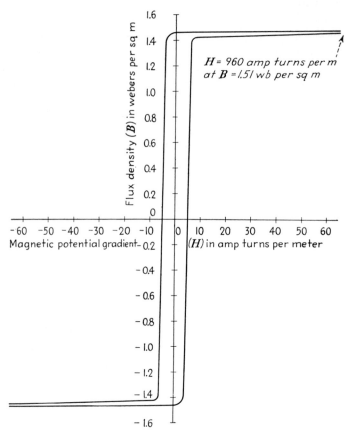

Fig. 7.43   A rectangular hysteresis loop of a Deltamax core.

other points on the core. The leakage paths are subjected to magnetic potentials much less than in the previous case and the leakage fluxes are reduced in direct proportion.

If it is not desirable or physically possible to place an exciting coil about an air gap in a magnetic circuit, it may be possible to divide the exciting coil and place one-half the turns on each side of and near the gap as in Fig. 7.42*c*. In other cases, as in a d-c generator, it may be necessary to place all the exciting turns on one side of the gap.

7.25. Rectangular Hysteresis Loops. For many applications, the shape of the hysteresis loop of the magnetic materials used is of no particular importance. In a power transformer it is desired that the loop have a small area in order that the hysteresis loss will be small and that saturation not occur until high values of flux density are attained in order that the mmf required to establish the flux will be small. However, there are applications for which what is called a rectangular hysteresis loop is desired. Actually, in addition to a rectangular loop it is desired that there be a region in which an intense degree of saturation occurs such that very little increase in the flux density results from a relatively great increase in the magnetic potential gradient. A rectangular hysteresis loop of a commercially available oriented 50 per cent nickel–50 per cent iron alloy is shown in Fig. 7.43. Some applications for material with such a hysteresis loop are discussed in Art. 8.22.

PROBLEMS

7.1. Compute the mmf acting on a magnetic circuit that is surrounded by a 200-turn coil carrying 3 amp.

7.2. A certain 500-turn coil has 100 ohms resistance and 120-v direct current is applied to it. Compute the coil mmf.

7.3. The coil of copper wire about a certain magnetic circuit produces 600 amp-turns and uses 50 w when 6-v direct current is applied to it. The coil is to be replaced by one that has an equal mean length of turn, and twenty times as many turns of wire with one-twentieth the cross section of that in the original coil. Compare the volumes of copper in the coils. Compare the resistances of the coils.

How much voltage should be applied to the second coil if the mmf is to equal that in the original coil? Compute the corresponding power input to the coil.

From the standpoint of the volume of copper required and that of the power input is one coil preferable to the other? State other factors that would be considered in choosing between the coils.

7.4. Ten turns of copper wire when wound about a certain magnetic circuit and connected to a 12-v d-c source produce an mmf of 2 amp-turns. A second coil, identical to the first, is also wound about the circuit. Compute the mmf if the two coils in series are connected across the source.

7.5. A sinusoidal current of 10 amp rms flows in a 40-turn coil. Compute the range through which the mmf acting on the magnetic circuit varies.

7.6. A certain 10-layer coil that is 4 in. long is wound of wire having a diameter, including the insulation, of 0.05 in. With 250 ma in the coil, compute the mmf acting on a magnetic circuit surrounded by the coil.

7.7. A certain d-c generator has 10 shunt-field coils that are to produce a total of 80,000 amp-turns. Compute the resistance of and the number of turns for each coil if the coils are to be in series and draw 16 amp from a 240-v d-c source.

Compute the resistance of and the number of turns for each coil if the coils are to be in parallel, and draw a total of 16 amp from a 240-v d-c source.

7.8. Compute the reluctance of an air gap that is 7 in. long and 1,100 sq in. in cross section.

7.9. Compute the reluctance of a magnetic path that has a length of 2 m, a cross section of 0.04 sq m, and a permeability of 2,000.

7.10. Compute the permeance of the air gap of Prob. 7.8.

7.11. Compute the permeance of the magnetic path of Prob. 7.9.

7.12. A magnetic path that has a permeance of 2×10^{-5} mks units is in parallel with one that has a permeance of 5×10^{-5} mks units. Compute the permeance and the reluctance of the combination.

7.13. The magnetic paths of Prob. 7.12 are in series. Compute the permeance and the reluctance of the combination.

7.14. The parallel combination of magnetic paths of Prob. 7.12 are in series with a third path that has a permeance of 10^{-5} mks units. The flux in the first path is 1,200 μwb. Compute the flux in and the reluctance drop in each of the other paths and the reluctance drop across the entire combination.

7.15. In a certain magnetic circuit that is 8 in. long and 2 sq in. in cross section, an mmf of 500 amp-turns produces a flux of 3,000 μwb. Compute the permeability of the material in the circuit.

7.16. In a certain air gap that is 0.1 in. long an mmf of 5,000 amp-turns produces a flux of 500 μwb. Compute the area of the gap.

7.17. In a certain magnetic circuit that is 20 in. long and 0.5 sq in. in cross section, an mmf of 400 amp-turns produces a flux of 800 μwb. Compute the magnetic potential gradient.

7.18. Compute the reluctance drop over a distance of 0.25 in. in a magnetic path in which the magnetic potential gradient is constant at 100,000 amp-turns per m.

7.19. The magnetic potential gradient along a straight line between two points varies with distance according to the equation $H = 50l$ amp-turns per m, where l is 0.1 m at the first point and 0.5 m at the other. The gradient is at all points directed along the line. Compute the reluctance drop between the points.

7.20. In a certain magnetic material a magnetic potential gradient of 200 amp-turns per m produces a flux density of 1.2 wb per sq m. For this flux density compute the permeability of the material.

7.21. In a certain magnetic material the permeability is 1,000 when the flux density is 0.8 wb per sq m. If the magnetic potential gradient is doubled, the flux density is increased 20 per cent. Compute the permeability at the higher density.

7.22. A flux of 2,000 μwb is to be established in an air gap that is 0.1 in. long and 5 sq in. in cross section. Compute the flux density, the magnetic potential gradient, and the reluctance drop.

7.23. The reluctance drop is 4,000 amp-turns across an air gap that is 0.2 in. long and 10 sq in. in cross section. Compute the magnetic potential gradient, the flux density, and the flux in the gap.

7.24. A toroid sample of sheet steel was tested in the circuit of Fig. 7.8. The mean length was 25 in. and the cross section was 1 by 1.25 in. The exciting coil had 4,000 turns. The fluxmeter calibration was 100 μwb per scale division with a one-turn search coil. A three-turn search coil was used. With the magnetic circuit initially demagnetized, a sudden current change from 0 to 125 ma caused a fluxmeter deflection of 37.5 divisions. Compute the flux density produced and the corresponding permeability.

7.25. For the magnetic circuit of Fig. 7.11 compute the current in the exciting coil to produce a flux of 500 μwb.

7.26. For the magnetic circuit of Fig. 7.11 compute the flux that would be produced by 1 amp in the exciting coil.

7.27. A certain magnetic circuit that consists of cast steel in series with an air gap may be considered to have a cross section of 0.8 sq in. throughout. The mean length of the magnetic path in the steel is 8 in. The length of the gap is 0.02 in. Compute the mmf required to produce a flux of 640 μwb.

7.28. The dimensions of a certain electromagnet are given in Fig. 7.44. The material in the magnetic circuit is all cast steel except for brass disks 0.01 in. thick, one of which is attached to each pole P between the pole face and the keeper. When the keeper is in contact with the disks, what mmf is required to produce a flux of 130 μwb?

7.29. For the magnet of Prob. 7.28, compute points for and plot the saturation curve showing the relation between the flux and the mmf.

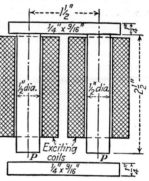

7.30. A certain magnetic circuit that consists of sheet steel in series with an air gap may be considered to have a cross section of 1.5 sq in. throughout. The mean length of the magnetic path in the steel is 12 in. The length of the gap is 0.05 in. By a graphical method compute the flux that would be produced by an mmf of 1,800 amp-turns.

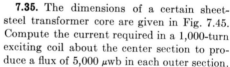

Fig. 7.44

7.31. A certain series magnetic circuit consists of a magnetic material portion 20 in. long and an air gap 0.05 in. long. For a certain flux density the reluctance drop in the magnetic material is 250 amp-turns and that in the gap is 500 amp-turns. For this flux density compute the permeability of the magnetic material.

7.32. A certain series magnetic circuit consists of a sheet-steel portion that is 20 in. long and has 2 sq in. cross section and a cast-steel portion that is 8 in. long and has 4 sq in. cross section. Compute the mmf that would be required to produce a flux of 1,800 μwb.

7.33. For the circuit of Prob. 7.32, compute the flux that would be produced by 400 amp-turns.

7.34. The material in a certain magnetic circuit is all cast steel. Throughout a length of 8 in. the cross section is 3 sq in. Throughout the remaining length of 20 in. the cross section is 2 sq in. Compute the current required in a 200-turn exciting coil to produce a flux of 2,000 μwb in the circuit.

7.35. The dimensions of a certain sheet-steel transformer core are given in Fig. 7.45. Compute the current required in a 1,000-turn exciting coil about the center section to produce a flux of 5,000 μwb in each outer section.

7.36. In Fig. 7.45 a 1,000-turn coil carrying 200 ma surrounds the center section. Compute the flux in each outer section of the sheet-steel core.

A second coil that has 200 turns is wound about one outer section. With the current in the first coil maintained at 200 ma, how much current in the second coil will reduce the flux through it to zero? Will the flux through the first coil remain at the original value? If not, compute its new value.

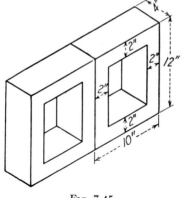

Fig. 7.45

With the current in the first coil maintained at 25 ma, how much current in the second coil will reduce the flux through the other outer section to zero?

7.37. Two sheet-steel magnetic paths are in parallel. The first has a length of 0.15 m and a cross section of 0.0015 sq m. The second has a length of 0.3 m and a cross section of 0.002 sq m. The flux in the first is 1,600 μwb. Compute the flux in the second and the total flux.

7.38. The total flux entering the two paths of Prob. 7.37 is 3,000 μwb. Compute the flux in and the reluctance drop across each path.

7.39. The stacking factor for a transformer core is the ratio of the cross section of steel in a core to the gross cross section of the core. With an insulation thickness of 1 mil, compute the stacking factor of a core in which the thickness of the steel of a lamination is 14 mils. Repeat for a thickness of the steel of 5 mils.

7.40. In the sheet-steel core of Fig. 7.46 the outside branches each have a mean length of 0.15 m and a cross section of 3.2×10^{-4} sq m; the center branch has a mean

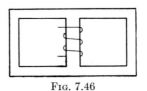

FIG. 7.46

length of 0.05 m and a cross section of 5×10^{-4} sq m. Compute the mmf required in the coil to produce a flux of 600 μwb in the center branch.

7.41. Compute the flux that would be produced in the center branch of Fig. 7.46 by 165 amp-turns in the exciting coil.

7.42. In Fig. 7.17 the flux in leg B is 1,600 μwb. Compute the fluxes in legs A and C and the mmf required in the exciting coil.

7.43. In Fig. 7.17 the mmf of the exciting coil is 1,200 amp-turns. Compute the flux in each branch.

7.44. The metal in the magnetic circuit of Fig. 7.47 is sheet steel. Compute the mmf required in an exciting coil about the center leg to produce a flux of 6,000 μwb across the air gap. Neglect any fringing at the gap.

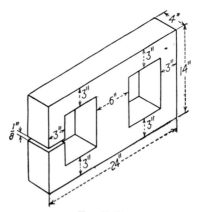

FIG. 7.47

Compute the fluxes in the three branches that would be produced by 1,500 amp-turns in an exciting coil about the center leg.

7.45. A certain cast-iron toroid that had a mean length of 0.5 m and a cross section of 4.5×10^{-4} sq m was wound with an exciting coil of 1,300 turns. A fluxmeter that had a calibration of 100 μwb per division with a one-turn search coil was connected to a twenty-turn search coil on the toroid. The exciting current was varied from 0 to 1 amp and back several times to ensure that a repeating magnetic cycle was produced. The data in the accompanying table were taken to determine points on the hysteresis loop being traversed. In each case the circuit was so manipulated as to keep the material in the original magnetic cycle.

It had been determined previously that the flux corresponding to 1 amp was 300 μwb. From the data compute points for and plot the displaced hysteresis loop traversed.

Initial current, amp	Final current, amp	Fluxmeter reading, divisions	Initial current, amp	Final current, amp	Fluxmeter reading, divisions
0	0.1	1.6	1	0.9	1.0
0	0.2	3.8	1	0.8	2.3
0	0.3	5.8	1	0.7	3.7
0	0.4	8.0	1	0.6	5.2
0	0.5	10.5	1	0.5	7.0
0	0.6	12.7	1	0.4	9.0
0	0.7	15.0	1	0.3	11.5
0	0.8	17.0	1	0.2	14.2
0	0.9	19.7	1	0.1	17.5
0	1.0	21.7	1	0	21.7

7.46. The accompanying hysteresis loop data were taken on a sheet-steel toroid that had a mean length of 0.35 m, a cross section of 8×10^{-4} sq m, and a 450-turn exciting coil. Plot the loop in terms of B and H.

Current, amp	Flux, μwb	Current, amp	Flux, μwb	Current, amp	Flux, μwb
0.5	1,020	0	780	0.1	210
0.4	1,000	−0.1	230	0.2	720
0.3	980	−0.2	−660	0.3	870
0.2	950	−0.1	−630	0.4	950
0.1	900	0	−510	0.5	1,020

7.47. A sheet-steel toroid that had a mean length of 1 m, a cross section of 0.0015 sq m, and a 1,750-turn exciting coil was connected as in Fig. 7.30. The fluxmeter calibration was 100 μwb per division with a one-turn search coil. A maximum current of 100 ma was used. The electric circuit was so manipulated as to keep the magnetic material operating on a symmetrical hysteresis loop. The data are recorded in the accompanying table. Plot the hysteresis loop in terms of B and H.

Initial current, ma	Final current, ma	Fluxmeter reading, divisions	Turns in search coil
100	57	18	20
100	25	29	10
100	8	25	5
100	0	26	4
0	−14	26	4
0	−22	21	2
0	−53	31	2
0	−100	39	2

7.48. In the magnetic circuit of Fig. 7.36 a residual flux density of 0.25 wb per sq m is to be produced in the air gap. Determine the length l_m of the magnet if Alnico IV is used.

7.49. In the magnetic circuit of Fig. 7.36 a length $l_m = 0.1$ m of Alnico III is used. Compute the residual flux in the air gap.

7.50. In Fig. 7.48 are two toroids, one wound with a uniformly distributed winding, the other with a concentrated winding. In each case the exciting coil is producing 500 amp-turns. For each toroid, compute the approximate magnetic potential acting to produce leakage flux between the points A and B.

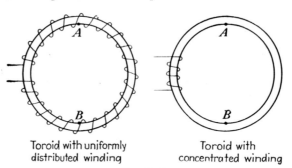

Toroid with uniformly distributed winding

Toroid with concentrated winding

Fig. 7.48

CHAPTER 8

MAGNETICALLY INDUCED ELECTROMOTIVE FORCES

8.1. Flux Linkages. Current in a conductor establishes flux in the conductor and in the medium surrounding it. A flux line surrounds the current that produces it. A closed circuit is at least one turn; therefore the flux passing through the area bounded by the turn encloses at least one turn. The linking of flux lines with a turn (or turns) constitutes flux linkages. The weber-turn is the mks unit of flux linkage.

With current in a coil of wire it may be that many turns are linked by certain flux lines. If all the flux linked all turns of the coil, the flux linkages would equal the product of the flux and the number of turns. The condition of all the flux linking all the turns of a coil is not physically realizable, but it can be closely approached by winding closely spaced turns in a single layer on a toroid core.

If the various turns of a coil are linked by different values of flux, the total flux linkages are equal to the sum of the fluxes through the individual turns. If Φ_1 is the flux in webers through turn 1, Φ_2 that through turn 2, etc., the flux linkages of turn 1 are Φ_1 wb-turns, those of turn 2 are Φ_2 wb-turns, etc. Hence the total flux linkages are $\Phi_1 + \Phi_2 \cdots$. It is usually difficult to compute the fluxes through the individual turns, given the geometry of a coil and the current in it. However, the total flux linkages corresponding to a given current in a given coil can be measured readily with instruments. If the total flux linkages λ wb-turns are produced in N turns in series, then λ/N is an equivalent flux in webers. The equivalent flux is that value which, linking all the turns of a coil, would produce a number of flux linkages equal to that actually present in the coil.

If the magnetic circuit of a coil has constant permeability, the relative distribution of the flux over a given area within the coil is unchanged if the flux is changed and the total flux is directly proportional to the current in the coil. If the current is doubled, the total flux is doubled, and the flux linkages are doubled.

If the magnetic circuit of a coil contains steel, the relative distribution of the flux over the steel cross section changes if the flux is changed, because of the changed permeability of the steel. If the current is doubled, the exciting mmf is doubled, and the total flux is changed in accordance with the magnetization curve of the steel. The flux linkages do not increase in exact proportion with the increase in the flux. However, in many cases where an exciting coil surrounds a steel core, an analysis suitable for many purposes can be based on the assumption that all the flux is confined to the core and links all the turns of the coil.

8.2. Induced EMF. Faraday proved in 1831 that an emf appeared in a conductor whenever there was a change in the flux linking the conductor. One can illustrate the principle with a horseshoe magnet, a coil of wire, and a millivoltmeter. Place the coil over one leg of the magnet, and then connect the coil ends to the millivoltmeter. Now observe the instrument pointer while holding the coil and moving the magnet. The pointer deflects in one direction when the magnet is moved toward the coil and in the opposite direction when the magnet is moved away from the coil. More rapid movement of the magnet causes a greater pointer deflection. If the magnet is held stationary, a pointer deflection occurs if the coil is moved. If the magnet and the coil are moved together so that there is no relative motion between them, no pointer deflection occurs. If the coil is about a leg of the magnet and both are held stationary while a piece of steel is moved to make and break contact with the poles, a pointer deflection occurs when the steel is moved. The deflection is in one direction while the steel is moved toward the poles and in the opposite direction while the steel is moved away from the poles.

An emf that is produced in a conductor by a changing magnetic field without movement of either the conductor or the medium in which the field exists is usually called an induced emf. When a conductor moves through a magnetic field or the field moves across the conductor, the emf produced is usually called a generated emf.

The instantaneous emf induced in a conductor is proportional to the rate of change of the conductor flux linkages. This is Faraday's law of induction although he did not definitely so state it.* In equational form

$$e = \frac{d\lambda}{dt} \tag{8.1}$$

where e is the instantaneous emf in volts and $d\lambda/dt$ is the rate of change of flux linkages in weber-turns per second.

---

* For a discussion on this point and other historical facts, see T. J. Higgins, The Origins and Developments of the Concepts of Inductance, Skin Effect, and Proximity Effects, *Am. J. Phys.*, vol. 9, no. 6, pp. 337–346, December, 1941.

When the flux linkages are directly proportional to the flux, the instantaneous emf e is

$$e = N \frac{d\phi}{dt} \quad \text{v} \qquad (8.2)$$

where N is the number of turns in series and $d\phi/dt$ is the rate of change in webers per second of the equivalent flux linking the turns. Positive directions of e and ϕ are related as in Fig. 8.1a. Here a permanent magnet is being inserted in a coil such that the flux is increasing in the upward direction. The direction of the emf is determined by Lenz's law: *The direction of the emf produced in a coil by a changing flux is such that a current in the same direction would produce an mmf that would oppose the change in flux.* Here if one points the extended thumb of the right hand opposite to the direction of increasing flux and encircles the fingers about the coil, the fingers point in the direction of the emfs in the turns. The polarities of the coil terminals are shown.

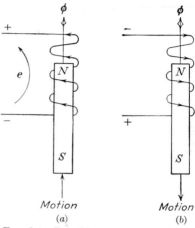

Fig. 8.1   Polarities of a coil produced by moving a magnet into and out of it.

In Fig. 8.1b the magnet is being removed from the coil. The flux is upward through the coil, but the amount of flux is decreasing. Here the direction of the emfs in the turns is such that currents in the same direction would establish flux in the upward direction. The polarities of the coil terminals are reversed from what they were in Fig. 8.1a. The positive direction of the emf was chosen according to the polarities produced by an increasing flux in the chosen positive direction. A flux in that direction that is decreasing has a negative rate of change and, by (8.2), induces a negative emf.

In graphical terms, (8.2) shows that the emf as a function of time is directly proportional (the proportionality factor being the number of turns N) to the slope of the curve of the flux as a function of time, since $d\phi/dt$ is a symbol for that slope.

Example 1. The coil of Fig. 8.1a has 500 turns. The magnet is moved in such a manner that the equivalent flux linking the turns increases linearly from 2×10^{-5} wb to 5×10^{-5} wb in 0.04 sec and then decreases linearly to 1×10^{-5} wb in the next 0.01 sec. Determine the manner in which the emf in the coil varies with time. Plot the flux-time and emf-time curves.

Solution. The flux-time curve plotted from the given information is in Fig. 8.2. During the interval from 0 to 0.04 sec the flux ϕ is increasing at a constant rate of $(5 - 2) \times 10^{-5}$ wb/0.04 sec $= 7.5 \times 10^{-4}$ wb per sec. During this interval the emf e is constant at 500 turns $\times 7.5 \times 10^{-4}$ wb per sec $= 0.375$ v

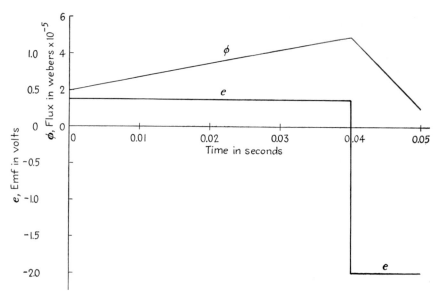

Fig. 8.2   Emf e induced in coil of Fig. 8.1 by a flux ϕ that varies as shown.

and is represented by a horizontal line in Fig. 8.2. During the interval from 0.04 to 0.05 sec the flux is changing at a constant rate of

$$\frac{(1 - 5) \times 10^{-5} \text{ wb}}{(0.05 - 0.04) \text{ sec}} = -4 \times 10^{-3} \text{ wb per sec}$$

During this interval the emf is constant at

$$500 \text{ turns} \times (-4 \times 10^{-3} \text{ wb per sec}) = -2 \text{ v}$$

and is represented by another horizontal line in Fig. 8.2. Note that a bidirectional emf is induced here by a flux that does not reverse in direction.

The preceding problem can be solved analytically as follows. During the first interval the equation of the flux-time curve is $\phi = 2 \times 10^{-5} + 7.5 \times 10^{-4}t$ wb, where t is in seconds. By (8.2),

$$e = 500 \frac{d\phi}{dt} = 500 \frac{d}{dt} (2.5 \times 10^{-5} + 7.5 \times 10^{-4}t) = 500(7.5 \times 10^{-4}) = 0.375 \text{ v}$$

a result that shows that the emf is constant during the interval.

During the second interval the equation of the flux-time curve is

$$\phi = 21 \times 10^{-5} - 4 \times 10^{-3}t \text{ wb}$$

where t is in seconds. By (8.2),

$$e = 500 \frac{d\phi}{dt} = 500 \frac{d}{dt} (21 \times 10^{-5} - 4 \times 10^{-3}t) = 500(-4 \times 10^{-3}) = -2 \text{ v}$$

Example 2. The coil of Fig. 8.1 has 2,000 turns. The magnet is moved in such a manner that the equivalent flux linking the coil alternates linearly between equal positive and negative values of 4×10^{-5} wb with a frequency of 1,000 c. Determine the manner in which the emf in the coil varies with time. Plot the flux-time and emf-time curves.

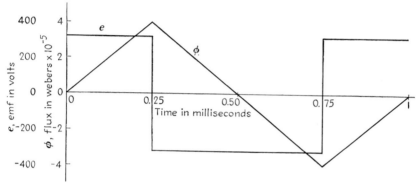

Fig. 8.3   Emf e induced in coil of Fig. 8.1 by a flux ϕ that varies as shown.

Solution. One cycle of the flux-time curve is plotted from the given information in Fig. 8.3. During the interval from 0 to 0.25×10^{-3} sec the flux ϕ is increasing at a constant rate of 4×10^{-5} wb/0.25×10^{-3} sec = 0.16 wb per sec. During this interval the emf is constant at 2,000 turns $\times$ 0.16 wb per sec = 320 v and is represented by a horizontal line in Fig. 8.3. During the interval from 0.25×10^{-3} to 0.75×10^{-3} sec the flux is changing at a constant rate of

$$\frac{(-4 - 4) \times 10^{-5} \text{ wb}}{(0.75 - 0.25) \times 10^{-3} \text{ sec}} = -0.16 \text{ wb per sec}$$

During this interval the emf e is constant at

$$2{,}000 \text{ turns} \times (-0.16 \text{ wb per sec}) = -320 \text{ v}$$

and is represented by a horizontal line in Fig. 8.3. During the interval from 0.75×10^{-3} to 1×10^{-3} sec the flux is changing at a constant rate of

$$\frac{0 - (-4 \times 10^{-5}) \text{ wb}}{(1 - 0.75) \times 10^{-3} \text{ sec}} = 0.16 \text{ wb per sec}$$

During this interval the emf is constant at 2,000 turns $\times$ 0.16 wb per sec = 320 v and is represented by a horizontal line in Fig. 8.3.

Figure 8.3 shows that if the flux linking a coil varies in such a manner as to cause the flux-time wave to be triangular the emf-time wave is rectangular.

Example 3. The coil in Fig. 8.1 has 2,000 turns. The magnet is moved in such a manner that the equivalent flux linking the coil alternates sinusoidally between equal positive and negative values of 4×10^{-5} wb with a frequency of 1,000 c. Determine the manner in which the emf in the coil varies with time. Plot the flux-time and the emf-time curves.

Solution. The general equation of the flux-time curve is $\phi = \Phi_m \sin 2\pi f t$ wb, where Φ_m wb is the maximum flux, f is the frequency in cycles per second, and t is the time in seconds following an instant when the flux is increasing from a zero value. Here $\Phi_m = 4 \times 10^{-5}$ wb and $f = 1,000$ c; hence

$$\phi = 4 \times 10^{-5} \sin 6{,}280t \qquad \text{wb}$$

To compute points from which the flux-time curve may be plotted, Table 8.1 will be used. In 0.001 sec the angle $6{,}280t$ varies through 2π radians and $360°$. Time intervals of $\frac{1}{12}$ cycle = $1/12{,}000$ sec = $30°$ have been chosen and entered

TABLE 8.1

Angle, degrees, $\dfrac{6{,}280t \times 360°}{2\pi}$	Sine of angle	ϕ, wb, $4 \times 10^{-5} \times$ sine of angle	Cosine of angle	$\dfrac{d\phi}{dt}$, wb per sec, $0.251 \times$ cosine of angle	e, v, $2{,}000\,\dfrac{d\phi}{dt}$
(1)	(2)	(3)	(4)	(5)	(6)
0	0	0	1	0.251	502
30	0.500	2×10^{-5}	0.866	0.218	436
60	0.866	3.46×10^{-5}	0.500	0.126	252
90	1.000	4×10^{-5}	0	0	0
120	0.866	3.46×10^{-5}	-0.500	-0.126	-252
150	0.500	2×10^{-5}	-0.866	-0.218	-436
180	0	0	-1.000	-0.251	-502
210	-0.500	-2×10^{-5}	-0.866	-0.218	-436
240	-0.866	-3.46×10^{-5}	-0.500	-0.126	-252
270	-1.000	-4×10^{-5}	0	0	0
300	-0.866	-3.46×10^{-5}	0.500	0.126	252
330	-0.500	-2×10^{-5}	0.866	0.218	436
360	0	0	1.000	0.251	502

in column 1. For each angle the sine was obtained from a trigonometric table and entered in column 2. The instantaneous flux values are computed and entered in column 3. These were plotted in Fig. 8.4 against the respective angles and the ϕ curve was drawn. Here the rate at which the flux is changing varies from instant to instant and can be obtained as the time derivative of the equation of flux as a function of time. Then

$$\frac{d\phi}{dt} = \frac{d}{dt}\,(4 \times 10^{-5} \sin 6{,}280t) = 0.251 \cos 6{,}280t$$

Values of $\cos 6{,}280t$ corresponding to the angles listed in column 1 were obtained from a trigonometric table and entered in column 5. Values of e entered in column 6 were obtained by multiplying each value in column 5 by 2,000, the number of turns. The values of e are plotted in Fig. 8.4 against the respective angles and the e curve drawn.

Figure 8.4 shows that if the flux linking a coil varies in such a manner as to cause the flux-time wave to be sinusoidal the emf-time wave is cosinusoidal.   Since a cosine wave has the same shape as a sine wave, a common statement is that a sinusoidal flux variation induces a sinusoidal emf variation.

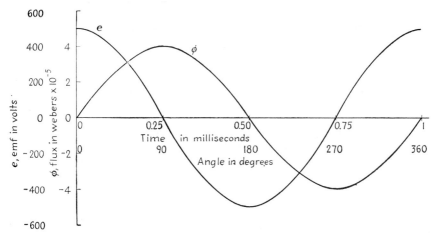

FIG. 8.4   Emf e induced in coil of Fig. 8.1 by a flux ϕ that varies sinusoidally.

From $e = N \, d\phi/dt$, $d\phi = e \, dt/N$.   Then the flux as a function of time during a time interval from t_1 to t seconds is

$$\phi = \frac{1}{N} \int_{t_1}^{t} e \, dt + \Phi_0 \qquad \text{wb} \tag{8.3}$$

where Φ_0 is the equivalent flux in webers linking the N turns at time t_1. The sign of Φ_0 is determined by its direction with respect to that positive for ϕ.   It is often convenient to consider time as zero at time t_1.   Then

$$\phi = \frac{1}{N} \int_{0}^{t} e \, dt + \Phi_0 \tag{8.4}$$

The preceding integrals can be evaluated if e is a constant or if it is a known function of time.   Graphically the evaluation of the integral represents the area in volt-seconds between the emf-time curve and the time axis within the time limits specified.

Example 4.   At $t = 0$, zero flux links the 2,000 turns of a certain coil.   First, the flux changes in such a manner that the emf induced in the coil increases linearly from 0 at $t = 0$ to 50 v at $t = 2$ msec and then decreases linearly to 0 at $t = 3$ msec.   Compute the equivalent flux linking the coil at $t = 2$ and that at $t = 3$ msec.   Determine and plot the flux-time curve.

Solution. The emf-time curve e is plotted in Fig. 8.5 from the given information. The area under this curve between $t = 0$ and $t = 2$ msec is

$$\tfrac{1}{2} \times 50 \text{ v} \times 2 \text{ msec} \times 1 \text{ sec}/1{,}000 \text{ msec} = 0.05 \text{ v-sec}$$

From (8.3), the flux at $t = 2$ msec is this area divided by the 2,000 turns in the coil. Hence, Φ at $t = 2$ msec is 0.05 v-sec/2,000 turns $= 2.5 \times 10^{-5}$ wb.

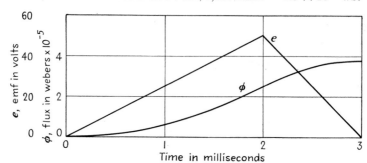

Fig. 8.5   Manner in which the flux ϕ linking the turns of a coil varies to induce the given emf e.

The area under the emf-time curve between $t = 2$ and $t = 3$ msec is one-half that during the former interval, or the area is 0.025 v-sec. Dividing this by the 2,000 turns yields 1.25×10^{-5} wb as the change of flux during the interval. Since the flux was 2.5×10^{-5} wb at $t = 2$ msec, the flux at $t = 3$ msec is

$$1.25 \times 10^{-5} \text{ wb} + 2.5 \times 10^{-5} \text{ wb} = 3.75 \times 10^{-5} \text{ wb}$$

Since the voltage is zero at $t = 0$, the slope of the flux-time curve is zero at $t = 0$ and therefore tangent to the horizontal axis at $t = 0$. That the flux-time curve will be a parabola that is concave upward, during the interval $t = 0$ to $t = 2$ msec, can be seen from the fact that the area under the emf-time curve is increasing as the square of the time, or that the flux-time curve must be a second-degree curve in order that its derivative will be a linear curve. Since the flux is 2.5×10^{-5} wb at $t = 2$ msec, it will be $(1.5/2)^2 \times 2.5 \times 10^{-5}$ wb $= 1.41 \times 10^{-5}$ wb at $t = 1.5$ msec, $(\tfrac{1}{2})^2 \times 2.5 \times 10^{-5}$ wb $= 0.625 \times 10^{-5}$ wb at $t = 1$ msec, and $(0.5/2)^2 \times 2.5 \times 10^{-5}$ wb $= 0.156 \times 10^{-5}$ wb at $t = 0.5$ msec. From these plotted values part of the curve ϕ in Fig. 8.5 was drawn.

The preceding relations can be verified by an analytical method. The equation of the emf e, between $t = 0$ and $t = 2$ msec, is

$$e = 25{,}000t \qquad \text{v}$$

where t is in seconds. Since $\phi = 1/N \int_0^t e\, dt + \Phi_0$ and $\Phi_0 = 0$, then

$$\phi = \frac{1}{2{,}000} \int_0^t 25{,}000t\, dt = \frac{1}{4{,}000} [25{,}000t^2]_0^t = 6.25t^2 \qquad \text{wb}$$

is the equation of the flux-time curve. This verifies the statement above that the curve is a parabola. Substitution of the time values selected above checks the flux values obtained.

During the interval from 2 to 3 msec in Fig. 8.5 the flux-time curve will be a parabola having zero slope at $t = 3$ msec since the emf is zero at that instant. This parabola is concave downward. At $t = 2$ msec, it is tangent to the parabola of the first time interval.   The value of flux at $t = 2.5$ msec can be computed by noting that of the flux change of 1.25×10^{-5} wb from 2.5×10^{-5} wb at $t = 2$ msec to 3.75×10^{-5} wb at $t = 3$ msec, three-fourths will have occurred when

$$t = 2.5 \text{ msec}$$

Hence, the flux at $t = 2.5$ msec is

$$2.5 \times 10^{-5} \text{ wb} + (\tfrac{3}{4})1.25 \times 10^{-5} \text{ wb} = 3.44 \times 10^{-5} \qquad \text{wb}$$

The parabola was drawn in Fig. 8.5 through the points above.

The preceding relations can be verified by an analytical method.   The equation of the emf e, between $t = 2$ and $t = 3$ msec, is

$$e = 150 - 50{,}000t \qquad \text{v}$$

where t is in seconds.   Since $\phi = 1/N \int_{t_1}^{t} e\, dt + \Phi_0$, and $\Phi_0 = 2.5 \times 10^{-5}$ wb then

$$\phi = \frac{1}{2{,}000} \int_{0.002}^{t} (150 - 50{,}000t)\, dt + 2.5 \times 10^{-5} = \frac{1}{2{,}000}\left[150t - \frac{50{,}000t^2}{2} \right]_{0,002}^{t}$$

$$+ \; 2.5 \times 10^{-5} = \frac{1}{2{,}000}\left[150t - \frac{50{,}000t^2}{2} - 150(0.002) + \frac{50{,}000(0.002)^2}{2} \right]$$

$$+ \; 2.5 \times 10^{-5} = 0.075t - 12.5t^2 - 7.5 \times 10^{-5} \text{ wb}$$

is the equation of the flux-time curve.

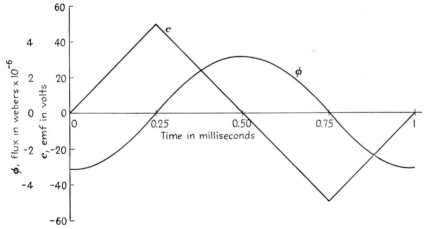

Fɪɢ. 8.6   Manner in which the flux ϕ linking the turns of a coil varies to induce the given emf e.

Example 5.   A flux that links the 2,000 turns of a certain coil alternates between equal positive and negative values in such a manner as to induce an alternating 1,000-c emf of triangular waveform with maxima of 50 v magnitude occurring midway between zero emf points.   Determine the flux waveform.

Solution.   The emf-time curve e was plotted in Fig. 8.6 from the given information.   The area under one-half cycle of the curve is

$$\tfrac{1}{2} \times 50 \text{ v} \times 0.5 \times 10^{-3} \text{ sec} = 12.5 \times 10^{-3} \text{ v-sec}$$

In one-half cycle the flux change will be

$$\frac{12.5 \times 10^{-3} \text{ v-sec}}{2,000 \text{ turns}} = 6.25 \times 10^{-6} \text{ wb}$$

Since the flux wave is symmetrical, the initial value is

$$-\tfrac{1}{2} \times 6.25 \times 10^{-6} = -3.13 \times 10^{-6} \text{ wb}$$

and the final value is $+3.13 \times 10^{-6}$ wb. The equation of the emf wave for the first quarter cycle is $e = 2 \times 10^5 t$ v, where t is in seconds. Then the equation of the flux-time curve during that interval is

$$\phi = \frac{1}{N} \int_0^t e \, dt + \Phi_0 = \frac{1}{2,000} \int_0^t 2 \times 10^5 t \, dt - 3.13 \times 10^5$$

$$= \frac{1}{2,000} \left[\frac{2 \times 10^5 t^2}{2} \right]_0^t - 3.13 \times 10^{-6} = 50t^2 - 3.13 \times 10^{-6} \text{ wb}$$

The section of a parabola corresponding to this equation for the given time interval is in Fig. 8.6. The flux is zero at $t = 0.25$ msec.

The equation of the emf curve between 0.25 and 0.75 msec is

$$e = 100 - 2 \times 10^5 t \qquad \text{v}$$

where t is in seconds. Then the equation of the flux-time curve during that interval is

$$\phi = \frac{1}{N} \int_{0.00025}^t e \, dt + \Phi_0 = \frac{1}{2,000} \int_{0.00025}^t (100 - 2 \times 10^5 t) \, dt$$

$$= \frac{1}{2,000} [100t - 10^5 t^2]_{0.00025}^t$$

$$= 0.05t - 50t^2 - 9.375 \times 10^{-6} \text{ wb}$$

The section of a parabola corresponding to this equation for the given time interval is in Fig. 8.6. The flux is zero at $t = 0.75$ msec.

The equation of the emf curve between 0.75 and 1 msec is

$$e = -200 + 2 \times 10^5 t \qquad \text{v}$$

where t is in seconds. Then the equation of the flux-time curve during that interval is

$$\phi = \frac{1}{N} \int_{0.00075}^t e \, dt + \Phi_0 = \frac{1}{2,000} \int_{0.00075}^t (-200 + 2 \times 10^5 t) \, dt$$

$$= \frac{1}{2,000} [-200t + 10^5 t^2]_{0.00075}^t$$

$$= -0.1t + 50t^2 + 4.69 \times 10^{-5} \text{ wb}$$

The section of a parabola corresponding to this equation for the given time interval is in Fig. 8.6.

Example 6. The rectangular loop of Fig. 8.7 has one side that is moving with a constant velocity v m per sec. The loop is normal to an unchanging magnetic field of uniform density B wb per sq m directed out of the paper. At time $t = 0$ the movable side is at a distance x_0 m from the left-hand side of the loop. At a time t sec the movable side is at a distance x m from its position at zero time.

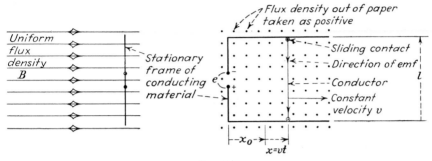

FIG. 8.7

Derive the equation that expresses the flux enclosed in the turn as a function of time. Derive the equation that expresses the emf in the coil as a function of time.

Solution. With the movable side at a distance x m from the initial position, the area enclosed by the turn is $l(x_0 + x)$ sq m. The flux ϕ enclosed is $Bl(x_0 + x)$ wb. With constant velocity v, then $x = vt$ and the equation of the enclosed flux as a function of time is $\phi = Bl(x_0 + vt)$. This shows that the flux is increasing linearly with time as in Fig. 8.8.

The coil emf e is $e = N \, d\phi/dt = 1 \cdot d[Bl(x_0 + vt)]/dt = Blv$ v. This shows that the emf is constant. The direction of the emf is such that current in the same direction would tend to send flux into the paper.

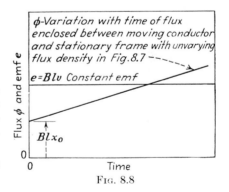

FIG. 8.8

In Fig. 8.7 the emf in the turn is all generated in the moving side. The result leads to the Blv rule as expressed by $e = Blv$ v for a conductor moving in an unvarying magnetic field of uniform density B wb per sq m. In the general case l m is the projection of the conductor in a plane normal to $\mathbf{B}$ and v m per sec is the component of the velocity of the conductor normal to $\mathbf{B}$. The directions of e, $\mathbf{B}$, and v are related by Fleming's right-hand rule: *Place the thumb, the first finger, and the second finger of the right hand mutually perpendicular. Point the first finger in the direction of the flux density and the thumb in the direction of the component of the velocity normal to the flux density. Then the second finger points in the direction of the emf in the conductor.*

If an unvarying magnetic field of uniform density moves across a stationary conductor, to apply Fleming's right-hand rule consider the motion of the conductor relative to the field to be opposite to that in which the field is moving.

Following the application of a constant d-c voltage to a permanent-magnet moving-coil voltmeter, the coil moves through an unvarying magnetic field of uniform density and moves the pointer from zero to a steady-state reading. While the coil is moving, an emf is generated in a direction opposite to that in which the current is being established. This emf is one of the factors that determines how quickly a pointer can assume a steady-state position, but it has nothing to do with determining what that position is.

If the armature and field structures of a d-c generator were kept stationary while a conductor was rotated at constant velocity in the air gap between them, the emf generated in the conductor would vary with time in about the same manner as the flux density was distributed in space. In a modern generator the conductors are placed in slots in the armature core. The teeth carry most of the flux. The flux density at their surface is much greater than that in the slots where the conductors are located. The emf generated in a conductor at a given instant is actually much greater than would be computed from the Blv rule, where B is the flux density in which the conductor is located.

In (8.4) the term $\int_0^t e\, dt$ represents the area under the emf-time curve between the time limits 0 and t sec. In a more general form $\int_{t_1}^t e\, dt$ represents the area under the emf-time curve between the time limits t_1 and t sec. This area divided by the time interval $t - t_1$ sec represents the average emf E_a during the interval. Hence

$$E_a = \frac{1}{t - t_1} \int_{t_1}^t e\, dt \qquad \text{v}$$

When e is being induced by an equivalent flux ϕ through N series turns that changes in some fashion from Φ_1 wb at t_1 to Φ_2 at t_2, then

$$e = \frac{N\, d\phi}{dt}$$

and

$$E_a = \frac{1}{t_2 - t_1} \int_{t_1}^{t_2} \left(N\, \frac{d\phi}{dt} \right) dt = \frac{1}{t_2 - t_1} \int_{\Phi_1}^{\Phi_2} N\, d\phi = \frac{N(\Phi_2 - \Phi_1)}{t_2 - t_1} \qquad \text{v}$$

$$(8.5)$$

This shows that the average emf induced in a given coil during a given time interval by a changing magnetic field depends only upon the initial and the final value of the flux and is independent of the shape of the flux wave during the interval. The average value of an emf is only a measure of the change of flux inducing it and in general conveys no information as to the waveshape of either the flux or the emf.

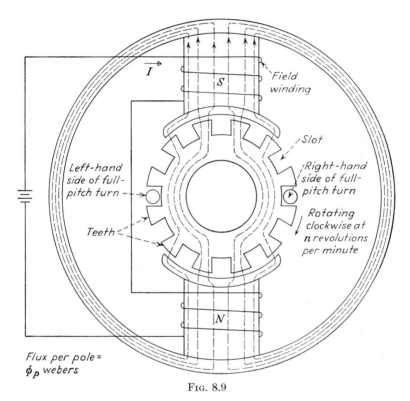

Fig. 8.9

In Fig. 8.9 are represented certain of the parts of a d-c generator. The armature is turning n revolutions per minute (rpm). With the full-pitch, one-turn coil in the position shown, it encloses the flux Φ_p wb per pole. Consider that instant as t_1 and $\Phi_p = -\Phi_1$. With p poles on the generator, the time required for the coil to make 1 revolution is $1/n$ min $= 60/n$ sec. The time required for the coil to move from the position shown to that where it encloses the flux Φ_p of the next pole is $60/np$ sec. Then $t_2 - t_1 = 60/np$ sec and $\Phi_2 = \Phi_p$. Since $N = 1$, then, from (8.5),

$$E_a = \frac{1[\Phi_p - (-\Phi_p)]}{60/np} = \frac{np\Phi_p}{30} \qquad \text{v per turn} \qquad (8.6)$$

In Fig. 8.9, if the armature core were a smooth cylinder of radius r m and a length l m, its surface area would be $2\pi r l$ sq m. The area that carries the flux Φ_p of one pole is $2\pi r l/p$ sq m. If the flux were distributed uniformly over this area with a density B wb per sq m, $\Phi_p = 2\pi r l B/p$ wb. A conductor rotating at n rpm at a radius of r m would have a velocity v m per sec, where $v = 2\pi r n/60$. From this $n = 30v/\pi r$. Substitution of the preceding values of Φ_p and n in (8.6) yields

$$E_a = \frac{(30v/\pi r)p(2\pi r l B/p)}{30} = 2Blv \qquad \text{v per turn}$$

Under the conditions assumed above, the emf generated in a turn is constant while the turn moves a pole pitch; hence the instantaneous emf is

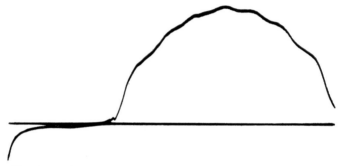

Fig. 8.10   Oscillogram of the emf generated in a d-c generator.

equal to the average emf during the interval. The emf of a full-pitch turn is twice that of a conductor that forms one-half of the turn.

The above derivation shows that when the conductors in a generator are placed in slots, regardless of how the flux of a pole is distributed over the armature surface within a pole pitch, the average emf generated in a full-pitch turn is equal to what it would be if the flux were distributed uniformly.

The emf generated in a turn on a d-c generator is alternating. It has a waveform that is fixed by the space distribution of the flux density and the span of the turn. In Fig. 8.10 is an oscillogram of the emf of a full-pitch turn on a certain d-c generator. Special collector rings were mounted on the armature shaft in order that connections could be made from the rotating turn to stationary external leads.

The coils in the armature winding of a d-c generator are connected in various ways to each other and to the commutator bars. Stationary brushes that ride on the rotating commutator provide contacts with the rotating coils such that a direct voltage is obtained externally between brushes. For most generators operating at constant speed and flux

density, this voltage varies so little with time that its average value is
about equal to its maximum value.

The average numerical value E_a of the emf between brushes on a d-c
generator is proportional to the flux per pole Φ_p and the speed of rotation n
of the armature. Hence $E_a = k_E \Phi_p n$ v. Here k_E is a proportionality factor that is equal to the emf generated per unit of flux and per unit of
speed. If a d-c generator is driven at constant speed with no load connected to its brushes, a d-c voltmeter between the brushes has a reading
that is proportional to the flux per pole.

A virgin magnetization (or saturation) curve of a d-c generator shows
the relation between the generated emf and the field current for a given

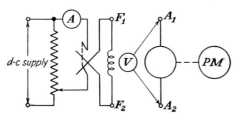

FIG. 8.11   Circuit for obtaining the magnetization curve and hysteresis loops of a
d-c generator.   The armature terminals are A_1 and A_2.   The field winding terminals
are F_1 and F_2.

speed of armature rotation, starting with the magnetic circuit demagnetized.   Data for such a curve can be obtained with the circuit of Fig. 8.11.
The generator armature is rotated by a prime mover whose speed is kept
constant.   If voltage is registered on the voltmeter when no current is
being sent through the field winding, the magnetic circuit is not demagnetized.   To demagnetize the magnetic circuit, the current should be
increased to a value that will produce saturation in the magnetic circuit.
Then, as the reversing switch is being thrown slowly from one closed
position to the other, the maximum current should be reduced to zero by
moving the voltage divider slowly to the zero output voltage position.
Now if the voltmeter reads zero, the magnetic circuit is demagnetized.
To obtain points on the magnetization curve, the field current is increased
to a desired value and the corresponding generated emf read on the voltmeter.   Then the field current is increased further, a second voltmeter
reading taken, and so on.   The field current should be increased only
until all desired values have been obtained.   If one overshoots a desired
current value and then reduces the current to it, hysteresis causes the
generated emf to be greater than if the value had not been overshot.   A
virgin magnetization curve for one d-c generator is in Fig. 8.12.

A symmetrical hysteresis loop of a d-c generator can be obtained with
the circuit of Fig. 8.11.   After one has demagnetized the magnetic cir-

cuit, one increases the field current to the value corresponding to the tip of the desired loop. Then the reversing switch is reversed, say ten times, to get the magnetic material in a cyclic state. Next for maximum field current the voltmeter is read. The current is reduced to a second value and the corresponding voltmeter reading taken. By continuing this process, current values from a positive maximum to a negative maximum and back again can be set and the corresponding voltmeter readings taken. The current should be varied in such a manner as to

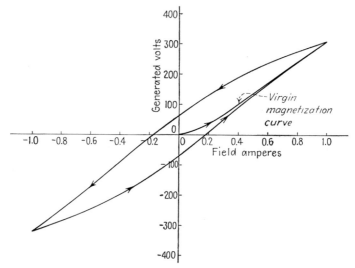

FIG. 8.12   Virgin magnetization curve and hysteresis loop of a d-c generator.

keep the magnetic material operating on the desired hysteresis loop. A loop for one generator is in Fig. 8.12. The emf corresponding to zero field current is about 20 per cent of that at the tip of the loop.

In a d-c generator driven at constant speed, the generated emf is directly proportional to the flux in the magnetic circuit. Because of this, certain magnetic phenomena can be demonstrated. In Fig. 8.13 are some results that were obtained with a 1,000-v generator. With no field current the residual emf was 55 v. When the field current was increased from 0 to 0.2 amp, the generated emf increased, as shown by curve 1. Then, when the current was reduced from 0.2 amp to 0, the generated emf decreased as shown by curve 2 to a residual value of 57 v. Next as the field current was varied from 0 to −0.2 amp, the generated emf decreased as shown by curve 3 to −11 v. Following this, the current was varied from −0.2 to 0.2 amp and back several times with the generated emf varying as shown by curves 4 to 12. These show the manner in which a cyclic set of values is approached. They prove that varying the

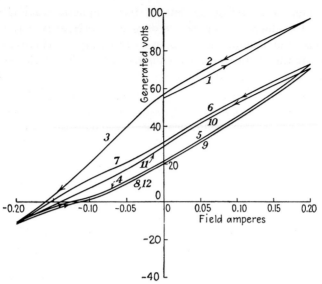

Fig. 8.13   Variations in the generated emf of a d-c generator as the field current is varied from 0 to 0.2 amp to −0.2 amp to 0 a number of times.   Residual flux was present initially.

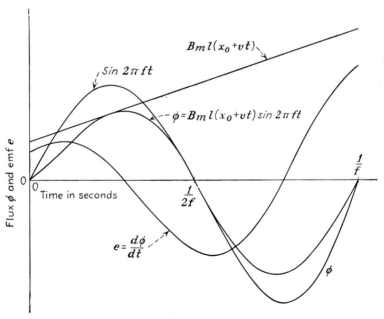

Fig. 8.14

exciting mmf of a circuit containing ferromagnetic material between equal positive and negative values does not necessarily cause the hysteresis loop to be symmetrical. If one wishes to be certain that a given magnetic circuit operates on a symmetrical loop, he must first demagnetize it.

Example 7. All conditions are the same as in Example 6 except that the flux density is alternating according to the equation $B = B_m \sin 2\pi ft$ wb per sq m, where B_m is the maximum instantaneous density and f is the frequency in cycles per second. Derive the equation that expresses the flux enclosed as a function of time. Plot the corresponding curve. Derive the equation that expresses the coil emf as a function of time. Plot the corresponding curve.

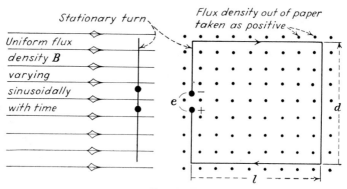

Fig. 8.15

Solution. As in Example 6, $\phi = Bl(x_0 + vt)$. Here $B = B_m \sin 2\pi ft$ so that $\phi = B_m l(x_0 + vt) \sin 2\pi ft$ wb. The flux-time curve ϕ is plotted in Fig. 8.14 as the product of the ordinates of the component curves $B_m l(x_0 + vt)$ and $\sin 2\pi ft$, each drawn as a function of time.

The coil emf e is

$$e = N\frac{d\phi}{dt} = 1\frac{d}{dt}\left[B_m l(x_0 + vt) \sin 2\pi ft\right]$$

$$= 2\pi f B_m l(x_0 + vt) \cos 2\pi ft + B_m lv \sin 2\pi ft \qquad \text{v}$$

The curve e representing this time variation of emf is in Fig. 8.14.

Example 8. In Fig. 8.15 is represented a stationary turn normal to a magnetic field of uniform flux density B that is varying sinusoidally with time according to the equation $B = B_m \sin 2\pi ft$ wb per sq m, where B_m is the maximum instantaneous density and f is the frequency in cycles per second. Derive the equation that expresses the flux enclosed as a function of time. Plot the corresponding curve. Derive the equation that expresses the coil emf as a function of time. Plot the corresponding curve.

Solution. The area of the given turn is ld sq m where l and d in meters are measured as in Fig. 8.15. Since flux = flux density $\times$ area, the flux ϕ linking the coil is given by $\phi = Bld = B_m ld \sin 2\pi ft$ wb. This sinusoidal variation of flux as a function of time is shown in Fig. 8.16.   The maximum flux Φ_m through the coil is $B_m ld$ wb and occurs at an instant when the angle $2\pi ft$ is equal to $\pi/2$ radians or any odd multiple thereof.   The coil emf e is

$$e = N\frac{d\phi}{dt} = 1\frac{d}{dt}[B_m ld \sin 2\pi ft] = 2\pi f B_m ld \cos 2\pi ft$$

$$= 2\pi f \Phi_m \cos 2\pi ft \qquad \text{v}$$

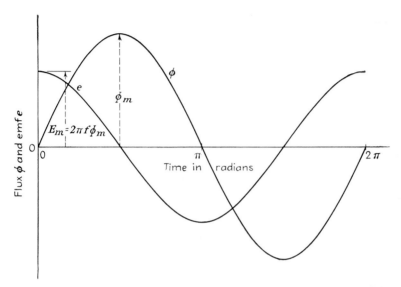

FIG. 8.16   A flux ϕ that varies sinusoidally with time induces the cosinusoidal emf e in a stationary turn.

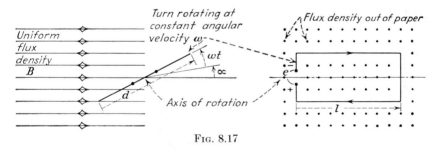

FIG. 8.17

The cosinusoidal variation of emf as a function of time is shown in Fig. 8.16. The maximum emf E_m is $2\pi f\Phi_m$ v and occurs when the angle $2\pi ft$ is equal to 0 or any multiple of π radians.

Example 9.   In Fig. 8.17 is represented a one-turn coil that is rotating with an angular velocity of ω radians per sec in an unvarying magnetic field of uniform flux density B wb per sq m.   Derive the equation that expresses the flux enclosed as a function of time.   Plot the corresponding curve.   Derive the equation that expresses the coil emf as a function of time.   Plot the corresponding curve.

Solution. The area of the given turn is ld sq m, where l and d in meters are measured as in Fig. 8.17. The projection of the area upon a plane normal to the flux density at an instant t is equal to ld times the sine of the angle $\omega t + \alpha$, where α is the angle that the coil makes with the horizontal at the instant chosen as $t = 0$. Then the flux ϕ linking the coil is given by $\phi = Bld \sin(\omega t + \alpha)$ wb. This sinusoidal variation of flux as a function of time is shown in Fig. 8.18. The maximum flux Φ_m through the coil is Bld wb and occurs at an instant when the angle $\omega t + \alpha$ is equal to $\pi/2$ radians or an odd multiple thereof.

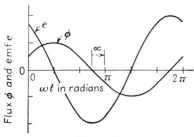

Fig. 8.18

The coil emf is

$$e = N\frac{d\phi}{dt} = 1\frac{d}{dt}[Bld \sin(\omega t + \alpha)] = \omega Bld \cos(\omega t + \alpha)$$

$$= \omega\Phi_m \cos(\omega t + \alpha) \quad \text{v}$$

The cosinusoidal variation of emf as a function of time is shown in Fig. 8.18. The maximum emf $E_m = \omega\Phi_m$ occurs when the flux linking the coil is zero, i.e., when the angle $\omega t + \alpha$ is equal to π radians or any multiple thereof. The flux linking the coil and the emf generated alternate at a frequency $f = \omega/2\pi$ c.

Example 10. In Fig. 8.17 the one-turn coil is rotating with a constant angular velocity ω radians per sec. Assume that the magnetic field of uniform density varies sinusoidally with time according to the equation

$$B = B_m \sin(2\pi ft + \theta) = B_m \sin(\omega_1 t + \theta) \quad \text{wb per sq m}$$

The frequency f c is such that ω_1 and ω may be equal or they may differ. θ is an angle such that $B_m \sin\theta$ is the flux density at the instant chosen for $t = 0$. Derive the equation that expresses the flux enclosed as a function of time. Derive the equation that expresses the coil emf as a function of time.

Solution. The projection of the surface within the turn upon a plane normal to the flux density at an instant t is $ld \sin(\omega t + \alpha)$ sq m. The flux linking the coil is $\phi = Bld \sin(\omega t + \alpha) = B_m ld \sin(\omega_1 t + \theta) \sin(\omega t + \alpha)$ wb. Since $\sin x \sin y = [\cos(x - y) - \cos(x + y)]/2$, then

$$\phi = \frac{B_m ld}{2}\cos[(\omega_1 - \omega)t + \theta - \alpha] - \frac{B_m ld}{2}\cos[(\omega_1 + \omega)t + \theta + \alpha] \quad \text{wb}$$

This shows that the flux variation is composed of a component of low-frequency $\omega_1 - \omega$ radians per sec and a component of equal amplitude of high-frequency $\omega_1 + \omega$ radians per sec. The graph of the time variation of the resultant flux linking the coil can have any one of an infinite variety of patterns, depending upon the values of ω_1, ω, θ, and α.

The coil emf is

$$e = N\frac{d\phi}{dt} = 1\frac{d}{dt}\left[\frac{B_m ld}{2}\cos[(\omega_1 - \omega)t + \theta - \alpha] - \frac{B_m ld}{2}\cos[(\omega_1 + \omega)t + \theta + \alpha]\right]$$

$$= (\omega - \omega_1)\frac{B_m ld}{2}\sin[(\omega_1 - \omega)t + \theta - \alpha] + (\omega_1 + \omega)\frac{B_m ld}{2}$$

$$\sin[(\omega_1 + \omega)t + \theta + \alpha] \quad \text{v}$$

The emf has components whose frequencies are equal, respectively, to those in the flux. The amplitudes of the components are in direct proportion to the frequencies.

8.3. Self-induction.

A current in an electric circuit establishes a magnetic field about the circuit. A change in the current changes the number of lines linking the circuit, and this in turn induces an emf in the circuit. The direction of the induced emf is such as to oppose the change of current, i.e., if the current is increasing, the emf is opposite in direction to the current and, if the current is decreasing, the emf is in the direction of the current. Self-induction is the property of a circuit that causes an emf to be induced in it by a change in the current in it. The factor by which the rate of change of the current is multiplied to obtain the value of the emf induced is the coefficient of self-induction, or the inductance, and is represented by the symbol L. In equational form the instantaneous induced emf e_L is $e_L = L \, di/dt$ v, where L is the inductance in henrys and di/dt is the rate of change of the current in amperes per second.

Since induced emf is also equal to $d\lambda/dt$, the rate of change of the flux linkages, then $L \, di/dt = d\lambda/dt$, from which $L = d\lambda/di$ h, where $d\lambda/di$ is in weber-turns per ampere. Then inductance is equal to the rate of change of the flux linkages with respect to the current.

For most electric circuits, $d\lambda = N d\phi$, either exactly or with sufficient accuracy for engineering computations. Then $L = N \, d\phi/di$ h, where $d\phi/di$ in webers per ampere is the rate of change of the equivalent flux with respect to the current. When the region about an electric circuit contains a magnetic material (such as steel), the flux linking the circuit is not directly proportional to the current. Then the inductance is not constant but varies with the current. An electric circuit surrounded by a nonmagnetic material has a constant inductance because the flux linking such a circuit is directly proportional to the current in the circuit. Graphically, the proportionality is represented by a straight line through the origin representing zero flux and current. The slope of the line, $d\phi/di$, is constant for all values of current and is equal to ϕ/i, where ϕ is the equivalent flux in webers corresponding to a current i amp. In the special case of constant inductance $L = N\phi/i$ h.

A device that is inserted in a circuit to introduce inductance is an inductor.

The inductance in henrys of a coil about a nonmagnetic core is equal to the flux linkages in weber-turns produced by 1 amp in the coil. This relation may be used in computing the inductance of a coil from its dimensions or in determining the effect of changes in the number of turns in a coil. Assume that a coil of N_1 turns is about a toroidal core. With 1 amp in the coil let Φ_1 wb be the equivalent flux. Then the coil inductance is $N_1\Phi_1$ h. Now let the original coil be replaced by one of N_2 turns of wire of such cross section that the second coil occupies the same space as the original coil. Now with 1 amp in the second coil, the mmf is N_2/N_1 times the original value and the flux will be N_2/N_1 times Φ_1. Since this flux links N_2 turns, the flux linkages are now $(N_2/N_1)^2$ times the original value. Here the flux linkages per ampere, or the inductance, varies as the square of the number of turns. In general, the inductances of two coils having different dimensions are not necessarily in the ratio of the square of the numbers of turns.

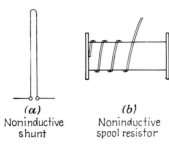

(a)   *(b)*
Noninductive   Noninductive
shunt   spool resistor

Fig. 8.19 Noninductive resistors. The mmf of one-half of the resistor nearly neutralizes the effect of the mmf of the other half.

The inductance of a given length of wire depends upon its configuration. If the inductance is to be large, the wire is wound into a coil so that the flux set up by the mmf of one turn will link with other turns. If the inductance is to be small, the wire is so arranged that little flux links it. A noninductive shunt may be made as in Fig. 8.19a. In winding resistance wire on spools to form a "noninductive" resistor, the wire may be doubled and then wound as in Fig. 8.19b.

8.4. Computation of Self-inductance. The inductance of a coil whose magnetic circuit contains nonmagnetic material is equal to the weber-turns of flux linkage per ampere. For such a magnetic circuit the flux linkages are proportional to the current. Any current value may be assumed when computing the inductance. There are few coil shapes for which the inductance can be computed by simple mathematics. Difficulty arises because the fluxes linking the individual turns may be unequal, the flux density may be nonuniform in the magnetic circuit, and some of the flux may pass through the conductor forming the turn. The inductance of a coil varies with the frequency of the current, because skin effect causes the current to be distributed nonuniformly over a conductor cross section. Despite these difficulties formulas have been derived and tables computed from which the self-inductances of coils of many shapes can be determined with accuracies ranging from a few per cent of error to an error no greater than one part in ten million.*

Example 1. A 2,000-turn coil surrounds a magnetic circuit that has a constant reluctance of 8×10^6 amp-turns per wb. Compute the inductance of the coil.

Solution. If I amp flows in the coil, the mmf is $2,000I$ amp-turns. Since flux equals mmf divided by reluctance, the flux is $2,000I/8 \times 10^6 = 2.5 \times 10^{-4}I$ wb.

---

* For a list of inductance formulas, see F. E. Terman, *Radio Engineers' Handbook*, McGraw-Hill Book Company, Inc., New York, 1943.

Assuming that all the flux links all the turns, then the flux linkages are

$$2.5 \times 10^{-4}I \times 2,000 = 0.5I \qquad \text{wb-turns}$$

Since inductance equals flux linkages per ampere, then $L = 0.5I/I = 0.5$ h.

Example 2. Compute the inductance of the toroid core of Fig. 7.6.

Solution. In Example 1, Art. 7.7, it was shown that, with 12 amp in the coil, the core flux was 2.29×10^{-6} wb. Little error will result if this flux is assumed to link the 125 turns of the coil; hence for 12 amp the flux linkages are

$$2.29 \times 10^{-6} \times 125 = 2.9 \times 10^{-4} \text{ wb-turns}$$

The inductance is 2.9×10^{-4} wb-turns/12 amp $= 2.41 \times 10^{-5}$ h, or 24.1 μh.

8.5. Effects of Inductance. In the circuit of Fig. 8.20 a varying emf of e v is suddenly impressed on a circuit of constant resistance R ohms and constant inductance L h. Time is taken as zero at the instant the switch is closed. The assumed positive direction of the current is indicated. The changing current induces an emf $L\,di/dt$ v. With increasing current the polarities of the inductor terminals are as shown. For most mathematical developments it is convenient to treat the effect of induct-

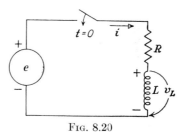

Fig. 8.20

ance as a voltage drop. This drop v_L is equal to $+L\,di/dt$ when taken positive in the direction of the current as in Fig. 8.20. With this convention, the voltage equation of the circuit is

$$e = iR + L\frac{di}{dt} \qquad (8.7)$$

Here the current was zero just before the switch was closed. The inductance causes the current to remain at zero momentarily when the switch is closed (that is, at $t = 0$). The rate of change of current at $t = 0$ instantly acquires a value such that $L\,di/dt$ is equal to the value of e at that instant. In a circuit containing much inductance it is easy to show experimentally that the current does not change instantly from one value to another. In a circuit of little inductance the current can be changed so rapidly that it is difficult to measure accurately the rate of change. The inductance of a circuit prevents an instantaneous change in the current by causing a voltage to be produced with the proper magnitude and polarity to hold the current momentarily at its original value when a change is made in the circuit.

If the emf in Fig. 8.20 is alternating, in a short time after $t = 0$ the current will settle into a cyclic or steady state. It is possible to have the frequency high enough and the ratio of L to R great enough, that in (8.7) the maximum instantaneous value of iR is small, say 5 per cent or less, compared with the maximum instantaneous value of $L\,di/dt$. In that case, it is a good approximation to write $e = L\,di/dt$. An oscillogram

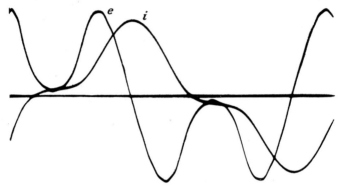

FIG. 8.21 Oscillogram of the current i produced in an inductor of constant inductance by the emf e.

that verifies this relation is in Fig. 8.21. The emf is greatest when the rate of change of current is greatest and is zero when the rate of change of current is zero.

8.6. Growth of Current. In Fig. 8.22 a battery having constant emf of E v is connected suddenly to a circuit of constant resistance R ohms and

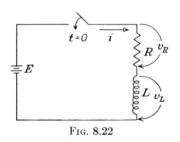

FIG. 8.22

constant inductance L h. Although here the resistance is represented as separate from the inductance, they may both be distributed throughout the length of an actual circuit. Here the voltage equation is

$$E = v_R + v_L = iR + L\frac{di}{dt} \qquad (8.8)$$

In equations relating voltages and currents it is to be understood that an equation applies only during the interval from an arbitrarily chosen instant (usually designated as $t = 0$) to a later instant when a change is made in the circuit.

Example 1. In Fig. 8.22, $E = 24$ v, $R = 6$ ohms, and $L = 50$ mh. (a) For the instant when the switch is closed, compute the resistive voltage, the inductive voltage, and the rate of change of the current. (b) For the instant when the current is 3 amp, compute the resistive voltage, the inductive voltage, and the rate of change of the current.

Solution. a. The given circuit is redrawn in Fig. 8.23a with the numerical values shown. Just before the switch was closed at $t = 0$, the current was zero. It will remain zero at $t = 0$ because of the inductance of the circuit. With zero current, the resistive voltage v_R is zero and the inductive voltage v_L is 24 v, the battery emf less the resistive voltage. Since $v_L = L\, di/dt$, then at $t = 0$, $di/dt = 24$ v/0.05 h $= 480$ amp per sec.

b. The given circuit is redrawn in Fig. 8.23b for the instant when the current is 3 amp. Now $v_R = 3$ amp $\times 6$ ohms $= 18$ v. Also $v_L = 24$ v $- 18$ v $= 6$ v. Now $di/dt = 6$ v/0.05 h $= 120$ amp per sec.

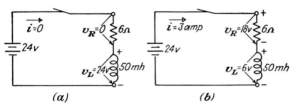

(a)   (b)

Fig. 8.23   (a) Circuit relations at $t = 0$.   (b) Circuit relations when $i = 3$ amp.

At an instant when a current of i amp is increasing in a series circuit of a resistor of constant resistance R ohms and an inductor of constant inductance L h, the power p_R being put into the resistor is

$$p_R = i^2 R = v_R i \qquad \text{w}$$

where v_R v is the voltage across the resistor. This power is the rate at which energy is being converted into heat in the resistor and is not directly recoverable in the circuit. The power p_L being put into the inductor is $p_L = iL\, di/dt = v_L i$ w, where di/dt amp per sec is the rate of change of the current and v_L v is the voltage across the inductor. This power is the rate at which energy is being put into the magnetic field of the inductor. The energy is stored to be released later when the current decreases.

The energy W_R converted into heat in a resistor of R ohms resistance by a varying current of i amp during a time interval from t_1 to t_2 sec is

$$W_R = \int_{t_1}^{t_2} i^2 R\, dt \qquad \text{w sec (or j)}$$

The value of this integral depends upon the manner in which the current varies during the interval.

The change in the energy W_L in the magnetic field of an inductor of L h inductance by a varying current of i amp during a time interval from t_1 to t_2 sec is

$$W_L = \int_{t_1}^{t_2} v_L i\, dt = \int_{t_1}^{t_2} Li \frac{di}{dt}\, dt = \int_{i_1}^{i_2} Li\, di = \frac{1}{2} Li^2 \bigg]_{i_1}^{i_2}$$
$$= \frac{1}{2} L(i_2^2 - i_1^2) \qquad \text{w sec (or j)}$$

where i_1 is the current at time t_1 and i_2 is the current at time t_2. If i_2 is greater than i_1, W_L is positive and energy has been stored in the magnetic field.   If i_2 is less than i_1, W_L is negative and energy has been extracted from the magnetic field.

If the energy in the magnetic field is taken as zero when the current producing the field is zero, when the current is i amp the energy stored is $W_L = \tfrac{1}{2}Li^2$ w sec (or j) and is independent of the manner in which the current varied with time as it varied from zero to i.

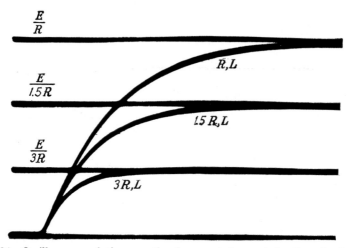

Fig. 8.24   Oscillograms of the growth of current in an inductive circuit.   The applied emf E and the inductance L were constant.   Three values of resistance were used.

Example 2.   For the instant when the current is 3 amp in the circuit of Fig. 8.23b, compute (a) the power being put into the resistance, (b) the power being put into the magnetic field, and (c) the energy stored in the magnetic field.

Solution.   For this instant the resistive voltage is 18 v; thus the power being put into the resistance is 18 v × 3 amp = 54 w.   The inductive voltage is 6 v; therefore the power being put into the magnetic field is 6 v × 3 amp = 18 w. The energy stored in the magnetic field is

$$W_L = \tfrac{1}{2}Li^2 = \tfrac{1}{2} \times 0.05 \times 3^2 = 0.225 \text{ wsec}$$

The rate of growth of current in the circuit of Fig. 8.22 is di/dt.   From (8.8), $di/dt = (E - iR)/L$.   This shows that the rate of growth of current is greatest when $i = 0$ and decreases as i increases.   Since $i = 0$ at $t = 0$

$$\text{Maximum } \frac{di}{dt} = \frac{di}{dt}\bigg|_{t=0} = \frac{E}{L} \qquad \text{amp per sec}$$

That the initial rate of growth of current is determined by E and L and is independent of R is verified by the oscillograms of Fig. 8.24.   These show the growths of current for three values of R with constant values of E and L.   The curves start with equal slopes and later diverge.   The greater the resistance, the less the steady-state current, and the more rapidly any given percentage of the steady-state current is attained. The oscillograms of Fig. 8.25 show the growths of current for three values of L with constant values of E and R. Each curve starts with a different slope and the greatest initial slope occurs when L is the least. All curves approach the same steady-state value of E/R amp.

In a series circuit resistance partly masks the effect of inductance. The greater the circuit resistance, the more difficult it is to measure the circuit

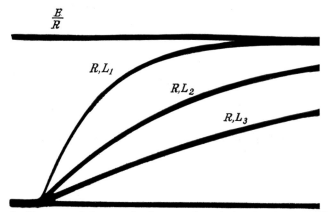

Fɪɢ. 8.25 Oscillograms of the growth of current in an inductive circuit. The applied emf E and the resistance R were constant. Inductances were $L_1 = 87$ mh, $L_2 = 180$ mh, and $L_3 = 480$ mh.

inductance. If the rate of growth of current in a given circuit element is to be increased without increasing the final current, additional resistance can be introduced in series with the element and then additional voltage applied. To obtain the original value of the final current, the voltage must be increased in the same ratio as the resistance was.

The equation of the current growth in Fig. 8.22 can be derived from (8.8). By separating the variables

$$\frac{di}{E - iR} = \frac{dt}{L}$$

from which
$$\frac{-R\,di}{E - iR} = \frac{-R\,dt}{L}$$

By integration $\ln (E - iR) = -Rt/L + k_1$, where k_1 is a constant of integration. The above may be written as $E - iR = \epsilon^{-Rt/L + k_1}$. But $\epsilon^{-Rt/L + k_1} = \epsilon^{-Rt/L}\epsilon^{k_1}$, and ϵ^{k_1} is another constant k_2. Hence

$$E - iR = k_2\epsilon^{-Rt/L}$$

from which $i = (E/R) - (k_2/R)\epsilon^{-Rt/L}$. Here k_2 can be evaluated from the boundary condition that $i = 0$ at $t = 0$. Since $\epsilon^0 = 1$, then

$$0 = \frac{E}{R} - \frac{k_2}{R}$$

and $k_2 = E$. Then

$$i = \frac{E}{R} - \frac{E}{R} \epsilon^{-Rt/L} = \frac{E}{R}(1 - \epsilon^{-Rt/L}) \qquad \text{amp} \qquad (8.9)$$

The term E/R in (8.9) is the steady-state component of current. The term $(E/R)\epsilon^{-Rt/L}$ is a transient component that has the value E/R at

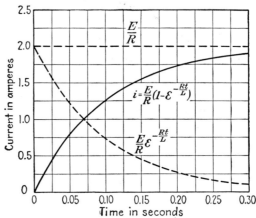

Fig. 8.26 Components of and total current during growth of current in an inductive circuit.

$t = 0$ and thereafter decreases exponentially with time. Theoretically, this component is not zero and the current is not E/R until time is infinite. In most circuits only a few seconds or less are required for the current to become constant as determined by an indicating instrument. The curves representing (8.9) are shown in Fig. 8.26.

Example 3. A 6-v direct current is suddenly applied to 20 ohms resistance in series with 400 mh inductance. At the instant when the current is 200 ma, what is the inductive power and how much energy is stored in the magnetic field? How much was the resistive energy during the time the current was increasing from 0 to 200 ma?

Solution. At the given instant the resistive voltage is

$$0.2 \text{ amp} \times 20 \text{ ohms} = 4 \text{ v}$$

The inductive voltage is the applied voltage less the resistive voltage, or 2 v. The inductive power is 2 v $\times$ 0.2 amp = 0.4 w.

At the given instant the energy stored in the magnetic field is

$$\tfrac{1}{2}Li^2 = \tfrac{1}{2} \times 0.4 \times 0.2^2 = 0.008 \text{ wsec, or 8 mj}$$

The resistive energy is

$$W_R = \int_0^{t_1} i^2R \, dt$$

or since $R = 20$ ohms,

$$W_R = 20 \int_0^{t_1} i^2 \, dt \qquad (8.10)$$

where t_1 is the time at which the current is 200 ma. Equation (8.10) can be integrated after expressing i in terms of t and determining t_1 by (8.9). It is also possible to solve (8.10) by a change in limits. The circuit voltage equation is $6 = 20i + 0.4 \, di/dt$, from which $dt = 0.4 \, di/(6 - 20i)$. By substituting this value of dt in (8.10), changing the limits, rearranging terms, simplifying, and integrating

$$W_R = -0.4 \int_0^{0.2} \frac{i^2 \, di}{i - 0.3} = -0.4 \int_0^{0.2} \left(i + 0.3 + \frac{0.09}{i - 0.3} \right) di$$

$$= -0.4 \left[\frac{i^2}{2} + 0.3i + 0.09 \ln (i - 0.3) \right]_0^{0.2}$$

After substitution of the limits $W_R = 0.0076$ wsec $= 7.6$ mj.

Example 4. In Fig. 8.27 switch S_1 is closed at $t = 0$. One-tenth second later switch S_2 is closed. At an infinitesimal instant before S_2 is closed, what are the inductive voltage and the rate of change of the current and how much energy is stored in the magnetic field? At the instant S_2 is closed, what are the inductive voltage and the rate of change of the current and how much energy is stored in the magnetic field?

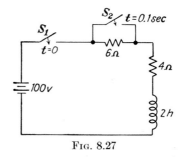

FIG. 8.27

Solution. After S_1 is closed, the current growth is expressed by

$$i = \frac{E}{R} (1 - \epsilon^{-Rt/L})$$

At $t = 0.1$ sec,

$$i = \tfrac{100}{10}(1 - \epsilon^{-\frac{10 \times 0.1}{2}}) = 10(1 - \epsilon^{-0.5}) = 3.93 \text{ amp}$$

This is the current just before S_2 is closed. Then the resistive voltage

$$v_R = 3.93 \text{ amp} \times 10 \text{ ohms} = 39.3 \text{ v}$$

and the inductive voltage $v_L = 100 - 39.3 = 60.7$ v. Since $v_L = L \, di/dt$, then at the instant being considered $di/dt = 60.7$ v/2 h $= 30.3$ amp per sec. The corresponding energy W_L stored in the magnetic field is

$$W_L = \tfrac{1}{2}Li^2 = \tfrac{1}{2} \times 2 \times 3.93^2 = 15 \text{ wsec} = 15 \text{ j}$$

When S_2 is closed, the circuit resistance is reduced from 10 to 4 ohms but the inductance prevents an instantaneous change of current so that the resistive

voltage v_R changes instantly from 39.3 to 15.7 v.   Since the inductive voltage
equals the difference between the applied and the resistive voltages, at the instant
S_2 is closed the inductive voltage changes instantly from

$$60.7 \text{ to } 100 - 15.7 = 84.3 \text{ v}$$

The corresponding rate of change of current is 84.3 v/2 h = 42.1 amp per sec.
Since the current did not change instantly, the energy stored in the magnetic
field remained momentarily at 15 j.

8.7. Time Constant.   A basis for comparing inductive circuits is the
time required for a given percentage change of current after a direct

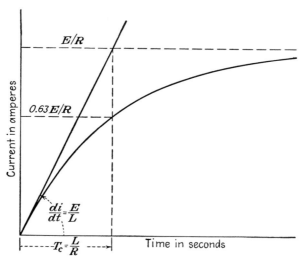

Fig. 8.28   Graphical representation of the time constant T_c of the inductive circuit
of Fig. 8.22. T_c is the time that would be required for the current to reach a steady-
state value E/R if the rate of increase had remained constant at the initial value of
E/L.   During the interval from 0 to T_c the current actually attains 63 per cent of its
steady-state value.

voltage is applied to the circuit.   There would be no distinction between
circuits if the comparison basis was the time required for the current to
change from zero to its steady-state value, since all theoretically require
infinite time.   The initial rate of current growth is fixed by the voltage
and the inductance, while the steady-state current is fixed by the voltage
and the resistance.   A convenient basis for comparing circuits is for a
time $T_c = L/R$ sec, where L is in henrys and R is in ohms. T_c is the time
constant of the circuit.   From (8.9), for $t = T_c = L/R$, the current is

$$i = \frac{E}{R}\left(1 - \epsilon^{-\frac{R}{L}\cdot\frac{L}{R}}\right) = \frac{E}{R}\left(1 - \frac{1}{\epsilon}\right) = 0.63\frac{E}{R} \qquad \text{amp}$$

The time constant of a series circuit of resistance and inductance is the time in seconds actually required for the current to reach 63 per cent of its steady-state value after a constant voltage is applied.

The principal reason for the choice of L/R as the time constant of the circuit of Fig. 8.22 is that if the current had continued to increase at the initial rate of E/L amp per sec, to reach the steady-state value of E/R amp would require E/R amp$/(E/L)$ amp per sec $= L/R$ sec.

The definitions of the time constant of the circuit of Fig. 8.22 are interpreted graphically in Fig. 8.28. A line tangent at the origin to the current-time curve has a slope of E/L amp per sec. The line represents what the current-time curve would have been if the current had continued to increase at the initial rate and intersects the steady-state value of E/R amp at $T_c = L/R$ sec. At this instant the current has actually attained 63 per cent of its steady-state value.

8.8. Voltage Relations during Current Growth. After a constant emf of E v has been applied suddenly to a series circuit of R ohms resistance and L h inductance, the resistive voltage is $v_R = iR$ v and the inductive voltage is $v_L = L\, di/dt$ v, where i is in amperes and t is in seconds. At any instant the sum of the two voltages is equal to the emf. At $t = 0$, there is no resistive voltage and the inductive voltage is equal to the applied emf. As time increases, the resistive voltage increases to a steady-state value of E and the inductive voltage decreases to zero. As in the case of current, steady-state voltages are reached at infinite time.

The equation of v_R, obtained by multiplying (8.9) by R, is

$$v_R = E(1 - \epsilon^{-Rt/L}) \qquad \text{v}$$

The equation of v_L, obtained by multiplying the time derivative of (8.9) by L, is

$$v_L = E\epsilon^{-Rt/L} \qquad \text{v} \qquad (8.11)$$

The voltages v_R and v_L as functions of time are given in Fig. 8.29.

The preceding voltage equation could have been derived directly without using (8.9). Since $v_L = L\, di/dt$, then $i = (1/L) \int_0^t v_L\, dt + I_0$. Here $i = 0$, at $t = 0$; thus $I_0 = 0$. The voltage equation $E = iR + L\dfrac{di}{dt}$ may be written as $E = (R/L) \int_0^t v_L\, dt + v_L$. The derivative of this with respect to time is

$$0 = \frac{Rv_L}{L} + \frac{dv_L}{dt}$$

from which $dv_L/v_L = -R\, dt/L$. By integration $\ln v_L = -Rt/L + k$,

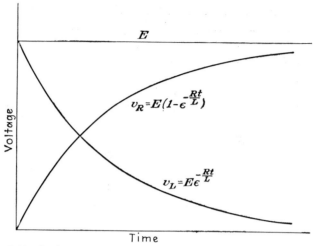

$$v_R = E(1 - \epsilon^{-\frac{Rt}{L}})$$

$$v_L = E\epsilon^{-\frac{Rt}{L}}$$

Time

FIG. 8.29   Resistive and inductive voltages in the circuit of Fig. 8.22.

where k is a constant of integration. Changing the form of the equation yields

$$v_L = \epsilon^{-Rt/L+k} = \epsilon^k \epsilon^{-Rt/L} = k_1 \epsilon^{-Rt/L} \qquad \text{v}$$

where k_1 is a new constant. At $t = 0$, $v_L = E$, and $\epsilon^0 = 1$; therefore $k_1 = E$ and $v_L = E\epsilon^{-Rt/L}$, a result that agrees with (8.11).

Example 1. For the circuit of Fig. 8.30 determine values of resistive power p_R and inductive power p_L that correspond to various current values.

Solution. The current starts at 0 and reaches a steady-state value of

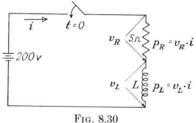

FIG. 8.30

$$\frac{200 \text{ v}}{5 \text{ ohms}} = 40 \text{ amp}$$

Computations will be made for currents in 5-amp steps in that range. For each value of current the resistive voltage, the resistive power, the inductive voltage, and the inductive power are computed as outlined in Table 8.2.

Note that the values in the table are independent of the value of inductance. However, the value of inductance is a factor in determining the time required for a given value of current to be attained. Also note that the inductive power starts at zero, increases to a maximum of 2,000 w, and then decreases to zero. The inductive power is a maximum when the inductive voltage is one-half the battery emf.

TABLE 8.2

i amp	v_R $i \times 5$ v	p_R $v_R \times i$ w	v_L $200 - v_R$ v	v_L $v_L \times i$ w
0	0	0	200	0
5	25	125	175	875
10	50	500	150	1,500
15	75	1,125	125	1,875
20	100	2,000	100	2,000
25	125	3,125	75	1,875
30	150	4,500	50	1,500
35	175	6,125	25	875
40	200	8,000	0	0

8.9. Decay of Current.   The circuit of Fig. 8.31 is assumed to have been closed long enough for the current to have a steady value of $E/(R_1 + R)$ amp, where E is in volts and R_1 and R are in ohms.   Time is counted from the instant when the switch of negligible resistance is closed.   The voltage equation for the right-hand loop is

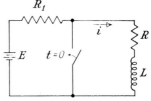

$$0 = iR + L\frac{di}{dt} \qquad (8.12)$$

where i is in amperes and L is in henrys. At $t = 0$, the current in the right-hand branch remains momentarily at $E/(R + R_1)$ amp because of the inductance there.   At $t = 0$, there are E v across R_1 so that the battery current changes instantly from $E/(R + R_1)$ to E/R_1 amp.   The initial current in the switch is the difference between the battery current and that in the right-hand branch, or $E/R_1 - E(R + R_1)$ amp.

Fig. 8.31   Inductive circuit in which the current i decays to zero after the switch is closed.

Closure of the switch in Fig. 8.31 does not cause the current in the right-hand branch to change instantly from its initial value of $E/(R + R_1)$, but it does cause the current to start to decrease.   Solving (8.12) for di/dt yields

$$\frac{di}{dt} = -\frac{iR}{L} \qquad (8.13)$$

which shows that the rate of current decay is greatest when the current is greatest.   Since $i = E/(R + R_1)$ at $t = 0$, then

$$\frac{di}{dt}\bigg|_{t=0} = -\frac{RE}{(R + R_1)L} \qquad \text{amp per sec}$$

Separation of the variables in (8.13) yields $di/i = -R\,dt/L$ which, by integration, yields $\ln i = -Rt/L + k$. This may be written as $i = k_1\epsilon^{-Rt/L}$, where $k_1 = \epsilon^k$. At $t = 0$, $i = E/(R + R_1)$, and $\epsilon^0 = 1$; hence $k_1 = E/(R + R_1)$ and

$$i = \frac{E}{R + R_1}\,\epsilon^{-Rt/L} \qquad (8.14)$$

In (8.14) the term $E/(R + R_1)$ is the initial current. This is often denoted as I_0 and the equation written as

$$i = I_0\epsilon^{-Rt/L} \qquad \text{amp}$$

The current decays to zero along an exponential curve determined by R and L. The energy required to maintain the current is supplied from

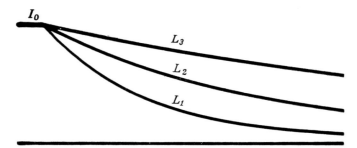

FIG. 8.32   Oscillograms of the decay of current in the circuit of Fig. 8.31.   Initial current $I_0 = 180$ ma.   Resistance of discharge circuit is 16 ohms. $L_1 = 87$ mh; $L_2 = 180$ mh; $L_3 = 480$ mh.   The distance representing I_0 on the vertical axis represents 6 msec on the horizontal axis.

that which was stored in the magnetic field during a previous interval when the current was increasing. The current becomes zero at infinite time. As in the case of the growth of current, the measurable change in most circuits occurs in a short time. If the current continued to decrease at the initial rate, it would be zero in L/R sec. At L/R sec the current has actually made 63 per cent of the total change and has decreased to 37 per cent of the initial value.

In Fig. 8.32 are oscillograms of the decaying current in the circuit of Fig. 8.31 for constant values of voltage and resistance and three values of inductance. These show that increasing the inductance increases proportionally the time required for the current to decrease to a given percentage of the initial value.

Example 1.   In Fig. 8.31, $E = 24$ v, $R_1 = 60$ ohms, $R = 40$ ohms, and $L = 0.05$ h.   Originally the circuit is in a steady state with the switch open. For the instant when the switch is closed determine (a) the initial currents in the branches; (b) the initial inductive voltage; (c) the initial rate of decay of the inductive branch current; (*d*) the initial energy stored in the magnetic field; (*e*) the initial power delivered by the magnetic field.

Solution.   *a.* The current in the original circuit is

$$\frac{24 \text{ v}}{60 + 40 \text{ ohms}} = 0.24 \text{ amp}$$

This is the current in the right-hand branch at $t = 0$.   The battery current at $t = 0$ is 24 v/60 ohms = 0.4 amp.   The switch current at $t = 0$ is

$$0.4 - 0.24 = 0.16 \text{ amp}$$

b. In Fig. 8.33 the circuit at $t = 0$ is represented.   Since the current in the right-hand branch is starting to decrease, the inductive voltage is maintaining the current.   The polarity of the inductive voltage is as indicated. With v_L taken positive in the direction of the current, then $40 \times 0.24 + v_L = 0$, from which $v_L = -9.6$ v.

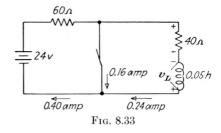

FIG. 8.33

c. Since v_L, or $L \, di/dt$, is -9.6 v at $t = 0$, the initial rate of change of the inductive branch current is $di/dt = v_L/L = -9.6$ v/0.05 h $= -192$ amp per sec, or the rate of decay is 192 amp per sec.

d. The initial energy stored in the magnetic field is

$$\tfrac{1}{2}Li^2 = \tfrac{1}{2} \times 0.05 \times (0.24)^2 = 0.00144 \text{ j, or } 1.44 \text{ mj}$$

e. The initial power input to the magnetic field is

$$v_L i = -9.6 \text{ v} \times 0.24 \text{ amp} = -2.3 \text{ w}$$

This means that the magnetic field is delivering 2.3 w.

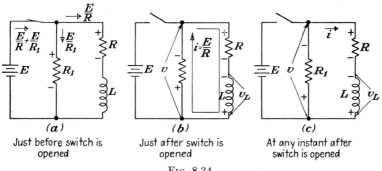

(*a*)
Just before switch is opened

(*b*)
Just after switch is opened

(*c*)
At any instant after switch is opened

FIG. 8.34

The circuit of Fig. 8.34*a* is assumed to have been closed long enough for the currents to have become constant.   At $t = 0$, the switch in series with the battery is opened.   In Fig. 8.34*b* are shown the relations that exist at an infinitesimal instant after the switch is opened.   At this instant current is maintained at E/R amp in the series circuit of R, L, and R_1 by power delivered by the magnetic field. Note that the current in R_1 changes instantly from E/R_1 amp in one direction to E/R amp in the other. To maintain momentarily the current of E/R, it is necessary for the inductance to produce $(E/R) \times (R + R_1)$ v. Just before $t = 0$, the voltage across R_1 was E v; just after $t = 0$, the voltage was ER_1/R v with a reversed polarity. Thus, in Fig. 8.34b the voltage $v = ER_1/R$ v at $t = 0$. This relation shows that v can exceed E. The transient voltage that appears across the terminals of an inductive circuit upon interruption of the current is an *inductive kick*.

The equations of the transient current i and the transient voltage v in Fig. 8.34c can be obtained from the voltage equation of the series circuit. Here $0 = i(R + R_1) + L\, di/dt$, from which

$$\frac{di}{i} = -\frac{R + R_1}{L} dt$$

From this, by integration,

$$\ln i = -\frac{(R + R_1)t}{L} + k \quad \text{or} \quad i = k_1 \epsilon^{-\frac{R+R_1}{L}t}$$

where $k_1 = \epsilon^k$. At $t = 0$, $i = E/R$ and $\epsilon^0 = 1$; thus

$$k_1 = \frac{E}{R} \quad \text{and} \quad i = \frac{E}{R} \epsilon^{-\frac{R+R_1}{L}t} \quad \text{amp}$$

Since $v = iR_1$, then

$$v = \frac{ER_1}{R} \epsilon^{-\frac{R+R_1}{L}t} \quad \text{v} \tag{8.15}$$

This voltage is a maximum of ER_1/R v at $t = 0$ and decreases exponentially to zero. If R_1 is large compared with R, the inductive kick may reach dangerous values. If a 150-v voltmeter whose resistance R_1 is 15,000 ohms were connected across the field winding of a d-c machine whose resistance R is 100 ohms, the voltmeter would be subjected momentarily to 150 times the supply voltage if the switch could open the circuit in zero time. In Fig. 8.35a, if R_1 were made infinite, a series circuit would remain and an infinite voltage would be produced when the switch is opened. In an actual circuit, conditions are never quite so extreme as represented by (8.15) because the inductive kick maintains for a time an arc across a switch that is opening. As a result, current continues for a time and a finite time is required for the switch to reduce the supply current to zero. Even so, inductive kicks may reach undesirable magnitudes. When a voltmeter is used for measurements across an inductive unit, it is well to connect the voltmeter only long enough to take a reading and not leave it connected continuously.

To limit the inductive voltage across the field-winding terminals of some motors and generators, a discharge resistor is connected as R_1 is in Fig. 8.35a. A special switch is used, which, on being opened, first connects the resistor across the winding terminals and then disconnects the supply. The resistance of the discharge resistor is a value that will limit

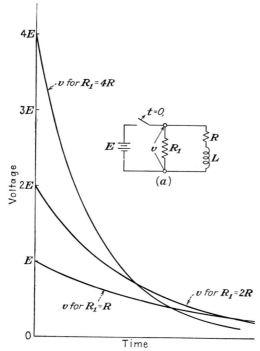

Fig. 8.35   Interrupting an inductive circuit.   Effect of increasing R_1 upon the initial value of v and rate of change of v.

the voltage to a reasonable value.   Increasing R_1 increases correspondingly the initial value of v and at the same time increases the initial rate of decrease of v, as shown in Fig. 8.35.

One should avoid contact with an inductive circuit when it is being interrupted.   Otherwise one may have sent through him a current about equal to that in the circuit just prior to the instant of interruption. Much of the energy originally stored in the magnetic field may be dissipated in the body of the person making the contact.   A small machine or a low-voltage circuit may have enough stored energy to cause a painful or fatal shock.

8.10. Mutual Induction.   Some of the flux set up by current in one circuit may link a second circuit.   A change in the current causes a change in the flux linkages of the second circuit and thus induces an emf in it by mutual induction at the same time another emf is induced in the first circuit by self-induction. The circuits are inductively coupled. The factor by which the rate of change of current in one circuit is multiplied to obtain the emf induced in a second circuit is the coefficient of mutual induction or the mutual inductance between the circuits and is denoted by the symbol M. When two circuits are inductively coupled, a changing current in either induces an emf in the other. There is mutual inductance from circuit 1 to circuit 2 and mutual inductance from circuit 2 to circuit 1. In equational form $e_2 = M_{12}\, di_1/dt$ v and

$$e_1 = M_{21} \frac{di_2}{dt} \quad \text{v}$$

where e_2 is the emf in volts induced in circuit 2, M_{12} is the mutual inductance in henrys from circuit 1 to circuit 2, di_1/dt in amperes per second is the rate of change of current in circuit 1, e_1 is the emf in volts induced in circuit 1, M_{21} is the mutual inductance in henrys from circuit 2 to circuit 1, and di_2/dt in amperes per second is the rate of change of current in circuit 2. M_{12} equals M_{21} when the medium surrounding the circuits has constant permeability. For the preceding equations the positive directions of the emfs and currents are related as in Fig. 8.36. When only two coupled circuits are being considered, the mutual inductance is designated commonly by the symbol M without subscripts.

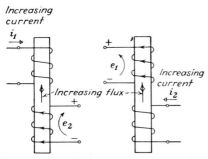

FIG. 8.36 Relations between positive current, positive flux, and positive emf.

The mutual inductance between two circuits may be defined also as the rate of change of the flux linkages of one circuit with respect to the current in the other. In equational form $M_{12} = d\lambda_{12}/di_1$ h and $M_{21} = d\lambda_{21}/di_2$ h, where M_{12} is the mutual inductance from circuit 1 to circuit 2, $d\lambda_{12}/di_1$ is the rate of change in weber-turns per ampere of the flux linkages of circuit 2 with respect to the current in circuit 1, M_{21} is the mutual inductance from circuit 2 to circuit 1, and $d\lambda_{21}/di_2$ is the rate of change in weber-turns per ampere of the flux linkages of circuit 1 with respect to the current in circuit 2.

In most cases it is exact or reasonably accurate to say that

$$d\lambda_{12} = N_2\, d\phi_{12}$$

and $d\lambda_{21} = N_1\, d\phi_{21}$. Then $M_{12} = N_2\, d\phi_{12}/di_1$ h and $M_{21} = N_1\, d\phi_{21}/di_2$ h, where N_2 and N_1 are the respective numbers of series turns in circuits 2 and 1, $d\phi_{12}/di_1$ is the rate of change in webers per ampere of the equivalent flux linking circuit 2 produced by the current in circuit 1, and $d\phi_{21}/di_2$ is the rate of change in webers per ampere of the equivalent flux linking circuit 1 produced by the current in circuit 2. When the medium surrounding two fixed, coupled circuits has constant permeability, the mutual inductance is a constant $M = M_{12} = M_{21} = N_2\phi_{12}/i_1 = N_1\phi_{21}/i_2$, where M h is the mutual inductance, ϕ_{12} wb is the equivalent flux linking circuit 2 produced by i_1 amp in circuit 1, and ϕ_{21} wb is the equivalent flux linking circuit 1 produced by i_2 amp in circuit 2.

Since $e_1 = L \, di_1/dt$ and $e_2 = M \, di_1/dt$, then $e_1/e_2 = L/M$, or the emf of self-induction in a circuit resulting from a changing current is to the emf of mutual induction in a second circuit at a given instant as the self-inductance of the first circuit is to the mutual inductance between circuits.

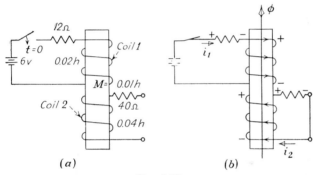

(a)   (b)

FIG. 8.37

Example 1. In Fig. 8.37 two coils are wound on a nonmagnetic core. At the instant when the switch is closed, how much emf is induced in each coil? At the instant when the current in coil 1 is 0.2 amp, how much emf is induced in each coil? Specify the polarities of the terminals of coil 2 in each case.

Solution. At $t = 0$, the current in coil 1 will be zero because of the inductance. To keep the current momentarily at zero, the induced emf of coil 1 must equal the battery emf, or 6 v. The upper terminal of coil 1 will be positive and the lower will be negative.

Since the mutual inductance between the coils is one-half the self-inductance of coil 1, the emf of mutual induction in coil 2 is one-half that of self-induction in coil 1, or 3 v.

The polarities of the terminals of coil 2 can be determined by noting that the coils are wound in the same direction. Since the changing flux induces the emf of self-induction in coil 1 and the emf of mutual induction in coil 2, the upper terminal of coil 2 will have the same polarity as the upper terminal of coil 1.

Another method for determining the polarities of the terminals of coil 2 is to determine the direction of current in the coil if its terminals were short-circuited when coil 1 is energized (see Fig. 8.37b). A short time after coil 1 is energized, there will be a current i_1 in the direction shown. By coiling the fingers of the right hand about the core in the direction i_1 encircles it, the extended thumb shows that the flux ϕ will be increasing in the upward direction. The current i_2 will be in the direction shown, since the mmf of coil 2 will oppose the increase of flux. The direction of i_2 fixes the polarities of the voltage across the resistance of coil 2 as shown. The lower terminal of the coil must be negative.

Referring again to Fig. 8.37a, when the current in coil 1 is 0.2 amp, the voltage across the 12 ohms of resistance is 0.2 amp × 12 ohms = 2.4 v. The emf of self-induction in coil 1 is the applied voltage of 6 v less the resistance drop of 2.4 v, or 3.6 v. As before the emf of mutual induction in coil 2 is one-half the emf of self-induction in coil 1, or 3.6 v/2 = 1.8 v. The polarities of the terminals of coil 2 will be the same as at $t = 0$ since the current in coil 1 is increasing in each case.

8.11. Coefficient of Coupling. When two coils are so situated that most of the flux set up by current in either coil links most of the turns of the other coil, the coils are said to be closely coupled. The degree of coupling between two coils is measured by the coefficient of coupling, which may have a value from zero to unity. The coefficient would be unity if all the flux set up by current in either coil linked all the turns of both. This condition can be approached closely but not actually attained. If i_1 amp in coil 1 produces a flux ϕ_1 wb that links all N_1 turns of that coil and all N_2 turns of coil 2, the self-inductance L_1 of coil 1 (flux linkages per ampere) is

$$L_1 = \frac{N_1\phi_1}{i_1} \quad \text{h}$$

and the mutual inductance M_{12} from coil 1 to coil 2 (flux linkages per ampere) is $M_{12} = N_2\phi_1/i_1$ h. Now if i_2 amp in coil 2 produces a flux ϕ_2 wb that links all N_2 turns of that coil and all N_1 turns of coil 1, the self-inductance L_2 of coil 2 is $L_2 = N_2\phi_2/i_2$ h, and the mutual inductance M_{21} from coil 2 to coil 1 is

$$M_{21} = \frac{N_1\phi_2}{i_2} \quad \text{h}$$

From the preceding equations it follows that

$$M_{12}M_{21} = L_1L_2$$

Since $M_{12} = M_{21} = M$, then with perfect coupling

$$M^2 = L_1L_2 \quad \text{and} \quad M = \sqrt{L_1L_2}$$

Since $\sqrt{L_1L_2}$ is the theoretical limit on the mutual inductance between two coils having self-inductances L_1 and L_2, the coefficient of coupling k between any two coils is taken as the ratio of M, the actual mutual inductance between them, to the theoretical limit. Hence, by definition,

$$k = \frac{M}{\sqrt{L_1L_2}}$$

where M, L_1, and L_2 are in the same unit.

Example 1.   A certain nonmagnetic toroidal core has a cross section of 0.001 sq m, a mean length of 0.4 m, and is wound with 200 closely spaced turns of wire. The core is also surrounded by a circular one-turn coil that has a diameter of 0.04 m.   Compute the mutual inductance between the coils.

Solution.   Here it is easy to compute the mutual inductance from the 200-turn coil to the one-turn coil but difficult to compute the mutual inductance in the reverse direction.   If the 200-turn coil is excited by i amp, nearly all the flux will be within the core and thus link all the turns of each coil.   The mmf acting on the core is $200i$ amp-turns.   The magnetic potential gradient H in the core is $200i$ amp-turns/0.4 m = $500i$ amp-turns per m.   With the core permeability unity, the flux density in the core is

$$B = 4\pi \times 10^{-7}H = 4\pi \times 10^{-7} \times 500i = 2\pi \times 10^{-4}i \text{ wb per sq m}$$

The flux in the core is $\phi = 2\pi \times 10^{-4}i$ wb per sq m $\times$ 0.001 sq m = $2\pi \times 10^{-7}i$ wb. The flux linkages of the one-turn coil are $2\pi \times 10^{-7}i$ wb-turns.   The mutual inductance between the coils is $M = 2\pi \times 10^{-7}i$ wb-turns/i amp = $2\pi \times 10^{-7}$ h, or 0.628 μh.

8.12. Measurement of Mutual Inductance.   Mutual inductance can be measured with the circuit of Fig. 8.38.   Here the reading of a fluxmeter connected to coil 2 is taken as a direct current is suddenly established in coil 1.   Coil 2 serves as a search coil for the fluxmeter.   If, as is usually the case, the fluxmeter calibration is given in terms of the deflection with a one-turn search coil, it is not necessary that the number of turns in coil 2 be known. Assume that the mutual inductance being measured is constant and that Φ wb is the equivalent flux linking the N_2

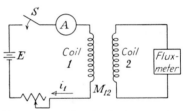

Fig. 8.38   Circuit for measuring mutual inductance with an ammeter and a fluxmeter.

turns of coil 2 when the current in coil 1 is I amp.   The fluxmeter actually measures flux linkages; thus $\Phi N_2 = FC$, where F divisions are read on the fluxmeter when I is established and C is the fluxmeter calibration in webers per division with a one-turn search coil.   Then the mutual inductance between the coils is

$$M = \frac{\text{flux linkages of coil 2}}{\text{current in coil 1}} = \frac{FC}{I} \quad \text{h} \qquad (8.16)$$

In using the circuit of Fig. 8.38, if one knows the approximate value of the mutual inductance to be measured, he can predict by (8.16) the current required for a satisfactory fluxmeter deflection.   Otherwise, to avoid an excessive deflection, a first trial should be made using a small current and in further trials increase it until a satisfactory fluxmeter deflection is obtained.   When a small mutual inductance is to be measured, the fluxmeter deflection for a given current can be doubled by introducing a reversing switch in the circuit and taking the fluxmeter reading as the current is suddenly reversed in direction. The reading would be divided by 2 when using (8.16) to compute the mutual inductance.

In using the circuit of Fig. 8.38, the resistance of coil 2 should not exceed the value specified for a search coil for the fluxmeter.

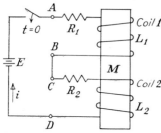

FIG. 8.39 Inductively coupled coils in series.

8.13. Coupled Circuit Relations. In Fig. 8.39 coil 1 of R_1 ohms resistance and L_1 h inductance is in series with coil 2 of R_2 ohms resistance and L_2 h inductance. The mutual inductance between the coils is M h. At $t = 0$, the battery of E v emf is suddenly connected to the coils by closing the switch. During the time the current is growing to its steady-state value of $E/(R_1 + R_2)$ amp, there are four inductive voltage drops in the coils:

$$L_1 \frac{di_1}{dt},$$ the drop of self-induction in coil 1

$$M \frac{di_2}{dt},$$ the drop of mutual induction in coil 1

$$L_2 \frac{di_2}{dt},$$ the drop of self-induction in coil 2

$$M \frac{di_1}{dt},$$ the drop of mutual induction in coil 2

In Fig. 8.39, $i_1 = i_2 = i$. When writing the voltage equations of a circuit, if the mmfs of the currents in the positive directions in the coils aid each other in setting up flux that links two coils, the sign of the $M\,di/dt$ drop is taken as positive when tracing through each coil in the direction of the current. If the mmfs oppose each other, the sign is taken as negative. In Fig. 8.39 the current i in coil 1 would establish flux in the core directed from the top to the bottom. The current i in coil 2 would establish flux in the core directed from the bottom to the top. Hence the coil mmfs oppose and a negative sign should be assigned to the $M\,di/dt$ terms in a voltage equation for the circuit traced in the direction of i.

In Fig. 8.39 the core is nonmagnetic; therefore the self-inductances and the mutual inductances are constant. The circuit voltage equation is

$$E = iR_1 + L_1 \frac{di}{dt} - M \frac{di}{dt} + iR_2 + L_2 \frac{di}{dt} - M \frac{di}{dt}$$

or
$$E = (R_1 + R_2)i + (L_1 + L_2 - 2M) \frac{di}{dt}$$

Here $R_1 + R_2$ is the equivalent resistance of the coils in series, and $L_1 + L_2 - 2M$ h is the equivalent self-inductance of the coils in series bucking.

In Fig. 8.39, if the connections on either coil were to be reversed, the mmfs of the coils would aid each other and the signs of the $M\ di/dt$ terms would be positive.   The equivalent self-inductance of the coils in series aiding is $L_1 + L_2 + 2M$ h.

In Fig. 8.39 the principal reason for showing the core was so that it would be possible to tell how the coils were wound with respect to each other.   Equivalent information can be conveyed by a statement as to whether the coils are in series aiding or bucking.

For inductively coupled coils of respective self-inductances L_1 and L_2 with mutual inductance M between them, the equivalent self-inductance is $L_A = L_1 + L_2 + 2M$ for a series aiding connection, and is

$$L_B = L_1 + L_2 - 2M$$

for a series bucking connection.   A method for obtaining adjustable self-inductance is to connect two coils in series and then vary the coupling between them by moving one coil with respect to the other.

Solving the preceding equations for M yields

$$M = \frac{L_A - L_B}{4}$$

Hence, if the measured equivalent self-inductance of two coils in series bucking is subtracted from their measured self-inductance in series aiding and the result divided by 4, the mutual-inductance between the coils is obtained.   If the mutual-inductance is small compared with the individual self-inductances, M as computed may be inaccurate. L_A and L_B will be nearly equal and a small percentage error in measuring either may result in a much larger percentage error in the value of M.

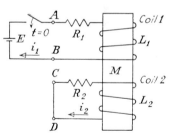

Fig. 8.40   Inductively coupled coils that are electrically isolated.

In Fig. 8.40 are two coils that are inductively coupled but electrically isolated.   All inductances are assumed constant.   A direct voltage is applied to coil 1 at $t = 0$ with coil 2 short-circuited.   The voltage equation of the circuit of coil 1 (the primary circuit) is

$$E = i_1 R_1 + L_1 \frac{di_1}{dt} - M \frac{di_2}{dt} \qquad (8.17)$$

and that of circuit 2 (the secondary circuit) is

$$0 = i_2 R_2 + L_2 \frac{di_2}{dt} - M \frac{di_1}{dt} \qquad (8.18)$$

where the respective units are in volts, amperes, ohms, henrys, and seconds. Although the circuits are electrically isolated, neither reacts as it would if the other were not coupled to it. For example, if the coils were not coupled, or if coil 2 were open-circuited at $t = 0$, $i_1 = 0$ and the initial rate of increase of i_1 (that is, di_1/dt) would be E/L_1. With coupling between the coils and coil 2 short-circuited, it can be seen from

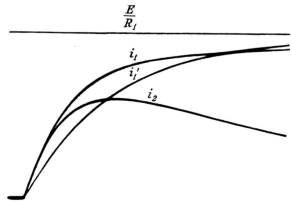

FIG. 8.41   Oscillograms of the currents in the circuit of Fig. 8.40. i_1 = primary current with secondary closed; i_1' = primary current with secondary open; i_2 = secondary current.

(8.17) that although at $t = 0$, $i_1 = 0$, the initial rate of increase of i_1 is not E/L_1 but $(E + M\ di_2/dt)/L_1$. Here the initial rate of increase of i_1 is greater than it would have been with no coupling or if coil 2 were open-circuited. The voltage of self-induction in coil 1 at $t = 0$ is greater than the applied voltage, the difference being the voltage of mutual-induction. In coil 2, at $t = 0$, the voltages of self-induction and mutual induction are equal in magnitude but opposite in polarity.

In Fig. 8.40 neither current can become steady until the other does and this does not occur until time is infinite. i_1 approaches a steady value of E/R_1 and i_2 approaches zero.   In Fig. 8.41 are oscillograms of the growths of the currents in Fig. 8.40 and one of the growth of i_1 when circuit 2 is open.   The primary current grows initially at a faster rate with the secondary circuit closed than with it open.   After a time the rate of growth is less in the first case than it is in the second. i_2 starts at zero, increases to a maximum, and then decreases asymptotically to zero.

The initial rates of increase of the currents in Fig. 8.40 can be obtained from (8.17) and (8.18). At $t = 0$, $i_1 = 0$, and $i_2 = 0$. Then

$$E = L_1 \frac{di_1}{dt}\Big|_{t=0} - M \frac{di_2}{dt}\Big|_{t=0} \quad \text{and} \quad 0 = L_2 \frac{di_2}{dt}\Big|_{t=0} - M \frac{di_1}{dt}\Big|_{t=0}$$

from which
$$\frac{di_1}{dt}\Big|_{t=0} = \frac{EL_2}{L_1L_2 - M^2} \quad \text{amp per sec}$$

and
$$\frac{di_2}{dt}\Big|_{t=0} = \frac{EM}{L_1L_2 - M^2} \quad \text{amp per sec}$$

Since $M^2 = k^2L_1L_2$, where k is the coefficient of coupling, the denominator in these equations may be written as $(1 - k^2)L_1L_2$.

Example 1. In Fig. 8.40, $E = 100$ v, $R_1 = 10$ ohms, $L_1 = 0.2$ h, $R_2 = 5$ ohms, $L_2 = 0.08$ h, and $M = 0.1$ h. For the instant when the switch is closed, compute the voltages of self-induction and mutual induction in each coil.

Solution. In accordance with (8.17) and (8.18) the circuit voltage equations are

$$100 = 10i_1 + 0.2 \frac{di_1}{dt} - 0.1 \frac{di_2}{dt}, \quad \text{and} \quad 0 = 5i_2 + 0.08 \frac{di_2}{dt} - 0.1 \frac{di_1}{dt}$$

At $t = 0$, $i_1 = 0$, and $i_2 = 0$; hence

$$100 = 0.2 \frac{di_1}{dt}\Big|_{t=0} - 0.1 \frac{di_2}{dt}\Big|_{t=0} \quad \text{and} \quad 0 = -0.1 \frac{di_1}{dt}\Big|_{t=0} + 0.08 \frac{di_2}{dt}\Big|_{t=0}$$

from which

$$\frac{di_1}{dt}\Big|_{t=0} = 1{,}330 \text{ amp per sec} \quad \text{and} \quad \frac{di_2}{dt}\Big|_{t=0} = 1{,}670 \text{ amp per sec}$$

The voltages of self-induction are 0.2 h $\times$ 1,330 amp per sec = 267 v in the primary coil and 0.08 h $\times$ 1,670 amp per sec = 133 v in the secondary coil. The voltages of mutual induction are 0.1 h $\times$ 1,670 amp per sec = 167 v in the primary coil and 0.1 h $\times$ 1,330 amp per sec = 133 v in the secondary coil.

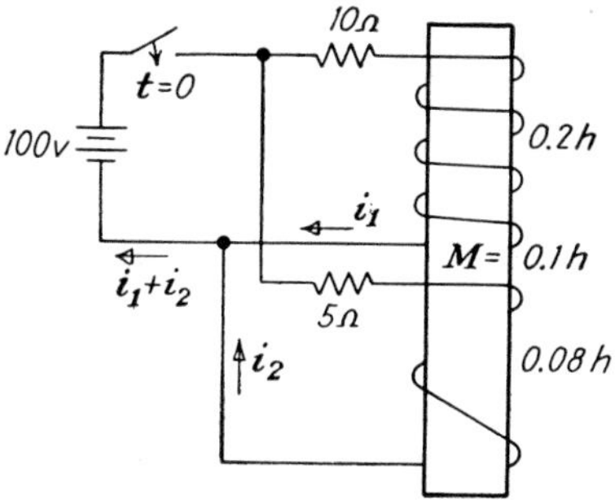

Example 2. In Fig. 8.42, compute for $t = 0$, the rate of increase of each current and the voltages of self-induction and mutual inductance.

Solution. The coils are electrically connected as well as inductively coupled. However, the principles involved in writing the voltage equations are the same

Fig. 8.42

as used previously. For the path through the battery and the upper coil, the voltage equation is

$$100 = 10i_1 + 0.2 \frac{di_1}{dt} + 0.1 \frac{di_2}{dt} \tag{1}$$

For the path through the battery and the lower coil, the voltage equation is

$$100 = 5i_2 + 0.08 \frac{di_2}{dt} + 0.1 \frac{di_1}{dt} \qquad (2)$$

The signs of the M terms in these equations are positive because, when i_1 and i_2 are each in a positive direction, the coil mmfs aid in establishing mutual flux through the coils.

Because of self-inductance in each coil, at $t = 0$, $i_1 = 0$, and $i_2 = 0$. At that instant (1) and (2) become

$$100 = 0.2 \frac{di_1}{dt} + 0.1 \frac{di_2}{dt} \qquad (3)$$

and

$$100 = 0.08 \frac{di_2}{dt} + 0.1 \frac{di_1}{dt} \qquad (4)$$

From (3) and (4),

$$\frac{di_1}{dt}\bigg|_{t=0} = -333 \text{ amp per sec} \quad \text{and} \quad \frac{di_2}{dt}\bigg|_{t=0} = 1{,}667 \text{ amp per sec}$$

The negative value for $di_1/dt\big|_{t=0}$ shows that i_1 starts and flows for a time in a direction opposite to that reached in a steady state. This occurs because the voltage of mutual induction in coil 1 for a short time interval is greater than and directed opposite to the battery voltage applied to the coil.

The voltage of self-induction in coil 1 at $t = 0$ is

$$0.2 \text{ h} \times (-333 \text{ amp per sec}) = -66.7 \text{ v}$$

and that in coil 2 is 0.08 h $\times$ 1,667 amp per sec = 133 v.

The voltage of mutual induction in coil 1 at $t = 0$ is

$$0.1 \text{ h} \times 1{,}667 \text{ amp per sec} = 167 \text{ v}$$

and that in coil 2 is 0.1 h $\times$ (−333 amp per sec) = −33.3 v.

Assume that circuit 1 having a resistance R_1 ohms and a self-inductance L_1 h is coupled with a constant mutual inductance M h to circuit 2 having a resistance R_2 ohms and a self-inductance L_2 h. Let a battery of emf E_1 v and negligible resistance be connected to circuit 1 and a battery of emf E_2 v and negligible resistance be connected to circuit 2 at $t = 0$. At any instant thereafter the circuit voltage equations are

$$E_1 = i_1 R_1 + L_1 \frac{di_1}{dt} \pm M \frac{di_2}{dt} \qquad (8.19)$$

and

$$E_2 = i_2 R_2 + L_2 \frac{di_2}{dt} \pm M \frac{di_1}{dt} \qquad (8.20)$$

where i_1 and i_2 amp are the respective currents in circuits 1 and 2 and are directed out of the positive battery terminals. Let (8.19) be multiplied by i_1 and (8.20) be multiplied by i_2.   After rearrangement of terms

$$E_1 i_1 - i_1^2 R_1 = L_1 i_1 \frac{di_1}{dt} \pm M i_1 \frac{di_2}{dt}$$

$$E_2 i_2 - i_2^2 R_2 = L_2 i_2 \frac{di_2}{dt} \pm M i_2 \frac{di_1}{dt}$$

where each term has the dimension of power.   Here $E_1 i_1$ is the instantaneous power delivered by battery 1, $E_2 i_2$ is the instantaneous power delivered by battery 2, $i_1^2 R_1$ is the instantaneous power converted into heat in circuit 1, and $i_2^2 R_2$ is the instantaneous power converted into heat in circuit 2.   But the sum of the powers delivered by the batteries less the power converted into heat in the circuits is p_{mag}, the power being put into the magnetic field.   Hence

$$p_{\text{mag}} = \frac{L_1 i_1 \, di_1}{dt} \pm \frac{M i_1 \, di_2}{dt} \pm \frac{M i_2 \, di_1}{dt} + \frac{L_2 i_2 \, di_2}{dt}$$

Since $dw_{\text{mag}} = p_{\text{mag}} \, dt$ j, where dw_{mag} is the infinitesimal amount of energy stored in the magnetic field during the infinitesimal interval of time dt, then

$$dw_{\text{mag}} = L_1 i_1 \, di_1 \pm M i_1 \, di_2 \pm M i_2 \, di_1 + L_2 i_2 \, di_2$$

With L_1, M, and L_2 constant, this can be integrated into

$$W_{\text{mag}} = \tfrac{1}{2} L_1 i_1^2 \pm M i_1 i_2 + \tfrac{1}{2} L_2 i_2^2 \qquad \text{j} \qquad (8.21)$$

Here the constant of integration is zero since the energy stored is zero when the currents are zero.

8.14. Eddy Currents.   The steel that is used in electric apparatus to provide a high-permeability path for the flux is an electric conductor. In a steel magnetic circuit, a change of flux induces emfs in the steel and these in turn produce eddy currents in the steel.   The $I^2 R$ caused by these currents is an eddy-current loss.   In a steel magnetic circuit that is excited by a coil carrying direct current, eddy currents usually exist only during the short intervals when current is being established or interrupted.   Here the eddy-current energy loss is usually unimportant. When the flux in a steel core is alternating (as in a transformer), the eddy currents are also alternating and an eddy-current loss exists as long as the core is excited.   The eddy-current loss in a core is a function of the magnitude of the flux, the rate at which it is changing, and the dimensions and the material of the core.   For most magnetic circuits carrying an alternating flux, the eddy-current loss would be objectionably high if the core were solid.   The loss in a given volume of a magnetic material can be reduced to a value that can be tolerated by division of the material into small units called laminations. Figure 8.43a represents a solid core with a radius r_1 and a length l m. The core is carrying a sinusoidal alternating flux of maximum value Φ_m wb that varies according to the equation $\phi = \Phi_m \sin 2\pi f t$ wb, where ϕ is the instantaneous value of the flux, f is the frequency in cycles per second, and t is the time in seconds after the flux goes through zero in a positive direction. Within the core consider the cylindrical shell of radius r m, of thickness dr m, and of length l m. The changing flux ϕ_r within the shell induces an emf e in the

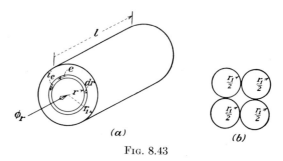

(a)   (b)

FIG. 8.43

shell normal to the direction of the flux. The emf produces the eddy current i_e in the shell. If the flux density is uniform over the core cross section, then ϕ_r is to ϕ as the area πr^2 within the shell is to the area πr_1^2 of the core. Hence $\phi_r/\phi = \pi r^2/\pi r_1^2$, from which $\phi_r = \phi r^2/r_1^2$. But $\phi = \Phi_m \sin 2\pi f t$, so that $\phi_r = (\Phi_m r^2/r_1^2) \sin 2\pi f t$ wb. Since the shell constitutes a single turn about ϕ_r, then

$$e = \frac{d\phi_r}{dt} = \frac{d}{dt}\left(\frac{\Phi_m r^2}{r_1^2} \sin 2\pi f t\right) = \frac{2\pi f \Phi_m r^2}{r_1^2} \cos 2\pi f t \qquad \mathbf{v}$$

The emf is sinusoidal with a maximum value E_m of $2\pi f \phi_m r^2/r_1^2$ $\mathbf{v}$ and an rms value of

$$E = \frac{E_m}{\sqrt{2}} = \frac{2\pi f \phi_m r^2}{\sqrt{2}\, r_1^2} \qquad \mathrm{v}$$

The length of the path followed by the eddy current in the shell is $2\pi r$ m. The section of the shell normal to the direction of the eddy current is dr m by l m and has an area of $l\, dr$ sq m. The resistance of the shell is

$$R = \frac{\text{resistivity} \times \text{length}}{\text{area}} = \frac{\rho 2\pi r}{l\, dr} \qquad \text{ohms}$$

where ρ is in ohm-meters. At low frequencies the effect of the inductance of an eddy-current path is negligible compared with that of the resistance and the loss is nearly equal to the square of the rms voltage acting on the path divided by the resistance of the path.   The infinitesimal power loss dP in the shell of Fig. 8.43a is

$$dP = \frac{E^2}{R} = \frac{(2\pi f \Phi_m r^2 / \sqrt{2}\, r_1^2)^2}{2\pi \rho r / l \; dr} = \frac{\pi f^2 l \Phi_m^2 r^3 \; dr}{\rho r_1^4} \qquad \text{w} \qquad (8.22)$$

The total eddy-current loss P_e in the core of Fig. 8.43a is obtained by integrating (8.22) with limits $r = 0$ to $r = r_1$.   Hence

$$P_e = \frac{\pi f^2 l \Phi_m^2}{\rho r_1^4} \int_0^{r_1} r^3 \; dr = \frac{\pi f^2 l \Phi_m^2}{\rho r_1^4} \left[\frac{r^4}{4}\right]_0^{r_1} = \frac{\pi f^2 l \Phi_m^2}{4\rho} \qquad \text{w} \qquad (8.23)$$

This shows that with a sinusoidally varying flux in the core of Fig. 8.43a the eddy-current loss varies directly as the squares of the frequency and the maximum flux, directly as the length, and inversely as the resistivity. Since r_1 does not appear in (8.23), then for a given length of core of given resistivity, carrying a sinusoidal flux at a given frequency, the eddy-current loss is independent of the radius of the core.

Now let the core of Fig. 8.43a be subdivided into four smaller cores as in Fig. 8.43b. If each smaller core has a radius of $r_1/2$ m, each has an area of $\pi r_1^2/4$ and the area of the four is πr_1^2 sq m, equal to that of the core of Fig. 8.43a. If the total flux carried by the four cores equals that in the larger core, the maximum flux in each smaller core is $\Phi_m/4$. The eddy-current loss varies as the square of the maximum flux and $(\frac{1}{4})^2 = \frac{1}{16}$; thus the loss in each smaller core is $\frac{1}{16}$ that in the larger core. The loss in the four smaller cores is $4 \times \frac{1}{16} = \frac{1}{4}$ that in the larger core. In a similar manner it can be shown that the total eddy-current loss can be reduced to $1/n$ part of the original value by dividing the original core into n identical circular elements.

Although laminations of circular cross section are used in some magnetic circuits, a more common type is one that is stamped from a steel sheet and has a rectangular cross section normal to the flux. Laminations are stacked together to form a complete core. Individual laminations are electrically insulated from each other by an oxide film formed on the surface during heat treatments given the laminations. When the lamination thickness is small compared with the width, the eddy-current loss for a given volume of steel of a given resistivity that is carrying a given sinusoidal flux at a given frequency is approximately proportional to the square of the thickness of the laminations. There is an economic limit to the thinness of laminations because of the increased cost of making and handling a greater number of laminations. The thickness of the oxide film is about the same for any thickness of lamination. As a result, the thinner that laminations are made, the less is the proportion of the gross cross section of a core that is steel. In 60-c transformers, a common lamination thickness is 14 mils (0.014 in.). For higher frequencies, laminations as thin as 2 mils or powdered iron cores are often used. For radio frequencies, it is usually undesirable to use a metallic core because excessive eddy-current loss would occur in it.

The eddy currents in a steel core cause the flux density to be nonuniform over the cross section of a lamination, it being least at the center and greatest at the surface. The variation of the flux density over the cross section of a lamination is small for the frequency and the lamination thickness used in commercial power transformers.

8.15. Induction Heating. This is a process in which desired heating is produced in a metallic substance by eddy currents. An alternating current is sent through a coil that surrounds the object to be heated. The heat can be concentrated in a small region of a metal object and applied so quickly that the remainder of the object stays relatively cool. Metal parts within a glass-walled envelope can be heated by induction. The frequency used for a given induction-heating application depends upon the cross section and the resistivity of the object to be heated and whether the object is to be heated uniformly throughout or mainly near the surface. For applications where the object has a large cross section and a low resistivity and is to be heated uniformly throughout, 60 c are used. When an object is to be heated near the surface, frequencies ranging from 3,000 to 450,000 c are used. At these frequencies, skin effect causes most of the current to flow near the surface of the object and concentrate most of the heat there.

8.16. Skin Effect. Within a circular conductor that is carrying current there is a magnetic flux. In Fig. 8.44 is such a conductor that is divided into three elements of equal cross section. The inner element is a cylinder of radius r_1, the second element is a tube of inner radius r_1 and an outer radius r_2, and the outer element is a tube of inner radius r_2 and an outer radius r_3. With direct current in the conductor the flux density varies

Fig. 8.44

linearly from zero at the center to a maximum at the conductor surface. The currents in the elements would be equal since the element resistances are equal. The outer element is surrounded by the flux external to the conductor. The second element is surrounded by the flux external to the conductor plus that within the outer element. The inner element is surrounded by the flux external to the conductor plus that within the other elements. The elements have unequal inductances because they are linked by unequal fluxes when carrying equal currents.

The conductor of Fig. 8.44 may be represented as in Fig. 8.45. Here the conductor elements have a resistance R each, respective self-inductances of L_1, L_2, and L_3, and mutual inductances of M_{12}, M_{23}, and M_{31}. Because of the inductances, the division of an alternating current between the elements is a function of the frequency. The higher the frequency, the greater the proportion of the current that is carried in the outer element, a manifestation known as skin effect.

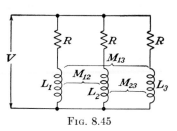

The nonuniform distribution of current over the cross section of a conductor that accompanies skin effect causes the heat loss in the conductor to be greater than it would be if an equal current were distributed uniformly. The a-c resistance of a

conductor increases with the frequency but not in a direct proportion.

8.17. Magnetic Pull. In Fig. 8.46 is represented an electromagnet excited by a coil of N turns carrying I amp. The magnet sections, having two contact surfaces of A sq m each, are assumed to be in contact initially and are then separated a distance of dl m by the force $2P$ newtons acting upon the lower section. In an actual circuit the coil has resistance and a battery might be used to establish the current. With the two sections in contact, as the current grows to a steady state, energy is stored in the magnetic field. With the current in a steady state, all energy delivered by the battery is converted into heat in the resistance. Now if the section is moved by the applied force, the motion causes a rate of decrease of the flux through the turns and induces an emf in them. The polarity of the emf is such that an increase of current occurs. During an interval in which motion occurs, more energy is delivered by the battery than during an equal interval when the current was steady. Also during the interval of motion, energy is put into the system equal to the mechanical energy resulting from the product of the force and the distance through which it moves. During an interval the energy delivered by the battery plus that converted from the mechanical form equals the energy converted into heat in the resistance plus the change in the energy stored in the magnetic field. A derivation for the force required, considering all the above factors, is quite involved. A derivation that leads to the same result can be obtained by using certain special conditions. Assume that the flux Φ wb is established by a current I amp in the resistanceless coil of N turns and

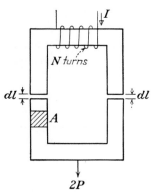

Fig. 8.46   Pull in a magnetic circuit.

then the turns are short-circuited. With no air gap in the magnetic circuit let its reluctance be $\mathcal{R}_o$ mks units. Then, since mmf = flux × reluctance

$$NI = \Phi\mathcal{R}_o \quad \text{amp-turns}$$

The original inductance of the coil is $L_o = N\Phi/I$ h and the original energy stored in the magnetic field is $W_o = \frac{1}{2}L_oI^2 = \frac{1}{2}N\Phi I = \frac{1}{2}\Phi^2\mathcal{R}_o$ j.

Now let a constant force of $2P$ newtons move the section a distance dl m, thereby doing $2P\,dl$ j of work. Two air gaps, each of length dl, are introduced in the magnetic circuit. The reluctance of each is dl/μ_vA mks units. The reluctance of the magnetic circuit is now $\mathcal{R}_o + 2\,dl/\mu_vA$ mks units. With a resistanceless coil the current will at once assume the new value I_1 required to maintain the flux at the original value of Φ, where $NI_1 = \Phi\mathcal{R}_o + 2\Phi\,dl/\mu_vA$ amp-turns. The inductance of the coil is now $L_1 = N\Phi/I_1$ h and the energy now stored in the magnetic field is $W_1 = \frac{1}{2}L_1I_1^2 = \frac{1}{2}N\Phi I_1 = \frac{1}{2}\Phi^2\mathcal{R}_o + \Phi^2\,dl/\mu_vA$ j. The change in the energy stored in the magnetic field equals the mechanical work done. Hence $2P\,dl = W_1 - W_o = \Phi^2\,dl/\mu_vA$, from which $P = \Phi^2/2\mu_vA$ newtons. The preceding derivation is based on the assumption that all the flux is confined to the core and that there is no fringing of the flux when an air gap is introduced. Also it is assumed that the permeability of the core material is, say, 100 or more. If the permeability were unity, introducing the air gaps would cause no change in the reluctance of the magnetic circuit and no magnetic pull would result. In an actual electromagnet fringing of flux occurs at an air gap and the flux density may be non-uniform over the pole face area where pull is being produced. These factors make it necessary to use various approximations in computing magnetic pull.

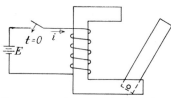

FIG. 8.47 Closing circuit of a magnetically operated switch.

The device of Fig. 8.47 is one in which a direct voltage is applied to an exciting coil to produce magnetic pull on a movable portion of a magnetic circuit. Following the closing of the switch in the exciting coil circuit, the current increases for a time about as it would in a circuit of constant inductance. The flux increases also, but it and the magnetic pull are small because of the high reluctance in the long air gap. As the movable portion moves to close the magnetic circuit, the flux increases at a more rapid rate than the current because of the decreasing reluctance. At the same time the pull is increasing about as the square of the flux. As the movable portion nears its closed position, the rapid rate of decrease of reluctance results in the induction of enough emf to cause a momentary decrease of the current.   Later the current increases to its steady-state value.   The current variation is shown in Fig. 8.48.   Note that the current had reached its E/R value before the dip in current occurred.   The reversal in the curvature of the current curve following the dip is caused by the varying permeability of the steel as the flux increases.

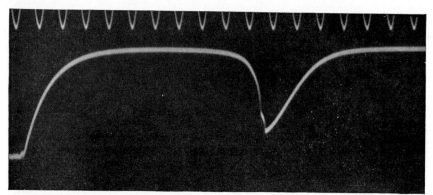

FIG. 8.48   Oscillogram of the growth of current in the circuit of Fig. 8.47.   The frequency of the timing wave is 60 c.

An alternating current in the exciting coil of an electromagnet produces an alternating flux.   When the flux is zero, the magnetic pull is zero. If the plunger is closed against either the pull of gravity or a spring, it will start to open as the flux nears zero.   Then an increase of flux in the reverse direction causes the plunger to be attracted again.   With the pull pulsating, the plunger may chatter objectionably.   One method for reducing the chatter is to cut a notch in the pole face and surround part of the pole face with a short-circuited turn of copper, a shading coil.   Induced currents in the turn prevent the flux within the turn from being zero when that over the remainder of the pole face is

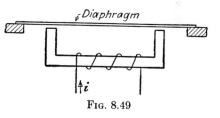

FIG. 8.49

zero.   Then there is no instant at which the total flux and pull are zero.

In Fig. 8.49 are represented the electric and the magnetic circuits of a receiver for a head set.   As current flows in the coil, magnetic pull causes the steel diaphragm to be deflected toward the pole faces.   It is desired that the pull should vary with time in the same manner as the current does.   Let us see if the desired response of the diaphragm would be obtained if soft steel were used in the electromagnet.   Assume that the current varies sinusoidally according to the equation

$$i = I_m \sin 2\pi ft \qquad \text{amp} \qquad (8.24)$$

where I_m amp is the maximum current, f c is the frequency of the current, and t is the time in seconds following an instant of zero current. The diaphragm is supported at such a distance from the pole pieces that there is always an air gap between them. If it is assumed that most of the reluctance drop in the magnetic circuit occurs in the air gap, the flux ϕ in the gap is proportional to the current i, or $\phi = k_1 i$, where k_1 is a proportionality factor. Since the pull p varies as the square of the flux, then $p = k_2 \phi^2 = k_3 i^2$, where k_2 and k_3 are other proportionality factors. Using the value of i from (8.24) yields $p = k_3 I_m^2 \sin^2 2\pi ft$. But $\sin^2 2\pi ft = (1 - \cos 4\pi ft)/2$; thus $p = k_3 I_m^2 (1 - \cos 4\pi ft)/2$, which may be written as $p = P_{\text{avg}}(1 - \cos 4\pi ft)$, where P_{avg} is the average pull. Time variations of the current and the pull are shown in Fig. 8.50. The pull varies cosinusoidally about the average pull but at twice the frequency of the current. A voice wave is composed of sine waves of various frequencies. If the coil current varies with time in the same manner as the voice wave at the transmitting end of the circuit, the response of the diaphragm will be such as to double each frequency component. The voice heard in the receiver will be high-pitched and unnatural.

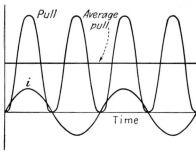

Fig. 8.50

Now let the electromagnet core in Fig. 8.49 be a permanent magnet that produces a residual flux Φ_o in the air gaps. With a sinusoidal current in the coil, the flux will vary as $\phi = \Phi_o + \Phi_1 \sin 2\pi ft$, where Φ_1 is the maximum value of the alternating component of the flux. Since the pull p varies as ϕ^2, then $p = k_4(\Phi_o + \Phi_1 \sin 2\pi ft)^2$, which, after expansion, can be expressed as

$$p = k_4 \left(\Phi_o^2 + \frac{\Phi_1^2}{2} + 2\Phi_o\Phi_1 \sin 2\pi ft - \frac{\Phi_1^2}{2} \cos 4\pi ft \right) \qquad (8.25)$$

where k_4 is a proportionality factor.

The first two terms in (8.25) are constants and represent a steady pull. The third term is a sinusoidal pull of the same frequency as the current and is a desired component. The last term is a cosinusoidal pull of twice the frequency of the current and is an undesired component. The amplitude of this component is small compared with that of the third term if Φ_o is large compared with Φ_1. By using a strong permanent magnet as the core and keeping the exciting current to a low value, the response of the diaphragm is satisfactory for speech reproduction.

8.18. Hysteresis Loss.   When the varying current i amp is established in a coil of N turns about a magnetic circuit, the voltage drop v_L produced by the changing flux ϕ wb is $v_L = N \, d\phi/dt$ v, where t is the time in seconds.   The instantaneous power input to the magnetic field is $p_L = v_L i = N i \, d\phi/dt$ w.   The energy input to the magnetic field is

$$W_L = \int_0^t p_L \, dt + W_0 = \int_0^t N i \frac{d\phi}{dt} \, dt + W_0 = \int_{\Phi_0}^{\Phi_1} N i \, d\phi + W_0 \qquad \text{j}$$

where W_0 is the energy stored in the field at $t = 0$, at which instant the flux is Φ_0 wb, and Φ_1 wb is the flux at t sec.   The sign of W_0 is positive if the integral term represents an increment of energy that adds to the energy originally present; otherwise the sign is negative.

The last integral above can be evaluated by formal integration if the equation is known or can be determined, that relates i and ϕ, as would be the case if a magnetic circuit of given dimensions were composed of a material of given constant permeability. The integral can be evaluated by graphical integration if the relation between i and ϕ is given by a curve (e.g., a magnetization curve).

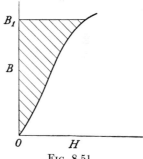

Fig. 8.51

If the flux density B wb per sq m and the magnetic potential gradient H amp-turns per m are uniform throughout the volume of a magnetic path, the energy stored may be expressed as

$$W_L = \int_{B_0}^{B_1} H l A \, dB + W_0 \qquad \text{j}$$

since here $d\phi = A \, dB$ and $Ni = Hl$, where A sq m is the cross section of the path, l m is its length, B_0 is the flux density at $t = 0$, and B_1 is the flux density at t sec.   Since lA is the volume of the path, then

$$\frac{W_L}{lA} = \int_{B_0}^{B_1} H \, dB + \frac{W_0}{lA} \qquad \text{j per cu m}$$

In Fig. 8.51 is a B-H curve for a steel core.   With the core initially demagnetized $W_0 = 0$ and $B_0 = 0$.   Then the energy input to the magnetic field as the flux density varies from 0 to B_1, in joules per cubic meter of the core, is equal to the shaded area in ampere-turns per meter times webers per square meter.

In Fig. 8.52 the energy input to the magnetic field as the flux density is increased from 0 to B_1 is proportional to the area OAB_1O.   When H is then reduced to zero, B does not decrease to zero but to a residual value B_2. The energy delivered by the magnetic field is proportional to the area AB_1B_2A. Since this area is less than that of OAB_1O, the energy delivered is less than that initially stored.

Figure 8.53 is a symmetrical hysteresis loop for a steel sample that has been subjected to several successive reversals of the magnetic potential gradient from $+H_1$ to $-H_1$. The flux density varies from $+B_1$ to $-B_1$.

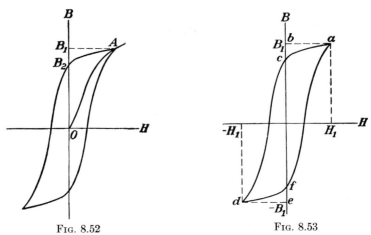

FIG. 8.52   FIG. 8.53

As the gradient is varied from $+H_1$ to 0, the magnetic field delivers energy proportional to the area $abca$. As H is varied from 0 to $-H_1$, energy proportional to the area $cdec$ is put into the magnetic field. As H is next varied from $-H_1$ to 0, energy proportional to the area $defd$ is delivered by the magnetic field. Finally, as H is increased from 0 to the original value of $+H_1$, energy proportional to the area $fabf$ is put into the magnetic field. The energy not returned by the magnetic field is proportional to the area $acdfa$, since

$$acdfa = cdec + fabf - defd - abca$$

The energy not returned, the hysteresis loss is equal to the area of the hysteresis loop in ampere-turns per meter times webers per square meter.

Hysteresis loss is of little importance in a d-c circuit that may remain closed for long periods. However, in an a-c circuit, where the magnetic field is constantly changing, the hysteresis loss may be an important item. The steel used for transformer cores has a narrow hysteresis loop and a low hysteresis loss. The hysteresis loss of a given sample of steel is usually determined from tests made with alternating current rather than by measuring the area of a hysteresis loop obtained with direct current.

8.19. Steinmetz Exponent. The hysteresis loss per cycle in steel subjected to a flux that alternates between equal positive and negative values is proportional to the area of the hysteresis loop.   During each cycle, the energy loss is repeated, so that the energy loss per second, which is the average power, is proportional to the frequency f in cycles per second.   In Fig. 8.54 as the maximum flux density is increased from B_1 to B_2 or B_3, the hysteresis loss per cycle increases in the ratio of the areas of the respective loops.   Steinmetz determined by experiment that, for certain grades of sheet steel used in transformers, the hysteresis loss at

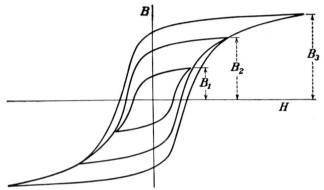

Fɪɢ. 8.54   Hysteresis loops corresponding to three values of maximum flux density.

constant frequency varied approximately as the 1.6 power of the maximum flux density.   This was equivalent to proving that the areas of two loops were in the ratio of the 1.6 power of their maximum ordinates.   For a steel core that is being carried through the cyclic alternations represented by symmetrical hysteresis loops,

$$P = kfB_m^{1.6}   \text{w}$$

where P is the average power loss, k is a proportionality factor, f is the frequency in cycles per second of the alternations, and B_m in webers per square meter is the maximum flux density.   The exponent is called the Steinmetz exponent.   Its value is not always 1.6 but may range from 1.4 to 2.5.

8.20. Magnetostriction.* This term applies to the change in the dimensions of a sample of ferromagnetic material that occurs when a magnetic field is established in the sample, or to the change in the strength of the magnetic field that occurs when an external force is applied to the sample.   Magnetostriction occurs in ferromagnetic materials, and in cobalt, iron, and nickel, and most of their alloys.

Magnetostriction effects are classified as:

1. Joule effect deals with the change in length of a material along the

* This article is based upon material in the booklet, "Magnetostriction," published by The International Nickel Company, Inc.

axis of the applied magnetic field when the field is changed. The longitudinal change is accompanied by a transverse and a volume change.

2. Villari effect deals with the change in the magnetization of a material in a magnetic field when the external stress is changed.

3. Wertheim effect deals with the transient voltage that appears between the ends of a wire in a longitudinal magnetic field while the wire is being twisted.

4. Wiedemann effect deals with the twist produced in a wire in a longitudinal magnetic field by a current in the wire. The inverse Wiedemann effect deals with the axial magnetization of a current-carrying wire when twisted.

A material has positive magnetostriction if it expands and negative magnetostriction if it contracts when a longitudinal magnetic field is established in it. The per unit change in length caused by magnetostriction is small. Nickel has negative magnetostriction, a reduction in length of about 20 parts in a million being caused by a change in the magnetic potential gradient from 0 to 6,000 amp-turns per m, 30 parts in a million by a change from 0 to 14,000 amp-turns per m, and 37 parts in a million by a change from 0 to 60,000 amp-turns per m. Iron has positive magnetostriction at low gradients up to 21,000 amp-turns per m, the maximum being about 4 parts in a million at 4,800 amp-turns per m. Iron has negative magnetostriction of 5 parts in a million for a gradient change from 21,000 to 50,000 amp-turns per m.

Magnetostriction may cause undesired noise and vibration and early studies of it were for the purpose of reducing its effects. However, magnetostriction now has commercial applications: in the Sonar, a device for detecting submarines and ships; in the Fathometer, a device for determining the depth of water and for locating schools of fish; in a bandpass filter for radio receiving sets; in homogenizing and sterilizing milk; in the acceleration of chemical reactions; in strain gages; in phonograph pickups; in frequency control of oscillators; and in dust precipitation.

8.21. Relations in Circuits with Variable Coupling. It was shown in Art. 8.13 that the stored energy W in the magnetic field about a coil having L_1 h constant self-inductance and carrying i_1 amp that is coupled with constant mutual inductance M h to a coil having L_2 h constant self-inductance and carrying i_2 amp is $W = \frac{1}{2}L_1 i_1^2 + M i_1 i_2 + \frac{1}{2}L_2 i_2^2$ j. If one of the coils is moving with respect to the other, or if some part of the magnetic circuits involved is moving in such a manner as to vary one or more of the circuit inductances, the differential energy change is

$$dw = \frac{1}{2}i_1^2\,dL_1 + L_1 i_1\,di_1 + i_1 i_2\,dM + M i_2\,di_1 + M i_1\,di_2 + \frac{1}{2}i_2^2\,dL_2$$
$$+ L_2 i_2\,di_2 \qquad j$$

The terms involving differential inductances represent energy being converted into mechanical form.   If rotational torque T newtons at 1-m radius acts through the differential angle $d\theta$ radian, the work done is $T\, d\theta = \frac{1}{2}i_1^2\, dL_1 + i_1 i_2\, dM + \frac{1}{2}i_2^2\, dL_2$ newton-m.   Then

$$T = \frac{1}{2}\, i_1^2 \frac{dL_1}{d\theta} + i_1 i_2 \frac{dM}{d\theta} + \frac{1}{2}\, i_2^2 \frac{dL_2}{d\theta} \qquad \text{newtons at 1-m radius} \quad (8.26)$$

If a linear force F newtons acts through the differential distance dx m, the work done is $F\, dx = \frac{1}{2}i_1^2\, dL_1 + i_1 i_2\, dM + \frac{1}{2}i_2^2\, dL_2$ newton-m.   Then

$$F = \frac{1}{2}\, i_1^2 \frac{dL_1}{dx} + i_1 i_2 \frac{dM}{dx} + \frac{1}{2}\, i_2^2 \frac{dL_2}{dx} \qquad \text{newtons} \quad (8.27)$$

In Fig. 8.55 are represented a magnetic circuit and two current-carrying coils.   The coupling between the coils can be varied by moving one coil in the air gap of the magnetic circuit. The expression for the force exerted on coil 2 is to be derived.   Even if coil 1 were not excited, the establishment of current in coil 2 in either direction would cause a force to be exerted on coil 2, tending to move it to the right to a position of symmetry about the core where the flux through it would be a maximum. With coil 2 in the position shown and carrying current, the establishment of current in coil 1 will cause an additional force to be exerted on coil 2. The direction of this force will depend upon the relative directions of the currents.   Assume   that   the

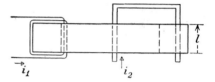

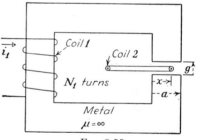

FIG. 8.55

metal in the magnetic circuit has infinite permeability and that there is no fringing of the flux at the air gap.   With these assumptions, with coil 2 not excited and coil 1 carrying i_1 amp in its N_1 turns, the reluctance drop across the gap would be $N_1 i_1$ amp-turns and the magnetic potential gradient in the gap would be $H_1 = N_1 i_1/g$ amp-turns per m, where g is the length of the gap in meters.   The uniform flux density produced in the gap would be

$$B_1 = \mu_v H_1 = \frac{\mu_v N_1 i_1}{g} \qquad \text{wb per sq m}$$

The cross section of the gap is al sq m, where a and l are the dimensions of the gap in meters normal to the flux.   The flux across the gap is $\phi_1 = B_1 al$ wb.   The self-inductance of coil 1 is $L_1 = N_1\phi_1/i_1 = \mu_v N_1^2 al/g$ h and is a constant, independent of the position of coil 2. With coil 2 in the position shown, the flux set up by coil 1 that links coil 2 is $\phi_{12} = B_1 lx$ wb, when $0 < x < a$. The mutual inductance between the coils is

$$M = \frac{\phi_{12}}{i_1} = \left(\frac{\mu_v N_1 i_1}{g}\right)\frac{lx}{i_1} = \frac{\mu_v N_1 lx}{g} \qquad \text{h}$$

Now assume that coil 1 is not excited and that the current i_2 is established in coil 2. Further assume that the number of flux lines about coil 2 whose path is entirely in the air is negligible and that the only flux established is that crossing the gap through the area lx. Since coil 2 is assumed to have one turn, the mmf of coil 2 is i_2 amp-turns. The corresponding magnetic potential gradient is $H_2 = i_2/g$ amp-turns per m. The corresponding flux density is $B_2 = \mu_v H_2 = \mu_v i_2/g$ wb per sq m. The flux linking coil 2 is $\phi_2 = B_2 lx = \mu_v lx i_2/g$ wb. The self-inductance of coil 2 is $L_2 = \phi_2/i_2 = \mu_v lx/g$ h.

Here L_1 is a constant; hence $dL_1/dx = 0$. Also

$$\frac{dM}{dx} = \frac{d(\mu_v N_1 lx/g)}{dx} = \frac{\mu_v N_1 l}{g}$$

and $dL_2/dx = d(\mu_v lx/g)/dx = \mu_v l/g$. Then, by (8.27)

$$f = i_1 i_2 \frac{\mu_v N_1 l}{g} + \frac{1}{2} i_2^2 \frac{\mu_v l}{g} = \frac{\mu_v l}{g}\left(i_1 i_2 N_1 + \frac{1}{2} i_2^2\right) \qquad \text{newtons} \qquad (8.28)$$

In Fig. 8.55 this force would act to move coil 2 toward the right and would represent motor action.

If the direction of i_2 in Fig. 8.55 were reversed, the sign of i_2 in (8.28) would be reversed and the two components of force would have opposite signs. The resultant force might be zero, or directed to the right, or directed to the left, the result depending upon the relative magnitudes of i_1 and i_2. If the resultant force is to the left, then if a mechanical force is applied to the coil to cause it to move to the right generator action occurs and energy is transferred from the mechanical system to the electrical system.

In Fig. 8.55, $B_1 = \mu_v N_1 i_1/g$. Then (8.28) may be expressed as

$$f = B_1 li_2 + \frac{\mu_v li_2^2}{2g} \qquad \text{newtons} \qquad (8.29)$$

Since the distance x in Fig. 8.55 does not appear in (8.29), then the force acting on coil 2 is a constant for any value from 0 to a. With the assumed flux-density distribution in space, all inductances become constant when the right-hand side of coil 2 is moved out from the air gap and the force on the coil becomes zero. In an actual case the fringing at the gap would determine the location of the coil when the force on it was zero and the flux through it was a maximum.

It is commonly stated that the force f exerted on a current-carrying conductor in a magnetic field of uniform density is given by the expression $f = Bli$ newtons, where B is in webers per square meter, l m is the length of the projection of the conductor upon a plane normal to the field, and i amp is the current. The directions of f, B, and i are expressed by Fleming's left-hand rule: if the thumb, the extended forefinger, and the second finger of the left hand are placed mutually perpendicular, when the first finger points in the direction of the magnetic field and the second finger in the direction of the current in the conductor, the thumb points in the direction of the force exerted on the conductor. An application of this rule is illustrated in Fig. 8.56. Note, however, that in (8.29) there are two terms involved and that the rule above neglects the presence of the second term. Hence the rule applies only when the second term is small compared with the first.

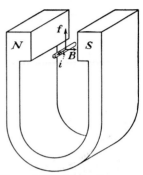

FIG. 8.56 Mutually perpendicular relations existing between the direction of the current i in a conductor, the direction of the density B of the magnetic field in which the conductor is located, and the direction of the force f that results.

The Bli principle is utilized in the permanent-magnet moving-coil d-c instruments. Parts of such an instrument are shown in Figs. 8.57 and 8.58. The moving coil of Fig. 8.57 is wound of fine, insulated copper wire

FIG. 8.57   Moving element of a permanent-magnet moving-coil instrument.   (*Weston Electrical Instrument Corporation.*)

on an aluminum frame. The number of turns is an integer plus one-half in order that one coil terminal will be at one end of the frame and the other terminal at the other end of the frame. To the coil, but insulated from it, are cemented two shafts whose ends are shaped to fit into V-shaped bearings. A spiral spring is mounted on each shaft, the end nearest the shaft being attached to the coil terminal. The active length of conductor in each turn is $2l$, l measured as in Fig. 8.58. The horseshoe permanent magnet of cross section A_m establishes flux that passes from a

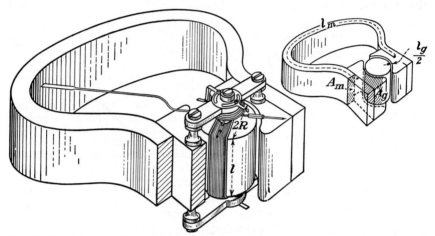

Fig. 8.58 Cutaway view of the mechanism of a permanent-magnet moving-coil instrument. (*Weston Electrical Instrument Corporation.*)

soft-iron pole piece through an air gap of cross section A_g and length $l_g/2$ to a stationary cylindrical soft-iron core. From the core the flux passes through a second air gap and a second pole piece back to the other leg of the magnet.

In a permanent-magnet moving-coil mechanism B, l, R, and N are fixed in manufacture. Hence, the upscale torque is directly proportional to the current. The springs tend to hold the pointer at the zero position and produce a downscale torque that is directly proportional to the angle θ radians that the pointer is turned from the zero position. With a constant current in the coil, the pointer moves to a position where the

Assume that the flux passes radially from the pole pieces to the core and that the force represented by the second term in (8.29) is negligible. Here the flux density B wb per sq m in the air gaps is established by the permanent magnet. The force produced by a half turn is normal to the plane of a coil and acts at a radius R m about the coil axis. It is $f = Bli$ newtons, where l in meters is the active length of a half turn as shown and i amp is the coil current. The torque produced by a half turn is $BliR$ and the total torque for N turns is $T = 2BliRN$ newton-m.

upscale and downscale torques balance.   The instrument has a linear scale.

When a cyclic current is sent through the coil of Fig. 8.58, the pointer response depends upon the frequency of the current.   If the frequency is of the order of a cycle per second or less, the pointer will move back and forth attempting to follow the instantaneous current values.   Because of the coil inertia and instrument damping, the pointer will register less than

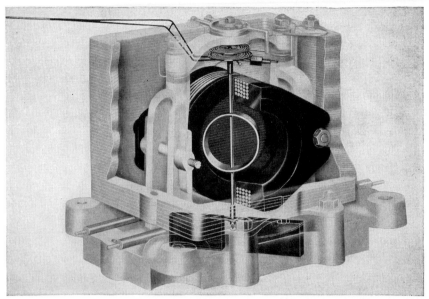

FIG. 8.59   Cutaway view of the mechanism of an electrodynamometer instrument. (*Weston Electrical Instrument Corporation.*)

the instantaneous current during part of the cycle and more than that during another part.   If the frequency is of the order of 60 c or more, the pointer will indicate the average value of the current.   With alternating current the reading is zero.

Figure 8.59 represents two fixed and one moving coils of an electro-dynamometer movement for an instrument.   Current is carried into and out of the moving coil through springs which here are both at the same end of the shaft that supports the coil.   To form a milliammeter, all coils would be wound of the same size of fine wire and connected in series. Since there are no magnetic materials within the coils, the coil self-inductances are constant and not functions of the position of the moving coil.   Then in (8.26), $dL_1/d\theta$ and $dL_2/d\theta$ are zero and the upscale torque on the moving coil is given by $T = i_1 i_2 \, dM/d\theta$.   If the coils are in series, $i_1 = i_2$.   Then for a given position of the moving coil, the torque acting on it is proportional to the square of the instantaneous current. When a cyclic current of a frequency of perhaps 10 c or higher is sent through the coils in series, the pointer will indicate the average of the squared values of the instantaneous current. This is a measure of the square of the rms current value; hence an electrodynamometer milliammeter is suitable for measuring the rms value of a current.

If $dM/d\theta$ were a constant, independent of the position of the moving coil, in an electrodynamometer milliammeter the scale would be a square-law one, i.e., the distance on the scale from 0 to 1 ma would be one-fourth that from 0 to 2 ma, one-ninth that from 0 to 3 ma, etc. Electrodynamometer instruments are often said to have a square-law scale, but

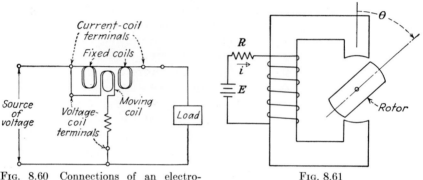

FIG. 8.60 Connections of an electro-dynamometer movement as a wattmeter.   FIG. 8.61

observation will show that the statement is seldom exact. This means that in most instruments $dM/d\theta$ varies as θ varies.

An electrodynamometer voltmeter differs from a milliammeter in that a resistor is connected in series with the coils. The resistor resistance is such that the current is limited to that necessary for full-scale deflection when full voltage is applied.

Most wattmeters utilize an electrodynamometer movement. As in Fig. 8.60, the fixed coils are in series with the load and are wound of wire of sufficient cross section to carry the load current without overheating. The movable coil is wound of fine wire and is connected in series with a resistor across the voltage source. Here the upscale torque is $T = i_1 i_2 \, dM/d\theta$, where i_2 is the current in the movable coil and i_1 is that in the fixed coils. The resistance of the voltage-coil circuit is made great enough that the effects of its self-inductance are negligible. Then $i_2 = v/R_2$ and $T = (vi_1/R_2) \, dM/d\theta$, where v is the instantaneous voltage. Here vi_1 is the instantaneous power and, except for frequencies below about 10 c, the pointer indicates the average power.

In Fig. 8.61 is represented a magnetic circuit, excited by a battery, whose reluctance can be varied by changing the position of the rotor. Assume that all portions of the circuit have constant permeability. The reluctance is a minimum when the long axis of the rotor is vertical and a maximum when it is horizontal. The reluctance varies through a cycle of values from a minimum to a maximum and back to a minimum in one-half revolution of the rotor. The inductance of the coil varies cyclically also, being a maximum when the reluctance is a minimum and a minimum when the reluctance is a maximum.

In Fig. 8.61 assume that with the rotor stationary and no external torque applied to it, the battery is connected to the exciting coil. Except for one position of the rotor, a magnetic torque will be exerted on it that will tend to turn it to the position of minimum reluctance. Whether the rotor turns clockwise or counterclockwise depends upon the initial rotor position since it will turn in the direction that will require a movement of less than 90° to reach the position of minimum reluctance. If the long axis of the rotor is horizontal initially, the rotor is in a position where no torque acts on it. The torque acting on the rotor is $T = \frac{1}{2}i^2\,dL/d\theta$, where L h is the inductance and θ is the space angle measured as in Fig. 8.61. Since $dL/d\theta = 0$ at the value of θ for which L is a maximum and also at the value of θ for which L is a minimum, this expression for torque shows that points of zero torque occur at each quarter revolution.

The principles illustrated in Fig. 8.61 are those used in the iron-vane (or moving iron) type of ammeter or voltmeter. In the instrument the rotor contains the only iron present, that in the core being omitted in order to make the flux established almost directly proportional to the current. Springs on the shaft that supports the rotor hold the rotor at a position between that for minimum and that for maximum reluctance when there is no current in the coil. How nearly the scale is a square-law one is determined by how nearly $dL/d\theta$ is a constant over the range through which θ varies as the instrument pointer moves from zero to full-scale deflection.

When used with direct current, an iron-vane instrument gives an upscale reading with either direction of current through it. Because of possible error due to the effect of residual magnetism in the rotor it is advisable to read the instrument with each direction of current and use an average of the two readings as the current value.

When used with alternating current with a frequency greater than about 10 c, the instrument reads the rms value of the current since for a given rotor position the instantaneous torque is proportional to the square of the instantaneous current.

8.22. Magnetic Amplifiers. A magnetic amplifier is a control device in which a small amount of energy is used to control a much larger amount by the use of magnetic characteristics of materials. In Fig. 8.62 is a diagram of one type of magnetic amplifier. Here two identical iron cores are wound with identical coils of N turns each. The two cores are surrounded by a control winding of N_c turns. This winding can be supplied with a variable direct current, by varying either the resistance of the circuit or the value of voltage applied.

With no current in the control winding, when the load current i_L is in the direction indicated the equal fluxes ϕ_A and ϕ_B are clockwise as shown and induce equal voltages in the main windings. Each of these voltages

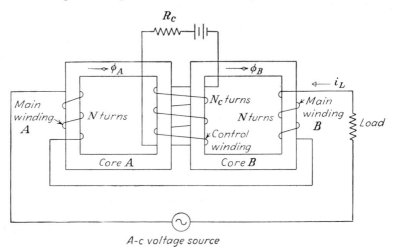

Fig. 8.62   A magnetic amplifier circuit.

cannot exceed in magnitude one-half of the a-c source voltage since some of the source voltage is used in sending i_L through the load resistance. Thus the two main windings serve as choke coils in limiting the current through the load. The voltage across each winding for a given value of load current depends upon the number of turns, the frequency of the current, the cross section and the mean length of the magnetic path in the core, and the magnetic properties of the core material.

First, assume that the core material has no hysteresis, that the magnetization curve rises very steeply to a certain saturation flux density B_s, and that above B_s the curve is nearly horizontal. With no current in the control winding, the behavior of the circuit would depend upon the rms value of the voltage applied. With a value such that the maximum flux density in the cores was less than B_s, the main windings would have high inductance and very little current would flow. Most of the applied voltage would appear across the main windings and very little across the load. If the voltage were increased until the maximum flux density exceeded B_s, during the portion of a cycle in which that density is exceeded the inductance of the main windings would be very small and most of the applied voltage would appear across the load and the load current would

be much greater than before.   The greater the value of the applied voltage, the greater is the maximum instantaneous current and the greater is
the percentage of a cycle during which most of the voltage appears across
the load.

With no current in the control winding, no voltage is induced in it,
since the net flux through it is $\phi_A - \phi_B$, and ϕ_A is always equal to ϕ_B.

When current is established in the control winding, during one-half
cycle the resulting mmf aids the mmf of one main winding and opposes
that of the other.   During the next one-half cycle conditions are reversed.
As a result the fluxes ϕ_A and ϕ_B are no longer equal.   When saturation
occurs in one core, very little voltage appears across the main winding on
that core.   Now with the fluxes unequal a voltage is induced in the control winding and produces a current in the control circuit.   The magnitude of this current depends in part upon the resistance of the control
circuit.   Since it is desired that this current not be limited by unnecessary
resistance, it is better to vary the control current by varying the voltage
applied to the control winding than by adding resistance in series with a
constant voltage source.   The mmf resulting from the control-winding
current opposes that of the main winding on the unsaturated core and
causes the flux in that core and the voltage across the main winding on it
to be less than they are for an equal load current with no current in the
control winding.   Hence, during a portion of each half cycle there is
little voltage across either main winding, little across one because of
saturation in the core and little across the other because of coupling
between a main winding and the control winding.   Changing the control-winding current changes the percentage of the time of a cycle during
which nearly all the applied voltage is used across the load.   Thus with
the control of a small value of power applied to the control winding a much
greater value of load power can be controlled, a property that represents
amplification.

Since magnetic materials operate on a hysteresis loop, a material with
a rectangular loop such as that in Fig. 7.43 is well suited for use in a magnetic amplifier.

PROBLEMS

8.1. A certain air-core coil has 10 turns.   With a fluxmeter it is found that with
80 amp in the coil the fluxes through the various coils are:

Turn numbers	Flux, μwb	Turn numbers	Flux, μwb
1 and 10	0.8	4 and 7	2.2
2 and 9	1	5 and 6	3
3 and 8	1.5		

Compute the flux linkages present. Compute the equivalent flux. Compute the equivalent flux that would be produced by 400 amp in the coil.

8.2. The equivalent flux linking a certain 2,000-turn coil decreases linearly from 5 μwb to 1 μwb in 100 msec and then increases linearly to 10 μwb in the next 40 msec. Determine the manner in which the emf in the coil varies with time. Sketch the flux-time and emf-time curves. Compute the maximum, the average, and the rms values of the emf during the 140-msec interval.

8.3. The equivalent flux linking a certain 800-turn coil alternates linearly at a frequency of 2,000 c between equal positive and negative values of 25 μwb. Determine the manner in which the emf in the coil varies with time. Sketch the flux-time and the emf-time curves. Compute the maximum, the average, and the rms values of the emf over a time interval equal to that between successive zero values.

8.4. An emf that alternates linearly between equal positive and negative maxima of 50 v is induced in a 200-turn coil by an equivalent flux that alternates between equal positive and negative values at a frequency of 100 c. Determine the maximum flux, and sketch the flux-time curve.

8.5. The equivalent flux linking a certain 200-turn coil alternates cyclically at 200 c as follows: During the first one-third cycle it increases linearly from 0 to 500 μwb; during the next one-sixth cycle it decreases linearly to 0; during the next one-third cycle it decreases linearly to −500 μwb; and during the last one-sixth cycle it increases linearly to zero. Sketch the flux-time curve. Determine and sketch the emf-time curve.

8.6. The equivalent flux linking a certain 200-turn coil alternates cyclically at 400 c as follows: During the first one-third cycle it increases linearly from 0 to 500 μwb; during the next one-sixth cycle it decreases linearly to 0; during the next one-sixth cycle it decreases linearly to −500 μwb; and during the last one-third cycle it increases linearly to zero. Sketch the flux-time curve. Determine and sketch the emf-time curve.

8.7. The equivalent flux linking a certain 800-turn coil alternates cyclically at 500 c as follows: During the first one-eighth cycle it increases linearly from 0 to 400 μwb; during the next one-fourth cycle it is constant at 400 μwb; during the next one-eighth cycle it decreases linearly to 0. The negative half cycle is identical in shape with that of the positive half cycle except for the sign of the ordinates. Sketch the flux-time curve. Determine and sketch the emf-time curve. Compute the maximum, the average, and rms values of the emf during a positive one-half cycle of the emf.

8.8. A certain copper washer has an inside diameter of 1 in., an outside diameter of 2 in., and a thickness of 0.05 in. The washer surrounds a steel core in which a changing magnetic field exists. At a certain instant the emf induced in the washer is 4 mv along any path concentric with the inner surface of the washer. Assume that resistance is the only effect that limits the current in the washer. Write the equation that expresses the variation of the current density from the inner to the outer surface of the washer. Compute the total current and the power developed in the washer.

8.9. A copper washer 0.1 in. thick, of inner radius 2 in., and outer radius 5 in. is in a uniform alternating magnetic field normal to the plane of the washer. The flux density varies according to the equation $B = 10,000 \sin 500 \, t$ μwb per sq m, where t is in seconds.

a. Derive the equation of the emf that is induced in an element of the washer near the inner surface and that of the emf induced in an element near the outer surface.

b. Compute the maximum current density produced in an element near the inner surface and that in an element near the outer surface.

c. Compute the power developed in the ring.

8.10. Determine and sketch the time variations of the equivalent flux which alternating at 1,000 c induces in a 50-turn coil an emf that varies as follows: During the first one-eighth cycle it increases linearly from 0 to 100 v; during the next one-quarter cycle it is constant at 100 v; during the next one-eighth cycle it decreases linearly to zero. The negative half cycle is identical with that of the positive half cycle except that the ordinates are negative.

8.11. Compute the self-inductance of a circuit in which 40 v are induced when the current is changing at the rate of 500 amp per sec.

8.12. At what rate is the current changing when 50 mv are induced in a circuit that has an inductance of 80 μh?

8.13. How much emf is induced in a circuit of 120 mh when the current is changing at the rate of 500 ma per sec?

8.14. In a certain circuit that has a self-inductance of 200 mh the current first increases linearly from 0 to 80 ma in 40 μsec. Then the current is constant at 80 ma for the next 20 μsec. Finally, the current decreases linearly from 80 to 10 ma during the next 10 μsec. Sketch the curve showing the time variation of the induced emf during the entire interval, and determine the maximum emf.

8.15. A certain circuit has a resistance of 2 ohms and a self-inductance of 80 mh. Determine the equation of the voltage that when applied to the circuit will establish the current $i = 20t$ amp, where t is in seconds. Sketch curves showing the time variations of the current, the resistive voltage drop, the inductive voltage drop, and the applied voltage.

8.16. A certain circuit has a resistance of 10 ohms and a self-inductance of 200 mh. Determine the equation of the voltage that when applied to the circuit will establish the current $i = 5 - 5\epsilon^{-50t}$ amp, where ϵ is the base of natural logarithms and t is in seconds. Sketch curves showing the time variations of the current, the resistive voltage drop, the inductive voltage drop, and the applied voltage.

8.17. A certain circuit has a resistance of 8 ohms and a self-inductance of 400 mh. Determine the equation of the voltage that when applied to the circuit will produce the current $i = 20t^2$ amp, where t is in seconds. Sketch curves showing the time variations of the current, the resistive voltage drop, the inductive voltage drop, and the applied voltage.

8.18. The current $i = 8(\epsilon^{-10t} - \epsilon^{-50t})$ amp, where ϵ is the base of natural logarithms and t is in seconds, is established in a circuit containing 2 ohms resistance and 40 mh self-inductance. Sketch the current-time curve and determine the maximum current. Derive the equation of the voltage applied to the circuit. Sketch the voltage-time curve.

8.19. The current $i = 10t\epsilon^{-100t}$ amp, where t is in seconds and ϵ is the base of natural logarithms, is established in a circuit containing 5 ohms resistance and 80 mh self-inductance. Sketch the current-time curve and determine the maximum current. Derive the equation of the voltage applied to the circuit. Sketch the voltage-time curve.

8.20. A certain sheet-steel toroid has a cross section of 0.001 sq m, an average length of 1 m, and is wound with 500 turns. Assume that the magnetization curve of the steel can be expressed by the Froelich equation $B = 2H/(160 + H)$ wb per sq m, where H is in amp-turns per m. Compute the inductance of the coil for 0.1 amp and that for 2 amp.

8.21. Compute the equivalent flux produced by 50 ma in a 300-turn coil that has a self-inductance of 40 mh.

8.22. A certain nonmagnetic toroid core is 0.04 m square in cross section and is wound with a uniformly distributed winding of 500 turns. The inner diameter of the coil is 0.1 m.

a. Compute the inductance of the coil, assuming that the flux density is uniform in the core and using the length of the magnetic path as that at the center of the core.

b. Compute the inductance of the coil, taking into account the nonuniform flux density in the core.

8.23. Solve Prob. 8.22 if the inner diameter is 0.5 m.

8.24. A certain inductor consists of a 200-turn coil surrounding a sheet-steel core of 0.01 sq m cross section. In order that the inductance will be nearly constant, a 2.5-mm air gap is cut in the core. Assuming that the reluctance of the steel is negligible compared with that of the gap, compute the inductance.

8.25. In Prob. 8.24 the inductance of the coil is to be 50 mh. What should be the length of the air gap?

8.26. A d-c voltage of 120 v is suddenly applied to a circuit that has a resistance of 20 ohms and an inductance of 50 mh. For $t = 0$, compute the induced voltage and the rate of change of the current. For the instant when the current is 4 amp, compute the induced voltage and the rate of change of the current.

8.27. A d-c voltage of 120 v is suddenly applied to a circuit that has a resistance of 30 ohms and an inductance of 100 mh. For the instant when the current is 1.2 amp, compute the induced voltage, the rate of change of the current, the power input to the magnetic field, and the energy stored in the magnetic field.

8.28. For the circuit of Prob. 8.27, compute the points for and plot the curve showing the time variations of the power input to and the energy stored in the magnetic field.

8.29. *a.* Draw the diagram of a circuit in which the steady-state current is 50 ma and 5 μsec are required for the current to increase from 0 to 31.5 ma.

b. If the resistance of the circuit in *a* is doubled, how much time is required for the current to increase from 0 to 15.8 ma?

c. If the inductance of the circuit in *a* is doubled, how much time is required for the current to increase from 0 to 31.5 ma?

8.30. In a certain circuit of resistance and inductance in series, when a certain d-c voltage was applied the initial rate of current increase was 400 amp per sec. If the voltage were halved and the resistance and inductance were doubled, what would be the initial rate of current increase?

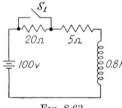

Fig. 8.63

8.31. The circuit of Fig. 8.63 is in a steady state with switch S_1 open. Then at $t = 0$, S_1 is closed. For that instant compute the induced voltage, the rate of change of current, and the power input to the magnetic field.

8.32. The circuit of Fig. 8.63 is in a steady state with switch S_1 closed. Then at $t = 0$, S_1 is opened. For that instant compute the induced voltage, the rate of change of current, and the power delivered by the magnetic field.

8.33. A d-c voltage of 120 v is suddenly applied to a circuit that has 15 ohms resistance and 200 mh inductance. How much energy is converted into heat by the resistance of the circuit while the current is increasing to 5 amp? How much energy is stored in the magnetic field when the current is 5 amp?

8.34. The field circuit of a certain generator has a resistance of 12 ohms. For the purpose of this problem assume that the circuit inductance is constant at 20 h. This circuit is connected in series with a 188-ohm resistor across 240-v direct current. The generator output voltage is controlled by a vibrating-type voltage regulator that periodically closes a contact across the resistor. The average output voltage depends upon the length of time the contact is closed.

a. The contact is closed for 0.12 sec and opened for 0.08 sec and this cycle repeated continuously. Compute the minimum, maximum, and average values of the field current.

b. The contact is closed for 0.15 sec and opened for 0.05 sec and this cycle repeated continuously. Compute the maximum, minimum, and average values of the field current.

8.35. In Fig. 8.34, E = 200 v, R_1 = 40 ohms, R = 10 ohms, and L = 200 mh. For t = 0, compute the induced voltage and the power delivered by the magnetic field.

8.36. In Fig. 8.64, for t = 0 compute the value of each current and that of the induced voltage. Compute the steady-state value of each current. Sketch the curves showing the time variations of the currents.

8.37. In Fig. 8.64, for the instant when the battery current is 5 amp compute the induced voltage. At that instant is power being delivered to or by the inductance and how much?

8.38. For Fig. 8.64 derive the equations of the currents following t = 0.

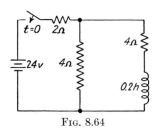

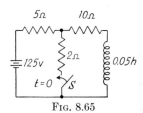

Fɪɢ. 8.64   Fɪɢ. 8.65

8.39. The circuit of Fig. 8.65 is in a steady state with the switch open. For the instant t = 0 when the switch is closed, compute the induced voltage and the rate of change of the current in the inductor.

8.40. For Fig. 8.65 derive the equations of the currents following t = 0.

8.41. In Fig. 8.34, E = 240 v, R = 60 ohms, and L = 12 h. Compute the value of R_1 that will limit the voltage v to 400 v when the circuit is interrupted. With this value of R_1 compute the voltage across the switch at the instant it is opened.

8.42. A 200-ohm discharge resistor is used with a field winding of 40 ohms resistance and 8 h inductance. The winding is excited from a 120-v source. Compute the initial voltage across the field terminals if the source is suddenly disconnected and the initial rate of decrease of the winding current.

8.43. A certain circuit that has 25 ohms resistance and 2 h inductance is excited from a 125-v source. A Thyrite resistor whose current-voltage characteristic has the equation $i = 10^{-9}v^4$ amp, where v is in volts, is permanently connected across the terminals as a discharge resistor.

a. Compute the current in the resistor while the current in the circuit is in a steady state.

b. Compute the voltage across the resistor at the instant when the source is disconnected.

c. Derive the equation of the resistor current following the disconnection of the source.

8.44. The current $i = 2 \sin 1{,}000t$ amp, where t is in seconds, flows in a circuit that has an inductance of 40 mh. Compute the maximum current, the rate of change of the current when the current is a maximum, and the voltage induced when the current is a maximum.

Compute the rate of change of the current when the current is zero, and the voltage induced when the current is zero.

8.45. The current in a certain 50-mh coil varies with time according to the equation $i = 5 + 4 \sin 500t$ amp, where t is in seconds. Sketch the current-time curve.

Compute the time in seconds between two successive maximum current values. Compute the maximum induced voltage. Sketch the voltage-time curve.

8.46. The coil of Prob. 8.45 has 20 ohms resistance. Compute the voltage that must be applied to it to produce the given current. How could such a voltage be obtained in an electrical laboratory?

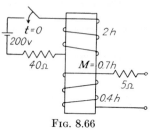

8.47. In Fig. 8.66 the secondary circuit is open. At the instant when the switch in the primary circuit is closed, how much voltage is induced in each circuit? Specify the polarities of the secondary terminals.

8.48. In Fig. 8.66, how much voltage is induced in the secondary circuit at the instant when the primary current is 3 amp?

FIG. 8.66

8.49. A 400-turn coil that has a self-inductance of 50 mh is inductively coupled to a 1,000-turn coil that has a self-inductance of 8 mh. When 200 ma flows in the first coil, 10^{-3} wb-turns of flux linkage exists in the second. Compute the mutual inductance between the coils and the coefficient of coupling.

8.50. The mutual inductance between two coils is 50 mh. How much direct current suddenly established in one coil will produce a deflection of 15 divisions on a fluxmeter connected across the other? The fluxmeter calibration is 100 μwb per division with a one-turn search coil.

8.51. When 12-ma direct current was suddenly reversed in one of two inductively coupled coils, nine divisions deflection was produced on a fluxmeter connected across the other. The fluxmeter calibration was 100 μwb per division with a one-turn search coil. Compute the mutual inductance between the coils.

8.52. In Fig. 8.66 the secondary terminals are short-circuited. Compute the rate of change of each current at the instant when the primary circuit is closed. Compare the initial rate of change of the primary current with what it would have been with the secondary circuit open.

8.53. In Prob. 8.52, for the instant when the primary circuit is closed, compute the voltages of self-induction and those of mutual induction.

8.54. A 200-v direct current is suddenly applied to the two coils of Fig. 8.66 in series. Compute the initial voltages across the coils, first if the mmfs are aiding, and next if the mmfs are opposing.

8.55. A coil of 0.1 ohm resistance and 30 mh self-inductance is coupled by 60 mh mutual inductance to a coil of 2 ohms resistance and 250 mh self-inductance. Compute the initial rates of change of the coil currents for both aiding and opposing mmfs when 24-v direct current is suddenly applied to the coils in parallel.

8.56. Two identical coils have 10 ohms resistance and 400 mh inductance. Assume that the coefficient of coupling between the coils is unity. A direct current of 120-v is suddenly applied to one coil with the other short-circuited. From the voltage equations prove that the currents are not zero at $t = 0$. Determine the initial values of the currents making use of the principle that the flux linking the coils does not change instantly at $t = 0$. Determine the equations of the currents. Compute the initial rate of change of each current. Sketch the current-time relations.

8.57. The coils of Prob. 8.56 are in a steady state with 120-v direct current applied to one coil and a short circuit across the other. Derive the equation of the current in the short-circuited coil following the sudden opening of the excited circuit.

8.58. Two identical coils are inductively coupled. The equivalent self-inductance is 120 mh for a series aiding and 20 mh for a series bucking connection. Compute the self-inductance of each coil, the mutual inductance between them, and the coefficient of coupling.

8.59. Two coupled coils, one of which can be rotated within the other, have equal self-inductances and are connected in series. The equivalent self-inductance of the series combination can be varied through a ratio of 8 to 1. Compute the maximum coefficient of coupling between the coils.

8.60. When one coil that has 4 ohms resistance and 80 mh inductance is in series aiding with one that has 5 ohms resistance and 20 mh inductance, the equivalent self-inductance is 150 mh. Compute the equivalent resistance and self-inductance of the coils in series bucking.

8.61. How much energy is stored in an air gap 5 mm long and 250 sq cm in cross section when the flux crossing the gap is 0.012 wb?

8.62. A certain electromagnet exerts a pull of 2 lb. If the flux is doubled and the area of the pole faces increased by 40 per cent, what will be the pull?

8.63. In a certain electromagnet with a fixed exciting current, the pull is 40 lb with a 0.1-in. air gap between the pole faces and the load. Compute the pull if the air-gap length were increased to 0.15 in. Assume that the reluctance of the steel portion of the magnetic circuit is negligible compared with that of the gap.

8.64. In a certain electromagnet with a fixed exciting current, the pull is 50 lb with an 0.08-in. air gap between the pole faces and the load. For what length of gap would the pull be 32 lb? Assume that the reluctance of the steel portion of the magnetic circuit is negligible compared with that of the gap.

8.65. The electromagnet and the keeper of Fig. 8.67 are made of cast steel. A 400-turn exciting coil surrounds the electromagnet. The flux is 0.001 wb. There is an air gap of 5 mils at each pole face. Compute the pull on the keeper and the exciting current.

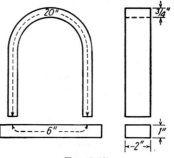

Fig. 8.67

8.66. A certain coil that has 80 mh self-inductance can be revolved inside another that has 120 mh self-inductance. The coefficient of coupling between the coils can be varied from 0.5 aiding through zero to 0.5 bucking. The coils in series carry 400 ma. Through what range can the energy stored in the magnetic field about the coils be varied as the inner coil is turned?

8.67. As the inner coil of Prob. 8.66 is turned, the coefficient of coupling between the coils varies according to the equation $k = 0.5 \cos \theta$, where θ is the angle in space radians turned through from the position of maximum coupling. The current in the coils in series is kept constant at 400 ma. Derive the equation of the torque exerted on the inner coil as a function of θ. Sketch the curve represented by the equation.

CHAPTER 9

DIELECTRIC CIRCUITS

9.1. Capacitance. The parallel metal plates A and B of Fig. 9.1 are separated a short distance in air. When a potential, such as the emf of the battery, is applied between the plates, electrons move counterclockwise in the circuit. The removal of electrons from A causes it to acquire a positive charge since the number of electrons there is less than the number of positive charges. The excess of electrons on B causes it to acquire a negative charge equal in magnitude to the positive charge on A.

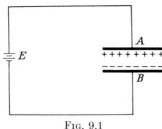

FIG. 9.1

An emf exists between the plates. If the plates are fixed in position, the magnitude of the emf is directly proportional to the number of electrons moved. The displacement of the electrons causes an electric current that continues until the plates acquire sufficient charge to make the emf between them equal to that of the battery. When the emfs become equal, the current becomes zero. The current is transient in nature, starting when the battery is connected to the plates and approaching zero as the emfs approach equality. The time during which a measurable current exists depends upon the magnitude of the battery emf, the area of and the distance between the plates, and the resistance of the circuit.

In Fig. 9.1 energy is required to charge the plates and is supplied by the battery. After the current has ceased, if the battery is disconnected from the plates, for a time the emf between plates will equal that of the battery. With increasing time, the emf between plates decreases to zero, usually at a slow rate. The material that supports the plates is not a perfect insulator; therefore the excess electrons on B trickle back to A through the material. In time the number of electrons on each plate becomes equal to the number of positive charges and the emf disappears.

The plates of Fig. 9.1 constitute a capacitor or a condenser. The property by which a capacitor may act as a reservoir for electric charges

when a voltage is applied is capacitance.   In a capacitor, electrons leave
one plate at the same rate that others arrive at the other plate; i.e., the
current entering the capacitor at one terminal is equal to that leaving at
the other.   It is customary to speak of the current through a capacitor
although there are relatively few electrons that cross the space between
the plates if they are separated by a good insulating material.

An electron in space near a charged capacitor is attracted by the positive plate and repelled by the negative plate.   A region in which a force
is exerted upon a stationary electric charge contains an electric (also
called dielectric) field.   The material in which the field exists is a
dielectric.

An electric field exists between any two conducting surfaces when voltage exists between them.   Let short fibers of silk be placed in a liquid
dielectric in which are immersed two metal plates connected one to each
terminal of a source of emf.   The fibers move into positions in lines
extending from one plate to the other and suggest that something is
moving from one plate to the other.   The concept of electric or dielectric
flux aids in visualizing the relations in an electric field.   The symbol Ψ is
used for electric flux and the mks unit of it is the coulomb.   The amount
of flux in coulombs entering or emanating from a given electric charge is
numerically equal to the magnitude of the charge in coulombs.

Electric flux lines are represented as lines that emanate from positive
charges or end on negative ones, or as endless lines surrounding a changing magnetic field.   Consider a charge of $+Q$ coul concentrated at the
center of a spherical shell on the inner surface of which there is a uniformly distributed charge of $-Q$ coul.   Here the electric flux lines
emanate radially from the concentrated charge and end on the inner
surface of the shell.   In an electric field an equipotential surface is at any
point normal to the flux line through the point.   The equipotential
surfaces within the shell are spherical with the concentrated charge at
their center.   If a plane is passed through the concentrated charge, the
traces of the equipotential traces in the plane are concentric circles as in
Fig. 9.2.   Each surface has its own potential, such as E_1, with respect to
the shell.   The direction of an electric flux line at a point is that in which
a positive charge at the point would be urged.

Two concentrated charges of $+Q_1$ and $+Q_2$ coul are represented at a
distance d m apart in Fig. 9.3.   Each charge acting alone would establish
electric flux lines radiating outward.   Each charge exerts a repelling
force on the other.   The force is

$$F = 9 \times 10^9 \frac{Q_1 Q_2}{\epsilon d^2} \qquad \text{newtons}$$

where ϵ is the dielectric constant (or specific permittivity) of the medium

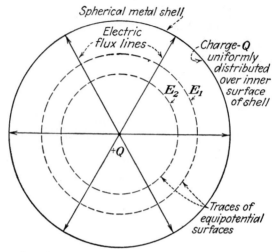

FIG. 9.2   Traces of equipotential surfaces in a plane passed through a concentrated charge $+Q$ at the center of a spherical metal shell.

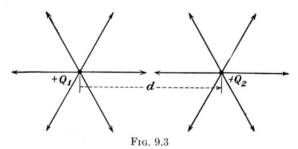

FIG. 9.3

in which the charges are located.   The dielectric constant is taken as 1 for a vacuum.   The dielectric constant of air at 0 C and atmospheric pressure is about 0.06 per cent greater than that of a vacuum but it is used as 1 for most engineering computations.

9.2. Capacitance in the Electric Circuit.   The capacitance C f of a capacitor is the factor by which the voltage v v across the capacitor is multiplied to obtain the magnitude of the charge q coul on each capacitor plate.   For most computations a microfarad (μf) or a micromicrofarad ($\mu\mu$f) is used as the unit of capacitance.

Since $q = vC$,   then $dq/dt = C(dv/dt) + v(dC/dt)$.   By definition $dq/dt = i$; hence $i = C(dv/dt) + v(dC/dt)$ amp, where C is in farads, v is in volts, and t is in seconds.   For most capacitors the capacitance is constant and not a function of time.   In such cases $dC/dt = 0$ and

$$i = C\frac{dv}{dt} \qquad \text{amp} \qquad (9.1)$$

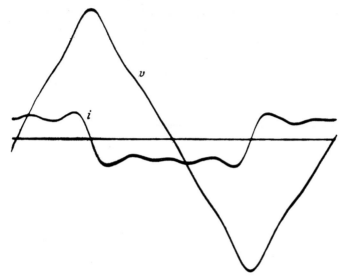

FIG. 9.4   Oscillograms of the voltage v across and the current i in a capacitor.

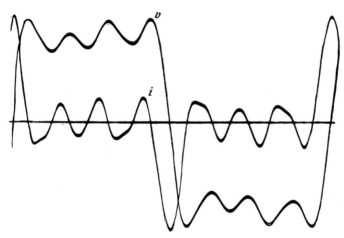

FIG. 9.5   Oscillograms of the voltage v across and the current i in a capacitor.

This shows that the current in a capacitor depends not upon the magnitude of the voltage across it but upon the rate at which the voltage is changing.   Graphically, the time rate of change of a voltage at a given instant is equal to the slope of the voltage-time curve at that instant. These statements are verified by the oscillograms of Figs. 9.4 and 9.5. Note that the current is zero when the rate of change of the voltage is zero and that the current is a maximum when the slope of the voltage curve is the greatest.

In some capacitor applications, the applied voltage is kept constant and current is produced by varying the capacitance. In such cases $dv/dt = 0$ and $i = v\, dC/dt$ amp. In a condenser microphone, the capacitance is varied by the motion of one plate resulting from sound waves striking it.

For a capacitor of constant capacitance, from (9.1) $dv_c = i\, dt/C$, from which

$$v_c = \frac{1}{C} \int_0^t i\, dt + V_0 \qquad \text{v} \qquad (9.2)$$

where V_0 is the voltage in volts across the capacitor at $t = 0$. The sign

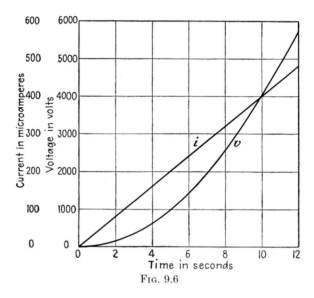

FIG. 9.6

of V_0 is positive if the direction, known or assumed, of the current is into the capacitor terminal that was positive at $t = 0$. If the current is in the opposite direction, the sign of V_0 is negative. If a capacitor is uncharged at $t = 0$, $V_0 = 0$.

Example 1. The voltage applied to a 0.5-μf capacitor varies according to the equation $v = 40t^2$ v, where t is in seconds. Derive the equation of the capacitor current. Plot the voltage and current curves.

Solution. Here

$$i = C \frac{dv}{dt} = 0.5 \times 10^{-6} \frac{d}{dt}(40t^2) = 0.5 \times 10^{-6}(80t) = 4 \times 10^{-5}t \qquad \text{amp}$$

thus the current increases linearly.

The curves in Fig. 9.6 were plotted by assuming various values of time and computing the corresponding values of voltage and current.

Example 2. A constant current of 5 ma flows for 2 sec into a 0.2-μf capacitor that was initially uncharged. To what voltage will the capacitor be charged?

Solution. The charge put into the capacitor will be

$$5 \text{ ma} \times \frac{1 \text{ amp}}{1,000 \text{ ma}} \times 2 \text{ sec} = 0.01 \text{ amp-sec} = 0.01 \text{ coul}$$

Since voltage equals charge divided by capacitance, then the voltage will be 0.01 coul/0.2 $\times$ 10^{-6} f = 50,000 v.

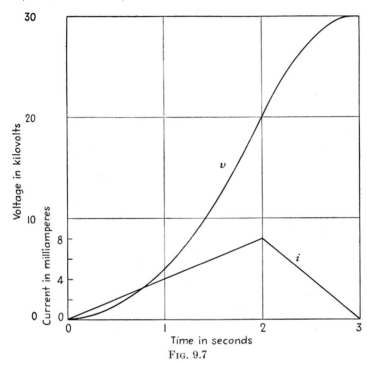

FIG. 9.7

Example 3. From $t = 0$ to $t = 2$ sec the current into a 0.4-μf capacitor that was initially uncharged increases linearly from 0 to 8 ma. From $t = 2$ to $t = 3$ sec, the current decreases linearly from 8 ma to 0. Determine the capacitor voltage at $t = 2$ and at $t = 3$ sec. Sketch the current and voltage waves.

Solution. The current wave was plotted in Fig. 9.7 from the given information. The area under the wave from $t = 0$ to $t = 2$ sec is ½ $\times$ 8 ma $\times$ 2 sec = 8 ma-sec = 0.008 amp-sec. This is the charge in coulombs put into the capacitor during the interval. The voltage at $t = 2$ sec will be 0.008 coul/0.4 $\times$ 10^{-6} f = 20,000 v.

The area under the current wave from $t = 2$ to $t = 3$ sec is

$$\text{½} \times 8 \text{ ma} \times 1 \text{ sec} = 4 \text{ ma-sec} = 0.004 \text{ amp-sec}$$

The charge put into the capacitor during this interval is one-half that put into it during the previous interval. Hence 10,000 v will be added and the voltage will be 20,000 + 10,000 = 30,000 v at $t = 3$ sec.

Since the current increases linearly during the first interval, the voltage increases along a parabola. Since the current is zero at $t = 0$, the slope of the voltage curve is zero at $t = 0$. The voltage curve is sketched in Fig. 9.7 as a section of a parabola starting with zero value and zero slope at $t = 0$ and ending at 20,000 v (20 kv) at $t = 2$ sec.

The current decreases linearly during the second interval. However, since the current values are all positive, the slope of the voltage curve must also be positive, the voltage increases throughout the interval with a slope that is greatest at $t = 2$ sec and decreases to zero at $t = 3$ sec. The voltage curve is a section of a parabola that has its vertex at $t = 3$ sec and $v = 30,000$ v (30 kv). This section of a parabola is tangent at $t = 2$ sec to the section of the other parabola. The voltage wave is sketched in Fig. 9.7.

9.3. Elastance. The factor capacitance is most often used when the effect of a capacitor in an electric circuit is to be determined. For determining relations in an electric field, an additional useful factor is elastance. It is the reciprocal of capacitance. Capacitance is defined by the equation $q = Cv$ and elastance by the equation $v = \psi S$, where v is the voltage in volts between the terminals of a capacitor, ψ is the dielectric flux in coulombs from plate to plate in the capacitor, and S is the elastance in darafs. The term daraf was obtained by spelling farad backward. Inasmuch as the farad is too large a unit for common use and the microfarad is more often used, the daraf is too small a unit of elastance for common use and the megadaraf is more often used.

The elastance of a dielectric conductor depends upon the length, the cross section, and the material of the conductor. Elastance in a dielectric conductor corresponds to resistance in an electric conductor and to reluctance in a magnetic material. If the dielectric flux density is uniform over a cross-sectional area A sq m throughout a length l m of a dielectric conductor between two conducting surfaces, the elastance S between the surfaces is

$$S = \frac{l}{\epsilon_v \epsilon A} \qquad \text{darafs} \qquad (9.3)$$

where $\epsilon_v = 8.85 \times 10^{-12}$ is the permittivity of a vacuum and ϵ is the relative permittivity of the material with respect to that of a vacuum.

The relative permittivity ϵ of a material is the ratio of the number of dielectric lines that would be established in a dielectric circuit composed of the material to the number of lines that would be established if the material were replaced by a vacuum and the applied voltage kept constant. The relative permittivity is commonly called the dielectric constant, despite the fact that this "constant" varies with operating conditions, such as the waveform and the frequency of the applied voltage, and the temperature. The dielectric constant of most insulating materials is rather low as shown by the typical values listed in Table 9.1.

TABLE 9.1. DIELECTRIC CONSTANTS AND DIELECTRIC STRENGTHS OF
INSULATING MATERIALS

Material	Dielectric constant ϵ	Dielectric strength, kv per mm
Air	1	3
Amber	2.9	
Asphalt	2.7	4–15
Bakelite	4.5–5.5	6–20
Ebonite	2.8	30–110
Fiber	2.5–5	2
Glass	5.4–9.9	30–150
Marble	8.3	2.5
Mica	2.5–6.6	30–220
Oil	2.2–4.7	4–20
Paper	2–2.6	10–25
Paraffin	2.1–2.5	12
Porcelain	5.7–6.8	3.5–10
Rubber	2–3.5	16–50
Slate	6.6–7.4	0.3
Water	81	15
Wood	2.5–7.7	1–3

Since $S = l/\epsilon_v \epsilon A$, and $C = 1/S$, then

$$C = \frac{\epsilon_v \epsilon A}{l} \qquad \text{f} \qquad (9.4)$$

where ϵ_v, ϵ, A, and l are in the same units as in (9.3).

It is often not possible to compute accurately the capacitance of a capacitor by (9.4). The main source of inaccuracy is that the air surrounding any other dielectric material is nearly as good a dielectric conductor per unit volume as the material is. For a parallel-plate capacitor having a solid dielectric material between the plates and air surrounding them, the dielectric lines spread out from a plate so that the dielectric flux density is not uniform either in the air or in the solid material. The actual capacitance is greater than a computed value considering only the solid material. In Fig. 9.8 is an approximate representation of some of the dielectric lines about the plates of an air capacitor.

FIG. 9.8 Approximate representation of some of the electric lines surrounding the plates of a charged air capacitor.

Example 1. Considering only the dielectric field between two plates that are separated 1 mm in air, compute the plate area required for 1 $\mu\mu f$ capacitance.

Solution. By (9.4),

$$A = \frac{Cl}{\epsilon_v\epsilon} = \frac{(1\ \mu\mu\text{f} \times 10^{-12}\ \text{f}/1\ \mu\mu\text{f})(1\ \text{mm} \times 1\ \text{m}/1,000\ \text{mm})}{(8.85 \times 10^{-12})(1)}$$
$$= 1.13 \times 10^{-4}\ \text{sq m}$$

Since there are 10^4 sq cm in 1 sq m, each plate area is 1.13 sq cm, which is equal to 0.175 sq in. Then two square plates about 0.4 in. on a side could be used.

9.4. Capacitors in Series. The three capacitors of Fig. 9.9 are in series with V v applied to the combination.

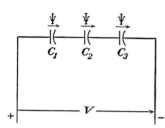

Fig. 9.9 Capacitors in series. If the capacitors were uncharged prior to the application of the voltage V, the electric flux ψ will be the same in each capacitor.

The respective capacitances are C_1, C_2, and C_3 f and the elastances are S_1, S_2, and S_3 darafs. If the capacitors were uncharged initially, the application of voltage will establish the same dielectric flux Ψ in each capacitor. Since the voltage across a capacitor is equal to the product of the dielectric flux and the elastance, the respective capacitor voltages V_1, V_2, and V_3 v are $V_1 = \Psi S_1$, $V_2 = \Psi S_2$, and $V_3 = \Psi S_3$. Since $V = V_1 + V_2 + V_3$, then

$$V = \Psi S_1 + \Psi S_2 + \Psi S_3$$

from which $V/\Psi = S_1 + S_2 + S_3$. But V/Ψ is the equivalent elastance S_e of the series combination; hence $S_e = S_1 + S_2 + S_3$. *The equivalent elastance of a number of capacitors in series is equal to the sum of the individual elastances.*

The equivalent capacitance C_e of the capacitors being considered is the reciprocal of their equivalent elastance. Since $S_e = 1/C_e$, $S_1 = 1/C_1$, etc., then

$$\frac{1}{C_e} = \frac{1}{C_1} + \frac{1}{C_2} + \frac{1}{C_3} \qquad \text{or} \qquad C_e = \frac{1}{1/C_1 + 1/C_2 + 1/C_3}$$

Hence the equivalent capacitance of a number of capacitors in series is equal to the reciprocal of the sum of the reciprocals of the individual capacitances. This means that capacitances in series combine like resistances in parallel. (1) When a number of capacitors are in series, the equivalent capacitance is less than that of the smallest capacitor. (2) When two capacitors of capacitance C_1 and C_2, respectively, are in series, the equivalent capacitance is $C_1C_2/(C_1 + C_2)$.

Dividing $V_1 = \Psi S_1$ by $V_2 = \Psi S_2$ yields $V_1/V_2 = S_1/S_2$. But $S_1 = 1/C_1$, and $S_2 = 1/C_2$; therefore $V_1/V_2 = C_2/C_1$. Hence, *when two capacitors are in series, the capacitor voltages are directly proportional to the respective elastances or inversely proportional to the respective capacitances.*

Since $V_1 = \Psi S_1$ and $V = \Psi(S_1 + S_2 + S_3)$, then

$$\frac{V_1}{V} = \frac{S_1}{S_1 + S_2 + S_3}$$

Hence, when a number of capacitors are in series, the voltage across one is to the voltage across all as the elastance of the one is to the equivalent elastance of the combination. This relation may also be expressed as: when several capacitors are in series, the voltage across one is to the voltage across all as the equivalent capacitance of the combination is to the capacitance of the one.

Example 1. A 2-, a 4-, and an 8-μf capacitor are in series across 220-v direct current. Compute the equivalent capacitance of the combination and the voltage across each capacitor.

Solution. The respective elastances are $\tfrac{1}{2} = 0.5$, $\tfrac{1}{4} = 0.25$, and

$$\tfrac{1}{8} = 0.125 \text{ megadarafs}$$

The equivalent elastance is $0.5 + 0.25 + 0.125 = 0.875$ megadarafs. The equivalent capacitance is $1/0.875 = 1.14 \ \mu f$.

Since the voltage across one capacitor is to the total voltage as the elastance of the one is to the equivalent elastance, then $V_2/220 = 0.5/0.875$, from which $V_2 = 126$ v, where V_2 is the voltage across the 2-μf capacitor.

Similarly, $V_4/220 = 0.25/0.875$, from which $V_4 = 63$ v, where V_4 is the voltage across the 4-μf capacitor.

Likewise, $V_8/220 = 0.125/0.875$, from which $V_8 = 31$ v, where V_8 is the voltage across the 8-μf capacitor.

9.5. Capacitors in Parallel. The capacitors of Fig. 9.10 are in parallel with V v applied to the combination. The respective capacitances are C_1, C_2, and C_3 f, the corresponding elastances are S_1, S_2, and S_3 darafs, and the corresponding dielectric fluxes are Ψ_1, Ψ_2, and Ψ_3 coul, where $\Psi_1 = V/S_1$, $\Psi_2 = V/S_2$, and $\Psi_3 = V/S_3$. The total dielectric flux Ψ_T is $\Psi_T = \Psi_1 + \Psi_2 + \Psi_3$,

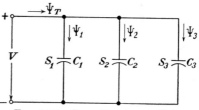

FIG. 9.10   Capacitors in parallel.

from which $\Psi_T = V(1/S_1 + 1/S_2 + 1/S_3)$. The equivalent elastance S_e of the parallel capacitors is

$$S_e = \frac{V}{\Psi_T} = \frac{1}{1/S_1 + 1/S_2 + 1/S_3}$$

Hence, *when several capacitors are in parallel, the equivalent elastance is equal to the reciprocal of the sum of the reciprocals of the individual elastances.* This relation may also be expressed as: *when several capacitors are in parallel, the equivalent capacitance is equal to the sum of the individual capacitances.*

Example 1. A 2-, a 4-, and an 8-μf capacitor are in parallel across 220 v. Compute the equivalent capacitance of the combination and the charge on each capacitor.

Solution. The equivalent capacitance is the sum of the individual capacitances, or $2 + 4 + 8 = 14$ μf.

There are 220 v across each capacitor. The charge Q_2 on the 2-μf capacitor is 220 v $\times$ 2 $\times$ 10^{-6} f $= 4.4 \times 10^{-4}$ coul.

The charge Q_4 on the 4-μf capacitor is 220 v $\times$ 4 $\times$ 10^{-6} f $= 8.8 \times 10^{-4}$ coul.

The charge Q_8 on the 8-μf capacitor is

$$220 \text{ v} \times 8 \times 10^{-6} \text{ farad} = 1.76 \times 10^{-3} \text{ coul}$$

9.6. Charging a Capacitor from a D-C Source.

In Fig. 9.11 a d-c voltage of E v is suddenly applied to a series circuit of constant resistance R ohms and constant capacitance C f by closing the switch at a time called $t = 0$. The capacitor is assumed to be uncharged initially. At $t = 0$ and thereafter, the voltage equation of the circuit is

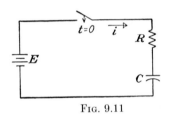

Fig. 9.11

$$E = iR + \frac{1}{C} \int_0^t i \, dt \qquad (9.5)$$

where i is the current in amperes and t is the time in seconds. Here iR is the resistor voltage and $(1/C) \int_0^t i \, dt$ is the capacitor voltage. From (9.5) an equation, containing no integrals or differentials, that expresses the current as a function of time is to be derived. However, without that equation certain relations in the circuit can be derived. Substitution of $t = 0$ in (9.5) causes the integral term to be zero. Then the current $I_0 = E/R$ amp. This result means that the current changes instantly from 0 to E/R at $t = 0$.

Differentiating (9.5) with respect to time yields $0 = R(di/dt) + (i/C)$, from which $di/dt = -i/RC$. This shows that the rate of change of the current is directly proportional to the current; hence it is greatest when the current is greatest. The negative sign shows that the current is decreasing. At $t = 0$, the current is E/R and the rate of change of the current is $-E/R^2C$ amp per sec.

Equation (9.5) is an integral equation. To obtain the equation of the current as a function of time directly from (9.5) requires that the answer (that is, i as a function of t) be known before the integral term can be evaluated. Equation (9.5) might be solved by trial by assuming different equations relating i and t until the one is found that satisfied (9.5). A

solution by trial is likely to be laborious.   A solution can be obtained by
starting with

$$0 = R\frac{di}{dt} + \frac{i}{C} \tag{9.6}$$

which is the time derivative of (9.5).   This can be rearranged as
$di/i = -dt/RC$, which after integration yields $\ln i = -t/RC + k$, where
k is a constant of integration.   In an exponential form of equation
$i = \epsilon^{-t/RC+k}$.   But $\epsilon^{-t/RC+k} = \epsilon^{-t/RC}\epsilon^{k} = k_1\epsilon^{-t/RC}$, where k_1 is another

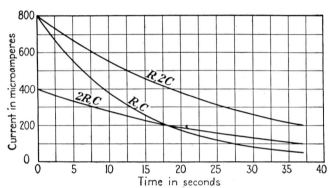

Fig. 9.12   Charging currents of capacitors with 120-v direct current applied.
$R = 150,000$ ohms; $C = 89$ μf.

constant.   Hence $i = k_1\epsilon^{-t/RC}$.   To determine k_1, substitute the known
boundary condition that $i = E/R$ amp at $t = 0$, and obtain $E/R = k_1\epsilon^0$.
But $\epsilon^0 = 1$; therefore $k_1 = E/R$ and

$$i = \frac{E}{R}\epsilon^{-t/RC}   \text{amp} \tag{9.7}$$

The voltage across a capacitor cannot be changed instantly from one
value to another.   The rate of change may be very great but it is always
finite.   When a change is made in a circuit containing a capacitor, the
capacitor permits an instantaneous change in current if necessary to hold
the voltage constant momentarily.   In the circuit of Fig. 9.11 the
capacitor was uncharged initially, i.e., just prior to $t = 0$.   At $t = 0$, the
capacitor voltage remains at zero, all the applied voltage is used by the
circuit resistance, and the current is E/R.   At the instant a circuit is
closed, an uncharged capacitor in it acts as a short circuit, a charged
capacitor in it acts as a source of emf with very little internal resistance.
In Fig. 9.12 are curves of the current-time relations in the circuit of Fig.
9.11 for several values of resistance and capacitance with a given applied
emf E.   With R ohms resistance and C f capacitance, the current changes
instantly from zero to E/R at $t = 0$ and then decays along an exponential

curve. Theoretically, the current is zero only after infinite time has elapsed. With R ohms resistance and $2C$ f capacitance the initial current is again E/R, but at $t = 0$ the rate of current decrease is one-half that in the previous case. Twice as much time is now required for the current to decrease to a given value. With $2R$ ohms resistance and C f capacitance, the initial current is $E/2R$. The initial rate of current decrease is one-fourth that with R ohms and C f, and twice as much time is required for the current to decrease to a given percentage of the initial value.

Figure 9.13 is an oscillogram of the current in the circuit of Fig. 9.11.

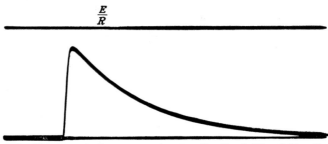

$\dfrac{E}{R}$

FIG. 9.13 Oscillogram of the current in the circuit of Fig. 9.11. $E = 7.75$ v; $R = 155$ ohms; $C = 22.7$ μf. The distance on the current axis representing E/R corresponds to 5.7 msec on the horizontal time axis.

Any circuit has inductance that prevents an instantaneous change of current. The inertia of the oscillograph vibrator prevented it from recording exactly the rapid change of current. Because of these factors, the oscillogram does not correspond exactly with the theoretical curves of Fig. 9.12. However, except for a short time interval following $t = 0$, the oscillogram should check with values computed from (9.7).

9.7. Time Constant of a Capacitive Circuit. For the circuit of Fig. 9.11 it was shown that the maximum rate of change of the current is $-E/R^2C$ amp per sec and occurs at $t = 0$. The current at $t = 0$ is E/R amp. If the current had continued to decrease at the initial rate, it would become zero in $(E/R)/(E/R^2C) = RC$ sec. The term RC is the time constant T_c of the circuit. In the equation $i = (E/R)\epsilon^{-t/RC}$, when $t = T_c = RC$, $i = (E/R)\epsilon^{-1} = E/R\epsilon$. But $1/\epsilon = 1/2.72 = 0.37$. Hence, at a time equal to the time constant, the current has decreased to 37 per cent of the initial value of E/R and has made $100 - 37 = 63$ per cent of the change from E/R to zero. Since the time constant of the circuit increases with both R and C, it is possible to obtain time constants ranging from microseconds to hours.

9.8. Voltage Transients in a Capacitive Circuit. In Fig. 9.11 the resistor voltage drop $v_R = iR$, taken positive in the direction of i. The current equation is $i = (E/R)\epsilon^{-t/RC}$; hence $v_R = E\epsilon^{-t/RC}$ v, where E is in volts, t is in seconds, R is in ohms, and C is in farads. $v_R = E$ at $t = 0$, and decreases exponentially to zero at $t = \infty$, as in Fig. 9.14.

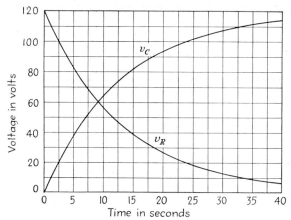

FIG. 9.14   Time variations of the resistive voltage and the capacitive voltage in the circuit of Fig. 9.11. $E = 120$ v; $R = 150{,}000$ ohms; $C = 89$ μf.

In Fig. 9.11 the capacitor voltage drop

$$v_C = E - v_R = E - E\epsilon^{-t/RC} = E(1 - \epsilon^{-t/RC}) \qquad \text{v}$$

$v_C = 0$ at $t = 0$, and increases exponentially to E at $t = \infty$, as in Fig. 9.14.

In Fig. 9.15, E v are suddenly applied to a resistor of R ohms resistance in series with a capacitor of C f capacitance. Because of a previous flow of current the capacitor has an initial voltage of E_0 v with polarities as indicated. The current and the voltage relations in the circuit are to be determined. The circuit voltage equation is $E = v_R + v_C$. But $v_R = iR$

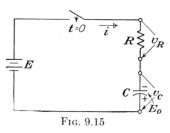

FIG. 9.15

and $v_C = (1/C) \int_0^t i\, dt - E_0$. The negative sign occurs because the direction of the current is into the capacitor terminal that was initially of negative polarity. Then $E = iR + (1/C) \int_0^t i\, dt - E_0$, which when differentiated with respect to time yields

$$0 = R\frac{di}{dt} + \frac{i}{C}$$

The general solution of this equation is the same as that of (9.6) and is $i = k_1\epsilon^{-t/RC}$ amp. At $t = 0$, the voltage equation becomes $E = iR - E_0$, from which the current at that instant is $i = (E + E_0)/R$. Hence

$(E + E_0)/R = k_1 \epsilon^0 = k_1.$ Then the current equation is

$$i = \frac{E + E_0}{R} \epsilon^{-t/RC} \qquad \text{amp}$$

The relation between current and time represented by this equation is the curve i in Fig. 9.16.

The capacitor voltage v_C is

$$v_C = \frac{1}{C} \int_0^t i \, dt - E_0 \qquad \text{v} \tag{9.8}$$

and can be obtained by substituting the derived equation of i in (9.8) and

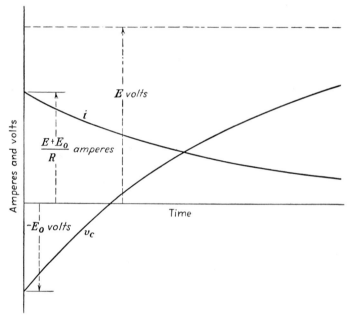

FIG. 9.16   Time variations of the current i and the capacitor voltage v_C in the circuit of Fig. 9.15.

integrating. v_C can also be obtained from the fact that here $v_C = E - iR$. Since i multiplied by R is $(E + E_0)\epsilon^{-t/RC}$, then

$$v_C = E - (E + E_0)\epsilon^{-t/RC} \qquad \text{v}$$

Inspection of this equation shows that the capacitor voltage is $-E_0$ at $t = 0$ and changes in polarity and magnitude to E at $t = \infty$.   Curves showing the time variations of the capacitor voltage are in Fig. 9.16.

The presence of an initial capacitor voltage E_0 in a circuit is equivalent to introducing a battery of emf E_0 in the circuit.   In making computations for a circuit containing a capacitor with an initial voltage, the capacitor may be replaced by an uncharged capacitor of equal capacitance and a battery whose emf is equal to the initial voltage on the original capacitor. The voltage across the original capacitor is the algebraic sum of the voltage across the second capacitor and that of the battery.

Example 1. Figure 9.17a contains two capacitors, each with an initial voltage. Following the closing of the switch, compute the steady-state voltage across each capacitor.

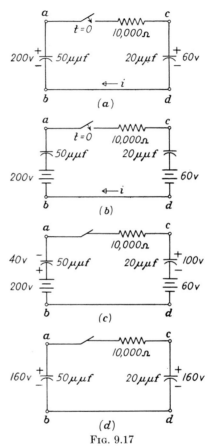

Solution. When the charged capacitors are replaced by uncharged capacitors and batteries, the circuit becomes that of Fig. 9.17b. Here the difference of $200 - 60 = 140$ v will divide between the capacitors, when a steady state is reached, inversely as the capacitances. Hence the 50-$\mu\mu$f capacitor will acquire $20/(50 + 20) = \frac{2}{7}$ of the 140 v, or 40 v with polarities as in Fig. 9.17c. The 20-$\mu\mu$f capacitor will acquire $50/(50 + 20) = \frac{5}{7}$ of the 140 v, or 100 v with polarities as in Fig. 9.17c. By recombination it is found that the voltage across each capacitor is 160 v, as in Fig. 9.17d.

9.9. Discharging a Capacitor. In Fig. 9.18 a capacitor of C f capacitance that has been charged previously to E_0 v is discharged by closing the switch that connects R ohms resistance across the capacitor terminals. The circuit voltage equation is $0 = v_R + v_C$. But $v_R = iR$ and

$$ v_C = \frac{1}{C} \int_0^t i\, dt - E_0; $$

Fig. 9.17

hence $0 = iR + 1/C \int_0^t i\, dt - E_0$. Differentiation of this with respect to time yields $0 = R(di/dt) + (i/C)$. Since this is the same as (9.6), its solution is the same, or $i = k_1 \epsilon^{-t/RC}$. At $t = 0$ in Fig. 9.18, the resistor voltage is equal to the capacitor voltage, which is E_0 v. The current is E_0/R amp. Hence $E_0/R = k_1 \epsilon^0 = k_1$, and

$$ i = \frac{E_0}{R} \epsilon^{-t/RC} \qquad \text{amp} $$

The form of the current equation during the discharge of a capacitor is the same as that during charge. However, during charge the current enters the positive capacitor terminal, while during discharge the current leaves the positive terminal.

During discharge the resistor voltage is $v_R = iR = E_0\epsilon^{-t/RC}$ and varies with time as v_R does in Fig. 9.14. The capacitor voltage is equal numerically to the resistor voltage and decreases in the same manner.

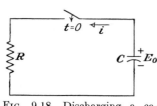

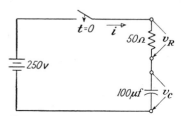

FIG. 9.18 Discharging a capacitor.

FIG. 9.19 Capacitive circuit for which the power variations have been computed in Table 9.2.

9.10. Power and Energy Relations in a Capacitor. In Fig. 9.19, the power input p_C to the electric field of the capacitor at any instant is equal to the product of the capacitor voltage v_C and the current i. The variation of the power with the current can be computed by assuming various values of current as shown in Table 9.2.

TABLE 9.2. CAPACITOR POWER VARIATIONS IN FIG. 9.19

i, amp	$v_R = 50i$, v	$v_C = 250 - 50i$, v	$p_C = v_C i$, w
5	250	0	0
4.5	225	25	112.5
4	200	50	200
3.5	175	75	262.5
3	150	100	300
2.5	125	125	312.5
2	100	150	300
1.5	75	175	262.5
1	50	200	200
0.5	25	225	112.5
0	0	250	0

Note that the capacitor power is 0 at $t = 0$ when $i = 5$ amp, rises to a maximum of 312.5 w when the current is 2.5 amp, and then decreases to 0 at infinite time when the current becomes 0.

While a capacitor of C f capacitance is being charged from 0 to v v, the energy input W_C to the dielectric field is $W_C = \int_0^t p_C\, dt$, where t is the time in seconds at which v volts is attained. Since $p_C = v_C i$, then

$$W_C = \int_0^t v_C i \, dt. \quad \text{But } i = C \, dv_C/dt; \text{ therefore } W_C = \int_0^t v_C \left(C \frac{dv_C}{dt} \right) dt, \text{ or}$$

$$W_C = \int_0^v C v_C \, dv_C$$

from which $W_C = \tfrac{1}{2} C v^2$ j (or wsec)   (9.9)

Equation (9.9) shows that the energy stored in a capacitor varies directly with the capacitance and with the square of the voltage to which the capacitor is charged.   In deriving (9.9), it was not necessary that the time variation of the capacitor voltage be known as it changed from 0 to v v.   This means that, when the voltage across a given capacitor attains a certain value, the energy stored is the same regardless of previous time variations in the voltage.

After a capacitor has been charged and then disconnected from a source of emf, it may retain some charge for a considerable time.   As a safety precaution such a capacitor should be discharged by connecting a discharge resistor across the terminals for a time before the terminals are touched with the hands.   The length of time required for a capacitor to discharge below a certain voltage depends upon the capacitance of the capacitor and the resistance of the discharge resistor.   The energy that a charged capacitor can deliver depends upon its capacitance and the voltage to which it is charged.   The hazard of touching a charged capacitor depends both upon the voltage to which it is charged and the amount of energy stored.

9.11. Capacitor Leakage Resistance. In Fig. 9.20 a voltage V v is suddenly applied to a voltmeter of resistance R ohms in series with a capacitor of capacitance C f by closing the switch.   At $t = 0$, the capacitor voltage is zero and the voltmeter voltage is V.   The voltmeter pointer swings quickly up scale, but it is not likely that it would read V momentarily because of the instrument damping and the inertia of the moving parts.   From a maximum of V, the voltage across the voltmeter would decrease with increasing time at a rate that depends upon the voltmeter resistance and the capacitor capacitance.   If the rate of decrease were not too great, after a short interval following $t = 0$ the voltmeter reading would be about equal to the voltage across the voltmeter.   In the derivation of the transient current in this type of circuit, it was stated that the current would decrease to zero.   In Fig. 9.20, it might be found that the voltmeter reading becomes steady at a value V_2 that is not

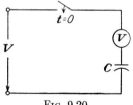

Fig. 9.20

zero.   In such a case, the capacitor current is V_2/R and not zero.   The presence of this current shows that some current passes by conduction from one capacitor terminal to the other.   This is leakage current.   The resistance through which the current flows is the leakage resistance of the capacitor.   A leaky capacitor is represented by a resistor of R_L ohms in parallel with a capacitor of capacitance C f, as in Fig. 9.21.   In Fig. 9.20 if the voltmeter reading is constant at V_2, the cur-

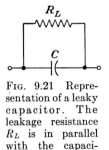

rent through the leakage resistance is equal to that through the voltmeter.   Then the ratio of the leakage resistance R_L to the voltmeter resistance R is equal to the ratio of the voltage $V - V_2$ across the leakage resistance to the voltmeter reading V_2.   Hence

Fig. 9.21 Representation of a leaky capacitor.   The leakage resistance R_L is in parallel with the capacitance C.

$R_L/R = (V - V_2)/V_2$, from which

$$R_L = \frac{R(V - V_2)}{V_2} \quad \text{ohms}$$

This method for measuring leakage resistance is satisfactory if V_2 is not too small to be read with reasonable accuracy and is not so large as to be nearly equal to V.

The leakage resistance of a capacitor is not constant but decreases as the voltage applied to the capacitor is increased.   The results of theoretical circuit computations based on the assumption of constant leakage resistance are likely to differ from results obtained experimentally.

Example 1.   In Fig. 9.22 the capacitor capacitance is 200 μf and the voltmeter resistance is 150,000 ohms.   Derive the equation of and plot the curve showing

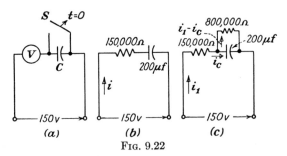

Fig. 9.22

the time variation of the voltmeter reading after the switch S is opened, for each of the following conditions: (a) neglecting the effect of the leakage resistance of the capacitor, and (b) the leakage resistance is 0.8 megohm.

Solution.   a.   With the effect of leakage neglected, the circuit to be solved is that of Fig. 9.22b.   The voltage equation is

$$150 = 150,000i + \frac{1}{200 \times 10^{-6}} \int_0^t i \, dt$$

Differentiating with respect to time and rearranging yields $di/i = -dt/30$, which integrates into $\ln i = -t/30 + k_1$. This can be expressed as $i = k_2\epsilon^{-t/30}$. Since $i = 150$ v/150,000 ohms $= 0.001$ amp at $t = 0$, then $k_2 = 0.001$ and $i = 0.001\epsilon^{-t/30}$ amp. The voltmeter reading $v = 150,000i$; thus

$$v = 150\epsilon^{-t/30} \quad \text{v} \tag{1}$$

The voltage-time curve representing (1) is that labeled 1 in Fig. 9.23.

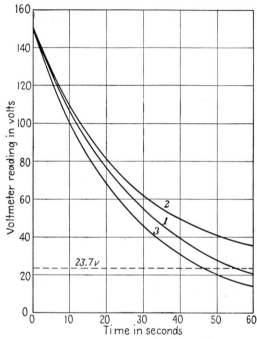

FIG. 9.23   Voltage-time curves for the circuits of Figs. 9.22a and 9.24a.

b. With the effect of leakage considered, the circuit to be solved is that of Fig. 9.22c. The voltage equations of the circuit are

$$150 = 150,000i_1 + \frac{1}{200 \times 10^{-6}} \int_0^t i_C \, dt \tag{2}$$

and

$$150 = 150,000i_1 + 800,000(i_1 - i_C) \tag{3}$$

Differentiating (2) with respect to time and simplifying yield $i_C = -30 \, di_1/dt$. Substitution of this for i_C in (3), simplifying, and rearranging yield

$$\frac{di_1}{1.5 - 9,500i_1} = \frac{dt}{240,000}.$$

Integration yields $\ln (1.5 - 9,500i_1) = -\dfrac{9,500t}{240,000} + k_1$, from which

$$1.5 - 9,500i_1 = \epsilon^{-t/25.3+k_1} = k_2\epsilon^{-t/25.3}$$

At $t = 0$, $i_1 = 150$ v/150,000 ohms $= 0.001$ amp; hence $k_2 = 1.5 - 9.5 = -8$. Then

$$i_1 = \frac{1.5 + 8\epsilon^{-t/25.3}}{9,500} = 0.000158 + 0.000842\epsilon^{-t/25.3} \text{ amp}$$

The voltmeter reading $v_1 = 150,000i_1$; thus $v_1 = 23.7 + 126.3\epsilon^{-t/25.3}$ v.

This voltage-time curve is that labeled (2) in Fig. 9.23. Comparison of curves 1 and 2 shows that the voltmeter reading at any instant is greater than it would have been with no leakage and that the voltmeter reading approaches a steady-state value of 23.7 v.

Example 2. The capacitor and the voltmeter of Example 1 are connected as in Fig. 9.24a. Derive the equation of and plot the curve showing the time variation

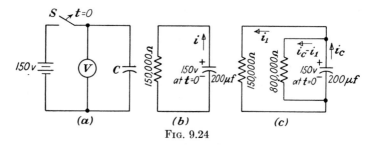

(a)   (b)   (c)

Fig. 9.24

of the voltmeter reading after the switch S is opened, for each of the following conditions: (a) neglecting the effect of the leakage resistance of the capacitor, and (b) the leakage resistance is constant at 0.8 megohm.

Solution. With S closed, the circuit is in a steady state with the capacitor charged to 150 v and the voltmeter reading at 150 v. After S is opened, the capacitor and the voltmeter are in series. The capacitor discharges through the voltmeter as in Fig. 9.24b. The voltage equation is

$$0 = 150,000i + \frac{1}{200 \times 10^{-6}} \int_0^t i \, dt - 150$$

which may be written as

$$150 = 150,000i + \frac{1}{200 \times 10^{-6}} \int_0^t i \, dt$$

Since this equation is identical to the voltage equation in Example 1, its solution is also $i = 0.001\epsilon^{-t/30}$ amp and the voltmeter reading is $v = 150,000i = 150\epsilon^{-t/30}$ v. The voltage-time curve is identical with curve 1 in Fig. 9.23.

b. When the effect of leakage is considered, the circuit is that of Fig. 9.24c. The voltage equations are

$$150 = 150,000i_1 + \frac{1}{200 \times 10^{-6}} \int_0^t i_c \, dt \tag{1}$$

and

$$0 = 800,000(i_c - i_1) - 150,000i_1 \tag{2}$$

Differentiating (1) with respect to time and simplifying yield $i_c = -30 \, di_1/dt$. Substitution of this value of i_c in (2), separation of the variables, and simplification yield $di_1/i_1 = -dt/25.3$. This integrates into $\ln i_1 = -t/25.3 + k$, which may be written as $i_1 = k_1\epsilon^{-t/25.3}$. When $t = 0$,

$$i_1 = \frac{150 \text{ v}}{150,000 \text{ ohms}} = 0.001 \text{ amp}$$

hence $k_1 = 0.001$ and $i_1 = 0.001\epsilon^{-t/25.3}$ amp. The voltmeter reading is

$$v_1 = 150,000i_1 = 150\epsilon^{-t/25.3} \quad \text{v}$$

The voltage-time curve representing this voltage is 3 in Fig. 9.23. The curve approaches zero as time increases, but at any instant the voltage is less than it would have been if there had been no leakage current. Comparison of curves 1 and 3 shows that leakage in a capacitor can cause a considerable difference between the curve for the capacitor voltage while charging and that while discharging.

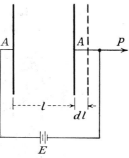

9.12. Electric Pull. In Fig. 9.25 is represented a capacitor each plate of which has an area of A sq m. The plates are separated l m. The capacitor is charged to E v by the battery shown. The pull required to separate the plates is to be computed. Assume that the left-hand plate is fixed and that the right-hand plate is moved dl m

FIG. 9.25   Electric pull.

by a pull P newtons. With the original plate separation, by (9.4), the capacitance $C_1 = \epsilon_v A/l$ f. The energy W_1 stored in the electric field is

$$W_1 = \tfrac{1}{2}C_1E^2 = \frac{\epsilon_v A E^2}{2l} \quad \text{j}$$

After the plates have been separated the additional distance dl, the capacitance $C_2 = \epsilon_v A/(l + dl)$ f, and the energy then stored in the electric field is $W_2 = \tfrac{1}{2}C_2E^2 = \epsilon_v A E^2/[2(l + dl)]$ j. Since C_2 is less than C_1, the electric field has given up energy of the amount

$$W_1 - W_2 = \frac{\epsilon_v A E^2}{2l} - \frac{\epsilon_v A E^2}{2(l + dl)} = \frac{\epsilon_v A E^2 \, dl}{2l(l + dl)} \quad \text{j}$$

If the circuit is assumed to have zero resistance, the battery maintains a constant voltage of E v across the capacitor. During the time the plate is moving, there is a current of i amp, where $i = E \, dC/dt$. Since $C = \epsilon_v A/l$, then $\dfrac{dC}{dt} = -\dfrac{\epsilon_v A}{l^2}\dfrac{dl}{dt}$ and $i = -\dfrac{\epsilon_v A E}{l^2}\dfrac{dl}{dt}$ amp. The negative sign shows that the capacitance is decreasing with time and that current is being delivered from (rather than to) the positively charged plate of that capacitor. The energy dw delivered to the battery during the time interval dt is $dw = -Ei \, dt = \epsilon_v A E^2/l^2 \, dl$ j. To separate the plates, mechanical work $P \, dl$ j must be done on them. The energy delivered to

the battery is equal to the sum of the mechanical work done and the
energy given up by the electric field; hence

$$P \, dl + \frac{\epsilon_v A E^2 \, dl}{2l(l + dl)} = \frac{\epsilon_v A E^2 \, dl}{l^2}$$

from which
$$P = \epsilon_v A E^2 \left[\frac{1}{l^2} - \frac{1}{2l(l + dl)} \right]$$

As dl becomes zero,

$$P = \frac{\epsilon_v A E^2}{2l^2} \quad \text{newtons} \tag{9.10}$$

By expressing (9.10) in other terms, a comparison can be made between
the expression for electric pull and that for magnetic pull. Since $E = \Psi S$,

Fig. 9.26   Elements of a capacitor (electrostatic) voltmeter. (*Sensitive Research Instrument Company.*)

and $S = l/\epsilon_v A$, then $E^2 = \Psi^2 l^2 / \epsilon_v^2 A^2$ and $P = \Psi^2 A / 2\epsilon_v A^2$.   But $(\Psi/A)^2 = D^2$, where D is the electric flux density in coulombs per square meter.
Hence $P = D^2 A / 2\epsilon_v$ newtons.   The expression for magnetic pull is $P = B^2 A / 2\mu_v$ newtons.   Hence, in the electric as well as in the magnetic
field, the pull is proportional to the product of the area and the square
of the flux density.

9.13. Capacitor Voltmeter.   In a capacitor voltmeter the attraction
between oppositely charged capacitor plates is used to measure the voltage applied between the plates.   Figure 9.26 shows a voltmeter in which
the plates are aluminum vanes, one set is fixed and the other pivoted so

that it can turn about the axis of suspension. The movable vanes turn against the restoring torque of a spring when voltage is applied between the movable and the fixed vanes.

Capacitor voltmeters are well suited for measuring high voltages. At one time they were not made with a full-scale capacity less than about 2,000 v. At present they are made with a capacity as low as 75 v.

Since the pull between the plates of a capacitor varies as the square of the voltage applied, when an alternating voltage is applied to a capacitor

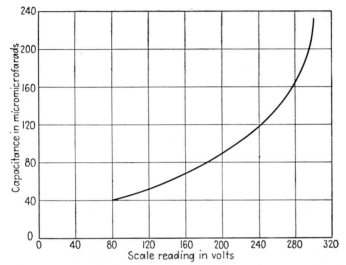

Fig. 9.27 Relation between the capacitance of a certain capacitor voltmeter and the scale reading.

voltmeter, the average torque produced is proportional to the average of the squared instantaneous voltages. Hence, the instrument is an rms voltmeter for any waveform.

When a capacitor voltmeter is used to measure a d-c voltage, it draws no current after the plates have become charged. However, if an alternating voltage across a capacitor is to be measured, the capacitance of the instrument may cause a change in the voltage being measured.

When a capacitor voltmeter is used to measure a voltage, either direct or alternating, and then disconnected, a charge may remain on the plates. If so, the instrument pointer does not return immediately to zero.

When a capacitor voltmeter is used to measure an alternating voltage, the steady-state reading is the rms voltage. When a capacitor voltmeter is disconnected from a 100-v rms sinusoidal voltage source, the instantaneous voltage left on the capacitor may have any value between 0 and the maximum of 141 v. If it should happen that the instrument is disconnected when the voltage is a maximum, one might expect the pointer to move from the original steady-state reading of 100 up to a new reading of 141 v. This does not happen. As the pointer moves upscale, the plates move closer together and increase the capacitance. With a given charge left on the plates, an increase in capacitance reduces the voltage below what it was when the pointer started to move upscale from 100. Figure 9.27 shows how the capacitance of a certain 300-v capacitor volt-meter varies with the scale reading.

9.14. Capacitance of a Cable. Figure 9.28 represents the cross section of a cable composed of a conductor of radius r_1 m, insulating material

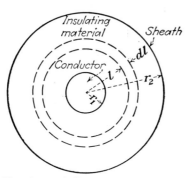

of dielectric constant ϵ, and a metallic sheath of inner radius r_2 m. The capacitance between the conductor and the sheath for a given length of cable is to be determined. The elastance per meter length of cable cannot be computed directly from the relation $S = l/\epsilon_v \epsilon A$ because the electric flux density is not uniform throughout the insulation when voltage is applied between the conductor and the sheath. The electric lines extend radially between the conductor surface and the sheath. The greatest electric flux den-

FIG. 9.28 A dielectric in which the electric flux density is not uniform.

sity occurs in the insulation at the conductor surface and the least density at the inner surface of the sheath. In the insulation equipotential surfaces are cylinders concentric with the conductor. Consider the surface that has a radius of l m and a second surface that is separated from the first by the infinitesimal distance dl m. The voltage between the surfaces is an infinitesimal dv v. Here $dv = \Psi \, dS$, where, for the 1-m length of cable, Ψ is the dielectric flux between the conductor and the sheath and dS is the infinitesimal elastance between the chosen equipotential surfaces. The elastance of the differential volume is $dS = dl/\epsilon_v \epsilon A$. The total elastance S between the conductor and sheath is obtained by integrating this expression between the limits r_1 and r_2. Hence

$$S = \int_{r_1}^{r_2} \frac{dl}{\epsilon_v \epsilon A} \tag{9.11}$$

The area A of a cylindrical equipotential surface normal to the dielectric flux is a function of l and is $2\pi l$ m, the perimeter of a cylinder, times the 1-m length of the cylinder, or $A = 2\pi l$ sq m. Substitution of this value of A in (9.11), integration, and substitution of the limits yield

$$S = \frac{1}{2\pi\epsilon_v\epsilon} \int_{r_1}^{r_2} \frac{dl}{l} = \frac{1}{2\pi\epsilon_v\epsilon} [\ln l]_{r_1}^{r_2} = \frac{1}{2\pi\epsilon_v\epsilon} \ln \frac{r_2}{r_1} \qquad \text{darafs per m length}$$

The capacitance C of the cable is the reciprocal of S, or

$$C = \frac{2\pi\epsilon_v\epsilon}{\ln(r_2/r_1)} \qquad \text{f per m length}$$

The capacitance of a cable L m long is

$$C = \frac{2\pi\epsilon_v\epsilon L}{\ln(r_2/r_1)} \qquad \text{f}$$

9.15. Voltage Gradients in Dielectrics.

The voltage gradient $\mathcal{E}$ in a dielectric is $\mathcal{E} = dv/dl$ v per m, where dv v is the infinitesimal voltage drop over a length dl m. If the dielectric flux density D in a given insulating material is uniform throughout the length of a material, the gradient is also v/l v per m, where v v is the voltage drop across the length l. There are few types of dielectric circuits in which the dielectric flux density is uniform throughout. In parallel-plate capacitors the density is approximately uniform if the distance between the plates is small compared with the dimensions of the plates.

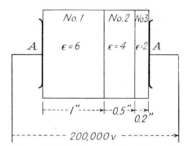

FIG. 9.29 Three dielectrics in series.

Example 1. The parallel-plate capacitor of Fig. 9.29 has three dielectrics as shown. Compute the voltage gradient in each dielectric.

Solution. Assuming a uniform dielectric flux density, the elastance S_1 of dielectric 1 is, from (9.3),

$$S_1 = \frac{l_1}{\epsilon_v\epsilon_1 A} = \frac{1 \text{ in.} \times 0.0254 \text{ m}/1 \text{ in.}}{6\epsilon_v A} = \frac{0.167 \times 0.0254}{\epsilon_v A} \qquad \text{darafs}$$

The elastance S_2 of dielectric 2 is

$$S_2 = \frac{l_2}{\epsilon_v\epsilon_2 A} = \frac{0.5 \text{ in.} \times 0.0254 \text{ m}/1 \text{ in.}}{4\epsilon_v A} = \frac{0.125 \times 0.0254}{\epsilon_v A} \qquad \text{darafs}$$

The elastance S_3 of dielectric 3 is

$$S_3 = \frac{l_3}{\epsilon_v\epsilon_3 A} = \frac{0.2 \text{ in.} \times 0.0254 \text{ m}/1 \text{ in.}}{2\epsilon_v A} = \frac{0.1 \times 0.0254}{\epsilon_v A} \qquad \text{darafs}$$

The elastance S of the capacitor is

$$S = S_1 + S_2 + S_3 = \frac{0.392 \times 0.0254}{\epsilon_v A} \qquad \text{darafs}$$

For elastors in series, the voltage across one elastor is to the total voltage as the elastance of the elastor is to the total elastance. Then $V_1/V = S_1/S$, where V_1 is the voltage across dielectric 1 and V is the voltage between the plates. Then $V_1/200,000 = 0.167/0.392$, from which $V_1 = 85,000$ v. Assuming the dielectric flux density to be uniform, the voltage gradient $\mathcal{E}_1$ in dielectric 1 is

$$\frac{V_1}{l_1} = \frac{85,000 \text{ v}}{1 \text{ in.} \times 0.0254 \text{ m/1 in.}} = 3.3 \times 10^6 \text{ v per m}$$

In a similar manner, $V_2/V = S_2/S$, where V_2 is the voltage across dielectric 2. Then $V_2/200,000 = 0.125/0.392$, from which $V_2 = 64,000$ v. The voltage gradient $\mathcal{E}_2$ in dielectric 2 is

$$\frac{V_2}{l_2} = \frac{64,000 \text{ v}}{0.5 \text{ in.} \times 0.0254 \text{ m/1 in.}} = 5 \times 10^6 \text{ v per m}$$

Likewise, $V_3/V = S_3/S$, where V_3 is the voltage across dielectric 3. Then $V_3/200,000 = 0.1/0.392$, from which $V_3 = 51,000$ v. The voltage gradient $\mathcal{E}_3$ in dielectric 3 is $V_3/l_3 = 51,000 \text{ v}/(0.2 \text{ in.} \times 0.0254 \text{ m/in.}) = 10^7$ v per m.

In Example 1 the term ϵ_v and the conversion factor from inches to meters canceled with identical terms when the ratio of elastances was set up. This means that the division of a given applied voltage between the various sections of a capacitor may be determined without using the numerical value of ϵ_v and with any common unit of length. If actual values of elastance and capacitance are desired, then the numerical value of ϵ_v is required and the lengths must be in meters.

In the cable of Fig. 9.28 the dielectric flux density is not uniform. The voltage gradient $\mathcal{E}$ at a point in the insulating material is $\mathcal{E} = dv/dl$. Let Ψ be the dielectric flux in coulombs per meter length of the cable that passes through the infinitesimal elastance dS daraf between the two equipotential surfaces that are separated by the infinitesimal distance dl m. The infinitesimal voltage dv v between the surfaces is $dv = \Psi \, dS$. It was shown in Art. 9.14 that $dS = dl/\epsilon_v \epsilon A$; hence $dv = \Psi \, dl/\epsilon_v \epsilon A$. From this $dv/dl = \Psi/\epsilon_v \epsilon A$. But $dv/dl = \mathcal{E}$, $A = 2\pi l$ sq m per meter length of cable (see Art. 9.14), and $\Psi = V/S$, where V v is the voltage and S is the elastance between conductor and sheath. In Art. 9.14 it was shown that $S = \ln (r_2/r_1)/(2\pi\epsilon_v \epsilon)$. Combining these relations yields

$$\mathcal{E} = \frac{V}{l \ln (r_2/r_1)} \qquad \text{v per m} \qquad (9.12)$$

For a given cable, r_1 and r_2 are fixed. Equation (9.12) shows that, for a given voltage V between the conductor and the sheath, the voltage gradient in the insulation varies inversely as the distance l of the point from the conductor center. The insulation extends only from $l = r_1$ to $l = r_2$; hence the minimum gradient $\mathcal{E}_{min}$ occurs at $l = r_2$, at the outer surface of the insulation, and is

$$\mathcal{E}_{min} = \frac{V}{r_2 \ln (r_2/r_1)} \qquad \text{v per m}$$

The maximum gradient $\mathcal{E}_{max}$ occurs at $l = r_1$, at the inner surface of the insulation, and is

$$\mathcal{E}_{max} = \frac{V}{r_1 \ln (r_2/r_1)} \qquad \text{v per m} \tag{9.13}$$

For fixed values of V and r_2 there is a ratio of r_2/r_1 for which the maximum voltage gradient is a minimum. With V and r_2 constant, the value of r_1 that makes $\mathcal{E}_{max}$ a minimum can be found by differentiating (9.13) with respect to r_1 and setting the result equal to zero. When this is done, it is found that $r_1 = r_2/\epsilon = 0.368r_2$. Here ϵ is the natural logarithm base.

9.16. Dielectric Strength. As the voltage gradient in a dielectric is increased, a value is reached at which the dielectric ceases to act as an insulator and breaks down, i.e., becomes a conductor. The gradient at which breakdown occurs is the dielectric strength. The dielectric strength of air is about 3,000 kv per m and depends upon the temperature, the humidity, and the pressure. In a solid dielectric the dielectric strength depends also upon the thickness of the sample tested. In insulating oil the presence of moisture in the ratio of 1 part in 10,000 reduces the dielectric strength to as low as one-half that for moisture-free oil.

In Table 9.1 are listed dielectric strengths of some insulating materials. These represent averages of values obtained from a number of tests. Samples taken from a given piece of insulating material may yield values that differ considerably.

There is no direct correspondence between the dielectric constant of a material and its dielectric strength. Each is a distinct property of a material to be considered in the design or the computation of a dielectric circuit.

When an insulation breakdown occurs in one part of a dielectric circuit, the voltage gradient in another part of the circuit may increase to a value that causes breakdown there.

Example 1. Figure 9.30 represents a capacitor with air and glass as dielectrics between parallel plates. The glass has a dielectric constant of 6 and a dielectric strength of 10,000 kv per m. Each plate area is A sq m. The voltage between plates is 50 kv.

The elastance S_a of the air is

$$S_a = \frac{0.5 \text{ cm} \times 0.01 \text{ m}/1 \text{ cm}}{\epsilon_v A} = \frac{0.005}{\epsilon_v A} \quad \text{darafs}$$

The elastance S_g of the glass is

$$S_g = \frac{1 \text{ cm} \times 0.01 \text{ m}/1 \text{ cm}}{6\epsilon_v A} = \frac{0.00167}{\epsilon_v A} \quad \text{darafs}$$

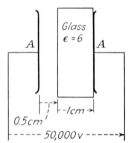

The equivalent elastance S_e of the capacitor is

$$S_e = S_a + S_g = \frac{0.00667}{\epsilon_v A} \quad \text{darafs}$$

The voltage V_a across the air is 50 kv $\times S_a/S_e = 37.5$ kv. If the air did not break down, the voltage gradient in it would be

$$\frac{37.5 \text{ kv}}{0.5 \text{ cm} \times 0.01 \text{ m}/1 \text{ cm}} = 7{,}500 \text{ kv per m}$$

FIG. 9.30 A capacitor having dielectrics of air and glass.

Since this gradient exceeds the 3,000 kv per m that air will stand, the air will break down and the full 50 kv will be applied to the glass. The resulting gradient in the glass would be 50 kv/(1 cm $\times$ 0.01 m/1 cm) = 5,000 kv per m. This is less than the 10,000 kv per m dielectric strength of the glass. If the voltage were direct, the glass would not break down. However, the breakdown of air under an alternating voltage is accompanied by a discharge called corona, which produces a pale violet light and an energy loss. In this capacitor the energy loss would heat the glass and in time would probably reduce its dielectric strength until it broke down.

In solid dielectrics air pockets in which corona might form are undesirable. Oil is sometimes forced into high-voltage cables and kept under pressure to eliminate air that would be present otherwise.

9.17. Electrolytic Capacitors. An electrolytic capacitor is formed if an aluminum and a steel bar are placed in a solution of baking soda in water. If a source of d-c voltage is connected between the bars, with the aluminum bar positive, at first there is a flow of current limited largely by the resistance in the circuit. In a short time an insulating film of aluminum oxide forms and the current diminishes to a low value. The film acts as a dielectric and an electrolytic capacitor is formed. Since the capacitance of a capacitor is inversely proportional to the dielectric thickness and that of the film may be of the order of 10^{-7} m, more capacitance can be obtained in a given volume in an electrolytic capacitor than in one having a solid dielectric such as mica or paper.

Commercial electrolytic capacitors are made in both wet and dry types. The latter is not actually dry, but the moisture content is much less than in the wet type. Wet electrolytic capacitors often have a round alu-

minum can to hold the electrolyte. The electrolyte serves as one electrode; aluminum foil mounted at the center of the can in the electrolyte
serves as the other. The insulating oxide film is formed on the foil by
placing it in a solution and then applying voltage between the foil and the
solution. The thickness of the film increases as the magnitude of the
forming voltage is increased. As a result the
capacitance of a given capacitor decreases as
the forming voltage is increased.

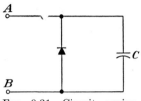

Electrolytic capacitors made as discussed
above are called polarized capacitors and may
be used in circuits where the polarity of the
capacitor voltage never reverses. Since a
polarized capacitor acts as a capacitor with
voltage of one polarity applied and conducts
readily when voltage of the reverse polarity

Fig. 9.31 Circuit equiva-
lent to a polarized electrolytic capacitor.

is applied, it is electrically equivalent to a rectifier in parallel with a
capacitor as in Fig. 9.31. Here, while terminal A is positive and B is
negative, no current passes through the rectifier (if it is assumed to
have infinite resistance to reverse current) and the circuit behaves as
a capacitor of capacitance C f. While terminal A is negative and B is
positive, the rectifier offers only its forward
resistance to the flow of current and thus is
nearly equivalent to a short circuit.

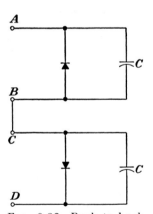

A nonpolarized capacitor is formed when
two polarized capacitors are connected back
to back, as in Fig. 9.32. Assume that a sinusoidal voltage of 100 v maximum is applied
between terminals A and D at the instant
when the voltage is passing through zero.
Assume further that the capacitors are initially
uncharged and that the rectifiers are perfect.
As A becomes positive with respect to D,
current flows from A to B through the upper
capacitor but from C to D through the lower
rectifier. With zero forward resistance in the
rectifier, there is no voltage drop from C to D.
The voltage across the upper capacitor is that
between A and D. This condition exists until
the applied voltage reaches a maximum of

Fig. 9.32 Back-to-back
connection of two polarized
electrolytic capacitors to
form a nonpolarized ca-
pacitor.

100 v. At this instant the voltage is not changing and the current is
zero. As the applied voltage decreases the upper capacitor begins to discharge and current begins to flow into terminal D and out of C. This
current enters the lower capacitor and charges the lower plate positively.

The process of discharging the upper capacitor and charging the lower capacitor continues until the applied voltage has reached a negative maximum of 100 v with terminal D positive with respect to A. At this instant the voltage across the upper capacitor is zero and the current is again zero. During the first quarter cycle of the applied voltage, the

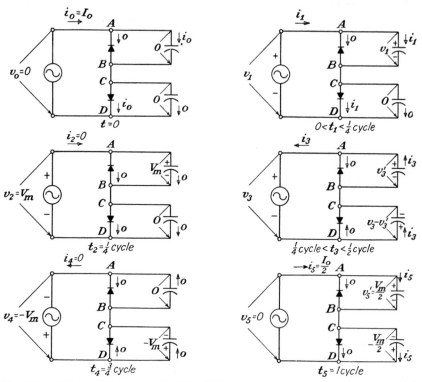

Fig. 9.33   Relations in the circuit of Fig. 9.32 following the application of a sinusoidal voltage between terminals A and D.

capacitance of the circuit is C f because the lower capacitor is short-circuited by the lower rectifier. During the second quarter cycle and thereafter, there is no current in either rectifier, the capacitors are in series, and the equivalent capacitance is $C/2$ f. Since $i = C\, dv/dt$, the maximum current is twice as great during the first quarter cycle of the voltage as it is during the second. After the second current zero, the current becomes cyclic, attaining the same maximum as that during the second quarter cycle. As a result the equivalent capacitance is then $C/2$ f.

The events just described are shown in the circuits of Fig. 9.33 and the curves in Fig. 9.34. The voltage across one capacitor is always of one polarity, varying between zero and the maximum of the applied voltage. The voltage across the other capacitor is always of the opposite polarity, varying between zero and the negative maximum of the applied voltage.

Since the back-to-back combination of two polarized capacitors of C f capacitance each forms a nonpolarized capacitor of $C/2$ f, four identical polarized capacitors of C f each are required to form a nonpolarized capacitor of C f capacitance. The maximum voltage rating of each of the four must be equal to the maximum voltage applied to the combination.

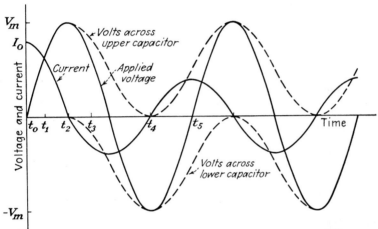

FIG. 9.34   Time variations of the applied voltage, the current, and the capacitor voltages in the circuit of Fig. 9.33.

An electrolytic capacitor has an undesirably low leakage resistance. Because of the accompanying high losses, this type is more limited in its applications than are oil-filled or paper-insulated capacitors. To represent better the equivalent circuit of an electrolytic capacitor, a resistor may be added in parallel with the rectifier and the capacitor in Fig. 9.31.

PROBLEMS

9.1. A positive charge of 2 $\mu\mu$coul, one of 4 $\mu\mu$coul, and one of 5 $\mu\mu$coul are in air at the respective vertices of a triangle, 0.5 cm on a side. Compute the magnitude and the direction of the force exerted on each charge.

9.2. An electron is placed at the center of the triangle of Prob. 9.1. Compute the magnitude and the direction of the force exerted on it.

9.3. Equal positive charges of 4 $\mu\mu$coul are 0.2 cm apart. A positive charge of 1 $\mu\mu$coul is moved slowly along the line joining the other charges, starting at a point 0.01 cm from one charge. Write the equation that expresses the force exerted on the moving charge as a function of the distance from a stationary charge. Compute the work done on (or by) the moving charge as it moves to the point midway between the stationary charges.

9.4. Two identical charges that are separated 4 cm in air exert a force of 3.6×10^{-10} newton on each other. Compute the magnitude of the charge.

9.5. When a 2-μf capacitor is charged to 400 v, how much charge is on each plate? How much dielectric flux exists between the plates?

9.6. How much voltage is required to store 50 μcoul on a 4-μf capacitor? How many electrons are added to one plate during the charging interval? How long would be required for a constant current of 25 ma to deliver this charge?

9.7. At what rate is the voltage across a 0.2-μf capacitor changing when the current in it is 4 ma?

9.8. The voltage across a certain 5-μf capacitor increases linearly from 0 at $t = 0$ to 200 v at $t = 5$ msec. Then it decreases linearly to 100 v at $t = 10$ msec. Sketch the current-time curve.

9.9. The equation of the voltage applied to a certain 2-μf capacitor is $v = 50t^2$ v, where t is in seconds. Derive the equation of and sketch the current-time curve. Compute the current when the voltage is 50 v and that when it is 200 v.

9.10. The current in a certain 0.8-μf capacitor increases linearly from 0 at $t = 0$ to 200 ma at $t = 5$ msec. Then it decreases linearly to 100 ma at $t = 10$ msec. Sketch the voltage-time curve, assuming that the capacitor is initially uncharged.

9.11. The equation of the voltage applied to a certain 0.1-μf capacitor is $v = 50$ $(1 - \epsilon^{-10t})$ v, where ϵ is the natural logarithm base and t is in seconds. Derive the equation of and sketch the current-time curve. Compute the current when the voltage is 10 v.

9.12. The equation of the current in a certain 0.2-μf capacitor is

$$i = 50(1 - \epsilon^{-10t}) \qquad \text{ma}$$

where ϵ is the natural logarithm base and t is in seconds. Sketch the voltage-time curve assuming that the capacitor is initially uncharged. Compute the voltage when the current is 40 ma.

9.13. The equation of the voltage applied to a certain 0.1-μf capacitor is

$$v = 100t\epsilon^{-10t} \qquad \text{v}$$

where ϵ is the natural logarithm base, and t is in seconds. Plot the voltage-time curve. Derive the equation of and plot the current-time curve.

9.14. The equation of the current in a 0.05-μf capacitor is $i = 5t\epsilon^{-20t}$ μamp, where ϵ is the natural logarithm base and t is in seconds. The capacitor was initially uncharged. Derive the equation of and plot the voltage-time curve.

9.15. If the voltage across a condenser microphone is constant at 150 v and the capacitance is changing at the rate of 80 μf per min, what is the current?

9.16. The output voltage of a certain d-c generator is directly proportional to the speed and is 240 v at 1,200 rpm. A 10-μf capacitor and an ammeter are in series across the armature. When the current is 50 μa, what is the acceleration of the armature?

9.17. The current in a certain 2-μf capacitor decreases linearly from 8 ma at $t = 0$ to 2 ma at $t = 3$ msec. The capacitor is initially uncharged.

a. Sketch the current-time curve and determine its equation.

b. How much charge does the capacitor receive during the 3-msec interval?

c. Derive the equation of the voltage-time curve. Sketch the curve.

d. What is the capacitor voltage at $t = 2$ and that at $t = 3$ msec?

e. A 15,000-ohm resistor is in series with the capacitor. Determine the equation of the voltage applied to the combination to produce the given current.

9.18. The current in a certain 0.02-μf capacitor increases linearly from 0 at $t = 0$ to

4 ma at $t = 400$ μsec. The capacitor is charged initially to 40 v. Determine the equation of the voltage required to produce the current if the current enters the capacitor terminal that was positive initially. Compute the voltage at $t = 200$ and that at 400 μsec.

9.19. Solve Prob. 9.18 if the current enters the capacitor terminal that was negative initially.

9.20. The current in a certain 0.5-μf capacitor varied according to the equation $i = 10\epsilon^{-200t}$ ma, where ϵ is the natural logarithm base and t is in seconds. The capacitor was uncharged initially. What was the capacitor voltage at $t = 2$ msec?

9.21. How many electrons are required to produce 400 v on a 4-μf capacitor?

9.22. Compute the elastance of a 2-μf capacitor.

9.23. How much dielectric flux would 2,000 v produce in a dielectric circuit that has an elastance of 0.5 megadaraf?

9.24. Compute the elastance and the capacitance of a dielectric circuit in which 0.5 μcoul are produced by 2,000 v.

9.25. In a certain cathode-ray tube the deflecting plates are parallel and are trapezoidal in shape. The parallel sides of each plate are 1.1 and 0.8 in. long. The altitude of the surface of each plate is 0.75 in. The plates are 0.25 in. apart. What is the approximate capacitance between them when in a vacuum?

9.26. Considering only the electric flux in the space between the parallel plates of a capacitor, what plate area is required for a capacitance of 0.4 μf if the plates are 0.1 in. apart in air?

9.27. When 3,000 v are applied to the parallel plates of an air capacitor, a dielectric flux of 0.2 μcoul is produced. With mica between the plates, that voltage produces 0.8 μcoul. Compute the dielectric constant of the mica.

9.28. A certain 0.4-μf capacitor consists of interleaved sheets of tin foil and paper. The paper sheets are 10 mils thick and have a dielectric constant of 2.5. Alternate tin-foil sheets are connected to one terminal. The other tin-foil sheets are connected to the other terminal. How many tin-foil sheets are required if each has an area of 50 sq in?

9.29. A 2-, a 4-, and a 5-μf capacitor are in series across 400-v direct current. Compute the elastance of each capacitor and that of the combination. Compute the capacitance of the combination. Compute the voltage across the 2-μf capacitor.

9.30. Compute the capacitance between points A and B in Fig. 9.35. If 400-v direct current is applied between A and B, what will be the voltage across the 2-μf capacitor?

9.31. In a triode the capacitances between the various electrodes form a pi system. In one triode the capacitances are: grid to filament, 9 μμf; filament to plate, 4 μμf; and plate to grid, 12 μμf. Compute the capacitance that would be measured externally between the grid and the plate terminals.

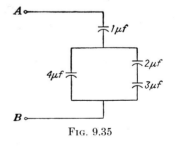

Fig. 9.35

9.32. With the grid and plate terminals connected together, the capacitance between a filament terminal and the grid terminal of a certain triode was measured as 10 μμf. With a filament terminal and the grid terminal connected together, the capacitance between the grid terminal and the plate terminal was measured as 14 μμf. With a filament terminal and the plate terminal connected together, the capacitance between the grid terminal and the plate terminal was measured as 16 μμf. Compute the capacitance between each pair of electrodes.

9.33. Six 5-μf capacitors are connected as the lamps are in Fig. 2.17.   What are the switch settings for minimum capacitance and what is the minimum capacitance?

A d-c source of 120 v is available.   Explain how to manipulate the switches so that each capacitor can be charged to 120 v with a total of 720 v across the group.   During the charging process how many coulombs are taken from the source?   If the capacitors are discharged after being connected for an initial voltage of 720 v, how many coulombs pass through the discharge circuit?   Explain why the number of coulombs delivered during discharge is not equal to the number acquired during the charging period.

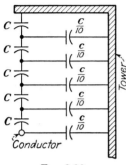

FIG. 9.36

9.34. A 0.2- and a 0.4-μf capacitor are in parallel. This combination is in series with a 1.4-μf capacitor across 200-v direct current.   Compute the charge on and the voltage across each capacitor.

9.35. In Fig. 9.36 there is an equivalent circuit for a string of five suspension insulators.   The capacitances between adjacent metal portions are represented by C-μf capacitors.   The capacitances between the metal portions and the tower are represented by 0.1C-μf capacitors.   At a certain instant the voltage between the conductor and the tower is 100,000 v.   Compute the voltage across each insulator.   (Compare this problem with Prob. 3.39.)

9.36. A d-c voltage of 200 v is suddenly applied to a 500-ohm resistor and a 4-μf capacitor in series.

a. Compute the initial current.

b. Compute the steady-state current.

c. Compute the charge in coulombs on the capacitor when the current is 100 ma.

9.37. A 0.1-μf capacitor that is initially charged to 400 v is connected to a 100-v d-c source in series with a 2,000-ohm resistor.   Compute the two possible values of the initial current.   Derive the equation of the capacitor voltage-time curve for each case.

9.38. In Fig. 9.37 the 5-μf capacitor has an initial charge of 300 v with the upper terminal negative.   The 10-μf capacitor has an initial charge of 160 v with the upper terminal positive. After the switch is closed, at the instant when the current is 100 ma what is the voltage across each capacitor?   What is the steady-state voltage across each capacitor?

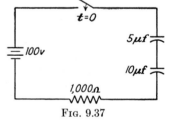

FIG. 9.37

9.39. Draw a series circuit containing resistance and capacitance in which the initial current is 2 ma and 4 sec are required for the current to decrease to 0.74 ma.

a. If the capacitance of the above circuit were doubled, in what time would the current decrease to 0.74 ma?

b. If the resistance of the original circuit were doubled, in what time would the current decrease to 0.37 ma?

9.40. The National Electric Code specifies that a capacitor with a voltage rating of 600 v or less, used for power factor correction, shall be equipped with a discharge resistor that will reduce the capacitor voltage to 50 v or less within 1 min after it is disconnected from a voltage source.   Compute the resistance required with a 4-μf capacitor used in a circuit whose voltage is sinusoidal with an rms value of 460 v.

With the maximum permissible resistance, compute the power loss in the resistor during normal operation of the circuit.

9.41. A 100-μf capacitor that has an insulation resistance of 2 megohms is in series with a 150-v voltmeter that has a resistance of 1,000 ohms per v. Compute the voltmeter reading 20 sec after 120-v direct current is applied to the series combination.

9.42. A certain automobile that has a capacitance to ground of 500 μμf is charged at $t = 0$ with 12,000 v to ground. One-half hour later the voltage is 10,000 v.

a. Compute the insulation resistance to ground.

b. A person whose resistance is 15,000 ohms from fingers to ground touches the automobile when the voltage to ground is 12,000 v. What momentary current is produced in the person? How much time is required for the current to decrease to 20 per cent of the initial value?

9.43. Draw two circuits, one containing no inductance and the other no capacitance, in which the current in a 5-ohm resistor is caused to vary according to the equation $i = 4\epsilon^{-2,000t}$ amp, where ϵ is the natural logarithm base and t is in seconds.

9.44. A d-c voltage of 250 v is suddenly applied to a 5,000-ohm resistor in series with a 0.05-μf capacitor. During the time the capacitor is charging, determine the maximum power delivered to the resistor and the maximum power delivered by the voltage source.

9.45. A d-c voltage of 400 v is suddenly applied to a 500-ohm resistor in series with a 20-μf capacitor. At the instant when the current is 0.3 amp, how many coulombs are stored on the capacitor, how much energy is stored in the electric field, and how much power is being delivered to the electric field?

9.46. A d-c voltage of 200 v is suddenly applied to a 1,000-ohm resistor in series with a 0.2-μf capacitor.

a. Compute the initial current, the initial rate of change of the capacitor voltage, and the initial rate of change of the current.

b. When the current is 40 ma, how much power is being delivered to the capacitor and how much energy is stored in the capacitor?

9.47. To what voltage is a 0.01-μf capacitor charged if the energy stored is equal to that in a 100-μf capacitor that is charged to 10 v? Which capacitor would be more hazardous to touch?

9.48. A certain lamp is flashed by the discharge of a 4-μf capacitor that is charged to 2,000 v. Compute the energy initially stored in the capacitor. If the capacitor is discharged in 25 μsec, compute the average power delivered.

9.49. In a certain nonlinear resistor the current varies as the square of the voltage and is 10 ma when the voltage is 200 v. At $t = 0$ the resistor is connected to a 2-μf capacitor that is charged to 200 v. Determine the initial rate of change of the resistor voltage, the equation of the resistor voltage as a function of time, and the time at which the capacitor voltage is 100 v.

9.50. A certain capacitor welding installation has 2,640 μf capacitance. The capacitors are charged at a uniform rate to 3,000 v in 1.5 sec. Compute the charging current. When the capacitors are charged to 3,000 v, how much energy and how many coulombs are stored in them?

9.51. In Fig. 9.38, compute the initial and the final values of each current. At the instant when the current in the 1,000-

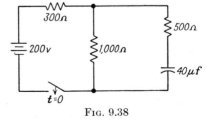

Fig. 9.38

ohm resistor is 110 ma, how much power is being delivered to the electric field of the capacitor and how much energy is stored in the field?

9.52. In Fig. 9.38, derive the equations that express the time variations of the currents after the switch is closed.

9.53. A 4-μf capacitor is to be charged from a 120-v d-c source.

a. The circuit resistance is 2,000 ohms. Determine the final energy stored in the capacitor and the energy loss in the resistance during the charging process.

b. Solve (*a*) if the circuit resistance is 2 ohms.

9.54. Compute the initial and the steady-state values of all the currents and the steady-state capacitor voltage in Fig. 9.39.

9.55. Derive the current-time equations for Fig. 9.39.

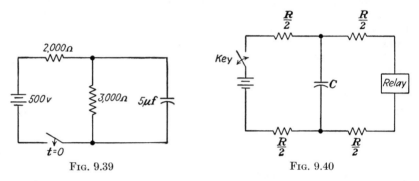

FIG. 9.39   FIG. 9.40

9.56. In a long teletypewriter system the capacitance between wires is represented sometimes by that of a capacitor at the center of the system. In Fig. 9.40 each line has R ohms resistance and the capacitor has C f capacitance. A signal is sent by closing the key at the sending end for a specified time and then opening it. As current builds up in the relay at the receiving end, the signal is registered. Assume that the battery and the relay resistance are negligible compared with the line resistances.

a. Derive the equation of the relay current after the key is closed.

b. Assume that the key is kept closed long enough for the relay current to become constant. Derive the equation of the relay current after the key is opened.

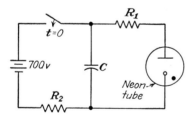

FIG. 9.41   Circuit of a neon-tube oscillator.

c. Sketch the current-time curves for *a* and *b.* Why does the relay current decay more slowly than it grows?

9.57. A neon-tube oscillator circuit is in Fig. 9.41. The tube does not conduct until the voltage across it reaches 500 v. Then the neon suddenly ionizes and the tube becomes conducting with a voltage drop that will be assumed constant at 150 v at any current greater than 1.5 ma. When the switch is first closed, the capacitor acts as a short circuit and the tube as an open circuit. The capacitor charges until the tube voltage reaches 500 v. Then the tube begins to conduct and the capacitor to discharge. This continues until the tube current has decreased to 1.5 ma, when the tube again ceases to conduct. The capacitor again starts to charge and the cycle is repeated. Determine the equations of and sketch the curve showing the time variations of the battery current if $R_1 = 50,000$ ohms, $R_2 = 800,000$ ohms, and $C = 0.06$ μf. Determine the frequency of the oscillation of the battery current.

9.58. At $t = 0$, 120-v direct current is applied to a 40-μf capacitor in series with a 150,000-ohm 150-v voltmeter. If the capacitor leakage resistance is infinite, compute the voltmeter reading at $t = 5$ sec.

If the capacitor leakage resistance is 2 megohms, compute the voltmeter reading at $t = 5$ sec.

9.59. A 150,000-ohm 150-v voltmeter was connected in parallel with a capacitor across 120-v direct current. The voltmeter read 80 v 4 sec after the voltage source was disconnected.

a. If the capacitor leakage resistance was infinite, what was its capacitance?

b. If the capacitor leakage resistance was 0.8 megohm, what was its capacitance?

9.60. When a 150,000-ohm voltmeter was connected in series with a capacitor across 120-v direct current, the steady-state reading was 5 v. Compute the capacitor leakage resistance.

9.61. In Fig. 9.42 the 20-μf capacitor is charged initially to 200 v and the 5-μf capacitor to 125 v. The upper plate of each is initially positive.

a. Compute the total energy stored initially in the capacitors.

b. Derive the equation of the current after the switch is closed.

c. Compute the steady-state voltage across each capacitor.

d. Compute the total energy stored in the capacitors in the steady state.

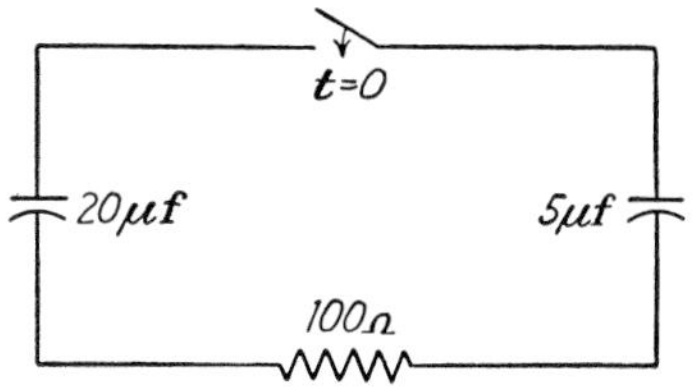

FIG. 9.42

e. Compute the energy converted into heat during the transient period.

9.62. Solve Prob. 9.61 if the initial polarity of one capacitor is reversed.

9.63. In a certain 0.5-μf parallel-plate capacitor the plates are separated 0.1 in. in air. If the capacitor is charged to 5 kv, compute the electric pull on the plates.

9.64. The electric pull between two capacitor plates is 2.5 mnewtons with 10,000 v applied. If the plate area is halved and the voltage doubled, what will be the pull?

9.65. The electric pull between two capacitor plates in air is 4 mnewton with 5 kv applied. If a material with a dielectric constant of 3 is introduced between the plates, what will be the pull?

9.66. The parallel plates are 0.2 in. apart in air in a capacitor that is charged to 12 kv. With no loss of charge the plates are moved until they are 0.25 in. apart. Compute the final value of voltage between the plates. Compare the final with the initial value of stored energy.

9.67. A 0.04- and a 0.06-μf capacitor are in series across 220-v direct current. A capacitor voltmeter is connected across the larger capacitor. Assume that its capacitance is constant at 100 $\mu\mu$f.

a. If the capacitors have infinite leakage resistance, compute the voltmeter reading.

b. If the respective leakage resistances are 5 and 15 megohms, compute the voltmeter reading.

9.68. Compute the capacitance per mile of a single conductor cable that consists of a No. 8 conductor surrounded by an 80-mil thickness of paper plus a lead sheath. The dielectric constant of the paper is 2.5.

9.69. Dielectric A of a certain parallel-plate capacitor is 4 mils thick and has a dielectric constant of 6. Dielectric B is 2 mils thick and has a dielectric constant of 2.5. What capacitor voltage will produce a voltage gradient of 50 v per mil in dielectric A?

9.70 Two parallel plates, each 100 sq in. on one side, are separated 0.75 in. in air.

Compute the approximate capacitance between the plates. What voltage will produce a voltage gradient of 50 kv per in. in the air between the plates?

9.71. One dielectric in a certain parallel-plate capacitor is paper that is 0.2 in. thick and has a dielectric constant of 2.5. The other dielectric is varnished cloth that is 0.3 in. thick and has a dielectric constant of 4. With 120 kv applied to the capacitor, compute the voltage gradient in each dielectric.

9.72. In the capacitor of Prob. 9.71 the dielectric strength of the paper is 12 kv per mm and that of the cloth is 30 kv per mm. What voltage applied to the capacitor will cause breakdown?

9.73. A certain sample of mica 4 mils thick broke down at 6 kv. Compute the dielectric strength.

9.74. A certain sample of impregnated cloth has a dielectric strength of 1.2 kv per mil. What thickness of cloth should be used for operation at 7.2 kv, allowing a safety factor of 2?

9.75. With 1.2 kv applied between the conductor and the sheath of the cable of Prob. 9.68, compute the maximum voltage gradient in the insulation.

9.76. A single conductor cable is to be operated with 2 kv between the conductor and the sheath whose inner diameter is 0.8 in. Compute the conductor diameter for which the voltage gradient is a minimum in the insulation at the conductor surface. Compute the minimum gradient.

9.77. A certain cable has a conductor 0.25 in. in diameter that is surrounded by impregnated paper that has a dielectric constant of 2 and is 0.1 in. thick. Outside the paper is a layer of rubber that has a dielectric constant of 3.5 and is 0.2 in. thick. Outside the rubber is a lead sheath. Compute the maximum voltage gradient in each dielectric when 25 kv are applied between the conductor and the sheath.

9.78. Compute the capacitance per mile for the cable of Prob. 9.77.

9.79. Between points A and B a 10-μf capacitor and a 1-megohm resistor are in parallel. Between B and C a second 10-μf capacitor and 1-megohm resistor are in parallel. Between A and C is a third 10-μf capacitor. The circuit is in a steady state with 450-v direct current applied between A and C. At $t = 0$, the voltage source is disconnected. Derive the equations of the capacitor voltages as the capacitors discharge. Sketch the voltage-time curves.

9.80. Solve Prob. 9.79 if the capacitor between A and B is initially charged to 450-v direct current with A positive, that between B and C is initially charged to 225-v direct current with C positive, and that between A and C is initially charged to 225-v direct current with A positive.

CHAPTER 10

MAGNETIC FIELDS

10.1. Magnetic Relations near an Isolated Conductor. In Fig. 10.1 is represented a straight cylindrical conductor of length l m that is carrying I amp. It is assumed that the conductor is isolated in air and that the magnetic effects of the current in the remainder of the circuit of which the conductor is a part may be neglected. Consider the point P which is at a radial distance of r m from the center of the conductor. The magnitude of the magnetic potential gradient $\mathbf{H}$ at a point in air near a conductor l m long and carrying I amp may be expressed as

$$H = \frac{Il}{4\pi b^2} \quad \text{amp-turns per m} \quad (10.1)$$

if all parts of the conductor are b m from the point, if all parts of the conductor and the point are in the same plane, and if the conductor diameter is small compared with b. $\mathbf{H}$ is a vector normal to the plane. Its direction can be determined by a right-hand rule: Grasp the conductor in the right hand with the extended thumb pointing in the direction of the current; then the fingers coil with the direction of the flux (and the magnetic potential gradient). Equation (10.1) is the mathematical expression of Ampère's law.

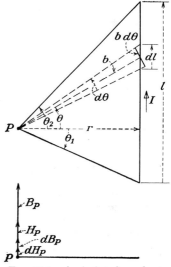

Fig. 10.1 An isolated conductor of length l carrying I amp. The magnetic effects at the point P are represented by the magnetic potential gradient $\mathbf{H}_P$ and the flux density $\mathbf{B}_P$. $\mathbf{H}_P$ and $\mathbf{B}_P$ are collinear and perpendicular to the plane containing the point and the conductor. The current in the infinitesimal length dl of the conductor produces the gradient $\mathbf{dH}_P$ and the density $\mathbf{dB}_P$.

In Fig. 10.1 all parts of the conductor are not equidistant from P; hence (10.1) may not be applied directly. Consider an infinitesimal section of the conductor that is dl m long with its center a distance b from P. The section is intercepted by the boundary lines of the infinitesimal angle $d\theta$ radian extending from P. If it is assumed that the infinitesimal gradient $\mathbf{dH}_P$ at P produced by I in the length dl is equal to what it would be if an equal current followed the arc of length $b\,d\theta$, then

$$dH_P = \frac{Ib\,d\theta}{4\pi b^2} = \frac{I\,d\theta}{4\pi b} \qquad \text{amp-turns per m}$$

As shown in Fig. 10.1 this gradient is normal to the plane containing P and the conductor and is collinear with the infinitesimal flux density $\mathbf{dB}$.

The total magnetic potential gradient at P in Fig. 10.1 can be computed by adding the component gradients produced by all the sections of the conductor. The addition should be vectorial, but in this case it happens to be numerical also since all the component gradients are collinear. Here the addition is performed by integration and is

$$H_P = \int_{\theta_1}^{\theta_2} dH_P = \int_{\theta_1}^{\theta_2} \frac{I\,d\theta}{4\pi b} \qquad \text{amp-turns per m}$$

where θ_1 and θ_2 are angles measured as in Fig. 10.1.   From the geometry of the figure, $b = r/\cos\theta$; hence

$$H_P = \int_{\theta_1}^{\theta_2} \frac{I\cos\theta\,d\theta}{4\pi r} = \frac{I}{4\pi r}[\sin\theta]_{\theta_1}^{\theta_2} = \frac{I}{4\pi r}(\sin\theta_2 - \sin\theta_1)$$

$$\text{amp-turns per m}$$

Since $B_P = 4\pi \times 10^{-7}H$ in air, then

$$B_P = \frac{I \times 10^{-7}}{r}(\sin\theta_2 - \sin\theta_1) \qquad \text{wb per sq m}$$

For the special case where in Fig. 10.1 the conductor is of infinite length, $\theta_2 = \pi/2$, $\sin\theta_2 = 1$, $\theta_1 = -\pi/2$, $\sin\theta_1 = -1$, $H_P = I/2\pi r$ amp-turns per m, and $B_P = (2I/r) \times 10^{-7}$ wb per sq m.

For the special case where in Fig. 10.1 P is located opposite the center of the given conductor, $\theta_2 = -\theta_1$, $\sin\theta_2 = l/2\sqrt{r^2 + (l/2)^2}$,

$$H_P = \frac{Il}{4\pi r\sqrt{r^2 + (l/2)^2}} \qquad \text{amp-turns per m}$$

and $B_P = Il \times 10^{-7}/r\sqrt{r^2 + (l/2)^2}$ wb per sq m.

If l is greater than $20r$, the expression $\sqrt{r^2 + (l/2)^2}$ may be replaced by $l/2$ with an error of $\frac{1}{2}$ per cent or less. With this substitution

$$H_P = \frac{I}{2\pi r} \qquad \text{amp-turns per m} \qquad (10.2)$$

which is equal to that for an infinitely long conductor. Hence a straight current-carrying conductor need not be very long in order that the magnetic relations near it will be almost the same as they would be if the conductor were infinitely long.

The relations just derived are based on the assumption that the conductor diameter is negligibly small compared with other dimensions involved. The expressions yield reasonably accurate results if the conductor diameter is small compared with the distance of the point P from

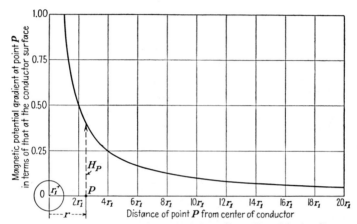

FIG. 10.2 Variation of the magnetic potential gradient $\mathbf{H}_P$ with the distance r from the center of a long, isolated current-carrying conductor of radius r_1.

the center of the conductor, or if the conductor is very long compared with the distance of the point P from the center of the conductor.

The manner in which the magnetic potential gradient at a point near a long current-carrying conductor varies with the distance of the point from the center of the conductor is shown graphically in Fig. 10.2. The curve was plotted from (10.2) by assigning values to r in terms of r_1, the conductor radius. At the conductor surface $r = r_1$ and the gradient is $I/2\pi r_1$. At $r = 2r_1$ the gradient is $I/4\pi r_1$, which is 0.5 that at the surface, and so on. The gradient decreases along a hyperbolic curve as r increases.

In Fig. 10.3 there is represented the cross section of a long, straight conductor that is carrying I amp into the page. A path of radius r m about the conductor is shown. If r is small compared with the conductor length, the gradient H_P at a point P in the path is $I/2\pi r$ amp-turns per m. The gradient is uniform along the path; thus the reluctance drop over the entire path is the gradient times the length of the path. But the length of the path is $2\pi r$, so that the reluctance drop is $(I/2\pi r) \times 2\pi r = I$ amp-turns. Hence along a closed circular path concentric with a long, circular isolated conductor the reluctance drop in ampere-turns is equal to the current in amperes in the conductor.

In an electric circuit the difference of electric potential between two points is independent of the path followed in going from one point to the other. In a magnetic field the difference of magnetic potential between two points is not necessarily the same by one path as it is by another. Consider points a and b in Fig. 10.3 that are separated $\pi r/2$ m, or one-fourth the circumference of the circle shown. Travel from a to b clockwise along the circle is in the direction of the magnetic potential gradient; therefore a is at a higher magnetic potential than b by

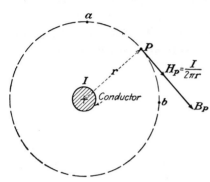

FIG. 10.3   Magnetic relations in air near a long, straight conductor. At any point P in the path of radius r about the conductor the magnetic gradient $\mathbf{H}_P$ is tangent to the path at the point.

$$\frac{I}{2\pi r} \times \frac{\pi r}{2} = \frac{I}{4} \qquad \text{amp-turns}$$

The distance from a to b counterclockwise along the circle is $3\pi r/2$ m. Travel from a to b along that path is against the direction of the magnetic potential gradient so that b is at a higher magnetic potential than a. The reluctance drop along the path is negative and is

$$-\frac{I}{2\pi r} \times \frac{3\pi r}{2} = -\frac{3I}{4} \qquad \text{amp-turns}$$

while between the same points by the other path it was $+I/4$ amp-turns. The two values differ by $I/4 - (-3I/4) = I$ amp-turns, the mmf produced by the current.

Besides the two values just computed for the magnetic potential from a to b in Fig. 10.3, there are an infinite number of other values, each differing from one of these by an integer times I amp-turns.

The preceding computations of the reluctance drop between a and b in Fig. 10.3 were made following paths in which the magnetic potential gradient was constant and directed along the path. Now the drop will be computed along the straight line between the points as shown in Fig. 10.4. At the point P, $H = I/2\pi r$ amp-turns per m. The reluctance drop along a length dl is equal to dl times the component of $\mathbf{H}$ collinear with it. Here the component is $H \cos \alpha$; thus the infinitesimal reluctance drop over dl is $H \cos \alpha \, dl$. The total reluctance drop from a to b is reluctance drop $a - b = \int_0^l H \cos \alpha \, dl$. As may be seen in Fig. 10.4, $\cos \alpha \, dl = -r \, d\theta$. When the point P is at a, $\theta = \pi/2$, and when it is at b, $\theta = 0$. Then

Reluctance drop $a - b = \int_{\pi/2}^{0} \frac{I}{2\pi r} (-r\, d\theta)$

$$= -\frac{I}{2\pi} \int_{\pi/2}^{0} d\theta = -\frac{I}{2\pi} [\theta]_{\pi/2}^{0} = \frac{I}{4} \qquad \text{amp-turns}$$

This is the same value for the magnetic potential between a and b as was obtained along the quadrant of radius r_1 between the points.

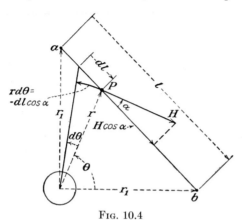

FIG. 10.4

According to (10.2) the magnetic potential gradient and hence the flux density at a point outside a long, straight, isolated conductor vary inversely as the distance from the center of the conductor. The expression for the flux Φ between the conductor surface and a concentric cylindrical surface with radius r_2 will be derived from Fig. 10.5. Since the flux density varies throughout this region, consider a thin tube of air with inner radius r m, thickness dr m, and length l m. The flux enclosed in this tube is designated as $d\phi$ wb. The area dA normal to the flux is that of a rectangle with dr as one side and l as the other, or $dA = l\, dr$ sq m. The flux density B over this area is $B = 2I \times 10^{-7}/r$ wb per sq m. Then $d\phi = B\, dA = 2Il \times 10^{-7}\, dr/r$, from which

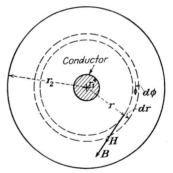

FIG. 10.5 Long isolated conductor in air surrounded by an imaginary surface of radius r_2. The flux enclosed between the conductor and the surface is to be computed.

$$\Phi = 2Il \times 10^{-7} \int_{r_1}^{r_2} \frac{dr}{r} = 2Il \times 10^{-7} [\ln r]_{r_1}^{r_2}$$

$$= 2Il \times 10^{-7} \ln \frac{r_2}{r_1} \qquad \text{wb}$$

10.2. Magnetic Relations near a Long, Rectangular Conductor. For a circular, isolated, current-carrying conductor it can be seen by symmetry that the flux lines about it are circles concentric with the conductor. For a rectangular conductor, the flux lines about it will not all have the same shape and none will be rectangles. Near the conductor the lines will follow somewhat, but not exactly, the outline of the conductor. At a considerable distance from the conductor the lines will be nearly circular. In Fig. 10.6 is represented a long, thin rectangular conductor of width $2a$ m and thickness b m. I amp is assumed to be distributed uniformly

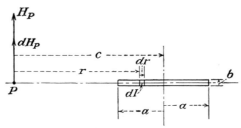

Fig. 10.6   A thin rectangular conductor that is carrying a uniformly distributed current I away from the observer.   The magnetic gradient $\mathbf{H}_P$ at the point P is to be computed.

over the cross section of the conductor. The magnetic potential gradient at a point P, which is in the plane of the conductor and c m from the conductor center, is to be computed. Consider a small element of the conductor of thickness b and width dr m that is a distance r m from P. The current dI in this element is to the total current I as the area $b\,dr$ of the element is to the area $2ab$ of the conductor; hence $dI/I = b\,dr/2ab$, from which $dI = I\,dr/2a$.

If the conductor is long compared with r, from (10.2) the gradient dH_P produced at P by the current dI is

$$dH_P = \frac{dI}{2\pi r} = \frac{I\,dr/2a}{2\pi r} = \frac{I\,dr}{4\pi ra} \tag{10.3}$$

The total gradient H_P at P may be obtained by integrating (10.3) from $r = c - a$ to $r = c + a$.   Hence

$$H_P = \frac{I}{4\pi a} \int_{c-a}^{c+a} \frac{dr}{r} = \frac{I}{4\pi a} \left[\ln r\right]_{c-a}^{c+a}$$

or
$$H_P = \frac{I}{4\pi a} \ln \frac{c + a}{c - a} \qquad \text{amp-turns per m} \tag{10.4}$$

Example 1.   For the conductor of Fig. 10.6 when $c = 5a$, compare the gradient at P as computed by (10.4) with that which would be produced by an equal current in a circular conductor whose center is c m from P.

Solution. By (10.4),

$$H_P = \frac{I}{4\pi(c/5)} \ln \frac{5a + a}{5a - a} = \frac{5I}{4\pi c} \ln \frac{6}{4} = \frac{5I}{4\pi c} \times 0.4055 = \frac{1.014I}{2\pi c} \text{ amp-turns per m}$$

If I were in a circular conductor whose center is c m from P, the gradient at P from (10.2) is $H_P = I/(2\pi c)$ amp-turns per m, a value that is only 1.4 per cent less than the more accurate one.

Example 2. Derive the expression for the magnetic potential gradient at a point that is near to and on the center line of a rectangular current-carrying conductor whose thickness is not small compared with the width.

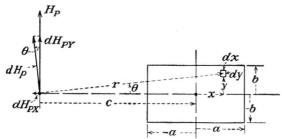

FIG. 10.7　A rectangular conductor that is carrying a uniformly distributed current I away from the observer. The magnetic gradient $\mathbf{H}_P$ is to be computed.

Solution. In Fig. 10.7 an element of the conductor with sides dx and dy m is carrying a current dI amp into the page. Assuming that the total current I is distributed uniformly over the conductor area, then $dI/I = dx\, dy/4ab$ from which $dI = I\, dx\, dy/4ab$.

The gradient $\mathbf{dH}_P$ produced at P by dI is directed at an angle θ with the vertical and may be resolved into the components $\mathbf{dH}_{PX}$ and $\mathbf{dH}_{PY}$. With P on the center line of the conductor, for every element above the center line producing a component gradient along the horizontal there is an element below the center line producing an equal, but oppositely directed, component gradient. As a result, the gradient $\mathbf{H}_P$, which is the resultant produced by all the current elements, will have no horizontal component. From (10.2), $dH_P = dI/2\pi r$. As may be seen in Fig. 10.7, $dH_{PY} = dH_P \cos\theta$, from which

$$dH_{PY} = \frac{dI}{2\pi r} \cos\theta$$

But $\cos\theta = (c + x)/r$ and $dI = I\, dx\, dy/4ab$; hence

$$dH_{PY} = \frac{c + x}{8\pi abr^2} I\, dx\, dy$$

Since $r^2 = (c + x)^2 + y^2$, then

$$dH_{PY} = \frac{(c + x)I\, dx\, dy}{8\pi ab[(c + x)^2 + y^2]}$$

The value of $H_P = H_{PY}$ may be obtained from this by double integration with the limits on x being $x = -a$ and $x = a$, while those on y are $y = -b$ and $y = b$. Hence

$$H_P = \frac{I}{8\pi ab} \int_{-b}^{b} \int_{-a}^{a} \frac{c + x}{(c + x)^2 + y^2} \, dx \, dy$$

The first integration is performed in terms of x with y and dy treated as constants. If both numerator and denominator are multiplied by 2, then

$$H_P = \frac{I}{16\pi ab} \int_{-b}^{b} \int_{-a}^{a} \frac{2(c + x)}{(c + x)^2 + y^2} \, dx \, dy$$

Now $2(c + x) \, dx$ is the differential of the term $(c + x)^2 + y^2$, with y treated as a constant; thus the above expression is in the form of the differential of a quantity over the quantity. This form integrates into the logarithm of the quantity; therefore

$$H_P = \frac{I}{16\pi ab} \int_{-b}^{b} \Big[\ln [(c + x)^2 + y^2] \Big]_{-a}^{a} \, dy$$

or $\quad H_P = \dfrac{I}{16\pi ab} \displaystyle\int_{-b}^{b} \Big[\ln [(c + a)^2 + y^2] - \ln [(c - a)^2 + y^2] \Big] \, dy \quad (10.5)$

In integrating this, y is the variable. The expression is not of a form listed in most integral tables. It can be integrated by use of the familiar relation

$$\int u \, dv = uv - \int v \, du$$

To integrate the term $\ln [(c + a)^2 + y^2] \, dy$, let $u = \ln [(c + a)^2 + y^2]$ and $dv = dy$. Then $du = 2y \, dy/[(c + a)^2 + y^2]$, $v = y$, and $uv = y \ln [(c + a)^2 + y^2]$. Then $\int v \, du = \int 2y^2 \, dy/[(c + a)^2 + y^2]$ which, as determined from a table of integrals, integrates into $2y - 2(c + a) \tan^{-1} [y/(c + a)]$. Combining results,

$$\int \ln [(c + a)^2 + y^2] \, dy = y \ln [(c + a)^2 + y^2] - 2y + 2(c + a) \tan^{-1} \frac{y}{c + a}$$
$$(10.6)$$

By similarity, the integral of the second term in (10.5) is

$$\int \ln [(c - a)^2 + y^2] \, dy = y \ln [(c - a)^2 + y^2] - 2y + 2(c - a) \tan^{-1} \frac{y}{c - a}$$
$$(10.7)$$

Combining (10.5), (10.6), and (10.7) yields

$$H_P = \frac{I}{16\pi ab} \Big[y \ln [(c + a)^2 + y^2] + 2(c + a) \tan^{-1} \frac{y}{c + a}$$
$$- y \ln [(c - a)^2 + y^2] - 2(c - a) \tan^{-1} \frac{y}{c - a} \Big]_{-b}^{b}$$

Substitution of the limits and a change of form yields

$$H_P = \frac{I}{8\pi ab} \Big[b \ln \frac{(c + a)^2 + b^2}{(c - a)^2 + b^2} + 2(c + a) \tan^{-1} \frac{b}{c + a} - 2(c - a) \tan^{-1} \frac{b}{c - a} \Big]$$
$$\text{amp-turns per m} \quad (10.8)$$

Example 3. A certain square conductor that is 0.2 in. on each side is carrying I amp uniformly distributed. Compute the magnetic potential gradient at the center of a side and compare with what it would be at the surface of a cylindrical conductor 0.2 in. in diameter carrying an equal current.

Solution. In (10.8), if all dimensions are in inches, the result will be in ampere-turns per inch. For the given square conductor, $a = b = 0.1$ in. and at the conductor surface $c = a$. Substitution of these values in (10.8) and simplification yields $H_P = 4.33I/\pi$ amp-turns per in. For the cylindrical conductor, from (10.2), $H_P = I/0.2\pi = 5I/\pi$ amp-turns per in.

Comparison of results shows that the gradient at the surface of the cylindrical conductor is $5/4.33 = 1.15$ times as great as at the center of the surface of the square conductor.

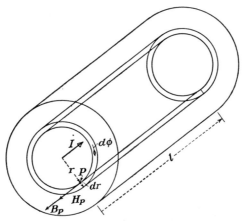

F<small>IG</small>. 10.8 Magnetic relations within a current-carrying conductor. A current I, directed away from the observer, is distributed uniformly over the cross section of the conductor. At the point P the magnetic gradient $\mathbf{H}_P$ is produced by the portion of the current enclosed by the circle of radius r.

10.3. Magnetic Relations within a Conductor.

In the circular conductor of Fig. 10.8, I amp, directed into the page, is assumed to be distributed uniformly over the cross section. The magnetic relations at a point P, which is r m from the center of the conductor, are to be computed. The flux line through P is a circle of radius r. The reluctance drop in ampere-turns along the complete circle is equal to the number of amperes encircled. The current I_r encircled is to the total current I as the area within the circle is to the area of the conductor. Hence $I_r/I = \pi r^2/\pi r_1^2$, from which $I_r = Ir^2/r_1^2$, where r_1 m is the conductor radius.

Since the reluctance drop of I_r amp-turns occurs in a length of $2\pi r$ m, the magnetic gradient H_P at P (or at any other point on the circle of radius r) is

$$H_P = \frac{\text{reluctance drop}}{\text{length}} = \frac{I_r}{2\pi r} = \frac{Ir}{2\pi r_1^2} \qquad \text{amp-turns per m} \qquad (10.9)$$

This shows that the magnetic gradient at a point within the conductor varies linearly from zero at the center where $r = 0$ to a maximum of $I/2\pi r_1$ at the surface where $r = r_1$.

The manner in which the magnetic potential gradient at a point varies as the point moves from the center of a conductor to the region without it is shown graphically in Fig. 10.9. The graph corresponds to (10.9) when the point is within the conductor and to (10.2) when the point is outside

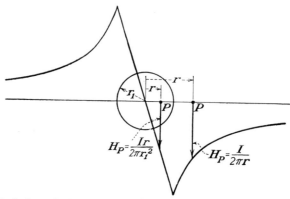

Fig. 10.9 Variation of the magnetic potential gradient along a horizontal line through the center of a circular current-carrying conductor. The conductor is carrying a current I uniformly distributed over the cross section and directed away from the observer. At any point on the line the gradient $\mathbf{H}_P$ is normal to the line. The magnitude of the gradient at a point on the line is represented by the vertical distance from the point to the curve.

the conductor. The gradient increases linearly as the point moves from the center of the conductor to its surface. Outside the surface it decreases along a hyperbola. Theoretically, the gradient becomes zero only at an infinite distance from the center. However, one cannot proceed very far from a conductor before the gradient is so small that its presence can be detected only with a sensitive measuring device.

The flux density B_P at a point P within the conductor of Fig. 10.8 is related to the gradient H_P at the point by the relation $B = 4\pi \times 10^{-7}\,\mu H$; hence

$$B = 2\mu I r / r_1^2 \times 10^{-7} \text{ wb per sq m} \tag{10.10}$$

Most conductors are made of nonmagnetic materials for which $\mu = 1$.

The flux within the conductor for a length l m in Fig. 10.8 will now be computed. Consider the infinitesimal element of volume included between the cylinder of radius r and that of radius $r + dr$. As indicated, the surface normal to the flux has one dimension dr and the other l. Call this area dA; then $dA = l\,dr$. The flux $d\phi$ through this area is $B\,dA$.

Then, using the value of B from (10.10),

$$d\phi = B\,dA = \frac{2\mu I r}{r_1^2} \times 10^{-7}(l\,dr) \qquad (10.11)$$

The total flux Φ within the conductor in the length l is obtained by integrating (10.11). Hence

$$\Phi = \frac{2Il \times 10^{-7}}{r_1^2} \int_0^{r_1} \mu r\,dr \qquad \text{wb}$$

This can be solved by formal integration if μ is a constant. For most conductors,

$$\mu = 1 \qquad \text{and} \qquad \Phi = Il \times 10^{-7} \text{ wb} \qquad (10.12)$$

This shows that the flux within a given length of circular nonmagnetic conductor is independent of the radius of the conductor and is proportional to the current. A 0.1-m section of a long copper conductor has within it one line of flux for each ampere carried.

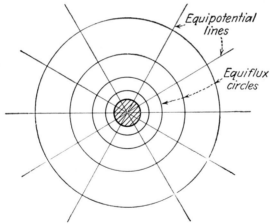

FIG. 10.10   Relative flux distribution within and about a long, circular, nonmagnetic current-carrying conductor. The flux between adjacent cylindrical surfaces is equal to that within the conductor. The radial lines are magnetic equi-potential lines.

In Fig. 10.10 are circles about a circular nonmagnetic current-carrying conductor whose radii are such that the flux between two cylinders, whose traces are represented by adjacent circles, is equal to the flux within the wire. According to (10.12) the flux within the wire is $Il \times 10^{-7}$ wb. The flux outside the wire between two cylindrical surfaces with the respective radii of r_1 and r_2 is $2Il \times 10^{-7} \ln (r_2/r_1)$ wb. Equating the two flux values yields $\ln(r_2/r_1) = 0.5$, from which $r_2/r_1 = 1.65$. Hence, if the radius of each circle in Fig. 10.10 is 1.65 times that of the next smaller circle, equal amounts of flux are included between adjacent cylinders.

In a magnetic field the equipotential surfaces are everywhere normal to the direction of the flux. In Fig. 10.10 the equipotential surfaces are planes through the conductor center. The traces of the planes in the page are equipotential lines, some of which are indicated.

10.4. Magnetic Relations near Parallel Current-carrying Conductors. In Fig. 10.11 are represented end views of two long, parallel, circular, isolated, nonmagnetic conductors carrying equal currents of I amp in

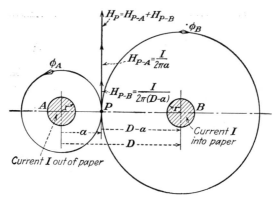

FIG. 10.11   Component and resultant magnetic gradients at a point P on the line through the centers of two long, parallel current-carrying conductors.

opposite directions. The magnetic potential gradient at a point P on the line through the centers of the conductors is to be computed. The relations derived previously for an isolated conductor may be used to compute the component gradient caused by the current in each conductor. The components may be combined vectorially to obtain the resultant gradient at a point. This procedure is not always correct because the current in each conductor may cause the current in the other to be distributed nonuniformly over the conductor cross section. The error is likely to be appreciable only if the conductors are very close together or if the current frequency is high.

In Fig. 10.11 are represented the flux line ϕ_A that would pass through P if the I amp in conductor A were acting alone and the flux line ϕ_B that would pass through the point if the current I amp in B were acting alone. The reluctance drop along the path of each flux line is equal to the amperes encircled, or I amp-turns along each. The length of flux line ϕ_A is $2\pi a$ m, where a m is the distance from the center of conductor A to P. The magnitude of the gradient $\mathbf{H}_{P-A}$ produced at P by the current in conductor A is $I/2\pi a$ amp-turns per m. $\mathbf{H}_{P-A}$ is normal to the line joining the conductor centers. The length of flux line ϕ_B is $2\pi(D - a)$, where D m is the distance from the center of conductor A to that of conductor B. The magnitude of the gradient $\mathbf{H}_{P-B}$ produced at P by the current in conductor B is $I/2\pi(D - a)$ amp-turns per m. $\mathbf{H}_{P-B}$ is also normal to the line joining the centers, and therefore collinear with $\mathbf{H}_{P-A}$. The resultant gradient $\mathbf{H}_P$ is their numerical sum and collinear with them. From the preceding $H_P = H_{P-A} + H_{P-B} = I/2\pi a + I/2\pi(D - a)$ amp-turns per m. This equation applies only for points outside the conductors on the line through their centers. Within conductor A, with

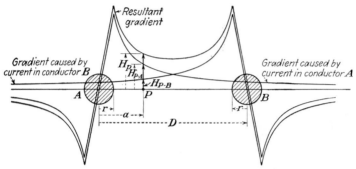

FIG. 10.12 Magnetic gradient at points along the line through the centers of two parallel current-carrying conductors. $\mathbf{H}_{P-A}$ is the component gradient at the point P produced by the current I in the conductor A coming toward the observer. $\mathbf{H}_{P-B}$ is the component gradient at P produced by the current I in conductor B going away from the observer. $\mathbf{H}_P$ is the resultant gradient at P. The component and the resultant gradient at any point on the line are collinear and normal to the line. The curves shown are correct only for a uniform distribution of the currents over the cross sections of the conductors.

uniform current density in it, according to (10.9) the magnitude of the gradient is $H_{P-A} = Ia/2\pi r^2$ amp-turns per m. The magnitude of the gradient $\mathbf{H}_P$ is

$$H_P = \frac{Ia}{2\pi r^2} + \frac{I}{2\pi(D - a)} \qquad \text{amp-turns per m}$$

In Fig. 10.12 are represented graphically the component and the resultant gradients as the point P moves along the line through the conductor centers. It is assumed that the conductors are nonmagnetic. In the region between the wires the component gradients add. The resultant gradient is greatest at the surface of a conductor. The resultant gradient is zero here a short distance from the center of each conductor. A reduction in the distance between conductor centers will shift the point of zero gradient farther away from the centers.

In the region on the line through the conductor centers and not within or between the conductors, the component gradients are oppositely directed. The resultant gradient is greatest at the conductor surface and decreases rapidly as the point moves away from a surface.

The total flux in a length of l m between two long, straight, parallel circular conductors isolated in air will be computed from Fig. 10.13. The conductors are each carrying I amp, uniformly distributed and in opposite directions. Each conductor has a radius of r m, and it is D m from

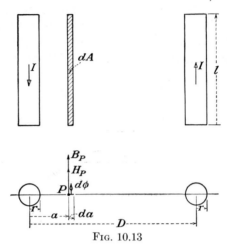

FIG. 10.13

one center to the other. The magnitude of the magnetic potential gradient $\mathbf{H}_P$ at a point P, on the line joining the conductor centers and a m to the right of the center of the left-hand conductor, is

$$H_P = \frac{I}{2\pi a} + \frac{I}{2\pi(D - a)} \qquad \text{amp-turns per m}$$

Since the flux density $B = 4\pi \times 10^{-7}H$ in air, then the magnitude of the flux density $\mathbf{B}_P$ at the point is $B_P = 2I \times 10^{-7}[1/a + 1/(D - a)]$ wb per sq m.

This density may be assumed to be constant over the infinitesimal area $dA = l\,da$. The infinitesimal flux $d\phi = B_P l\,da$, from which

$$d\phi = 2Il \times 10^{-7}\left(\frac{1}{a} + \frac{1}{D - a}\right)da \qquad \text{wb} \qquad (10.13)$$

The total flux Φ between the wires is obtained by integrating this from $a = r$ to $a = D - r$. Hence

$$\Phi = 2Il \times 10^{-7} \int_r^{D-r}\left[\frac{da}{a} + \frac{da}{D - a}\right] \qquad \text{wb}$$

from which $\Phi = 2Il \times 10^{-7}[\ln a - \ln (D - a)]_r^{D-r}$. Substitution of the limits and simplification yields

$$\Phi = 4Il \times 10^{-7} \ln \frac{D - r}{r} \qquad \text{wb} \qquad (10.14)$$

In many cases the radius r of the conductors is so small compared with the distance D from center to center that $D - r$ is nearly equal to D. In those cases (10.14) may be written as $\Phi = 4Il \times 10^{-7} \ln (D/r)$ wb.

At a point near two long current-carrying conductors, not on the line joining the centers, the component magnetic potential gradients may be computed in a manner similar to that used previously. However, the components are not collinear and must be added vectorially to obtain the resultant gradient. In Fig. 10.14 the gradient at a point P, a m from the

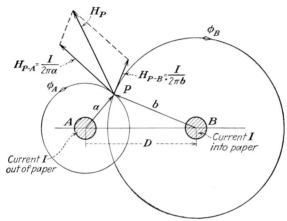

FIG. 10.14 Component and resultant gradients at a point P near two long, straight, current-carrying conductors. Each component gradient is normal to the line joining P and the center of the conductor carrying the current that produces the respective gradient.

center of conductor A and b m from the center of conductor B, is to be computed. The flux line ϕ_A that would be established by the current in A acting alone and the flux line ϕ_B that would be established by the current in B acting alone are indicated. The gradient $\mathbf{H}_{P-A}$, of magnitude $I/2\pi a$, is normal to the radius a, and the gradient $\mathbf{H}_{P-B}$, of magnitude $I/2\pi b$, is normal to the radius b. The resultant gradient $\mathbf{H}_P$ is less than the numerical sum of its components and is directed between them.

Example 1. Two circular conductors that are carrying equal currents of 200 amp in opposite directions are spaced 0.3 m apart center to center. Compute the magnetic gradient and the flux density at a point 0.15 m from the center of one conductor and 0.25 m from the center of the other.

Solution. As shown in Fig. 10.15, the magnitudes of the two component gradients are $H_A = 212$ amp-turns per m, and $H_B = 127$ amp-turns per m. From the geometry of the figure the angles α and β can be computed. Their functions are $\cos \alpha = 0.555$, $\sin \alpha = 0.832$, $\cos \beta = 0.867$, and $\sin \beta = 0.499$.

The vertical component of $\mathbf{H}$ is equal to the vertical component of $\mathbf{H}_A$ plus that of $\mathbf{H}_B$, or

$$H_{\text{vert}} = H_A \cos \alpha + H_B \cos \beta = 212 \times 0.555 + 127 \times 0.867$$
$$= 228 \text{ amp-turns per m}$$

The horizontal component of **H** is equal to the horizontal component of $\mathbf{H}_B$ less that of $\mathbf{H}_A$, or

$$H_{\text{hor}} = -H_A \sin \alpha + H_B \sin \beta = -212 \times 0.832 + 127 \times 0.499$$
$$= -113 \text{ amp-turns per m}$$

The magnitude of **H** is the square root of the sum of the squares of the vertical

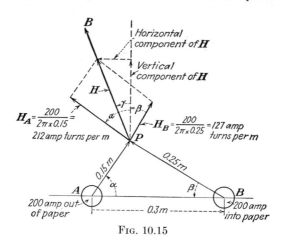

Fig. 10.15

and horizontal components, or $H = \sqrt{228^2 + (-113)^2} = 254$ amp-turns per m. Since $B = 4\pi \times 10^{-7}H$ in air, the flux density at P is

$$B = 4\pi \times 10^{-7} \times 254 = 3.2 \times 10^{-4} \text{ wb per sq m}$$

In Fig. 10.15, γ is an angle whose tangent is equal in magnitude to the horizontal component of **H** divided by the vertical component of **H**, or

$$\gamma = \tan^{-1} (^{113}\!/_{228}) = 26.4°$$

Then **B** and **H** are directed at an angle of 26.4° to the left of the vertical.

Consider two long, isolated, round, parallel circular conductors in a horizontal plane, the left-hand one carrying i_1 amp away from an observer and the other carrying i_2 amp toward him. Each conductor is in a magnetic field established by the current in the other conductor and each experiences a force that may be computed by the Bli rule. Consider the left-hand conductor. The flux line ϕ_2 passing downward through it is produced by i_2 in the right-hand conductor. Along ϕ_2 the total reluctance drop of i_2 amp-turns is distributed uniformly over a length $2\pi D$ m, where D is the distance from one conductor center to the other. The magnetic potential gradient at the center of the left-hand conductor is $H_2 = i_2/2\pi D$ amp-turns per m. In air $B = 4\pi \times 10^{-7}H$; hence the flux density at the center of the left-hand conductor is

$$B_2 = (4\pi \times 10^{-7}) \frac{i_2}{2\pi D} = \frac{2 \times 10^{-7} i_2}{D} \qquad \text{wb per sq m}$$

By the *Bli* rule the force acting on the left-hand conductor is

$$f_1 = \frac{2 \times 10^{-7} i_2}{D} (l) (i_1) = \frac{2 \times 10^{-7} i_1 i_2 l}{D} \qquad \text{newtons}$$

for a length l m of the conductors. Fleming's left-hand rule shows that f_1 is directed to the left.

Now consider the right-hand conductor. The flux line ϕ_1 passing through it is produced by the current i_1 in the left-hand conductor. The magnetic potential gradient at the center of the right-hand conductor is $H_1 = i_1/2\pi D$ amp-turns per m. The flux density at the center of the right-hand conductor is $B_1 = 2 \times 10^{-7} i_1/D$ wb per sq m. By the *Bli* rule the force acting on the right-hand conductor is

$$f_2 = \frac{2 \times 10^{-7} i_1 i_2 l}{D} \qquad \text{newtons}$$

Fleming's left-hand rule shows that the force is directed to the right.

Comparison of the preceding expressions shows that $f_1 = f_2$. Hence, parallel conductors carrying currents in opposite directions experience equal forces tending to separate them. The magnitude of the force is proportional to the product of the currents and to the length of the conductors, and is inversely proportional to the distance between conductor centers.

The expressions for f_1 and f_2 would be exact if a short section of two infinitely long conductors of infinitesimal cross section were being considered. The equations lead to this definition: An absolute ampere is that value of current which when flowing in each of two infinitely long, parallel, circular conductors of very small cross section separated 1 m in air causes each conductor to experience a force of 2×10^{-7} newton per meter length of conductor.

When two parallel conductors carry the outgoing and returning currents in a circuit, i_1 and i_2 are equal. The force exerted on each conductor is $f = ki^2$, where k is a proportionality factor. For conductors of finite length and diameter, k may differ considerably from $2 \times 10^{-7} l/D$.

Parallel conductors carrying currents in the same direction experience forces that tend to cause the conductors to move toward each other. In a mercury column this pinch effect causes a reduction in the cross section when current flows.

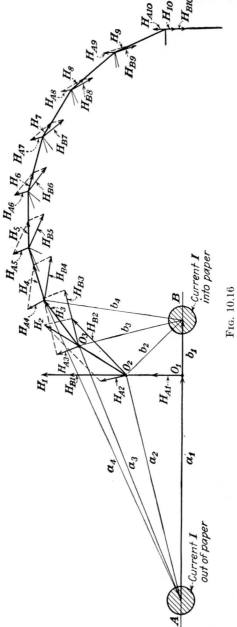

Fig. 10.16

10.5. Flux Lines about Parallel Current-carrying Conductors.

In Fig. 10.16 are represented two long, straight, parallel, circular, isolated non-magnetic conductors that are separated D m from center to center and carrying I amp in opposite directions. In Fig. 10.15 it was shown how the magnetic potential gradient at any point in space about the conductors could be determined. A flux line is the locus of the path followed by a point that moves in a magnetic field such that it is always traveling in, or opposite to, the direction of the gradient. This definition will be used to determine the approximate shape of the flux line through the point O_1, which is on the line joining the conductor centers and four times as far from the center of conductor A as from that of conductor B. The distance from the center of conductor A to O_1 is a_1 and the distance from O_1 to the center of conductor B_1 is b_1. The gradient $\mathbf{H}_{A1}$ at O_1 is that produced by the current in conductor A; $\mathbf{H}_{B1}$ is produced by the current in conductor B. Since the magnitude of the gradient produced at a point in space by the current in a circular conductor is inversely proportional to the distance of the point from the conductor center, H_{B1} is four times as great as H_{A1}. At O_1 the resultant gradient $\mathbf{H}_1$ is collinear with $\mathbf{H}_{A1}$ and $\mathbf{H}_{B1}$ in a vertical direction. Now move from O_1 along $\mathbf{H}_1$ an arbitrary distance to the point O_2. Next the lengths of a_2 and b_2 are measured and the new gradients $\mathbf{H}_{A2}$ and $\mathbf{H}_{B2}$ are drawn normal, respectively, to a_2 and b_2. The magnitude of $\mathbf{H}_{A2}$ is to that of $\mathbf{H}_{B2}$ as b_2 is to a_2. The resultant gradient $\mathbf{H}_2$ is the vector sum of $\mathbf{H}_{A2}$ and $\mathbf{H}_{B2}$ as shown. Now move from O_2 along $\mathbf{H}_2$ to O_3, where the distance from O_2 to O_3 equals that from O_1 to O_2. At O_3 the directions and magnitudes of the component and the resultant gradients are determined as before. The process is continued until the extension of the line joining the centers of the conductors is reached. If the construction had been started in a counterclockwise direction from O_1, it would have been symmetrical with that in Fig. 10.16. Hence a flux line through O_1 encircles conductor B and a crude representation of its shape has been obtained.

To obtain a closer approximation to the shape of the flux line through O_1, a second construction was made in which the distance traversed along a gradient was only one-half that in the previous construction. The result of this construction is shown as path b in Fig. 10.17, while that of the previous construction is redrawn as path a. The two paths have the same general form of a circle but they fail to coincide closely. This suggests that, although the second construction probably gives a more accurate picture of the flux line than did the first, even the second may be considerably in error. The flux line through O_1 as determined by an exact method is path c in Fig. 10.17.

The graphical method of determining flux lines used in Fig. 10.16 is a tedious process and the accuracy may be poor unless very small increments of distance along the various resultant gradients are used. The method has little practical value but the principles are useful in the exact method that will now be explained.

In Fig. 10.18 are represented two long, straight, parallel, circular, isolated nonmagnetic conductors that are carrying I amp in opposite

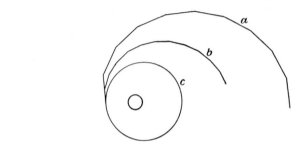

FIG. 10.17   Flux paths about two parallel current-carrying conductors.   (a) Path determined in Fig. 10.16.   (b) Path determined using an increment of distance one-half that used for (a).   (c) Path determined by an exact method.

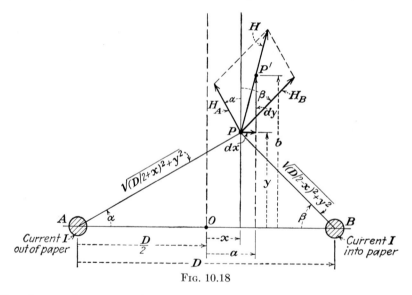

FIG. 10.18

directions and are spaced D m center to center. The point O midway between the centers is chosen as the origin of a coordinate system with the line joining the centers as one axis and the bisector of the line as the other axis. The form of a flux line through P', where P' is a distance a m to the right of and a distance b m above O, is to be determined. A second chosen point is P whose coordinates are x m and y m and which is on the flux line through P'. P' is a distance dx to the right of and a distance dy above P. The vertical component of $\mathbf{H}$, the magnetic potential gradient at P, is $H_A \cos \alpha + H_B \cos \beta$, where $\mathbf{H}_A$ and $\mathbf{H}_B$ are respective gradients produced at P by the currents in conductors A and B and α and β are angles as designated. Since $H_A = I/[2\pi \sqrt{(D/2 + x)^2 + y^2}]$, $\cos \alpha = (D/2 + x)/\sqrt{(D/2 + x)^2 + y^2}$, $H_B = I/[2\pi \sqrt{(D/2 - x)^2 + y^2}]$, and $\cos \beta = (D/2 - x)/\sqrt{(D/2 - x)^2 + y^2}$, then the magnitude of the vertical component of $\mathbf{H}$ is

$$H_{\text{vert}} = \frac{I}{2\pi} \left[\frac{D/2 + x}{(D/2 + x)^2 + y^2} + \frac{D/2 - x}{(D/2 - x)^2 + y^2} \right] \quad \text{amp-turns per m}$$

The magnitude of the horizontal component of $\mathbf{H}$ in Fig. 10.18 is $H_B \sin \beta - H_A \sin \alpha$. Since $\sin \beta = y/\sqrt{(D/2 - x)^2 + y^2}$ and $\sin \alpha = y/\sqrt{(D/2 + x)^2 + y^2}$, then the magnitude of the horizontal component of $\mathbf{H}$ is

$$H_{\text{hor}} = \frac{I}{2\pi} \left[\frac{y}{(D/2 - x)^2 + y^2} - \frac{y}{(D/2 + x)^2 + y^2} \right] \quad \text{amp-turns per m}$$

The tangent of the angle that $\mathbf{H}$ in Fig. 10.18 makes with the horizontal is dy/dx. It is also equal to the magnitude of the vertical component of $\mathbf{H}$ divided by that of the horizontal component. Equating the two values of the tangent of the angle yields $dy/dx = [(D/2)^2 - x^2 + y^2]/2xy$, which may be rearranged as

$$\frac{2xy\,dy - y^2\,dx}{x^2} = \left[\frac{(D/2)^2}{x^2} - 1 \right] dx$$

in which each side of the equality may be integrated. The result is $y^2/x = -(D/2)^2/x - x + k$ which may be arranged as

$$x^2 - kx + y^2 = -\left(\frac{D}{2} \right)^2 \quad (10.15)$$

where k is a constant of integration. Equation (10.15) is the general equation of a family of circles whose centers are on the x axis. The value of k for the circle through P' can be determined by substituting in (10.15) the values $x = a$ and $y = b$. By this process $k = [a^2 + b^2 + (D/2)^2]/a$, and the equation of the flux circle through P' is

$$x^2 - \frac{a^2 + b^2 + (D/2)^2}{a} x + y^2 = -\left(\frac{D}{2} \right)^2 \quad (10.16)$$

To write the equation so that the radius and the location of the center of the circle can be recognized readily, complete the square by adding the term $\{[a^2 + b^2 + (D/2)^2]/2a\}^2$ to each side of the equality in (10.16). The result may be written as

$$\left[x - \frac{a^2 + b^2 + (D/2)^2}{2a} \right]^2 + y^2 = \left[\frac{a^2 + b^2 + (D/2)^2}{2a} \right]^2 - \left(\frac{D}{2} \right)^2 \quad (10.17)$$

This is the equation of a circle whose center is on the x axis at

$$x = \frac{a^2 + b^2 + (D/2)^2}{2a}$$

and whose radius is $\sqrt{\left[\dfrac{a^2 + b^2 + (D/2)^2}{2a}\right]^2 - \left(\dfrac{D}{2}\right)^2}$.

From the above relations any number of flux circles about the conductors in Fig. 10.18 can be located, each corresponding to a set of values

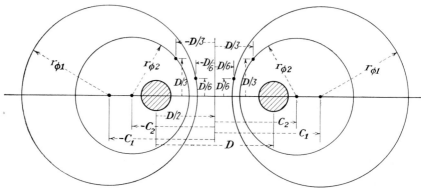

FIG. 10.19   Flux lines about two long, circular current-carrying conductors.

for a and b.   Let C be the distance from the point midway between the conductors to the center of a flux circle and r_ϕ be the radius of a flux circle. Then

$$C = \frac{a^2 + b^2 + (D/2)^2}{2a} \qquad \text{m} \qquad (10.18)$$

and

$$r_\phi = \sqrt{\left[\frac{a^2 + b^2 + (D/2)^2}{2a}\right]^2 - \left(\frac{D}{2}\right)^2} \qquad \text{m} \qquad (10.19)$$

From (10.18) it can be seen that with a given value of b the value of C has the same magnitude for a given positive value of a as it has for an equal negative value of a.   However, the sign of C reverses with the change of sign of a.   From (10.19) it can be seen that with a given value of b the value of r_ϕ has the same magnitude for a given positive value of a as it has for an equal negative value of a.   These results mean that for every flux circle linking conductor B in Fig. 10.18, there is a flux circle of equal radius located similarly with respect to conductor A.   In Fig. 10.19 are the flux circles through the points $a = D/6$, $b = D/6$; $a = -D/6$, $b = D/6$; $a = D/3$, $b = D/3$; and $a = -D/3$, $b = D/3$.   As determined by (10.18) and (10.19) the centers of the first pair of circles are at $C_1 = 0.92D$ and $C_1 = -0.92D$, and the radius of the circles is $r_{\phi 1} = 0.77D$.

The centers of the second pair of circles are at $C_2 = 0.71D$ and $C_2 = -0.71D$, and the radius of the circles is $r_{\phi 2} = 0.5D$.

If P' in Fig. 10.18 is on the perpendicular bisector of the line joining the conductor centers, $a = 0$. For this value of a, according to (10.18) and (10.19), for any value of b the center of the flux circle is at an infinite distance from O and the radius of the flux circle is infinite. Hence the bisector is a flux circle of infinite radius.

The flux circles of Fig. 10.19 are the traces in the plane of the paper of flux cylinders about the conductors. To provide information regarding

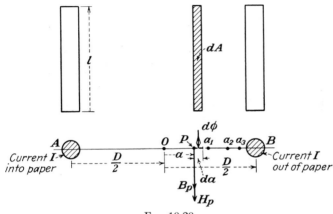

FIG. 10.20

the flux densities at various points near the conductors, a number of flux circles will be so located that equal amounts of flux will be included between the corresponding cylinders. Points of intersection of the flux circles on the line joining the conductor centers will be determined. These points are at respective distances of a_1, a_2, and a_3 m to the right of O in Fig. 10.20. Consider a point P at an arbitrary distance a to the right of O. The magnitude of the gradient $\mathbf{H}_p$ at P is

$$H_P = \frac{I}{2\pi(D/2 + a)} + \frac{I}{2\pi(D/2 - a)} \qquad \text{amp-turns per m}$$

Since, in air, $B = 4\pi \times 10^{-7}H$, then the flux density at P is

$$B_P = 2I \times 10^{-7}\left[\frac{1}{D/2 + a} + \frac{1}{D/2 - a}\right] \qquad \text{wb per sq m}$$

The area $dA = l\,da$ sq m. The flux through dA is

$$d\phi = B_P\,dA \qquad \text{or} \qquad d\phi = 2Il \times 10^{-7}\left(\frac{1}{D/2 + a} + \frac{1}{D/2 - a}\right) da \quad \text{wb}$$

$$(10.20)$$

The flux Φ_1 contained within the region between the flux cylinder through O and that through a_1 is obtained by integrating (10.20) from the limit 0 to the limit a_1. Hence

$$\Phi_1 = 2Il \times 10^{-7} \int_0^{a_1} \left(\frac{1}{D/2 + a} + \frac{1}{D/2 - a} \right) da$$

$$= 2Il \times 10^{-7} \left[\ln \left(\frac{D}{2} + a \right) - \ln \left(\frac{D}{2} - a \right) \right]_0^{a_1}$$

or
$$\Phi_1 = 2Il \times 10^{-7} \ln \frac{D/2 + a_1}{D/2 - a_1} \qquad \text{wb}$$

By analogy, the flux Φ_2 within the region from O to a_2 is

$$\Phi_2 = 2Il \times 10^{-7} \ln \frac{D/2 + a_2}{D/2 - a_2} \qquad \text{wb}$$

Since a_1, a_2, and a_3 are to be so located that equal amounts of flux are included between flux cylinders through adjacent points, then $\Phi_2 = 2\phi_1$, $\Phi_3 = 3\Phi_1$, etc. From $\Phi_2 = 2\Phi_1$,

$$\ln \frac{D/2 + a_2}{D/2 - a_2} = 2 \ln \frac{D/2 + a_1}{D/2 - a_1} \qquad (10.21)$$

which may be written as

$$\frac{D/2 + a_2}{D/2 - a_2} = \frac{(D/2 + a_1)^2}{(D/2 - a_1)^2}$$

From this
$$a_2 = \frac{D}{2} \frac{(D/2 + a_1)^2 - (D/2 - a_1)^2}{(D/2 + a_1)^2 + (D/2 - a_1)^2} \qquad (10.22)$$

From the relation $\Phi_3 = 3\Phi_1$ and substitutions similar to those just made

$$a_3 = \frac{D}{2} \frac{(D/2 + a_1)^3 - (D/2 - a_1)^3}{(D/2 + a_1)^3 + (D/2 - a_1)^3} \qquad (10.23)$$

By analogy it follows that

$$a_n = \frac{D}{2} \frac{(D/2 + a_1)^n - (D/2 - a_1)^n}{(D/2 + a_1)^n + (D/2 - a_1)^n} \qquad (10.24)$$

where a_n is a point so located that the flux Φ_n within the region between the flux cylinder through it and the one through O is n times Φ_1. Equation (10.24) is valid for values of a_n not greater than $D/2$ less the radius of the conductor.

To locate the points a_1, a_2, a_3, etc., where the flux circles cross the line joining the centers, a_1 was assigned arbitrarily a value of $0.2D/2$. Substitution of this value in (10.22) and (10.23) yields $a_2 = 0.385D/2$ and $a_3 = 0.543D/2$. Values of a_4, a_5, etc., were obtained from (10.24) by substituting in it the arbitrary value of a_1 and then assigning to n first a value of 4, next a value of 5, and so on. The results are tabulated in Table 10.1.

TABLE 10.1

n	a_n	$r_{\phi n}$	n	a_n	$r_{\phi n}$
1	$0.200D/2$	$2.400D/2$	6	$0.840D/2$	$0.175D/2$
2	$0.385D/2$	$1.105D/2$	7	$0.890D/2$	$0.117D/2$
3	$0.543D/2$	$0.648D/2$	8	$0.925D/2$	$0.078D/2$
4	$0.670D/2$	$0.411D/2$	9	$0.949D/2$	$0.052D/2$
5	$0.767D/2$	$0.268D/2$			

The radii of the various flux circles through the points a_1, a_2, etc., can be computed by (10.19). Since the points are on the line joining the conductor centers, $b = 0$ and the radius of a flux circle becomes

$$r_{\phi n} = \frac{(D/2)^2 - a_n^2}{2a_n} \tag{10.25}$$

where n is assigned the successive values of 1, 2, etc. Values of $r_{\phi n}$ computed from (10.25) are tabulated in Table 10.1. Flux circles drawn from values in the table are in Fig. 10.21.

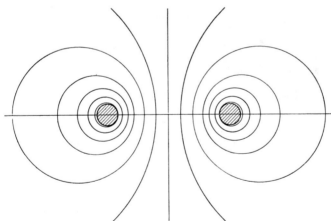

FIG. 10.21   Flux circles about two long, circular conductors carrying equal currents in opposite directions. Equal amounts of flux are included between adjacent circles.

10.6. Equipotential Lines about Parallel Current-carrying Conductors.

The slope of a flux line at a point P in space near the conductors of Fig. 10.18 is $dy/dx = [(D/2)^2 - x^2 + y^2]/2xy$. Since the equipotential line through a point is perpendicular to the flux line through the point, the slope of the equipotential line through P is

$$-\frac{dy}{dx} = \frac{2xy}{(D/2)^2 - x^2 + y^2} \tag{10.26}$$

From this the equation of the equipotential line through an arbitrary point will be derived.

In Fig. 10.22 the point O midway between the conductor centers is the

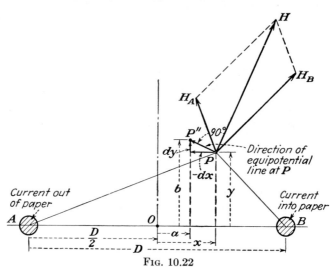

FIG. 10.22

origin of a coordinate system. Here two points P'' and P are on an equipotential line. P'' is a m to the right of and b m above O. P and P'' are separated a horizontal distance dx and a vertical distance dy.

Equation (10.26) may be rearranged as

$$\frac{2xy\,dx - x^2\,dy}{y^2} = \left[\frac{-(D/2)^2}{y^2} - 1\right]dy$$

in which each side of the equality may be integrated. The result is

$$\frac{x^2}{y} = \frac{(D/2)^2}{y} - y + k \tag{10.27}$$

where k is a constant of integration.

Equation (10.27) may be rearranged as

$$x^2 + y^2 - ky = \left(\frac{D}{2}\right)^2 \tag{10.28}$$

which is the general equation of a family of circles whose centers are on the y axis. The value of k for a circle through P'' can be obtained by substituting in (10.28) the values $x = a$ and $y = b$. From that $k = [a^2 + b^2 - (D/2)^2]/b$; thus

$$x^2 + y^2 - \left[a^2 + b^2 - \left(\frac{D}{2}\right)^2\right]\frac{y}{b} = \left(\frac{D}{2}\right)^2 \qquad (10.29)$$

Completing the square in (10.29) yields

$$x^2 + y^2 - \left[a^2 + b^2 - \left(\frac{D}{2}\right)^2\right]\frac{y}{b} + \frac{[a^2 + b^2 - (D/2)^2]^2}{(2b)^2}$$

$$= \frac{[a^2 + b^2 - (D/2)^2]^2}{(2b)^2} + \left(\frac{D}{2}\right)^2$$

which may be written as

$$x^2 + \left[y - \frac{a^2 + b^2 - (D/2)^2}{2b}\right]^2 = \frac{[a^2 + b^2 - (D/2)^2]^2}{(2b)^2} + \left(\frac{D}{2}\right)^2$$

This is the equation of a circle whose center is on the y axis at

$$y = \frac{a^2 + b^2 - (D/2)^2}{2b}$$

and whose radius is $\sqrt{[a^2 + b^2 - (D/2)^2]^2/(2b)^2 + (D/2)^2}$.

From the preceding any number of equipotential circles about the conductors of Fig. 10.22 can be located, each corresponding to a set of values for a and b. In Fig. 10.23, let d be the distance from O to the center of an equipotential circle and r_e be the radius of an equipotential circle. Then

$$d = \frac{a^2 + b^2 - (D/2)^2}{2b} \qquad (10.30)$$

and

$$r_e = \sqrt{\frac{[a^2 + b^2 - (D/2)^2]^2}{(2b)^2} + \left(\frac{D}{2}\right)^2} \qquad (10.31)$$

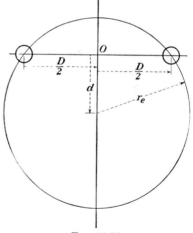

Fɪɢ. 10.23

Equation (10.30) shows that for a given value of a the value of d has the same magnitude for a given positive value of b as it has for an equal negative value of b. Note, however, that for positive values of both a and b the sign of d is negative if $a^2 + b^2$ is less than $(D/2)^2$, and positive if $a^2 + b^2$ is greater than $(D/2)^2$. When $a^2 + b^2 = (D/2)^2$, $d = 0$ and the center of the equipotential circle is at O. Note further that the sign of d reverses with a change of sign of b.

Equation (10.31) shows that for a given value of a the value of r_e has the same magnitude for a given positive value of b as it has for an equal negative value of b. Except for the circle whose center is at O, the equipotential, as well as the flux circles, occur in pairs.

If P'' in Fig. 10.22 is on the line joining the conductor centers, $b = 0$, for which, from (10.30) and (10.31), for any value of a the center of the equipotential circle is at an infinite distance from O and the radius of the circle is infinite. This means that the line joining the centers is part of an equipotential circle of infinite radius.

By inspection of (10.30) and (10.31) it can be seen that

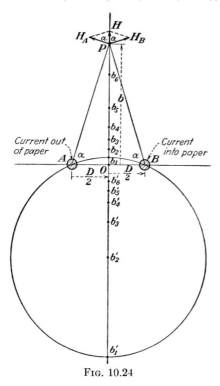

Fig. 10.24

$$r_e^2 = d^2 + (D/2)^2$$

Hence r_e is always of such length that each equipotential circle passes through the conductor centers.

In Fig. 10.24 the point P is on the perpendicular bisector of the line joining the conductor centers at a distance b m from O. The magnitude of the magnetic potential gradient $\mathbf{H}_A$ produced at P by I amp in conductor A is, by (10.2), $H_A = I/[2\pi \sqrt{(D/2)^2 + b^2}]$ amp-turns per m. The magnitude of the magnetic potential gradient $\mathbf{H}_B$ produced at P by I amp in conductor B is equal to H_A. The horizontal components of $\mathbf{H}_A$ and $\mathbf{H}_B$ are equal and oppositely directed and neutralize each other. The resultant gradient $\mathbf{H}$ at P is the sum of the equal vertical components of $\mathbf{H}_A$ and $\mathbf{H}_B$; hence its magnitude is $2H_A \cos \alpha$. But

$$\cos \alpha = (D/2)/\sqrt{(D/2)^2 + b^2}$$

therefore $H = ID/2\pi[(D/2)^2 + b^2]$ amp-turns per m.

The reluctance drop from the point P to a point b_1 m above O along the line joining the points is $\int_0^{b_1} H\, db$; hence the *reluctance drop* from O to b_1 is

$$\int_0^{b_1} \frac{ID\, db}{2\pi[(D/2)^2 + b^2]} = \frac{ID}{2\pi} \left[\frac{\tan^{-1}[b/(D/2)]}{D/2} \right]_0^{b_1}$$

$$= \frac{I}{\pi} \tan^{-1} \frac{b_1}{D/2} \qquad \text{amp-turns} \qquad (10.32)$$

Let the arbitrary value of $I/16$ be assigned to the reluctance drop from O to b_1. From (10.32), $I/16 = (I/\pi) \tan^{-1} [b_1/(D/2)]$, from which $b_1 = (D/2) \tan (\pi/16) = (D/2) \tan 11.25° = 0.2D/2$ m. The center of the equipotential circle through b_1 is equidistant from it and the conductor centers. The radius of the equipotential circle can be computed from (10.31) and is $2.6D/2$ m.

For a reason that will now be explained it is better to speak of equipotential arcs rather than circles. All points on the circular arc extending from the surface of conductor A through b_1 to the surface of conductor B are at the same magnetic potential. The circle of which this arc is a part also intersects the perpendicular bisector of the line joining the conductor centers at the point b_1' below the conductors. Since the radius of the circle is $2.6D/2$, its diameter is $5.2D/2$. Also, since the distance from O to b_1 is $0.2D/2$, then the distance from O to

$$b_1' = \frac{5.2D}{2} - \frac{0.2D}{2} = \frac{5D}{2} \quad \text{m}$$

The reluctance drop from O to b_1' along the bisector will be computed to see if it is equal to that from O to b_1. By similarity to the preceding computation

$$\text{Reluctance drop from } O \text{ to } b_1' = - \int_0^{5D/2} \frac{ID \, db}{2\pi[(D/2)^2 + b^2]} \quad (10.33)$$

The negative sign is used here because the path of integration is opposite to the direction of $\mathbf{H}$.

Integration of (10.33) and substitution of the limits yields

$$\text{Reluctance drop from } O \text{ to } b_1' = - \frac{I}{\pi} \tan^{-1} 5$$

But $\tan^{-1} 5 = 78.65°$, or $7\pi/16$ radians. Hence

$$\text{Reluctance drop from } O \text{ to } b_1' = - \frac{7I}{16} \quad \text{amp-turns}$$

This result shows that b_1' is not at the same magnetic potential as b_1 even though they both lie on the same circle. The line joining the conductor centers must be treated as a line of discontinuity dividing a circle into two arcs. All points on one arc are at one magnetic potential. All points on the other arc are at a second common magnetic potential. The reluctance drop from b_1' to b_1 is $-(-7I/16) + I/16 = I/2$ amp-turns. The difference of magnetic potential between any point on an equipotential arc below the line joining the conductor centers and any point on the arc of the same circle above the line is $I/2$ amp-turns.

In Fig. 10.24 the point b_1 was chosen so that the reluctance drop from O to b_1 was $I/16$ amp-turns. The points b_2, b_3, etc., are to be so located that the reluctance drop from b_1 to b_2, that from b_2 to b_3, etc., are also $I/16$ amp-turns. Then the reluctance drop from O to b_2, is twice that from O to b_1, the reluctance drop from O to b_3 is three times that from O to b_1, etc. By similarity to the derivation used in obtaining (10.32)

$$\text{Reluctance drop from } O \text{ to } b_n = \frac{I}{\pi} \tan^{-1} \frac{b_n}{D/2} \qquad \text{amp-turns} \qquad (10.34)$$

where n may be assigned the successive values of 1, 2, 3, etc., in computing the reluctance drops from O to b_1, O to b_2, O to b_3, etc. The reluctance drop from O to b_n is to be n times that from O to b_1; hence, from (10.32) and (10.34), $(I/\pi) \tan^{-1} [b_n/(D/2)] = (nI/\pi) \tan^{-1} [b_1/(D/2)]$, from which

$$b_n = \frac{D}{2} \tan \left(n \tan^{-1} \frac{b_1}{D/2} \right) \qquad (10.35)$$

Values of b_2, b_3, etc., computed from (10.35) are tabulated in Table 10.2 with b_1 so chosen that $\tan^{-1} [b_1/(D/2)] = \pi/16$.

TABLE 10.2

n	Reluctance drop from point O, amp-turns	$n \tan^{-1} b_1/(D/2)$	$b_n = (D/2) \tan [n \tan^{-1} b_1/(D/2)]$
1	$I/16$	$\pi/16$	$0.20D/2$
2	$I/8$	$\pi/8$	$0.41D/2$
3	$3I/16$	$3\pi/16$	$0.67D/2$
4	$I/4$	$\pi/4$	$1.00D/2$
5	$5I/16$	$5\pi/16$	$1.50D/2$
6	$3I/8$	$3\pi/8$	$2.41D/2$

The radii of the equipotential arcs through the points b_1, b_2, etc., can be computed by (10.31). However, since it is known that each arc also passes through the conductor centers, the centers of the arcs can be located quickly by trial. Equipotential arcs have been drawn in Fig. 10.25 along with a number of flux circles.

In Fig. 10.26 are represented two long, parallel, isolated, circular, nonmagnetic conductors carrying I amp each in opposite directions. The variation of the magnetic potential gradient at a point P as it moves along the perpendicular bisector of the line joining the conductor centers is to be determined. From a previous derivation the gradient is

$$H_P = \frac{ID}{2\pi[(D/2)^2 + b^2]} \qquad \text{amp-turns per m} \qquad (10.36)$$

The gradient has its greatest value of $2I/(\pi D)$ when $b = 0$, that is, at the point midway between the centers. As b increases, the gradient decreases to zero at $b = \infty$. Points for the curve of Fig. 10.26 showing the relation

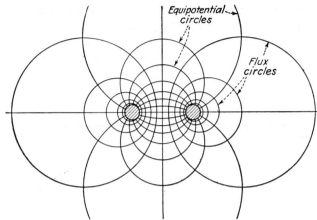

FIG. 10.25 Flux and magnetic equipotential circles for two conductors carrying equal currents in opposite directions.

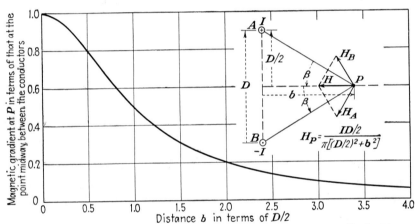

FIG. 10.26 Variation of the magnetic potential gradient along a perpendicular bisector of the line joining the centers of two conductors that are carrying equal currents in opposite directions.

between the gradient and b were obtained from (10.36) by assigning to b successive values such as $0.1D/2$, $0.2D/2$, etc.

Equation (10.36) may be written as

$$H_P = \frac{2I(D/2)^2}{\pi D[(D/2)^2 + b^2]} \qquad \text{amp-turns per m}$$

But $(D/2)^2/[(D/2)^2 + b^2] = \sin^2 \beta$, where β is measured as in Fig. 10.26. The magnitude of the gradient varies as the square of $\sin \beta$. As β decreases from 90°, $\sin \beta$ at first decreases slowly and $\sin^2 \beta$ also decreases slowly. As β nears 45°, $\sin \beta$ and $\sin^2 \beta$ are decreasing more rapidly per degree change in β than for any other values of β. The rate of change of the gradient with respect to β is greatest at $\beta = 45°$. Below that value of β the gradient decreases less and less rapidly as β decreases.

10.7. Parallel Conductors Carrying Currents in Same Direction. In Fig. 10.27 are represented two long, parallel, isolated, circular, nonmagnetic conductors carrying I amp each in the same direction. The variation of the magnetic potential gradient at a point P as it moves along the

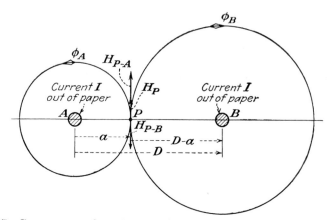

FIG. 10.27 Component and resultant gradients at a point P on the line through the centers of two long, parallel, circular conductors that are carrying equal currents in the same direction.

line joining the conductor centers is to be computed. At P the component gradient produced by current in one conductor will be added vectorially to that produced by current in the other. The currents will be assumed to be distributed uniformly over the conductors.

In Fig. 10.27 are represented the flux line ϕ_A that would pass through P if I amp in conductor A acted alone and the flux line ϕ_B that would pass through P if I amp in conductor B were acting alone. As shown earlier, the magnitude of the gradient $\mathbf{H}_{P-A}$ established at P by the current in conductor A is $I/2\pi a$ amp-turns per m and that of the gradient $\mathbf{H}_{P-B}$ established at P by the current in conductor B is $I/2\pi(D-a)$ amp-turns per m. The component gradients are collinear and oppositely directed when P is between the conductors. The magnitude of the resultant gradient $\mathbf{H}_P$ is

$$H_P = \frac{I}{2\pi a} - \frac{I}{2\pi(D-a)} \qquad \text{amp-turns per m} \qquad (10.37)$$

where a and D are in meters.

Equation (10.37) is valid when P is outside the conductors on the line between the centers. Within the left-hand conductor, by analogy to (10.9), the magnitude of the gradient $\mathbf{H}_P$ is

$$H_P = \frac{Ia}{2\pi r^2} - \frac{I}{2\pi(D-a)} \qquad \text{amp-turns per m}$$

Figure 10.28 shows graphically the variations in the component and

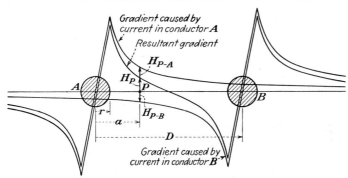

FIG. 10.28   Magnetic gradients at points along the line through the centers of two current-carrying conductors. $\mathbf{H}_{P-A}$ is the component gradient at the point P produced by the current I in conductor A coming toward the observer. $\mathbf{H}_{P-B}$ is the component gradient at P produced by the current I in conductor B coming toward the observer. $\mathbf{H}_P$ is the resultant gradient at P. The component and resultant gradients at any point on the line are collinear and normal to the line.

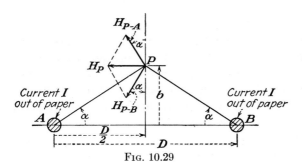

FIG. 10.29

resultant gradients as P moves along the line through the conductor centers. The resultant gradient is greatest near the surface of a conductor that is farthest from the other conductor. The resultant gradient is zero at the point midway between the conductor centers and also at points near the centers.

In Fig. 10.29 are represented two long, parallel, isolated, circular, non-magnetic conductors carrying I amp each in the same direction. The variation in the magnetic potential gradient at a point P as it moves along the perpendicular bisector of the line joining the conductor centers is to be computed. From (10.2), the magnitude of the gradient $\mathbf{H}_{P-A}$ produced at P by the current in conductor A and that of the gradient $\mathbf{H}_{P-B}$ produced at P by the current in conductor B are each $I/[2\pi\sqrt{(D/2)^2 + b^2}]$ amp-turns per m, where b and D are in meters. The vertical components of these gradients are equal and oppositely directed and neutralize each other. The magnitudes of the horizontal components of $\mathbf{H}_{P-A}$ and $\mathbf{H}_{P-B}$ are each

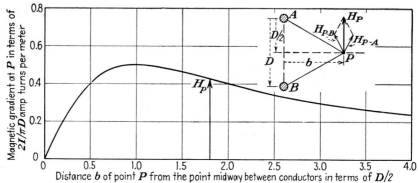

FIG. 10.30   Variation of the magnetic potential gradient along a perpendicular bisector of the line joining the centers of two conductors that are carrying equal currents in the same direction.

equal to $I/[2\pi\sqrt{(D/2)^2 + b^2}]\sin\alpha$ and that of $\mathbf{H}_P$ is twice that. Hence

$$H_P = \frac{I\sin\alpha}{\pi\sqrt{(D/2)^2 + b^2}} \qquad \text{but} \qquad \sin\alpha = \frac{b}{\sqrt{(D/2)^2 + b^2}}$$

thus
$$H_P = \frac{Ib}{\pi[(D/2)^2 + b^2]} \qquad \text{amp-turns per m} \qquad (10.38)$$

The gradient is zero at $b = 0$, that is, at the point midway between conductors. As b increases, the gradient at first increases until it reaches a maximum value of $I/\pi D$ amp-turns per m at $b = D/2$. Beyond that value of b the gradient decreases and becomes zero at $b = \infty$. Points for the curve of Fig. 10.30 were computed from (10.38) by assigning to b successive values such as $0.1D/2$, $0.2D/2$, etc.

In (10.38) if b^2 is large compared with $(D/2)^2$, the term $(D/2)^2 + b^2$ may be replaced by b^2 with little error. With this substitution, (10.38) reduces to $H_P = I/\pi b$ amp-turns per m. This is equal to the gradient that would be produced at a distance b from the center of a circular conductor carrying $2I$ amp. Hence the two conductors in Fig. 10.28 could be replaced by a single circular conductor, carrying $2I$ amp and with its center at the point midway between the conductor centers, without changing the gradient at a considerable distance from the point. Figure

10.31 is a graphical comparison of the gradient that would be produced by I amp in each of two conductors with the gradient that would be produced by $2I$ amp in a conductor whose center is at the point midway between the original conductors. For values of b greater than $4D/2$ the curves nearly coincide.

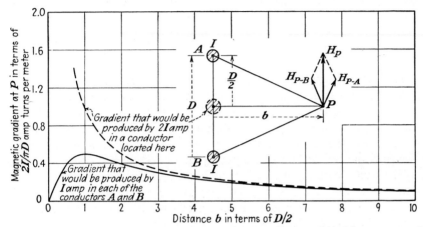

FIG. 10.31   Comparison of the magnetic potential gradient produced by a current I in each of two conductors separated a distance D with that produced by a current $2I$ in one conductor located midway between the two conductors.

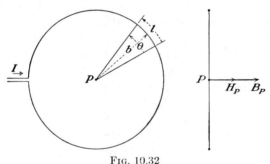

FIG. 10.32

10.8. Magnetic Relations near a Circular One-turn Coil.

Consider a section l m long of the circular one-turn coil of Fig. 10.32. If the diameter of the conductor forming the turn is very small compared with the radius b m of the turn, then all elements of the turn may be considered as equidistant b m from the point P at the center of the turn. Then Ampère's law as expressed by (10.1) may be applied directly and the magnitude of the magnetic potential gradient $\mathbf{H}_P$ at P produced by I amp in the length l is

$$H_P = \frac{Il}{4\pi b^2} \quad \text{amp-turns per m} \quad (10.39)$$

By the rule, "coil the fingers of the right hand in the direction of the current, then the extended thumb points the direction of the flux," it follows that $\mathbf{H}_P$ is directed as shown in Fig. 10.32. The flux density $\mathbf{B}_P$ is collinear with $\mathbf{H}_P$.

In Fig. 10.32, $l = b\theta$, where θ is the angle in radians subtended by the arc of length l. Substitution of this value in (10.39) yields

$$H_P = \frac{I\theta}{4\pi b} \qquad \text{amp-turns per m} \qquad (10.40)$$

The magnetic potential gradient at the center of the turn of Fig. 10.30 produced by the mmf of the complete turn can be obtained from (10.39) by substituting $l = 2\pi b$, or from (10.40) by substituting $\theta = 2\pi$. Either method yields $H_P = I/2b$ amp-turns per m. The corresponding flux density can be obtained from the relation $B = 4\pi \times 10^{-7}H$ in air. Hence $B_P = 2\pi I \times 10^{-7}/b$ wb per sq m.

The two preceding expressions yield reasonably accurate results if the diameter of the conductor is small (say 10 per cent or less) compared with the diameter of a turn and if b is measured from the center of a turn to the center of the conductor.

$H_P = I/2b$ is the expression for the magnetic potential gradient at the center of a current-carrying one-turn coil of fine wire. Now consider what the gradient will be at a point that is in the plane of the turn but not at the center. In Fig. 10.33 a point P has been chosen that is halfway from the center to the wire. The various elements of the turn are not at equal distances from P. An approximate solution based on (10.40) will be used. The portion of the turn below the diameter through P produces a magnetic potential gradient at P that is equal to and in the same direction as that produced at P by the portion of the turn above the diameter. The gradient produced by the upper portion of the turn will be computed and the result doubled to obtain the total gradient at P. From P seven lines are drawn, with 30° between adjacent lines. The first and the last of these lines lie along the diameter through P. Each line is extended until it intersects the turn, giving the intersection points a, b, c, d, e, f, and g. Each of the bisectors of the 30° angles is drawn and extended to give the intersection points h, i, j, k, l, and m. Then arcs are drawn as shown, the first having a radius Ph, with the points n and o at the extremities of the arc. The arcs pq, rs, tu, vw, and xy have the respective radii, Pi, Pj, Pk, Pl, and Pm.

Assume that the gradient produced at P by the current I amp in the element ab of the turn is equal to that which would be produced at P by an equal current in a conductor that coincides with the arc no. Likewise assume that the gradient produced at P by the currents in the elements bc, cd, de, ef, and fg are equal, respectively, to those that would be pro-

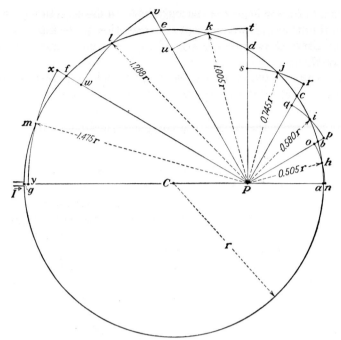

FIG. 10.33 Approximate determination of magnetic potential gradient at a point not at the center but in the plane of a one-turn coil.

duced by equal currents in conductors that coincide with the arcs pq, rs, tu, vw, and xy.

The turn being considered has a radius r m. The distances Ph, Pi, Pj, Pk, Pl, and Pm are next measured and found to be, respectively, $0.505r$, $0.580r$, $0.745r$, $1.005r$, $1.288r$, and $1.475r$ m. According to (10.40) the magnitude of the gradient $\mathbf{H}_{P-no}$ at P produced by the current I in the arc no is equal to $I\theta$ divided by 4π times the radius of the arc. Here $\theta = 30° = \pi/6$ radians. Hence

$$H_{P-no} = \frac{I\pi/6}{4\pi \times 0.505r} = \frac{I}{24r} \times 1.98 \text{ amp-turns per m}$$

Similarly

$$H_{P-pq} = \frac{I}{24r} \times \frac{1}{0.580} = \frac{I}{24r} \times 1.72$$

$$H_{P-rs} = \frac{I}{24r} \times \frac{1}{0.745} = \frac{I}{24r} \times 1.34$$

$$H_{P-tu} = \frac{I}{24r} \times \frac{1}{1.005} = \frac{I}{24r} \times 0.99$$

$$H_{P-vw} = \frac{I}{24r} \times \frac{1}{1.288} = \frac{I}{24r} \times 0.78$$

and

$$H_{P-xy} = \frac{I}{24r} \times \frac{1}{1.475} = \frac{I}{24r} \times 0.68$$

The sum of these components is $0.312I/r$ amp-turns per m.   Since the other half of the turn produces an equal gradient at P, the total gradient $H_P = 0.624I/r$ amp-turns per m.

The gradient at the center of the turn of Fig. 10.33 is $0.5I/r$ amp-turns per m, a value that is less than that at P.   The gradient and the flux density are least at the center of the turn and increase as the point P moves farther from the center and nearer to the turn.   As the point moves away from the center, the component gradient produced by the

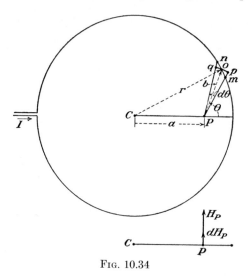

Fig. 10.34

current in the elements of the turn from which the point is moving decrease, while the component gradients produced by the current in the elements of the turn toward which the point is moving increase.   The increased effect of the latter more than compensates for the reduced effect of the former.   The net result is that the total gradient increases.   However, the increase in the gradient at the point moves away from the center is gradual at first.   When the point has moved halfway from the center to the turn, the gradient is $0.624/0.5 = 1.25$ times as great as that at the center.

An expression for the magnetic potential gradient at a point in the plane of a circular one-turn coil and within the turn will be derived by an extension of the method used in Fig. 10.33.   The turn will be divided into infinitesimal sections and the component gradients added by integration to obtain the resultant gradient.   The result will be inexact because the conductor forming a turn does not have zero diameter, as will be assumed. In Fig. 10.34 is a point P at a distance a m from the center C of a turn of radius r m.   From P are two radiating lines at the infinitesimal angle

$d\theta$ radian apart. The radiating lines intersect the turn at the points m and n. The bisector of $d\theta$ is also shown and intersects the turn at the point o. The distance from P to o is b m. With P as a center and a radius b, the arc pq was drawn. Assume that I amp in the arc pq produces an infinitesimal gradient dH_P at P equal to that produced by an equal current in the element mn of the turn. From (10.40),

$$dH_P = \frac{I\,d\theta}{4\pi b} \qquad \text{amp-turns per m}$$

The magnitude of the total gradient $\mathbf{H}_P$ at P in Fig. 10.34 can be obtained by integrating dH_P with the limits $\theta = 0$ to $\theta = 2\pi$ radians. Hence

$$H_P = \frac{I}{4\pi} \int_0^{2\pi} \frac{d\theta}{b} \qquad \text{amp-turns per m} \qquad (10.41)$$

To express the variable distance b in Fig. 10.34 as a function of the angle θ, the triangle CPo is redrawn in Fig. 10.35 and further construction

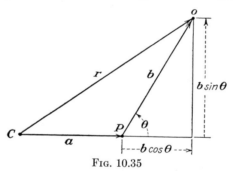

FIG. 10.35

lines added. By dropping a perpendicular from o to the line CP extended, a right triangle with r as a hypotenuse is formed. One side of the triangle is $a + b \cos \theta$; the other is $b \sin \theta$. Then

$$r^2 = (a + b \cos \theta)^2 + (b \sin \theta)^2$$

which can be simplified to $r^2 = a^2 + 2ab \cos \theta + b^2$. From this

$$b = -a \cos \theta \pm \sqrt{a^2 \cos^2 \theta - a^2 + r^2}$$

Of the two values of b the one with physical meaning in this case is the one that is positive, or

$$b = -a \cos \theta + \sqrt{a^2 \cos^2 \theta - a^2 + r^2} \qquad (10.42)$$

Substitution of this value of b in (10.41) yields

$$H_P = \frac{I}{4\pi} \int_0^{2\pi} \frac{d\theta}{\sqrt{a^2 \cos^2 \theta - a^2 + r^2} - a \cos \theta} \qquad (10.43)$$

Rationalizing this by multiplying both numerator and denominator by $\sqrt{a^2 \cos^2 \theta - a^2 + r^2} + a \cos \theta$ and simplifying yields

$$H_P = \frac{I}{4\pi(r^2 - a^2)} \int_0^{2\pi} (\sqrt{r^2 - a^2 \sin^2 \theta} + a \cos \theta)\, d\theta \quad (10.44)$$

The term $a \cos \theta\, d\theta$ in (10.44) integrates into $a \sin \theta$. The term $\sqrt{r^2 - a^2 \sin^2 \theta}\, d\theta$ cannot be integrated directly in the usual manner. However, tables of elliptic integrals can be computed, from which, for any ratio of a to r in Fig. 10.34, values of H_P can be obtained. For any value of θ the value of the term $\sqrt{r^2 - a^2 \sin^2 \theta}$ in (10.44) depends upon the value of a compared with that of r. Consider the case solved previously by an approximate method in which $a = r/2$. For this value of a, $\sqrt{r^2 - a^2 \sin^2 \theta} = r\sqrt{1 - 0.25 \sin^2 \theta}$. Values of this term were obtained for various assumed values of θ as shown in Table 10.3.

TABLE 10.3

θ	$\sin \theta$	$\sin^2 \theta$	$0.25 \sin^2 \theta$	$1 - 0.25 \sin^2 \theta$	$r\sqrt{1 - 0.25 \sin^2 \theta}$
0	0	0	0	1.000	1.000r
18°	0.309	0.096	0.024	0.976	0.988r
36°	0.588	0.346	0.087	0.913	0.956r
54°	0.809	0.655	0.164	0.836	0.914r
72°	0.951	0.904	0.226	0.774	0.880r
90°	1.000	1.000	0.250	0.750	0.866r
108°	0.951	0.904	0.226	0.774	0.880r
126°	0.809	0.655	0.164	0.836	0.914r
144°	0.588	0.346	0.087	0.913	0.956r
162°	0.309	0.096	0.024	0.976	0.988r
180°	0	0	0	1.000	1.000r

From the values in Table 10.3, curve 1 of Fig. 10.36 was plotted to show how $r\sqrt{1 - 0.25 \sin^2 \theta}$ varies as θ varies. The quantity varies cyclically over a period of π radians. The maximum value is r at $\theta = 0$ and the minimum is $0.866r$ at $\theta = 0.5\pi$.

For $a = r/2$, the term $a \cos \theta = 0.5r \cos \theta$. This term plotted against θ yields curve 2 in Fig. 10.36. The quantity is cyclic with a period of 2π radians. The maximum value is $0.5r$ at $\theta = 0$ and the minimum is $-0.5r$ at $\theta = \pi$.

Addition of the ordinates of curves 1 and 2 in Fig. 10.36 yields curve 3. This shows that the quantity $r\sqrt{1 - 0.25 \sin^2 \theta} + 0.5r \cos \theta$ is cyclic with a period of 2π radians. The maximum value is $1.5r$ at $\theta = 0$ and the minimum is $0.5r$ at $\theta = \pi$. This curve when studied in conjunction with Fig. 10.34 shows the relative magnetic effects produced at P by the currents in the various elements of the turn. With $\theta = 0$, the magnetic effect is the greatest because the element of the turn there is the one nearest to P. As θ increases, the magnetic effect of the elements decreases until, at $\theta = \pi$, the element there is farthest from P. As θ increases above π, the magnetic effect of the elements increases until a maximum is reached at $\theta = 2\pi$, at which the starting point is reached.

Graphically the result of the integration of the term behind the integral sign in (10.43) and the substitution of the limits represents the area under curve 3 between $\theta = 0$ and $\theta = 2\pi$ in Fig. 10.34. Between

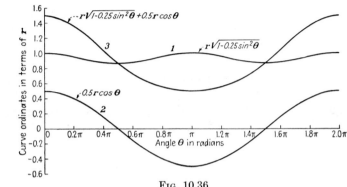

FIG. 10.36

these limits, under curve 2 there is as much negative as positive area, and the net area is zero. As a result, the area under curve 3 is equal to the area under curve 1. By symmetry, the area under curve 1 between $\theta = 0$ and $\theta = 2\pi$ equals four times the area under the curve between $\theta = 0$ and $\theta = \pi/2$. Hence, (10.43) may be written as

$$H_P = \frac{I}{\pi(r^2 - a^2)} \int_0^{\pi/2} \sqrt{r^2 - a^2 \sin^2 \theta}\; d\theta \qquad (10.45)$$

This equation can be integrated as an infinite series. For a given value of a the value of the integral can be obtained by substitution of the limits in the series. Tables of the values of the function are given in Dwight, "Mathematical Tables," p. 204. To convert (10.45) into the form used in the table, let $a = kr$, where k is a decimal. Substitution of this value of a in (10.45) and rearrangement yields

$$H_P = \frac{I}{\pi r(1 - k^2)} \int_0^{\pi/2} \sqrt{1 - k^2 \sin^2 \theta}\; d\theta \qquad (10.46)$$

The term $\int_0^{\pi/2} \sqrt{1 - k^2 \sin^2 \theta}\; d\theta$ is an elliptic integral of the second kind, values of which for various values of k^2 are given in Dwight, "Mathematical Tables." For the point used in the approximate solution of Fig. 10.33, $a = 0.5r$; hence $k = 0.5$ and $k^2 = 0.25$. For this value of k^2, according to Dwight, the integral is 1.47. Hence

$$H_P = \frac{I}{\pi r(1 - 0.25)} \times 1.47 = \frac{0.623I}{r} \qquad \text{amp-turns per m}$$

as compared with the previous approximate value of $0.624I/r$.

The variation in the flux density over the cross section within a circular turn will now be determined. If there is no magnetic material near the turn, the flux density at a point in the cross section within the turn is directly proportional to the magnetic potential gradient at the point. Since $B_P = 4\pi \times 10^{-7}H$, then by substituting the value of H_P from (10.46) and rearranging,

$$B_P = \frac{4I \times 10^{-7}}{r(1 - k^2)} \int_0^{\pi/2} \sqrt{1 - k^2 \sin \theta} \, d\theta \qquad \text{wb per sq m} \qquad (10.47)$$

By assigning various values to k and using Dwight's tables, corresponding values of B_P were computed, as listed in Table 10.4. The curve of

TABLE 10.4

k ratio a/r in Fig. 10.34	k^2	$1 - k^2$	$\dfrac{1}{1 - k^2}$	$\displaystyle\int_0^{\frac{\pi}{2}} \sqrt{1 - k^2 \sin^2 \theta}\, d\theta$ from table of elliptic integrals	B_P
0	0	1	1	1.57	$1.57 \times (4I \times 10^{-7}/r)$
0.1	0.01	0.99	1.01	1.57	$1.59 \times (4I \times 10^{-7}/r)$
0.2	0.04	0.96	1.04	1.55	$1.62 \times (4I \times 10^{-7}/r)$
0.3	0.09	0.91	1.10	1.53	$1.69 \times (4I \times 10^{-7}/r)$
0.4	0.16	0.84	1.19	1.51	$1.80 \times (4I \times 10^{-7}/r)$
0.5	0.25	0.75	1.33	1.47	$1.96 \times (4I \times 10^{-7}/r)$
0.6	0.36	0.64	1.56	1.42	$2.22 \times (4I \times 10^{-7}/r)$
0.7	0.49	0.51	1.96	1.36	$2.67 \times (4I \times 10^{-7}/r)$
0.8	0.64	0.36	2.78	1.28	$3.57 \times (4I \times 10^{-7}/r)$
0.85	0.7225	0.2775	3.60	1.23	$4.43 \times (4I \times 10^{-7}/r)$
0.9	0.81	0.19	5.26	1.17	$6.17 \times (4I \times 10^{-7}/r)$
0.95	0.9025	0.0975	10.25	1.10	$11.27 \times (4I \times 10^{-7}/r)$
1	1	0	∞	1.00	∞

B_P against kr, as plotted from values in the table, is shown in Fig. 10.37. The flux density is least at the center of the turn and increases as the point P moves radially from the center. The increase in density is gradual at first, being about 3 per cent greater at a distance $0.2r$ from the center than it is at the center. As P nears a distance r from the center, the density increases rapidly. In Table 10.4 the density is listed as

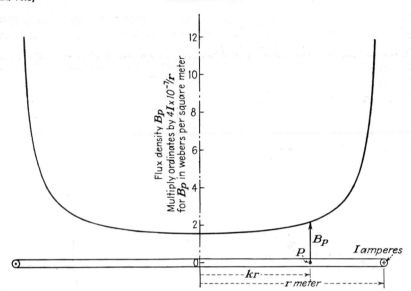

FIG. 10.37 Variation of the flux density over the plane within a current-carrying one-turn coil.

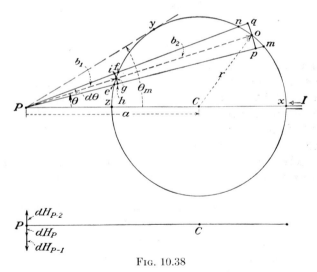

FIG. 10.38

infinite for $k = 1$ (that is, $a = r$). This would be correct if the conductor forming the turn had zero cross section. For a conductor of finite diameter d m, the maximum density will occur at the inner edge of the conductor and is approximately $4I \times 10^{-7}/d$ wb per sq m.

Consider the one-turn coil of Fig. 10.38. The current is I amp, the diameter of the conductor is very small, the radius of the turn is r m, and the turn is isolated in air. A point P has been chosen in the plane of the coil. The distance from P to the center C of the turn is a m. From P are drawn two radiating lines at the angle $d\theta$ radian from each other. The bisector of the angle is at the angle θ from the line through P and C. The radiating lines intersect the nearer side of the turn at e and f and the farther side at m and n. The bisector of $d\theta$ intersects the turn at g and o. The distance from P to g is b_1 and that from P to o is b_2. Assume that I amp in the arc hi produces an infinitesimal magnetic potential gradient dH_{P-1} at P equal to that produced by an equal current in the element ef of

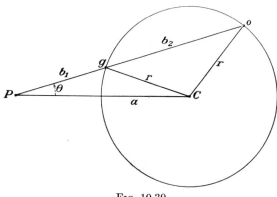

FIG. 10.39

the conductor. Also assume that I amp in the arc pq produces an infinitesimal gradient dH_{P-2} at P equal to that produced by an equal current in the element mn of the turn. $\mathbf{dH}_{P-1}$ is normal to the plane Phi and is directed into the paper at P. $\mathbf{dH}_{P-2}$ is normal to the plane Ppq and is directed out of the paper at P. Since these two component gradients are collinear and oppositely directed, the magnitude of their resultant is their numerical difference. According to (10.40), $dH_{P-1} = I\ d\theta/(4\pi b_1)$ and $dH_{P-2} = I\ d\theta/4\pi b_2$. Since $dH_P = dH_{P-1} - dH_{P-2}$, then

$$dH_P = \frac{I\ d\theta}{4\pi b_1} - \frac{I\ d\theta}{4\pi b_2} \tag{10.48}$$

Since b_1 is less than b_2, dH_{P-1} is greater than dH_{P-2} and $\mathbf{dH}_P$ is in the direction of $\mathbf{dH}_{P-1}$ or normal to and into the paper at P.

In Fig. 10.38, θ_m is the maximum value of the angle θ. The magnetic potential gradient H_P can be obtained by integrating (10.48) from $\theta = 0$ to $\theta = \theta_m$ and doubling the result since the lower half of the turn produces a gradient at P equal to that produced by the upper half. Hence

$$H_P = \frac{I}{2\pi} \int_0^{\theta_m} \left(\frac{1}{b_1} - \frac{1}{b_2} \right) d\theta \tag{10.49}$$

Since b_1 and b_2 vary as θ varies, to integrate (10.49), they may be expressed in terms of θ (see Fig. 10.39). From triangle PCg, by the law of cosines, $r^2 = b_1^2 + a^2 - 2b_1a \cos \theta$. From this, by the quadratic equation,

$$b_1 = a \cos \theta - \sqrt{a^2 \cos^2 \theta - a^2 + r^2} \qquad (10.50)$$

The negative sign in front of the radical is used since b_1 is always less than or equal to $a \cos \theta$. From triangle PCo, $r^2 = a^2 + b_2^2 - 2b_2a \cos \theta$. From this

$$b_2 = a \cos \theta + \sqrt{a^2 \cos^2 \theta - a^2 + r^2} \qquad (10.51)$$

The positive sign in front of the radical is used since b_2 is always greater than or equal to $a \cos \theta$.

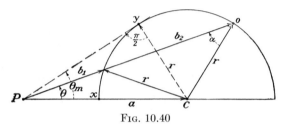

FIG. 10.40

Substituting the values of b_1 and b_2 from (10.50) and (10.51) in (10.49), arranging with a common denominator, and simplifying yields

$$H_P = \frac{I}{\pi(a^2 - r^2)} \int_0^{\theta_m} \sqrt{r^2 - a^2 \sin^2 \theta}\, d\theta \qquad (10.52)$$

To evaluate this integral, the variable may be changed from the angle θ to the angle α shown in Fig. 10.40. As θ varies from 0 to θ_m, α varies from 0 to $\pi/2$.

From triangle PCo, by the law of sines, $r/\sin \theta = a/\sin \alpha$, from which $a \sin \theta = r \sin \alpha$. Differentiating this expression yields

$$a \cos \theta\, d\theta = r \cos \alpha\, d\alpha$$

from which $d\theta = r \cos \alpha/(a \cos \theta)\, d\alpha$. Substituting the preceding values of $a \sin \theta$ and $d\theta$ in (10.52) and making use of some trigonometric identities yields

$$H_P = \frac{Ir^2}{\pi(a^2 - r^2)} \int_0^{\pi/2} \frac{\cos^2 \alpha\, d\alpha}{\sqrt{a^2 - r^2 \sin^2 \alpha}} \qquad (10.53)$$

Let the ratio $r/a = k$ in Fig. 10.39. Substituting $a = r/k$ in (10.53), making use of a trigonometric identity, and rearranging terms yields

$$H_P = \frac{Ik}{\pi r(1 - k^2)} \left[\int_0^{\pi/2} \frac{(k^2 - 1)\, d\alpha}{\sqrt{1 - k^2 \sin^2 \alpha}} \right.$$

$$\left. + \int_0^{\pi/2} \sqrt{1 - k^2 \sin^2 \alpha}\, d\alpha \right] \qquad (10.54)$$

The first integral in (10.54) is an elliptic integral of the first kind and can be evaluated for a given value of k by use of Dwight, "Mathematical Tables," p. 199.

The second integral in (10.54) is an elliptic integral of the second kind and was encountered previously. It can be evaluated for a given value of k by use of the table in Dwight, p. 204.

Let us compute the magnetic potential gradient in Fig. 10.38 at a point P that is a distance $a = 2r$ from the center of the turn. Here

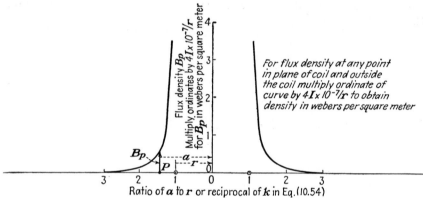

For flux density at any point in plane of coil and outside the coil multiply ordinate of curve by $4Ix10^{-7}/r$ to obtain density in webers per square meter

FIG. 10.41   Variation of the flux density over the plane of a current-carrying one-turn coil in the region without the coil.

$k = r/a = 0.5$ and $k^2 = 0.25$. According to the tables in Dwight, for this value of k^2

$$\int_0^{\pi/2} \frac{d\alpha}{\sqrt{1 - k^2 \sin^2 \alpha}} = 1.69 \quad \text{and} \quad \int_0^{\pi/2} \sqrt{1 - k^2 \sin^2 \alpha}\, d\alpha = 1.47$$

Substitution of these values in (10.54) yields $H_P = 0.0425I/r$ amp-turns per m.

Since $B = 4\pi \times 10^{-7}H$ in air, the flux density B_P at a point without a one-turn coil in the plane of the turn can be computed after the value of H is computed by (10.54). By assigning various values to k and using the tables of elliptic integrals, the variations in the flux density without the turn can be computed. The curve showing this relation is shown in Fig. 10.41.

The curve showing the variation of the flux density both within and without the turn is shown in Fig. 10.42.

10.9. Magnetic Relations on the Axis of a Circular One-turn Coil.

To compute the magnetic potential gradient at a point on the axis of the one-turn coil of radius r m in Fig. 10.43, consider the point P on the axis at a

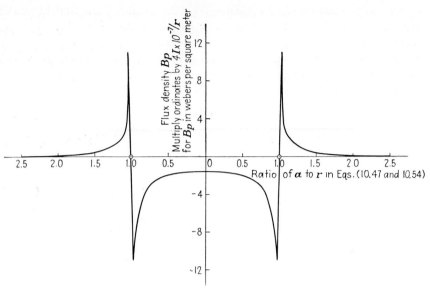

Fig. 10.42   Variation of the flux density over the plane of a current-carrying one-turn coil.

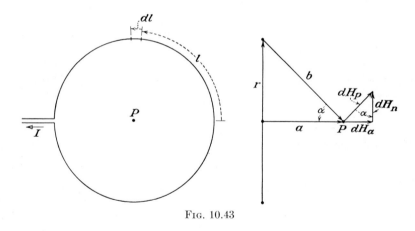

Fig. 10.43

distance a m from the plane of the turn.   The magnitude of the gradient $\mathbf{dH}_P$ produced at P by I amp by an element of the turn of length dl m is, by (10.1),

$$dH_P = \frac{I\,dl}{4\pi b^2} \qquad \text{amp-turns per m} \qquad (10.55)$$

This gradient is normal to the line b.   It is in the plane that contains the line and is normal to the plane of the turn as in Fig. 10.43. $\mathbf{dH}_P$ can be resolved into the gradient $\mathbf{dH}_a$ along the axis and the gradient $\mathbf{dH}_n$ normal to the axis. dH_n is neutralized by an equal and oppositely directed component produced by the current in the element of the turn diametrically opposite to the element in Fig. 10.43. Hence, the resultant gradient H_P at P is the summation of the axial components of all the infinitesimal elements of the turn.

In Fig. 10.43,

$$dH_a = dH_P \sin \alpha \qquad (10.56)$$

Combining (10.55) and (10.56) yields $dH_a = I\,dl/4\pi b^2 \sin \alpha$ amp-turns per m. But $b = \sqrt{r^2 + a^2}$ and $\sin \alpha = r/\sqrt{r^2 + a^2}$; hence

$$dH_a = \frac{Ir\,dl}{4\pi(r^2 + a^2)^{3/2}} \qquad \text{amp-turns per m} \qquad (10.57)$$

H_P is the integral of (10.57) as l varies from 0 to $2\pi r$, or

$$H_P = \frac{Ir}{4\pi(r^2 + a^2)^{3/2}} \int_0^{2\pi r} dl = \frac{Ir^2}{2(r^2 + a^2)^{3/2}} \qquad \text{amp-turns per m} \quad (10.58)$$

Equation (10.58) may be written as

$$H_P = \frac{I}{2r}\left(\frac{r}{\sqrt{r^2 + a^2}}\right)^3 = \frac{I\sin^3\alpha}{2r} \qquad \text{amp-turns per m}$$

where α radians is an angle measured as in Fig. 10.43.

Since $B = 4\pi \times 10^{-7}H$ in air, the flux density B_P at the point P in Fig. 10.43 is

$$B_P = \frac{2\pi r^2 I \times 10^{-7}}{(r^2 + a^2)^{3/2}} = \frac{2\pi I \times 10^{-7}}{r}\sin^3\alpha \qquad \text{amp-turns per m}$$

The flux density at a point on the axis of a one-turn coil is directed along the axis and is in the direction of the magnetic potential gradient at the point.

The flux density on the axis of a one-turn current-carrying coil is greatest when $a = 0$, that is, at the center of the turn. As a increases, the density decreases slowly at first when a is small compared with r, and then more and more rapidly until $a = r$. As a becomes large compared with r, the flux density becomes more and more nearly inversely proportional to a. These relations are shown graphically in Fig. 10.44. Here the distance from the center of the turn has been expressed in terms of the radius of the turn. At the center of the turn $a = 0$ and the flux density is $B_P = 2\pi I \times 10^{-7}/r$ wb per sq m. At $a = r$ the density is

$$B_P = 0.353\frac{2\pi I \times 10^{-7}}{r} \qquad \text{wb per sq m}$$

or the density at a point on the axis at a distance from the center equal to the radius of the turn is 0.353 times that at the center of the turn.   Hence, in Fig. 10.44, for a value of 1 on the abscissa the corresponding ordinate is 0.353.   Other points on the curve were located in a similar manner by assigning other values to a in terms of r.

While (10.58) was derived with the assumption that the conductor has a negligible diameter, the equation yields fair accuracy if the radius of the

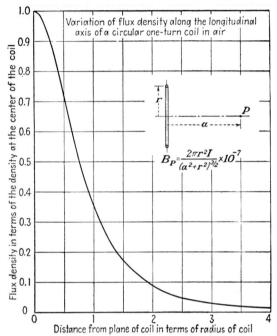

FIG. 10.44   Variation of the flux density along the longitudinal axis of a current-carrying circular one-turn coil.

turn is ten or more times the diameter of the conductor if r is taken as the mean radius of the turn.

10.10. Magnetic Relations on the Axis of a Solenoid.   An insulated conductor wound in the form of a helix is a single-layer solenoid.   Usually the adjacent turns on a solenoid are close together.   When a solenoid contains more than a single layer of turns, the successive layers are usually wound as helices with a pitch that is alternately right and left.   The axis of symmetry about which the turns are wound is the longitudinal axis.   An axis normal to the longitudinal axis and intersecting it at the center of the solenoid is a transverse axis.

For the single-layer solenoid of Fig. 10.45 an expression for the magnetic potential gradient at a point P on the longitudinal axis will be derived. P is at an arbitrary distance d m from the center C of the solenoid. It is assumed that there are no magnetic materials near the solenoid. The conductor is represented as of rectangular cross section. The radius of the turns is r m. Neglecting the pitch of the winding and the insulation between turns, the coil may be considered as producing a sheet of current. The total current in the sheet is NI amp, where N is

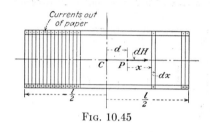

Currents out of paper

FIG. 10.45

the number of turns in the coil and I amp is the current in each turn. The current per meter length of the coil is NI/l amp, where l is the coil length in meters. An infinitesimal element of the coil of thickness dx m located a distance x m from P constitutes a one-turn coil for which the relations previously derived are approximately applicable. Since the current per meter length is NI/l amp, the current in the element of length dx is $(NI/l)\,dx$ amp. From (10.58), the infinitesimal magnetic potential gradient dH produced at P is

$$dH = \frac{r^2(NI/l)\,dx}{2(r^2 + x^2)^{3/2}} \quad \text{amp-turns per m} \tag{10.59}$$

The total magnetic potential gradient $\mathbf{H}_P$ at P is the summation of the gradients of all the infinitesimal elements of the coil and is directed along the longitudinal axis. The summation is obtained by integrating (10.59) from the limit $x = -l/2 - d$ to $x = l/2 - d$, since this is the range of values traversed by x in including all the elements of the coil. Hence

$$H_P = \frac{r^2 NI}{2l} \int_{-l/2-d}^{l/2-d} \frac{dx}{(r^2 + x^2)^{3/2}} \quad \text{amp-turns per m}$$

which, upon integration and substitution of the limits, yields

$$H_P = \frac{NI}{2l} \left[\frac{l/2 - d}{\sqrt{r^2 + (l/2 - d)^2}} + \frac{l/2 + d}{\sqrt{r^2 + (l/2 + d)^2}} \right]$$
$$\text{amp-turns per m} \tag{10.60}$$

The flux density $\mathbf{B}_P$ at a point on the longitudinal axis of an air-core solenoid is directed along the axis. Since $B = 4\pi \times 10^{-7} H$ in air, then

$$B_P = \frac{2\pi \times 10^{-7} NI}{l} \left[\frac{l/2 - d}{\sqrt{r^2 + (l/2 - d)^2}} + \frac{l/2 + d}{\sqrt{r^2 + (l/2 + d)^2}} \right]$$
$$\text{wb per sq m} \tag{10.61}$$

At the center of the solenoid, $d = 0$, and (10.61) reduces to

$$B_P = \frac{2\pi \times 10^{-7} NI}{\sqrt{r^2 + (l/2)^2}} \quad \text{wb per sq m}$$

At the end of the solenoid, $d = l/2$, and (10.61) reduces to

$$B_P = \frac{2\pi \times 10^{-7} NI}{\sqrt{r^2 + l^2}} \qquad \text{wb per sq m}$$

10.11. Magnetic Relations in a Long Air-core Solenoid. In Fig. 10.45 is represented an air-core solenoid in which N closely wound turns are distributed in a single layer along a length l m. Consider a solenoid as

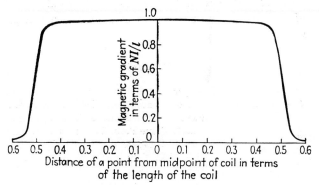

FIG. 10.46   Variation of the magnetic potential gradient along the longitudinal axis of a solenoid in which $l = 40r$.

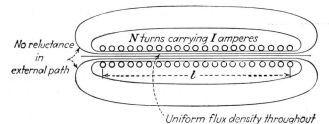

FIG. 10.47   Magnetic relations in a hypothetical long solenoid in which the flux density at the center is equal to what it is in an actual solenoid of the same dimensions.

"long" if its length is equal to or greater than ten times the diameter of the turns. Within a long solenoid the magnetic potential gradient and the flux density are greatest at the center cross section. Figure 10.46 shows how the gradient varies along the axis of a long solenoid in which the length is twenty times the diameter of the turns. The gradient decreases only slightly from the maximum at the center until points near the end of the solenoid are reached. Here the gradient decreases rapidly and at the end is almost exactly one-half that at the center.

   In Fig. 10.45 the gradient at the center of the solenoid on the longitudinal axis is very nearly NI/l amp-turns per m. This is the gradient that would occur throughout the entire length of the solenoid if the relations of Fig. 10.47 existed. Here a solenoid of N turns uniformly distributed over the length l encloses flux lines that are all parallel to the longitudinal axis within the solenoid. The external magnetic path between the ends of the solenoid is considered to have no reluctance. If conditions were as assumed the only reluctance in the magnetic circuit would be that of the air within the coil, the flux density would be uniform within the coil, and the gradient within the coil would be uniform at NI/l amp-turns per m. In a long air-core solenoid the flux density at the center is nearly uniform and nearly equal to what it would be if all the mmf of the solenoid were used in establishing a uniform magnetic field within the solenoid.

PROBLEMS

10.1. A section of a No. 18 copper wire is carrying 3 amp as in Fig. 10.48. If $r = 0.5$ in., $l_1 = -2$ in., and $l_2 = 5$ in., compute the flux density at the point P produced by the current in the section.

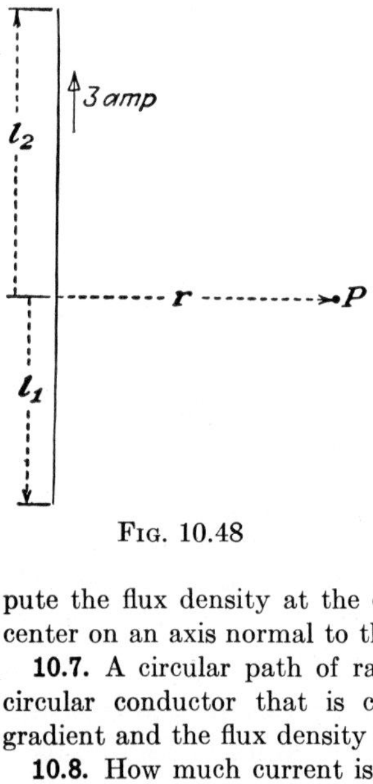

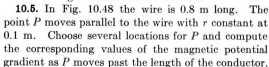

10.2. Solve Prob. 10.1 if r is changed to 2 in.

10.3. Compare the results in Probs. 10.1 and 10.2 with what they would be if the conductor were of infinite length.

10.4. In Fig. 10.48, $l_1 = -0.4$ m and $l_2 = 0.4$ m and the point P moves from the surface of the wire outward. Choose several values of r, and compute the corresponding values of the magnetic potential gradient at P. Plot the curve showing the relation between the gradient and the value of r.

10.5. In Fig. 10.48 the wire is 0.8 m long. The point P moves parallel to the wire with r constant at 0.1 m. Choose several locations for P and compute the corresponding values of the magnetic potential gradient as P moves past the length of the conductor.

FIG. 10.48

10.6. A certain isolated rectangular one-turn coil of fine wire is 0.2 by 0.5 m and carries 400 ma. Compute the flux density at the center of the turn and that at a point 0.4 m from the center on an axis normal to the plane of the turn.

10.7. A circular path of radius 0.05 m surrounds and is concentric with a long, circular conductor that is carrying 150 amp. Compute the magnetic potential gradient and the flux density at any point in the path.

10.8. How much current is required in a long, circular conductor to produce outside it a flux density of 8×10^{-5} wb per sq m at a distance of 0.2 m from the conductor center?

10.9. A point P moves in a horizontal line that is normal to and 0.1 m above a long, horizontal, circular conductor that is carrying 100 amp. Write the equation that expresses the relation between the magnetic potential gradient at P and the distance x of P from the point on the line directly above the conductor. Compute the reluctance drop from $x = 0$ to $x = 0.1$ m and that from $x = 0$ to $x = 0.2$ m.

10.10. A long No. 14 copper conductor is carrying 10 amp. For each meter of length compute the flux enclosed in the volume between the conductor surface and a surface of 0.5 m radius concentric with the conductor.

10.11. A certain long, rectangular, copper bus bar that is ⅛ in. by 1 in. is carrying 200 amp. Compute the flux density at the center of each side and that at a point 4 in. from the center of the longer side on a line normal to the surface.

10.12. Compute the flux density at the corner of a long copper conductor that is 0.2 in. square when the current is 80 amp.

10.13. A certain long copper conductor that has a diameter of 0.4 in. is carrying 100 amp. At what point within the conductor is the flux density equal to what it is at a distance of 5 in. from the conductor center?

10.14. At what point in the conductor of Prob. 10.13 is the flux density 0.001 wb per sq m?

10.15. Compute the flux per meter length of the conductor of Prob. 10.13.

10.16. Two parallel circular conductors spaced 0.3 m center to center form part of a closed circuit. For an instant when the current is 150 amp, compute the magnetic potential gradient and the flux density at a point 0.05 m from the center of one conductor on a line joining the conductor centers.

10.17. The two copper wires of a certain transmission line have a diameter of 0.325 in. and are spaced 2 ft center to center. For an instant when the currents in the wires are 150 amp, compute the flux between the wires for each mile of line.

10.18. Two long, circular conductors in a horizontal plane carry equal currents in opposite directions and are spaced 2 m center to center. The flux density at a point midway between the centers is 10 μwb per sq m.

a. Compute the flux density at a point between the centers, in the plane of the centers, 0.5 m from one center.

b. Compute the flux density at a point 1.5 m above one center.

c. Compute the flux density at a point not between the centers, in the plane of the centers, 0.5 m from one center.

10.19. Two long, parallel, circular copper conductors carry 200 amp in opposite directions and are spaced horizontally 0.2 m center to center. A point P moves at right angles to the conductors in a plane that is 0.04 m from and parallel to a plane through the centers. Determine the equation of the horizontal component and that of the vertical component of the magnetic potential gradient at P in terms of the distance x from a point directly above the left-hand conductor.

10.20. From the equations derived in Prob. 10.19 compute the horizontal and the vertical components of the gradient at P for various values of x in 0.025-m steps from -0.125 to $+0.125$ m. From these components construct diagrams showing the direction and the magnitude of the resultant gradient at each of the selected points.

10.21. For the conductors of Prob. 10.19 compute the reluctance drop as P moves from a point directly above one conductor to one directly above the other.

10.22. The conductors of Prob. 10.19 are 500 mils in diameter. Determine the radius of and the location of the center of the flux circle that passes through a point 1 in. above the center of one conductor. Repeat for a point that is 5 in. above the center of one conductor.

10 23. Determine the radii of and the location of the centers of the equipotential circles that pass through the points specified in Prob. 10.22.

10.24. Solve Prob. 10.19 if the currents are in the same direction.

10.25. Two long, parallel, circular conductors carry equal currents in the same direction and lie in a horizontal plane. The distance between conductor centers is D. The origin of a system of coordinate axes is at the point midway between the centers. Prove that the equations of the flux lines about the conductors is $(x^2 + y^2)^2 - D^2x^2/2 + D^2y^2/2 = C$, where C is a constant of integration.

10.26. For the conductors of Prob. 10.25 determine the value of C for the flux line through the point at a distance D directly above the point midway between the centers.

Compute the coordinates of enough points on the flux line to enable it to be sketched.

10.27. Prove that H_P in (10.38) is a maximum when $b = D/2$.

10.28. A certain circular one-turn coil of fine wire has a diameter of 0.25 m and carries 2 amp. Compute the flux density at the center of the coil.

10.29. At what point on the longitudinal axis of the coil of Prob. 10.28 is the flux density 25 per cent of that at the coil center?

10.30. A certain circular one-turn coil is 0.1 m in diameter and carries 120 amp. Compute the reluctance drop between two points on the longitudinal axis on opposite sides of the coil and each 0.1 m from the coil center.

10.31. From the center of the coil of Prob. 10.30 to what point on the longitudinal axis is the reluctance drop 48 per cent of the coil mmf?

10.32. A certain single-layer air-core solenoid is 0.2 m long and has a turn diameter of 0.05 m. There are 200 closely wound turns in it. With 2 amp in the solenoid compute the reluctance drop between points at the ends of the solenoid on the longitudinal axis.

10.33. For the solenoid of Prob. 10.32 compute the flux density at its center and that at the center of an end turn.

10.34. For the solenoid of Prob. 10.32 plot the curve showing how the flux density varies along the longitudinal axis.

10.35. A certain solenoid that is 0.125 m long has an inside diameter of 0.3 m and an outside diameter of 0.4 m. A one hundred-turn search coil that has an area of 0.001 sq m is placed so that its axes coincide with those of the solenoid. When 3 amp were suddenly reversed in the solenoid, a fluxmeter connected to the search coil had 15 divisions deflection. The fluxmeter calibration was 100 μwb per division with a one-turn search coil. Approximately how many turns are in the solenoid?

10.36. A certain coil consists of 11 turns of No. 18 wire spaced 0.01 m apart. With 5 amp in the coil compute the flux density at its center and at the center of an end turn. The diameter of each turn is 0.05 m.

10.37. A No. 24 enamel- and cotton-covered wire has an over-all diameter of 6.42×10^{-4} m. A single layer of this wire forms a solenoid 0.125 m long and 0.05 m in diameter. With 6 amp in the coil compute the flux density at its center and that at the center of an end turn.

10.38. A certain air-core solenoid that has a length of 1.5 m and a diameter of 0.05 m is wound with 2,000 closely spaced turns. With 2 amp in the solenoid compute the flux density at its center.

10.39. Solve Prob. 10.38 if the solenoid diameter is 0.025 m.

10.40. Two long, parallel, circular conductors are separated 0.25 m in air. One carries 200 amp, the other 400 amp in the same direction.

a. Compute the magnetic potential gradient and the flux density produced in the center of each conductor by the current in the other.

b. Compute the amount and the direction of the force exerted on each conductor per meter of length.

10.41. In a certain d-c voltmeter the flux density in the air gap is radial and uniform at 0.15 wb per sq m. The moving coil is 0.031 by 0.02 m and contains 60.5 turns. The instrument requires 10 ma for full-scale deflection of 80°. Compute the torque required per degree of deflection.

10.42. The three copper wires of a certain transmission line are spaced 0.3 m between centers in a horizontal plane. At a certain instant there are 120 amp in the center wire in one direction, and 80 and 40 amp, respectively, in the outer wires in the opposite direction.

a. For the given instant, compute the amount and the direction of the force exerted on each wire per mile of line.

b. For the given instant, compute the flux densities at points 0.1 m above each wire center.

10.43. Certain of the dimensions of a switch are in Fig. 10.49. During a short circuit on a system there were 2,000 amp in the switch. Assume that the relations

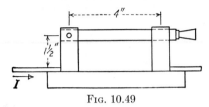

Fig. 10.49

derived for a circular conductor apply here, and compute the flux density at the center of the switch blade. For the same point compute the force per unit length tending to open the switch.

10.44. A circular current-carrying one-turn coil is in a uniform magnetic field with the plane of the coil parallel to the field. Prove that the torque T acting to rotate the coil is $T = \pi B r^2 I$ newton-m, where B is the flux density in webers per square meter, r is the radius of the coil in meters, and I is the current in amperes in the coil.

CHAPTER 11

ELECTRIC FIELDS

11.1. Electric Field about an Isolated Charge. When a concentrated charge of $+Q$ coul is isolated in air, electric flux lines emanate radially in all directions. Since an equipotential surface in an electric field is everywhere normal to the dielectric flux lines, an equipotential surface in this field is a spherical one whose center is at the point where the charge is located, and the trace of an equipotential surface in the plane is a circle, as in Fig. 11.1. The electric flux Ψ coul emanating from the charge of Q coul passes through the spherical equipotential surface. The surface at a distance r m from the point of charge concentration has an area of $4\pi r^2$ sq m. The electric flux density D normal to the surface is $D = \Psi/4\pi r^2$ coul per sq m.

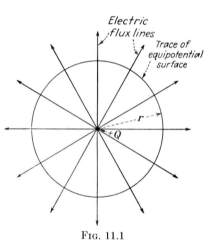

Electric
flux lines
Trace of
equipotential
surface

r

$+Q$

Fig. 11.1

In Fig. 11.2, two points a and b are at the respective distances r_1 and r_2 m from a charge of $+Q$ coul at a point O. For the present assume that O, a, and b are in the same plane. The voltage drop V_{ab} from a to b is to be computed. Consider two spherical equipotential surfaces whose respective radii are r and $r + dr$ m. The traces of the surfaces are the circles in Fig. 11.2. The elastance between the surfaces is the infinitesimal $dS = dr/\epsilon_v \epsilon A$ daraf, where A is the area in square meters of the spherical surface whose radius is r m. The infinitesimal voltage dv between the surfaces is $dv = \Psi \, dS = \Psi \, dr/\epsilon_v \epsilon A$ v. But Ψ/A is the dielectric flux density $D = \Psi/(4\pi r^2)$; thus

$$dv = \frac{\Psi \, dr}{4\pi \epsilon_v \epsilon r^2} \quad \text{v} \qquad (11.1)$$

The voltage drop V_{ab} can be obtained by integrating (11.1) from the limit $r = r_1$ to $r = r_2$. Hence

$$V_{ab} = \frac{\Psi}{4\pi\epsilon_v\epsilon} \int_{r_1}^{r_2} \frac{dr}{r^2} = \frac{\Psi}{4\pi\epsilon_v\epsilon} \left[-\frac{1}{r} \right]_{r_1}^{r_2} = \frac{\Psi}{4\pi\epsilon_v\epsilon} \left[\frac{1}{r_1} - \frac{1}{r_2} \right] \qquad \text{v} \quad (11.2)$$

Here $\epsilon_v = 8.85 \times 10^{-12}$ and ϵ is the dielectric constant of the material in which the charge is located.

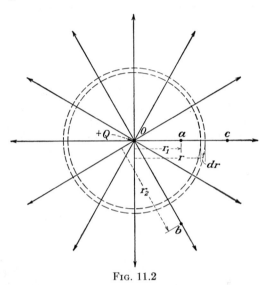

FIG. 11.2

The voltage gradient $\mathcal{E}$ in the electric field of a concentrated charge is dv/dr, which, from (11.1), is

$$\mathcal{E} = \frac{\Psi}{4\pi\epsilon_v\epsilon r^2} \qquad \text{v per m} \qquad (11.3)$$

This shows that the voltage gradient decreases inversely as the square of the distance from the point of charge concentration.

Since $\Psi/4\pi r^2 = D$, then $\mathcal{E} = D/\epsilon_v\epsilon$ v per m, showing that in the electric field being considered, the voltage gradient is directly proportional to the electric flux density and inversely proportional to the dielectric constant of the material.

In (11.2) the path of integration was radial from a spherical equipotential surface containing the point a to another spherical equipotential surface containing the point b. In Fig. 11.2 the point c is in the same surface as b so that the potential from a to c equals that from a to b. In an electric field the voltage gradient at a point is in the direction of the electric flux through the point. The difference in potential between two points along one path is equal to that along any other path and can be computed by the use of a line integral. The path of integration need not be in the direction of the voltage gradient. The voltage drop V_{ab} between two points a and b in an electric field is expressed as $V_{ab} = \int_{l_1}^{l_2} \mathcal{E} \cos \theta \, dl$, where θ is the angle in radians between the direction of the voltage gradient and the path of integration, l_1 and l_2 are the respective distances in meters from an arbitrary point to a and b, and dl m is an infinitesimal distance measured from an arbitrary point in the path of integration.

Example 1. In Fig. 11.3 are represented two points a and b in the electric field

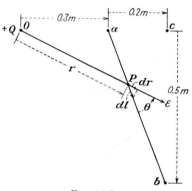

FIG. 11.3

established in air by a concentrated charge of $+Q$ coul at the point O. The charge is of such magnitude that the voltage gradient at a is 5 v per m. Compute the voltage drop from a to b by integration along the line joining the points.

Solution. From (11.3), $\Psi = 4\pi\epsilon_v\epsilon r^2\mathcal{E}$. Here $\epsilon_v = 8.85 \times 10^{-12}$, $\epsilon = 1$ (for air), $r = 0.3$ m, and $\mathcal{E} = 5$ v per m. Then

$$\Psi = 4\pi \times 8.85 \times 10^{-12} \times 1$$
$$\times 0.3^2 \times 5 = 50 \ \mu\mu\text{coul}$$

The charge is equal numerically to the number of electric lines, or 50 $\mu\mu$coul. To compute the voltage drop V_{ab} by integration along the line joining the points, let a point P on the line be chosen. The voltage gradient $\mathcal{E}$ at P is directed along the line OP as shown and makes an angle θ with the line ab. The voltage drop V_{ab} between a and b is $V_{ab} = \int_0^{l_{ab}} \mathcal{E} \cos \theta \, dl$ v, where $\mathcal{E} \cos \theta$ is the component of $\mathcal{E}$ that is directed along the line of length l_{ab} extending from a to b, and dl m is an infinitesimal length of the line measured from P toward b.

As P moves along the line ab, $\mathcal{E}$ changes in magnitude because the distance from O to P changes. θ also changes because $\mathcal{E}$ is always directed radially from O along the line OP. To integrate the previous expression, the variables $\mathcal{E}$, θ, and dl may be expressed in terms of the distance r. Here $\mathcal{E} = \Psi/4\pi\epsilon_v\epsilon r^2$, which may be written as $\mathcal{E} = k/r^2$ since Ψ, ϵ_v, and ϵ are constants. With $\mathcal{E}$ given as 5 v per m at $r = 0.3$ m, then $k = 5 \times 0.3^2 = 0.45$, and $\mathcal{E} = 0.45/r^2$ v per m. In Fig. 11.3 it can be seen that $dl \cos \theta = dr$. Hence

$$V_{ab} = \int_0^{l_{ab}} \mathcal{E} \cos \theta \, dl = \int_{0.3}^{0.707} \frac{0.45 \, dr}{r^2} = \left[\frac{-0.45}{r} \right]_{0.3}^{0.707}$$
$$= 0.45 \left[\frac{1}{0.3} - \frac{1}{0.707} \right] = 0.86 \text{ v}$$

If an electric field of uniform density D coul per sq m is normal to a surface of area A sq m, the electric flux passing through the surface is $\Psi = DA$ coul. If D makes an angle θ radians with a normal to the surface, then

$$\Psi = DA \cos \theta \text{ coul}$$

If D makes an angle θ radians with a normal to an infinitesimal surface of area dA sq m, the infinitesimal flux passing through the surface is

$$d\Psi = D \cos \theta \, dA \text{ coul}$$

Integration of the preceding expression over a given surface yields the net flux through the surface. To perform the integration analytically, it is necessary that the equation be known that expresses the magnitude and the direction of D as a function of any point in the surface being considered.

An extension of the above principle leads to Gauss' theorem which states that the result of integration over a closed surface is equal to the net charge in coulombs enclosed within the surface. The net charge is the algebraic sum of the individual positive and negatives charge on any bodies enclosed.

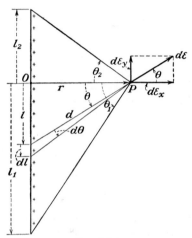

Fig. 11.4

11.2. Electric Field about an Isolated Charged Wire. Figure 11.4 represents an isolated wire of length $l_2 - l_1$ m that is charged with Q coul per m of length. The wire diameter is assumed to be negligible compared with the other dimensions involved. The voltage gradient $\mathcal{E}$ is to be computed at a point P, r m from the wire on a line normal to it. The line divides the wire at the point O into the lengths l_1 and l_2. Since all parts of the wire are not at the same distance from P, the wire may be divided into small elements and the effects of the charges on these elements at P added to obtain the combined effect. Consider the infinitesimal element dl m long at a distance l m from O. The element is d m from P and has a charge of $Q \, dl$ coul. The electric flux emanating from the charge is $\Psi \, dl$ lines, where Ψ is numerically equal to Q. Think of this flux as distributed uniformly normal to the surface of a sphere of d m radius with its center coincident with that of dl. Then P is in this surface. The gradient at the surface of a sphere of d m radius surrounding a charge at the center is equal to the charge divided by $4\pi\epsilon_v\epsilon \, d^2$ [see (11.3)]. The infinitesimal gradient $d\mathcal{E}$ at P is directed along line d as shown and is $d\mathcal{E} = \Psi \, dl/4\pi\epsilon_v\epsilon \, d^2$ v per m. As shown in Fig. 11.4, $d\mathcal{E}$ may be resolved into the normal components $d\mathcal{E}_y$ and $d\mathcal{E}_x$. But $d\mathcal{E}_y = d\mathcal{E} \sin \theta$, where θ is the angle between d and r.   Hence

$$d\mathcal{E}_y = \frac{\Psi \sin \theta \, dl}{4\pi\epsilon_v\epsilon \, d^2} \qquad \text{v per m} \tag{11.4}$$

The resultant gradient $\mathcal{E}_y$ at P parallel to the charged wire can be obtained by integrating (11.4).   Since both θ and d vary with l, it is necessary to express (11.4) in terms of a single variable before integrating.   Let θ be the variable.   From Fig. 11.4 it can be seen that $d = r \sec \theta$ and $l = r \tan \theta$. Then $dl = d(r \tan \theta) = r \sec^2 \theta \, d\theta$.   Substitution of the values of d and dl in (11.4) yields $d\mathcal{E}_y = \Psi \sin \theta \, d\theta/4\pi\epsilon_v\epsilon r$, from which

$$\mathcal{E}_y = \frac{\Psi}{4\pi\epsilon_v\epsilon r} \int_{\theta_1}^{\theta_2} \sin \theta \, d\theta = \frac{\Psi}{4\pi\epsilon_v\epsilon r} [-\cos \theta]_{\theta_1}^{\theta_2} = \frac{\Psi}{4\pi\epsilon_v\epsilon r}$$
$$(\cos \theta_1 - \cos \theta_2) \qquad \text{v per m} \tag{11.5}$$

If P is opposite the center of the charged wire, θ_2 is equal numerically to θ_1 and $\mathcal{E}_y$ is zero.   The y components at P of the gradient caused by the charges above O are neutralized by the y components there of the gradient caused by the charges below O.

In Fig. 11.4 the gradient $d\mathcal{E}_x$ at P is $d\mathcal{E} \cos \theta$; hence

$$d\mathcal{E}_x = \frac{\Psi \cos \theta \, dl}{4\pi\epsilon_v\epsilon \, d^2} \qquad \text{v per m} \tag{11.6}$$

The resultant gradient $\mathcal{E}_x$ at P normal to the charged wire is obtained by integrating (11.6).   By substituting for dl and d in terms of θ the values obtained above, the relation $d\mathcal{E}_x = \dfrac{\Psi}{4\pi\epsilon_v\epsilon r} \displaystyle\int_{\theta_1}^{\theta_2} \cos \theta \, d\theta$ is obtained.   Then

$$\mathcal{E}_x = \frac{\Psi}{4\pi\epsilon_v\epsilon} [\sin \theta]_{\theta_1}^{\theta_2} = \frac{\Psi}{4\pi\epsilon_v\epsilon r} (\sin \theta_2 - \sin \theta_1) \qquad \text{v per m} \tag{11.7}$$

The resultant gradient $\mathcal{E}$ at P in Fig. 11.4 is the square root of the sum of the squares of $\mathcal{E}_x$ and $\mathcal{E}_y$.   Hence

$$\mathcal{E} = \sqrt{\mathcal{E}_x^2 + \mathcal{E}_y^2} = \frac{\Psi}{4\pi\epsilon_v\epsilon r} \sqrt{(\cos \theta_1 - \cos \theta_2)^2 + (\sin \theta_2 - \sin \theta_1)^2}$$

which can be simplified to

$$\mathcal{E} = \frac{\Psi}{4\pi\epsilon_v\epsilon r} \sqrt{2[1 - \cos (\theta_1 - \theta_2)]} \qquad \text{v per m} \tag{11.8}$$

As P moves parallel to the charged wire at a constant r m from the wire, the voltage gradient at the point varies as expressed by (11.8).   The gradient is a maximum when $\cos (\theta_1 - \theta_2)$ is a minimum.   This occurs when $\theta_1 - \theta_2$ is a maximum with P opposite the center of the charged wire.   There $\mathcal{E}_y = 0$, and $\theta_1 = -\theta_2$; therefore

$$\text{Maximum } \mathcal{E} = \text{maximum } \mathcal{E}_x = \frac{\Psi}{2\pi\,\epsilon_v\epsilon r} \sin\theta_1 \qquad \text{v per m}$$

Example 1.   A small wire that is 4 m long is isolated in air and has $-16\ \mu\mu\text{coul}$ distributed uniformly along its length.   Compute the magnitude and the direction of the voltage gradient at the points P_1, P_2, and P_3, in Fig. 11.5.

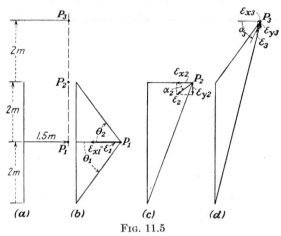

FIG. 11.5

Solution.   The electric flux per unit length is

$$\Psi = \frac{16 \times 10^{-12} \text{ coul}}{4 \text{ m}} = 4 \times 10^{-12} \text{ coul per m}$$

At each point the distance from the point to the wire or its extension is 1.5 m. This is the distance r in (11.5) and (11.7).

At P_1, $\theta_1 = -\theta_2$.   In Fig. 11.5b it can be seen that

$$\sin\theta_1 = \frac{2}{\sqrt{2^2 + 1.5^2}} = 0.8$$

Since P_1 is opposite the center of the wire, there is no gradient component there parallel to the wire.   The resultant gradient $\mathcal{E}_1$ is equal to the component gradient normal to the wire.   Since $\epsilon_v = 8.85 \times 10^{-12}$ and $\epsilon = 1$ for air, then, by (11.7),

$$\mathcal{E}_1 = \frac{4 \times 10^{-12}}{2\pi \times 8.85 \times 10^{-12} \times 1 \times 1.5} \times 0.8 = 0.0384 \text{ v per m}$$

At P_2, Fig. 11.5c shows that $\theta_2 = 0$; hence $\cos\theta_2 = 1$, and $\sin\theta_2 = 0$.   Also $\sin\theta_1 = 4/\sqrt{4^2 + 1.5^2} = 0.94$ and $\cos\theta_1 = 1.5/\sqrt{4^2 + 1.5^2} = 0.35$.
From (11.7),

$$\mathcal{E}_{x2} = \frac{4 \times 10^{-12}}{4\pi \times 8.85 \times 10^{-12} \times 1 \times 1.5} \times 0.94$$

$$= 0.0225 \text{ v per m}$$

From (11.5),

$$\mathcal{E}_{y2} = \frac{4 \times 10^{-12}}{4\pi \times 8.85 \times 10^{-12} \times 1 \times 1.5} (1 - 0.35)$$
$$= 0.0156 \text{ v per m}$$

The resultant gradient $\mathcal{E}_2$ at P_2 has the magnitude

$$\mathcal{E}_2 = \sqrt{0.0225^2 + 0.0156^2} = 0.0274 \text{ v per m}$$

It is directed toward the wire at the angle α_2 below the horizontal, where

$$\alpha_2 = \tan^{-1} \frac{0.0156}{0.0225} = 34.7°$$

At P_3, Fig. 11.5d shows that $\cos \theta_2 = 1.5/\sqrt{2^2 + 1.5^2} = 0.6$,

$$\sin \theta_2 = \frac{2}{\sqrt{2^2 + 1.5^2}} = 0.8$$

$\cos \theta_1 = 1.5/\sqrt{6^2 + 1.5^2} = 0.24$, and $\sin \theta_1 = 6/\sqrt{6^2 + 1.5^2} = 0.97$.
From (11.7),

$$\mathcal{E}_{z3} = \frac{4 \times 10^{-12}}{4\pi \times 8.85 \times 10^{-12} \times 1 \times 1.5}$$
$$(0.97 - 0.8) = 0.0041 \text{ v per m}$$

From (11.5),

$$\mathcal{E}_{y3} = \frac{4 \times 10^{-12}}{4\pi \times 8.85 \times 10^{-12} \times 1 \times 1.5}$$
$$(0.6 - 0.24) = 0.0086 \text{ v per m}$$

The resultant gradient $\mathcal{E}_3$ at P_3 has the magnitude

$$\mathcal{E}_3 = \sqrt{0.0041^2 + 0.0086^2} = 0.0095 \text{ v per m}$$

It is directed toward the wire at an angle α_3 below the horizontal, where

$$\alpha_3 = \tan^{-1} \frac{0.0086}{0.0041} = 64.5°$$

The electric fields relations in air near an infinitely long, charged, isolated conductor can be determined by an extension of the principles used in deriving (11.5) and (11.7). In Fig. 11.5, if the conductor is infinitely long, θ_1 becomes $\pi/2$ radians and θ_2 becomes $-\pi/2$ radians. Since $\cos (\pi/2) = \cos (-\pi/2)$, then (11.5) reduces to zero. This means that there is zero voltage gradient and no electric flux parallel to an infinitely long, charged conductor. Since $\sin (\pi/2) = -\sin (-\pi/2) = 1$, then (11.7) reduces to $\mathcal{E}_x = \Psi/(2\pi\epsilon_v\epsilon r)$ v per m as the gradient normal to an infinitely long, isolated, charged conductor at a distance r m from the conductor center.

In the preceding derivations it has been assumed that the charge was distributed uniformly along a conductor of negligible diameter. In Fig. 11.6 is represented a 1-m section of an infinitely long, charged conductor of radius r_1 m. Assume that a charge of Q coul per m is distributed uniformly over the conductor surface. The voltage gradient $\mathcal{E}$ is to be determined at a point P that is r m from the conductor center. Consider an infinitesimal element of area dA on the conductor surface, an element

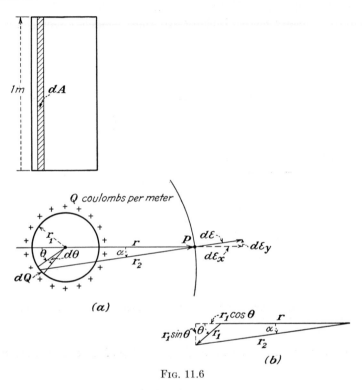

(a)

(b)

Fig. 11.6

intercepted by the angle $d\theta$. Consider the element as a section of an infinitely long, charged conductor of negligible diameter. The charge dQ on the infinitesimal element is to the charge Q as the angle $d\theta$ is to a complete revolution or 2π radians. Then $dQ = Q \, d\theta/2\pi$. The electric flux $d\Psi$ coul emanating per m length of the element is $d\Psi = \Psi \, d\theta/2\pi$, where Ψ is numerically equal to Q. Since element dA is a section of a conductor of infinite length, the electric flux lines emanate normal to and radially from dA. Think of the element as at the center of a cylindrical equipotential surface through P. In Fig. 11.6 the radius of this surface is r_2 m. The electric flux from dA through P produces the infinitesimal voltage gradient $d\mathcal{E}$ at P normal to the surface. By analogy to the conditions previously derived $d\mathcal{E} = d\Psi/2\pi\epsilon_v\epsilon r_2$. But $d\Psi = \Psi \, d\theta/2\pi$; thus

$d\mathcal{E} = \Psi \, d\theta / 4\pi^2 \epsilon_v \epsilon r_2$.   This gradient can be resolved into the normal components shown, $d\mathcal{E}_x$ and $d\mathcal{E}_y$.

The total voltage gradient $\mathcal{E}$ at P in Fig. 11.6 can be obtained by adding the component gradients produced by all the charged elements in the conductor surface.   Because of the conductor symmetry the summation of the y components is zero, since the y component of every element above the line through the conductor center and P is neutralized by the y component of another element below the line.   The x components of the

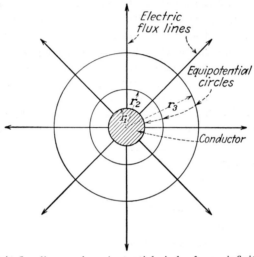

Fig. 11.7   Electric flux lines and equipotential circles for an infinitely long cylinder with uniformly distributed charge.

gradients all add directly.   From the geometry of the figure, it can be seen that

$$d\mathcal{E}_x = d\mathcal{E} \cos \alpha$$

and from Fig. 11.6b that $\cos \alpha = (r + r_1 \cos \theta)/r_2$ and

$$r_2^2 = (r + r_1 \cos \theta)^2 + (r_1 \sin \theta)^2 = r^2 + r_1^2 + 2rr_1 \cos \theta$$

Combination of relations above yields

$$d\mathcal{E}_x = \frac{\Psi (r + r_1 \cos \theta) \, d\theta}{4\pi^2 \epsilon_v \epsilon (r^2 + r_1^2 + 2rr_1 \cos \theta)} \tag{11.9}$$

The total voltage gradient $\mathcal{E}$ at P is obtained by integrating (11.9) with limits on θ from 0 to 2π radians.   Hence

$$\mathcal{E} = \frac{\Psi}{4\pi^2 \epsilon_v \epsilon} \int_0^{2\pi} \frac{(r + r_1 \cos \theta) \, d\theta}{r^2 + r_1^2 + 2rr_1 \cos \theta} \tag{11.10}$$

Integration of (11.10) and substitution of the limits yields

$$\mathcal{E} = \frac{\Psi}{2\pi\epsilon_v\epsilon r} \quad \text{v per m}$$

This result shows that a charge distributed uniformly over the surface of an infinitely long cylinder produces the same voltage gradient at a point outside the cylinder as would be produced at the point if all the charge were concentrated along the center line of the cylinder.

For an infinitely long, charged cylindrical conductor the electric flux lines and the equipotential lines can be represented as in Fig. 11.7. The electric flux lines extend radially outward from a positively charged conductor and radially inward to a negatively charged conductor. The equipotential lines are circles concentric with the conductor. The equipotential circles drawn have radii such that equal voltages exist between adjacent circles. The ratio of the radius of one circle to that of the next smaller circle is the same for each pair of circles.

11.3. Experimental Plotting of an Electric Field. The location of the equipotential lines in a given plane in an electric field can be determined by an experimental method using an electrolyte to represent the dielectric.*

A glass plate was coated with paraffin. To a uniform depth paraffin was then removed in the form of the cross section of a pin-type insulator. The plate was then covered with a copper sulfate solution until the liquid depth over the portion representing the insulator was five times that over the surrounding area. Thus was formed the equivalent of an insulator whose dielectric constant was five times that of the surrounding air.

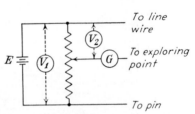

FIG. 11.8 Circuit used in drawing equipotential lines.

Copper conductors were used to represent the line and tie wires and the metal supporting pin. Copper strips were used in the insulator section to represent the conducting layers of the cemented joints. The electric circuit used is shown in Fig. 11.8. A constant d-c voltage was applied between the conductors representing the line wires and the pin.

To locate points on a given equipotential line, the reading on voltmeter V_2 was set to the desired value by moving the rheostat slider. The exploring point in the solution was then moved until the galvanometer G read zero. Thus a starting point on the equipotential line was obtained.

* See Roscoe H. George, Kirk A. Oplinger, and Charles F. Harding, "Improved Method of Visualizing and Photographing the Dielectric Field," *Purdue Univ. Expt. Sta. Bull.* 29, 1927.

The exploring point was then moved along a path such that the galvanometer deflection was kept at zero; hence the exploring point was following an equipotential line. The exploring point was connected to a pantograph (see Fig. 11.9) and the equipotential line was drawn directly on a sheet of paper. The reading of V_2 was set to a new value and the corresponding equipotential line drawn in the same manner as before. After the equipotential lines had been drawn, the electric flux lines were

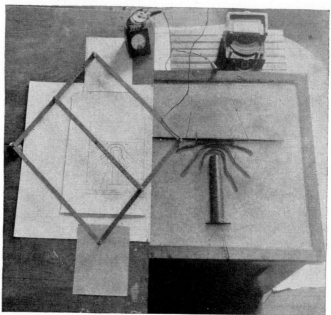

FIG. 11.9   Apparatus used in drawing equipotential lines.

sketched in normal to the equipotential lines. In Figs. 11.10 and 11.11 are shown the equipotential and the flux lines in two planes through the insulator perpendicular to each other. In any other plane a different field distribution exists.

11.4. Electric Field Relations about Transmission-line Conductors. In Fig. 11.12a are represented two parallel circular conductors such as might be used for a transmission line. Each has r m radius and they are spaced D m center to center. The shapes of the electric and the equipotential lines are to be determined for the case in which the charges on the conductors are equal in magnitude and opposite in sign. Consider a point P that is x m to the right of and y m above a point midway between the conductors. At P a voltage gradient ε_1 is established along the line r_1 by the positive charge on the left-hand conductor and a voltage gradient ε_2

along the line r_2 by the negative charge on the right-hand conductor. Let Ψ be the dielectric flux in coulombs per meter length of the conductors.

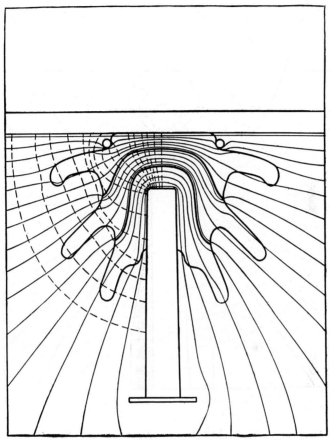

FIG. 11.10   Equipotential and electric flux lines in a plane through a pin-type insulator parallel to the conductor.

Assuming that the conductors are infinitely long,

$$\mathcal{E}_1 = \frac{\Psi}{2\pi\epsilon_v\epsilon r_1} \quad \text{and} \quad \mathcal{E}_2 = \frac{\Psi}{2\pi\epsilon_v\epsilon r_2}$$

The resultant voltage gradient $\mathcal{E}$ is the vector sum of $\mathcal{E}_1$ and $\mathcal{E}_2$. These may be resolved into the components $\mathcal{E}_{x1}$, $\mathcal{E}_{y1}$, $\mathcal{E}_{x2}$, and $\mathcal{E}_{y2}$, as shown in Fig. 11.12b. It can be seen that $\mathcal{E}_{x1} = \mathcal{E}_1 \cos \alpha_1$, $\mathcal{E}_{y1} = \mathcal{E}_1 \sin \alpha_1$, $\mathcal{E}_{x2} = \mathcal{E}_2 \cos \alpha_2$, and $\mathcal{E}_{y2} = \mathcal{E}_2 \sin \alpha_2$.

In Fig. 11.12a it can be seen that $\cos \alpha_1 = (D/2 + x)/r_1$, $\sin \alpha_1 = y/r_1$,

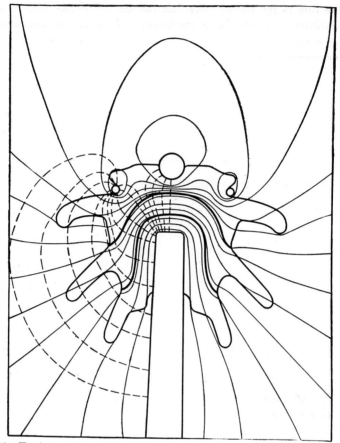

FIG. 11.11 Equipotential and electric flux lines in a plane through a pin-type insulator perpendicular to the conductor.

$\cos \alpha_2 = (D/2 - x)/r_2$, and $\sin \alpha_2 = y/r_2$. Then

$$\mathcal{E}_{x1} = \frac{\Psi(D/2 + x)}{2\pi\epsilon_v \epsilon r_1^2} \qquad \text{and} \qquad \mathcal{E}_{x2} = \frac{\Psi(D/2 - x)}{2\pi\epsilon_v \epsilon r_2^2}$$

Since $\mathcal{E}_x = \mathcal{E}_{x1} + \mathcal{E}_{x2}$, then

$$\mathcal{E}_x = \frac{\Psi}{2\pi\epsilon_v \epsilon}\left(\frac{D/2 + x}{r_1^2} + \frac{D/2 - x}{r_2^2}\right)$$

Also

$$\mathcal{E}_{y1} = \frac{\Psi y}{2\pi\epsilon_v \epsilon r_1^2} \qquad \text{and} \qquad \mathcal{E}_{y2} = \frac{\Psi y}{2\pi\epsilon_v \epsilon r_2^2}$$

Since $\mathcal{E}_y = \mathcal{E}_{y1} - \mathcal{E}_{y2}$, then

$$\mathcal{E}_y = \frac{\Psi y}{2\pi\epsilon_v \epsilon}\left(\frac{r_2^2 - r_1^2}{r_1^2 r_2^2}\right)$$

The direction of the electric flux line through P is that of the voltage gradient ε there. Let dy/dx be the slope at P of the electric flux line. This slope is also $\tan \gamma = \varepsilon_y/\varepsilon_x$ in Fig. 11.12b. From this fact and the above expressions for ε_y and ε_x

$$\frac{dy}{dx} = \frac{y(r_2^2 - r_1^2)}{(D/2)(r_2^2 + r_1^2) + x(r_2^2 - r_1^2)} \tag{11.11}$$

From Fig. 11.12a it can be seen that $r_1^2 = (D/2 + x)^2 + y^2$ and

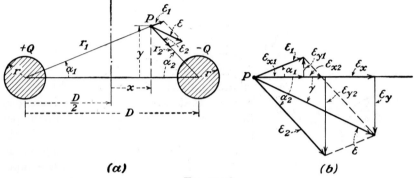

(a)   **(b)**

Fɪɢ. 11.12

$r_2^2 = (D/2 - x^2) + y^2$. Then

$$r_2^2 - r_1^2 = -2Dx \qquad \text{and} \qquad r_2^2 + r_1^2 = 2(D^2/4 + x^2 + y^2)$$

Substitution of these values of $r_2^2 - r_1^2$ and $r_2^2 + r_1^2$ in (11.11) and simplification yields

$$\frac{dy}{dx} = \frac{-2xy}{D^2/4 - x^2 + y^2} \tag{11.12}$$

Since (11.12) is the same as (10.26), Art. 10.6, its solution is the same and the equation of an electric flux line is

$$x^2 + y^2 - ky = \frac{D^2}{4} \tag{11.13}$$

This is the equation of a family of circles whose centers are on the y axis. The electric flux circles in Fig. 11.12 are identical to the equipotential circles in the magnetic field of Fig. 10.25. It follows that in Fig. 11.12a the electric flux circle through the point whose coordinates are $x = a$ and $y = b$ has its center at $x = 0$ and $y = [a^2 + b^2 - (D/2)^2]/2b$. The radius r_ψ of the circle is $r_\psi = \sqrt{[a^2 + b^2 - (D/2)^2]^2/4b^2 + D^2/4}$.

From the above relations any number of electric flux circles can be located in space about the conductors in Fig. 11.12a, each circle corresponding to a set of values for a and b. The circles are located with respect to each other in the same fashion as are the magnetic equipotential circles of Fig. 10.25.

Since the electric flux circles about the charged conductors of Fig. 11.12 are identical to the magnetic equipotential circles about the current-carrying conductors of Fig. 10.25, the electric equipotential lines about the charged conductors will be circles identical to the magnetic flux lines about the current-carrying conductors. An electric equipotential circle through the point $x = a$ and $y = b$ has its center on the x axis at the point $x = (a^2 + b^2 + D^2/4)/2a$ and a radius

$$r_e = \sqrt{\left[\frac{(a^2 + b^2 + D^2/4)}{2a}\right]^2 - \frac{D^2}{4}}$$

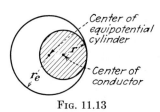

FIG. 11.13

In the above derivations it was assumed that the charge was distributed uniformly over the conductor surface and that this charge was equivalent in its effects to a charge of equal amount per unit length concentrated along the conductor center. That this assumption may be in error will be shown. Consider an equipotential cylinder that is tangent to a conductor as in Fig. 11.13. The radius r_e of this circle, obtained by assigning the values $a = -D/2 + r$ and $b = 0$, is

$$r_e = \frac{r(D - r)}{D - 2r} \qquad (11.14)$$

Such a result would mean that the radius of the equipotential cylinder is greater than that of the conductor and that the cylinder center does not coincide with the conductor center. However, the conductor surface is an equipotential surface. The charge will not be distributed uniformly over the conductor surface but will be so distributed as to cause the surface to be an equipotential one. Since the proper distribution of charge was not assumed in the preceding derivations, the results are not exact. However, if, as is often true, r is small compared with D, r_e will be nearly equal to r, and the derived results are accurate enough for most purposes.

For those cases in which r is not small compared with D, other expressions will be derived. The problem is this: Determine the location of a line along which a charge equal to that on the conductor may be concentrated and produce an electric field in space about the conductor identical to that produced by the nonuniformly distributed charge on the conductor surface. The line is called the electrical center of a conductor or a kernel. Since the charges on the conductor surfaces are distributed more densely on the facing portions of the conductors than on the other portions, the electrical centers are nearer each other than are the geometrical centers (see Fig. 11.14). Here the conductor radius is r, the geometrical centers are separated a distance D, and the electrical centers are separated a distance d. If the origin O of the coordinate axes is midway between the conductors, relations similar to those derived above hold if

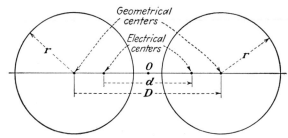

FIG. 11.14

r_1 and r_2 are measured from the electrical rather than the geometrical centers. The radius r_e of an equipotential cylinder is

$$r_e = \sqrt{\left[\frac{(a^2 + b^2 + d^2/4)}{2a}\right]^2 - \frac{d^2}{4}} \qquad (11.15)$$

The surface of the right-hand conductor is an equipotential cylinder of radius r. At the line in this cylinder nearest to O, $a = D/2 - r$ and $b = 0$. Substitution of these values in (11.14) yields

$$d = \sqrt{D^2 - 4r^2} \qquad (11.16)$$

or
$$d = \sqrt{D^2 - 8Dr + 12r^2} \qquad (11.17)$$

Consideration of the physical relations involved shows that

$$d = \sqrt{D^2 - 4r^2}$$

is the correct value. Hence the distance between the electrical centers of the conductors is less than that between the geometrical centers by an amount that depends upon the relative values of D and r.

When the radius r of two parallel conductors is not negligible compared with the distance D between the conductor centers, the radii of the flux and equipotential circles can be computed if the value of d computed from (11.16) is used instead of D in the equations derived from the assumption that the charges were concentrated along the conductor centers.

11.5. Capacitance of a Transmission Line. In Fig. 11.15 it is assumed that electric fluxes of $+\Psi$ and $-\Psi$ coul per m length are present between the electrical centers C_1 and C_2 of two parallel conductors of radius r m of a transmission line. Consider a point P that is x m from the electrical center of the left-hand conductor on the line joining the centers. The

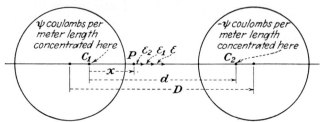

FIG. 11.15

voltage gradient $\mathcal{E}_1$ produced at P by the charge at C_1 is

$$\mathcal{E}_1 = \frac{\Psi}{2\pi\epsilon_v\epsilon x} \qquad \text{v per m} \qquad (11.18)$$

The gradient $\mathcal{E}_2$ produced at P by the charge at C_2 is

$$\mathcal{E}_2 = \frac{\Psi}{2\pi\epsilon_v\epsilon(d - x)} \qquad \text{v per m} \qquad (11.19)$$

The resultant gradient $\mathcal{E}$ at P is

$$\mathcal{E} = \mathcal{E}_1 + \mathcal{E}_2 = \frac{\Psi}{2\pi\epsilon_v\epsilon}\left(\frac{1}{x} + \frac{1}{d - x}\right) \qquad \text{v per m} \qquad (11.20)$$

The voltage drop V from the left- to the right-hand conductor is the line integral of the voltage gradient from one conductor surface to the other along the line joining the conductor centers. At the left-hand surface $x = r - (D - d)/2$, and at the right-hand surface, $x = (D + d)/2 - r$. Hence

$$V = \frac{\Psi}{2\pi\epsilon_v\epsilon}\int_{r-\frac{D-d}{2}}^{\frac{D+d}{2}-r}\left(\frac{dx}{x} + \frac{dx}{d - x}\right)$$

from which
$$V = \frac{\Psi}{2\pi\epsilon_v\epsilon}\left[\ln x - \ln (d - x)\right]_{r-\frac{D-d}{2}}^{\frac{D+d}{2}-r}$$

Substitution of the limits and simplification yield

$$V = \frac{\Psi}{\pi\epsilon_v\epsilon}\ln\frac{d + (D - 2r)}{d - (D - 2r)} \qquad \text{v}$$

Substitution of the value $d = \sqrt{D^2 - 4r^2}$ and simplification yield

$$V = \frac{\Psi}{\pi\epsilon_v\epsilon}\ln\frac{D + \sqrt{D^2 - 4r^2}}{2r} \qquad \text{v} \qquad (11.21)$$

The capacitance per unit length is

$$C = \frac{\Psi}{V} = \frac{\pi \epsilon_v \epsilon}{\ln \dfrac{D + \sqrt{D^2 - 4r^2}}{2r}} \qquad \text{f per m} \qquad (11.22)$$

Since $\epsilon_v = 8.85 \times 10^{-12}$, $\epsilon = 1$ for air, $\ln 10 = 2.3 \log 10$, 1 mile $= 1,609$ m. and 1 f $= 10^6$ μf, substitution of these values in (11.22) yields

$$C = \frac{0.0194}{\log \dfrac{D + \sqrt{D^2 - 4r^2}}{2r}} \qquad \mu\text{f per mi}$$

In many cases r is so small compared with D that the term $\sqrt{D^2 - 4r^2}$ is nearly equal to D. With this approximation $C = 0.0194/\log (D/r)$ μf per mi.

In the preceding derivations of the capacitance between transmission-line conductors it was assumed that they were isolated in air. The presence of the earth, the supporting insulators, and the towers cause the electric flux distribution about the conductors to differ from that assumed. The capacitance between two conductors is greater than that computed from the equations, though the difference is often negligible. Methods have been developed for taking into account the presence of the earth.

11.6. Electric Fields Relations on Axis of a Charged One-turn Coil. In Fig. 11.16 is represented an isolated one-turn coil that has $+\Psi$ coul of

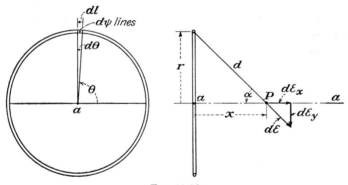

Fig. 11.16

electric flux distributed uniformly over its surface. Assume that the wire forming the turn is so small that its diameter is negligible compared with the other dimensions involved. The variation of the voltage gradient along the axis $a - a$ of the turn is to be determined. Consider a point P on the axis, x m from the center of the turn, and an element dl m of the turn. The flux is distributed uniformly over the full circle, or

$2\pi r$ m.   The flux per unit length of circumference is $\Psi/2\pi r$ coul per m.
The flux $d\Psi$ on the length dl is $\Psi\, dl/2\pi r$ coul.   Think of this flux as radial
from the center of a sphere with P in the surface of the sphere.   The
sphere radius is the distance d in Fig. 11.16.   As shown previously, the
voltage gradient at the surface of such a sphere is equal to the flux divided

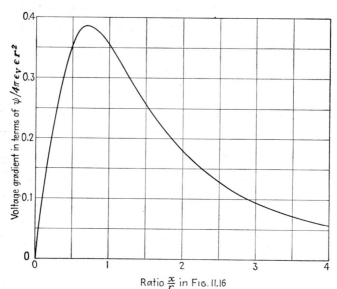

FIG. 11.17   Variation of the voltage gradient along the axis of a charged one-turn coil.

by $\epsilon_v\epsilon$ and the surface area $4\pi d^2$ of the sphere.   The gradient $d\mathcal{E}$ in Fig.
11.16 is directed through P and is

$$d\mathcal{E} = \frac{d\Psi}{4\pi\epsilon_v\epsilon d^2} = \frac{\Psi\, dl/2\pi r}{4\pi\epsilon_v\epsilon d^2} = \frac{\Psi\, dl}{8\pi^2\epsilon_v\epsilon r d^2} \qquad \text{v per m}$$

The component of the gradient directed along the axis and that normal
to the axis have been designated as $d\mathcal{E}_x$ and $d\mathcal{E}_y$, respectively.   For the
entire turn the resultant gradient will be directed along the axis since, for
each element of the turn that produces a component gradient normal to
the axis, there is an element diametrically opposite that produces a component gradient of equal magnitude and opposite direction.   Hence it is
necessary to consider only the component $d\mathcal{E}_x$.   From Fig. 11.16 it can be
seen that $d\mathcal{E}_x = \cos\alpha\, d\mathcal{E}$.   But $\cos\alpha = x/d$; hence

$$d\mathcal{E}_x = \frac{x}{d}\frac{\Psi\, dl}{8\pi^2\epsilon_v\epsilon r d^2} = \frac{\Psi x\, dl}{8\pi^2\epsilon_v\epsilon r d^3} \tag{11.23}$$

The total voltage gradient $\mathcal{E}$ along the axis in Fig. 11.16 is the sum of
the gradient components along that axis produced by the infinitesimal

elements of charge. For a given value of x the summation is obtained by integrating (11.23) from $l = 0$ to $l = 2\pi r$. Hence

$$\mathcal{E} = \frac{\Psi x}{8\pi^2 \epsilon_v \epsilon r d^3} \int_0^{2\pi r} dl = \frac{\Psi x}{4\pi \epsilon_v \epsilon d^3} \quad \text{v per m}$$

In Fig. 11.16, $d = \sqrt{x^2 + r^2}$; hence $d^3 = (x^2 + r^2)^{3/2}$. Then

$$\mathcal{E}_x = \frac{\Psi x}{4\pi \epsilon_v \epsilon (x^2 + r^2)^{3/2}} \quad \text{v per m} \qquad (11.24)$$

The variation of the potential gradient along the axis of the charged one-turn coil of Fig. 11.16 is shown in Fig. 11.17. The curve was plotted from points determined by substituting in (11.24) various values of x in terms of r (such as $x = 0$, $x = 0.5r$, etc.). The gradient is zero at the center of a turn, increases to a maximum at $x = r/\sqrt{2}$, and then decreases for greater values of x.

The voltage drop between two points located on the axis of a charged one-turn coil at the respective distances of a and b m from the center of the coil can be obtained as follows. Since $V_{ab} = \int_a^b \mathcal{E}\, dx$, then

$$V_{ab} = \frac{\Psi}{4\pi \epsilon_v \epsilon} \int_a^b \frac{x\, dx}{(x^2 + r^2)^{3/2}}$$

By integration

$$V_{ab} = \frac{\Psi}{4\pi \epsilon_v \epsilon} \left[\frac{-1}{\sqrt{x^2 + r^2}} \right]_a^b$$

from which

$$V_{ab} = \frac{\Psi}{4\pi \epsilon_v \epsilon} \left(\frac{1}{\sqrt{a^2 + r^2}} - \frac{1}{\sqrt{b^2 + r^2}} \right) \quad \text{v}$$

PROBLEMS

11.1. A charge of 1.5 μcoul is isolated in a medium whose dielectric constant is 3. Compute the electric flux density and the voltage gradient at a point 0.5 m from the charge.

11.2. Compute the voltage between two points that are, respectively, 0.4 and 0.6 m from the charge of Prob. 11.1.

11.3. For the charged wire of Fig. 11.5 locate the point on the line that is parallel to and 1.5 m from the wire at which the voltage gradient is 20 mv per in.

11.4. At 2 m from the center of a certain infinitely long conductor, the voltage gradient is 4 v per m. Compute the voltage between two points that are respectively, 1 and 3 m from the center.

11.5. Compute the charge on an infinitely long conductor required to produce in air a voltage gradient of 20 v per m at a point 20 m from the wire.

11.6. Two conductors are spaced 2 m between centers with 20,000 v between them. Compute the voltage gradient at the conductor surface for a conductor diameter of 0.0025 m and that for a diameter of 0.005 m.

11.7. The conductors in a certain transmission line are No. 1 solid copper. Compute the capacitance per mile between conductors for a spacing of 0.3 m between centers and that for a spacing of 0.6 m.

11.8. Two conductors that are 0.5 in. in diameter are spaced 2 in. between centers. For 400 v between conductors, locate and draw the equipotential circles that are at respective voltages of 50, 100, 150, and 200 v with respect to the point midway between the conductors. Also draw a number of the electric flux circles.

11.9. A fine wire that forms a one-turn coil 0.1 m in diameter has a charge of 8 $\mu\mu$coul. Compute the voltage gradient at a point on the longitudinal axis 0.125 m from the center of the turn. Compute the voltage between points on the axis that are, respectively, 0.1 and 0.15 m from the center.

11.10. The resistance from end to end of the rotor shaft of a certain capacitor is 0.08 ohm. When current is fed into the shaft from the end, the end section carries the current for all the plates attached to the shaft, the section between the first and second plates carries the current for all plates except the first, the section between the second and third plates carries the current for all plates except the first and second, etc. A curve showing the current distribution along the shaft has the appearance of stair steps. As an approximation, the current distribution may be assumed to vary linearly from a maximum at the input end of the shaft to zero at the other end. Using this approximation, compute the equivalent resistance of the shaft with respect to the input end.

11.11. The capacitor shaft of Prob. 11.10 is fed at the center instead of the end. Compute the equivalent resistance of the shaft with respect to the input point.

11.12. Air at certain specified standard temperature, humidity, and pressure ionizes and becomes a conductor at a voltage gradient of about 3,000 kv per m. If an electron velocity of 2×10^6 m per sec is required to produce ionization in air, how far must an electron travel in a uniform electric field with the above gradient to acquire the ionizing velocity? (This distance is called the mean free path of the electron.)

11.13. The ionization potential of a gas is defined as the potential through which an electron starting from rest must have passed in order to attain a velocity sufficient to ionize a neutral molecule of the gas. For argon the ionization potential is about 15 v. Compute the minimum velocity that an electron can possess and ionize a molecule of argon. How much energy is required to ionize an argon molecule?

11.14. A sphere of thin metal that has a radius of 0.1 m is within and concentric with a second sphere that has a radius of 0.15 m. The space between the spheres is filled with air. Compute the capacitance between the spheres.

For 5,000 v between spheres compute the maximum voltage gradient in the air between the spheres.

11.15. In Prob. 11.14 assume that the outer sphere has a radius of 0.15 m and that the voltage between spheres is maintained at 5,000 v. Determine the radius of the inner sphere that will cause the maximum voltage gradient in the air between the spheres to be a minimum and the value of the gradient.

CHAPTER 12

ELECTROCHEMISTRY

12.1. Electrolytic Conduction. There is a close relationship between chemical and electrical action. When two plates of unlike metals are placed in a solution that contains an acid, an alkali, or a salt, an electric potential exists between the plates. Such an arrangement is an elementary electrolytic cell. The plates are electrodes, and the solution is an electrolyte.

The electrodes of a cell are designated as positive and negative (or plus and minus). If a d-c voltmeter is so connected between the electrodes as to have an upscale reading, the electrode to which the plus terminal of the voltmeter is connected is the positive one and the other is the negative one. In a commercial cell a positive electrode may consist of one, two, or more plates connected together. A negative electrode usually consists of two or more plates connected together. The negative plates are intermeshed with but not in contact with the positive plates. Because there is usually one more negative plate than positive, the number of plates in a cell is usually odd.

There are certain differences between the conduction of electricity in a metal and that in a conducting solution. In a metal the positive charges are bound in position, and it is the movement of the electrons that constitutes the current. No chemical change occurs in the metal as a result of the electron flow. In a conducting solution there is not only a movement of free electrons in one direction, but there is also a movement of positive charges in the opposite direction. A chemical change occurs in a conducting solution as a result of the flow of current.

A crude representation of the action in a cell is shown in Fig. 12.1. Here copper and zinc electrodes are placed in a solution of sulfuric acid in water and connected externally by a voltmeter. The copper electrode is positive and the zinc electrode is negative. Some of the sulfuric acid is dissociated into hydrogen ions and sulfate ions. Each hydrogen ion carries a positive charge equal in magnitude to the charge of an electron. Each sulfate ion has a negative charge of two electrons. With the electrodes connected externally, some of the zinc goes into solution and displaces hydrogen ions to form zinc sulfate. Some of the zinc sulfate is dissociated into zinc ions and sulfate ions. Each zinc ion carries a positive charge equal to twice the magnitude of the charge of an electron. One difference between a zinc ion and the original zinc atom is that the ion has a positive charge because it left two electrons on the zinc electrode when it went into solution. The positively charged hydrogen ions that were displaced by the zinc ions move to the copper electrode; there each combines with an electron to become an atom of hydrogen gas that collects on the electrode or passes off into the air. In the solution there are some electrons that go directly to the zinc electrode. The result of the various ion movements described is that, in the external circuit through the voltmeter, there is a movement of electrons only; in the solution there is a movement of both positive ions and electrons. It is sometimes stated that there are two oppositely directed currents in an electrolytic solution. The total current is equal to the arithmetic sum of the current produced by position-ion motion and that produced by electron motion.

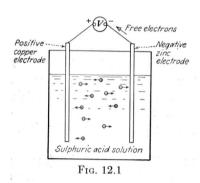

FIG. 12.1

The emf of a cell depends upon the materials used for the electrodes and upon the temperature and concentration of the electrolyte. The various elements may be classified in a series according to the value of the emf that each will produce in conjunction with a standard electrode. A standard electrode commonly used for this purpose is made of platinum and coated with hydrogen. The electrode is saturated and covered with hydrogen gas and placed in an acid solution containing a normal solution of hydrogen ions. A normal solution is of such strength that one liter contains one gram atom of replaceable hydrogen. The potentials of several elements arranged in the order of their potentials with respect to a standard hydrogen atom are in Table 12.1. In this table the element that is the higher in the list will be the positive electrode of a cell in which any element listed below it is the negative electrode. For example, in a cell having a silver and a zinc electrode, the silver electrode would be positive. The emf of the cell would be the algebraic difference between the emf of silver and that of zinc, or $0.800 - (-0.758) = 1.558$ v. The emf of the cell would have this value only as long as the electrolyte remained a normal solution. Any chemical action that changed the concentration of the solution would change the emf of the cell.

Cells are classified as primary and secondary cells. A primary cell is one in which the materials are used up as energy is converted from chemical to electrical form, and the process cannot be reversed. A secondary cell is one in which it is possible to convert energy from electrical to chemical form by using an external source of emf to force current through the cell in the direction opposite to that when the cell delivers electrical energy. A secondary cell is commonly called a *storage cell*.

A battery consists of two or more cells connected so as to provide a greater emf or current capacity than that of a single cell. In common

TABLE 12.1. POTENTIALS OF VARIOUS ELEMENTS*

Element	Potential against hydrogen electrode, volts
Silver	0.800
Mercury	0.799
Copper	0.345
Hydrogen	0.0
Lead	−0.122
Nickel	−0.231
Cobalt	−0.29
Cadmium	−0.398
Iron	−0.441
Zinc	−0.758
Potassium	−2.922
Lithium	−2.958

* Taken with permission from "Standard Handbook for Electrical Engineers," 8th ed., McGraw-Hill Book Company, Inc., New York, 1949.

usage a single cell is often called a *battery*. It is common practice to represent a battery as consisting of a single constant emf in series with what is called the *internal resistance* of the battery. Such a representation is satisfactory for some purposes but it is not sufficiently accurate for many circuit applications or computations. As an example, in a test on a certain dry cell the open-circuit voltage was read on a voltmeter as 1.55 v. When a resistor was connected across the terminals of the dry cell, the current was 0.8 amp and the terminal voltage was 1.45 v. The resistor was then disconnected and the open-circuit voltage was found to be 1.52 v at first. After several minutes it was noted that the open circuit voltage was rising very slowly and in about 2 hr had risen to 1.55 v. If one were to assume that the emf of the cell was constant at the original open-circuit voltage of 1.55 v, then he would say that the drop of $1.55 - 1.45 = 0.1$ v was the internal-resistance drop caused by the current of 0.8 amp and that the internal resistance was

$$\frac{0.1 \text{ v}}{0.8 \text{ amp}} = 0.125 \text{ ohm}$$

However, the fact that the open-circuit voltage was not the same immediately after the removal of the resistor as it was initially, shows that the process of drawing current causes a decrease in the original emf or else introduces an emf of opposite polarity in the cell. This additional emf is termed the emf of polarization. When it is considered, a battery when discharging may be represented as shown in Fig. 12.2a. For a battery, when charging, the emf of polarization has a polarity opposite to that when discharging. For this condition the battery may be represented as shown in Fig. 12.2b. The internal resistance of a battery is made up of the resistance of the electrodes and the electrolyte. The resistance of the electrodes is usually negligible compared with that of the electrolyte.

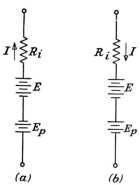

FIG. 12.2   Representation of a battery on discharge and on charge.

In a battery supplying any appreciable amount of current, the emf caused by chemical decomposition, the emf of polarization, and the internal resistance vary with so many factors that it is not possible to predict with accuracy the terminal voltages under various given sets of conditions.

12.2. Primary Cells. Although it is possible to produce emf with many different kinds of electrodes and electrolytes, only a few combinations have proved to be satisfactory for commercial cells. The most commonly used primary cell is the dry cell, which is not dry but has for an electrolyte a sal ammoniac solution held by capillary action in a porous material that separates the electrodes. The positive electrode is a rod or flat plate of carbon. The negative electrode is the zinc container that forms the outside of the cell. The sides and bottom of this container are lined with an absorbent material such as blotting paper, flour or starch paste, plaster of paris, or pulpboard. The carbon electrode is placed axially in the container, and the space between is filled with a mixture of finely crushed coke, manganese dioxide, and graphite. This material is tamped about the carbon rod to within a short distance from the top of the container. The absorbent material in the cell is then saturated with a solution of sal ammoniac and manganese dioxide or zinc chloride. The top of the cell is then sealed by a layer of asphaltum compound.

A new dry cell has an emf of about 1.5 v. The emf decreases with time and the active material in the cell is used up even if the cell is not used. When current is drawn from a dry cell, hydrogen is released at the carbon electrode. If the hydrogen bubbles were allowed to accumulate on the electrode, the emf of polarization and the internal resistance of the cell would become objectionably high. The coke, manganese dioxide, and graphite constitute a depolarizing agent and absorb most of the hydrogen.

One method of testing the condition of a dry cell is to short-circuit it with an ammeter and measure the current. A new cell may deliver as much as 30 amp when tested in this manner. A cell is considered as in good condition if it will deliver a short-circuit current of 15 amp or more. The amount of current that a dry cell will deliver on short circuit is not an accurate measure of the service capacity that the cell can deliver. Since testing a dry cell by short-circuiting it uses energy at a rapid rate, the testing period should be very short. The reader is cautioned that *a dry cell is one of the few sources of emf that is tested by short-circuiting it with an ammeter.* In general, one should never connect an ammeter directly across a source of emf. Even a dry cell would quickly damage an ammeter of less than 5 amp capacity connected across the cell terminals.

The capacity of a battery is expressed in ampere-hours. An ampere-hour is a measure of quantity of electricity and represents the number of coulombs that has moved through the battery and the external circuit during a period of 1 hr in which the current was kept constant at 1 amp. The ampere-hour capacity of a dry cell depends upon the volume and the quality of the materials used, upon the value of the discharge current, and whether the discharge is continuous or intermittent. A new $2\frac{1}{2}$- by 6-in. dry cell when discharged continuously through a 15-ohm resistor should deliver 25 amp-hr or more before the terminal voltage becomes less than 0.5 v. After the terminal voltage has fallen to this value, there is some energy left in the cell but the emf is so low and the internal resistance is so high that the cell is not satisfactory for most applications.

12.3. Standard Cells. A primary cell whose emf is used as a voltage standard is a standard cell. To be satisfactory as a standard, a cell must have an emf that remains constant for a long time, and it must be possible to reproduce the cell accurately. Two cells, a normal cell and an unsaturated cell, developed by the Weston Electrical Instrument Corporation, have proved to be satisfactory standards. The positive electrode of the cells is mercury; the negative electrode is amalgamated cadmium; and the electrolyte is a solution of mercurous sulfate and cadmium sulfate.

Weston normal cells are maintained in Washington, D.C., by the National Bureau of Standards and the emfs of these are compared with each other in determining the standard of emf of the United States. With careful manufacture following certain specifications, normal cells can be made whose emfs agree to within a few microvolts. In the normal cell the electrolyte is kept saturated by an excess of cadmium sulfate crystals introduced during manufacture. According to international agreement the international volt was defined as the 10,000/10,183 part of the emf of a Weston normal cell at 20 C. This definition of the international volt was discarded on Jan. 1, 1948. Since then the Weston normal cell is not the standard of emf, but will still be used as a means for maintaining the absolute volt. The absolute volt will be determined by measurement of the absolute ampere and the absolute ohm. Since 1 U.S. international volt = 1.000330 absolute volts, the emf of the Weston normal cell will be taken as 1.018636 absolute volts at 20 C.

The emf of a Weston normal cell decreases about 40 μv for 1 degree increase in temperature above 20 C. The variation in emf with temperature is not linear, the relation between the two being expressed by the equation

$$E = E_{20} - 0.0000406(t - 20) - 0.00000095(t - 20)^2 \\ + 0.00000001(t - 20)^3$$

where E is the emf in absolute volts at a temperature t C and E_{20} is the emf in absolute volts at 20 C.

The Weston unsaturated cell differs from the normal cell in that during manufacture the electrolyte is saturated at 4 C and no excess of cadmium sulfate crystals is left in the solution. The emf of an unsaturated cell cannot be reproduced so accurately, nor is it so permanent as that of the normal cell. The emf of an unsaturated cell decreases only about 10 μv for 1-degree increase in temperature above 20 C. Note that this change of voltage with temperature is only one-fourth that of the normal cell.

Most of the standard cells in use except those at standardizing laboratories are unsaturated cells whose emfs are measured and certified as of a certain date. At the National Bureau of Standards the emfs can be measured to the nearest microvolt (i.e., to seven significant figures) and are certified to six significant figures.

The internal resistance of an unsaturated standard cell is usually within the range from 100 to 500 ohms. Except for the effect upon the sensitivity of measuring instruments in the circuit, the exact value of the internal resistance of a given cell is of little importance because the cell current is zero when instrument readings are taken. In the use of a standard cell it is important that very little current should ever flow in the cell and that current for only short intervals. A current as small as 1 μa passing through a cell for several minutes produces a measurable change in the emf. After such a current flow has ceased, the emf will return to the original value in a few minutes. The current in a standard cell should never exceed 100 μa, and the period of use of current should always be short. In one test it was found that after 100 μa was drawn for 3 min, approximately 1 day was required for the emf to return to normal. If a standard cell is accidentally short-circuited for a short time, it may recover to its normal emf in a month or so. However, it should not be used as a standard again unless tests have shown that it is reliable.

12.4. Lead-acid Storage Batteries. Nearly everyone is familiar with at least some of the construction details of a lead-acid storage battery because of its universal use as an automobile accessory. In this type of battery each cell has several positive plates on which the active material is lead peroxide. Each cell also has several negative plates on which the active material is sponge lead. The plates of opposite polarity are interleaved and kept from contact with each other by separators made of glass, hard rubber, or wood.

The electrolyte in a lead-acid storage battery is a solution of water and sulfuric acid. During discharge the active materials on each plate are converted into lead sulfate and water is formed in the electrolyte. Oxygen is set free at the positive plate, and hydrogen at the negative plate. Since water has a lower specific gravity than sulfuric acid, the reduction in the amount of sulfuric acid and the increase in the amount of water in the solution will lower the specific gravity of the electrolyte. Because of this the most common method for determining the state of charge of such a battery is to measure the specific gravity of the electrolyte. During charge of a lead-acid storage battery, lead sulfate on one plate is reconverted into lead and that on the other into lead peroxide, the amount of sulfuric acid is increased, and the amount of water is decreased.

As with other batteries, the emf of a lead-acid storage battery increases during charge and decreases during discharge. Just when a battery is charged and when it is discharged is a matter of definition. The state of charge may be defined in terms of the cell emf or of the specific gravity of the electrolyte. For example, a battery with a certain type of plates might be said to be fully charged when the specific gravity has risen to, say, 1.280, even though further charging would result in further increase in the chemical energy stored. The same battery might be said to be discharged when the specific gravity has fallen to, say, 1.100, even though it is possible to obtain additional electrical energy from the battery. A lead-acid battery should not be allowed to remain in a discharged condition for long because the lead sulfate on the plates becomes partly crystallized and does not reduce readily when the battery is charged again.

The lead-acid storage battery has an emf of about 2.1 v per cell when fully charged. This type of battery can be built with an internal resistance so low that several hundred amperes can be delivered on short circuit. Such a battery is suited for starting service in an automobile because it can deliver the high current needed to produce good starting torque in a starter motor. Automobile storage batteries usually have a capacity of the order of 100 amp-hr based on a 20-hr discharge rate. This means that, starting fully charged, at 80 F, a 100-amp-hr battery should be able to deliver a constant current of 5 amp for a period of 20 hr without the terminal voltage falling below 1.75 v per cell. The battery has a second rating which is the number of amperes that, starting fully charged at 0 F, it can deliver for 20 min without the terminal voltage falling below 1.5 v per cell.

If a fully charged battery that is rated at 100 amp-hr on a 20-hr basis were to discharge 20 amp continuously for 5 hr, it would be found that the final state of charge would be less than if it were to discharge 5 amp for 20 hr. For still higher discharge currents, the capacity of the battery would be even further reduced. The reduction in capacity occurs because at the higher currents the electrolyte does not penetrate the pores of the active material rapidly enough to make the chemical changes uniformly in the material.

The ampere-hour efficiency of a battery is the ratio of the ampere-hour output of the battery to the ampere-hour input required to bring the battery back to the original state of charge under specified conditions of charging rate, final voltage, and temperature. Ampere-hour efficiency is not a true energy efficiency since the terminal voltage during charge is higher than during discharge. Ampere-hour efficiency can only be approximated since it is not possible to tell accurately when the original state of charge has been restored.

The capacity of a lead-acid storage battery depends upon the temperature. For example, the capacity of such a battery at 0 F is only about one-half of what it is at 100 F. This decrease in capacity with decrease in temperature is particularly disadvantageous in an automobile battery because the starting requirements are severe during cold weather.

The freezing point of the electrolyte in a fully charged lead-acid storage battery is so low that a battery is seldom damaged by freezing. However, a battery that is partially discharged might be damaged by freezing.

12.5. Alkaline Storage Batteries. The nickel-iron-alkaline cell made in the United States is also called the Edison cell after its inventor. In this cell the active materials of the positive plates are nickel oxide and flakes of metallic nickel. The active material of the negative plates is finely divided iron. The electrolyte is a 21 per cent solution of potassium and lithium hydroxides. The specific gravity of the electrolyte is about 1.200 at 60 F. Unlike that in the lead-acid battery, the specific gravity of the electrolyte in an alkaline battery changes very little with the state of charge. The best method for determining the state of charge of an alkaline battery is to measure the emf, which is about 1.5 v per cell in a fully charged battery and about 1 v per cell in a discharged battery.

An alkaline battery has a steel container that is not attacked by the electrolyte. As the internal resistance of an alkaline cell is considerably higher than that of a lead-acid cell, the alkaline cell is not well adapted for applications where heavy discharge currents are required. Like the lead-acid type the capacity of an alkaline cell decreases as the temperature decreases.

Unlike a lead-acid battery an alkaline battery can stand in a discharged condition for an indefinite period without any ill effects. For a given kilowatthour capacity an alkaline battery weighs less than a lead-acid battery. This fact is of commercial importance in portable services because less of the energy of an alkaline battery is required in moving its own weight than is the case for a lead-acid battery.

12.6. Faraday's First Law of Electrolysis. Faraday's first law of electrolysis states that *the mass of the products of an electrolytic process is equal to the quantity of electricity passed through the electrolyte times a factor that varies with the element deposited.* It matters not whether a small current exists for a long time or whether a large current exists for a short time; when a given number of coulombs pass through a given electrolyte, the mass of the material deposited on a cathode or an anode will be the same, provided the chemical reactions are the same. In some cases a change in the current through a given electrolyte causes a change in the chemical reactions produced. When this occurs, the mass of the products deposited depends upon the time required for a given number of coulombs to pass through the electrolyte.

12.7. Faraday's Second Law of Electrolysis. Faraday's second law states that *the mass of a metal deposited or of a gas set free by an electrolytic process by the passage of a given quantity of electricity is directly proportional to the gram equivalent of the metal or gas.* The gram equivalent of an element is equal to the atomic weight divided by the valence. The second law in equational form is

$$m = k \frac{qw}{n} \tag{12.1}$$

where m is the mass in grams of the metal deposited or of the gas set free, k is a proportionality factor, q is the quantity of electricity in coulombs passing through the electrolyte, w is the atomic weight of the element deposited or set free, and n is the valence of the element.

The value of k can be determined by experiment. The international ampere was defined as "the unvarying current which, when passed through a solution of silver nitrate in water in accordance with certain standard specifications, deposits silver at the rate of one thousand one hundred eighteen millionths (0.001118) of a gram per second." The atomic weight of silver is 107.88 and its valence is 1. With the current in a silver nitrate solution constant at an international ampere, a quantity of one coulomb of electricity would pass through the solution in one second. The value of k can be determined by substitution of the values $m = 0.001118$ gm, $q = 1$ coul, $w = 107.88$, and $n = 1$. Hence $0.001118 = k(1 \times 107.88)/1$ from which $k = 1.0363 \times 10^{-5}$ or $k = 1/96,494$ which is usually approximated by $k = 1/96,500$. Substituting this value of k in (12.1) yields

$$m = \frac{qw}{96,500n} \tag{12.2}$$

Solving (12.2) for q yields $q = 96,500(mn/w)$. For any element it can be said that, when $q = 96,500$ coul, the quantity $mn/w = 1$. This means that for any element the mass in grams of the products of an electrolytic process caused by the passage of 96,500 coul of electricity is equal to the atomic weight of the element divided by the valence. The quantity 96,500 coul is a faraday of electricity.

The international ampere was defined in terms of the electrochemical effect of current because it was thought that would make it possible for anyone who had the proper equipment to produce a standard current. However, the process is now seldom, if ever, used to establish a current standard.

The international ampere as defined here was discarded on Jan. 1, 1948. Since then the absolute ampere is the unit of current, where 1 international ampere = 0.999835 absolute ampere. The absolute ampere is determined from measurements of the force exerted on a current-carrying conductor in a magnetic field.

One of the first methods used by Edison for metering the energy used by a customer made use of the electrochemical effect of current. An electrolytic cell was so connected that all or a known portion of the current in one of the lines supplying the customer passed through the cell. Each time that a bill was to be made out, the plate on which metal had been deposited was taken out of the cell and weighed. From the increase in the weight of the plate during a billing period the amount of electricity that had passed through the circuit was determined. By this method the ampere-hours, and not the watthours, were measured. If the voltage supplied to a customer's lines could have been kept constant, the watthours would have been directly proportional to the ampere-hours. Because the voltage did vary some, the metering method was not exact.

Careful measurements have shown that Faraday's second law is exact. However, the amount of metal deposited from a given solution cannot always be computed correctly by (12.2). For example, in the process of depositing a metal such as copper, it may happen that hydrogen gas is freed at the electrode on which the copper is deposited. It might be that 80 per cent of the coulombs would deposit copper and the other 20 per cent would free hydrogen. If we are concerned only with depositing copper, we might say that the efficiency of the electrolytic process is 80 per cent. The term *current efficiency* is used to express this result. If Faraday's laws are to be used in determining the quantitative results of an electrolytic process, it is essential that all the chemical reactions be known that occur during the process.

12.8. Electroplating. Metal can be plated upon a conducting object by making that object the electrode at which the current leaves an electrolytic solution when the current is forced through the solution by an external emf. In this case the object is a cathode. The electrode at which the current enters the solution is an anode. If the anode is soluble in the solution and consists of the same metal that is to be plated out, the weight of the metal dissolved from the anode is equal to that deposited at the cathode and the solution is unchanged by the process. If the anode is not soluble, new material must be added to the solution occasionally to replace the metal plated out.

When the anode in an electrolytic solution is composed of the same material as that plated out, the chemical reactions that occur at the cathode are the reverse of those at the anode. In this case no emf is produced by the chemical reactions, and the voltage that must be applied to the electrodes is equal to the current multiplied by the resistance of the electrodes and the solution. Usually the resistance of the electrodes is negligible in comparison with that of the solution.

Since the resistance of an electrolytic solution causes an energy loss when current passes through the solution, the resistance is kept low by using electrodes of large area and with a short distance of separation. The electrodes cannot be placed too near each other, however, or the current density in the solution will not be uniform and the deposit on the cathode will be unevenly distributed. The resistance of an electrolytic solution varies with the amount of the current through the solution. For the current densities ordinarily used in commercial work, the resistance of a solution is so low that the voltage drop between electrodes may be only a fraction of a volt or a few volts at most. To produce large currents at low voltages is more costly than to produce the same amount of power at a higher voltage. Whenever possible, electrolytic cells are connected in series so that a higher applied voltage may be used.

12.9. Electrolytic Refining of Copper. If copper is to have a high conductivity, it must not contain more than a few thousandths of 1 per cent of antimony or arsenic. If brittleness in copper is to be prevented, there must be very little lead or tellurium present. These impurities as well as certain other elements can be removed by an electrolytic refining process if they are present in quantities that do not total more than 1 or 2 per cent. The impure copper is made the anode in a solution of copper sulfate that contains some uncombined sulfuric acid. The cathode is pure copper. When current is sent through the solution, copper is dissolved from the anode into the electrolyte. In turn from the electrolyte copper is deposited upon the cathode.   If they are not present in too great quantities, it is possible to keep most of the impurities from being deposited on the cathode.   The chief impurity in cathode copper is hydrogen.

In the refining process it is often possible to recover enough gold and silver to pay a considerable portion of the cost of the process.

The electrodes in cells used for electrolytic refining may be connected to form either a series or a parallel system.   In a series system the electrodes are rolled or cast plates which are placed parallel and relatively close together in the electrolytic solution.   The plate at which the current leaves the cell is made of pure copper.   The other plates are made of the copper that is to be refined.   All the plates except the first and the last have impure copper dissolved from one side and pure copper deposited upon the other.   The refining process is continued until all the plates have been changed to pure copper.

In a parallel system for an electrolytic cell the anodes, which are made of the impure copper, are all connected to the positive terminal and interleaved between the cathode plates.   The cathode plates, which are thin sheets of pure copper, are all connected to the negative terminal.   During the refining process the impure copper anodes are dissolved and additional copper is deposited on the cathode plates.

Electrolytic cells used for copper refining can be connected in various series and parallel combinations according to the voltage required per cell and the supply voltage available.

The current density used in refining is usually from 20 to 30 amp per sq ft.

12.10. Electrolytic Corrosion.   Certain electrical systems operate, intentionally or otherwise, with part of the circuit in contact with the earth.   Soil is a very poor conductor of electricity when dry, but becomes an electrolytic conductor when it contains moisture with salts in solution. In a street railway system the soil forms a conducting path that is in parallel with the rails.   At points where currents leave the rails and enter the soil, electrolytic action dissolves some metal from the rail.   If an underground pipe is located near the rails, currents may enter it from the soil, travel along it for a distance, and then leave in a more direct return path to the generator.   At points where currents leave the pipe, electrolysis occurs and dissolves metal from it.   The damage caused by earth currents is often found at a considerable distance from the conductor that is supposed to carry all the current in a system.

Electrolysis is produced by alternating as well as direct current.   However, with alternating current the metal that is dissolved during one half cycle may be redeposited during the next half cycle.   At points of contact where partial rectification happens to occur electrolytic damage may result.

PROBLEMS

12.1. What is the emf of a wet battery that has zinc and copper electrodes if the electrolyte is a normal solution?

12.2. In a "soda cell" one electrode is made of zinc, the other of black oxide of copper, and the electrolyte is a normal solution of caustic soda. If the emf of such a cell is 0.95 v, what is the potential of the copper oxide with respect to a hydrogen electrode?

12.3. For a certain dry cell it is specified that for continuous service the current density in the surface of the zinc should not exceed 2 ma per sq in. The cell is 2.5 in. in diameter and 6 in. in height. What is the allowable discharge current?

12.4. A certain dry cell had an open-circuit voltage of 1.61 v. When the terminals of the cell were short-circuited by a 50-amp ammeter, the current was 22 amp. What was the internal resistance of the cell?

12.5. A certain flashlight battery of two cells in series cost 20¢. Assume that during a life of 30 hr the battery delivered a current of 300 ma at a voltage of 1.1 v per cell. Compute the cost in cents per kilowatthour of the energy delivered by the battery.

12.6. A certain Weston saturated cell has an emf of 1.01865 v at a temperature of 20 C. What will be the emf at a temperature of 10 C?

12.7. The emf of a cell was measured by comparison with that of a standard cell by means of the circuit of Fig. 3.35. The current in the uniform slide wire AC was controlled by the rheostat R. The standard cell had an emf of 1.0186 v. With the switch S closed to the left, the galvanometer G had zero deflection when the slider B was 40.6 cm from C. With the switch S closed to the right, the galvanometer had zero deflection when the slider was 67.3 cm from C. Compute the unknown emf.

12.8. The terminal voltage of a certain lead-acid storage battery was measured at 1-hr intervals with the discharge current kept constant at 15 amp. The following data were taken:

Time, hr	Terminal voltage, v	Time, hr	Terminal voltage, v
0	6.06	5	5.92
1	6.03	6	5.85
2	6.00	7	5.70
3	5.97	8	5.52
4	5.94		

The battery was then charged with the current kept constant at 16 amp. The following data were taken:

Time, hr	Terminal voltage, v	Time, hr	Terminal voltage, v
0	6.53	5	6.96
1	6.57	6	7.10
2	6.67	7	7.35
3	6.72	8	7.62
4	6.82		

Compute the approximate energy efficiency for the given cycle of discharge and charge.

12.9. In the Edison ampere-hour meter mentioned in Art. 12.7 two zinc plates were used in a zinc sulfate solution. What change in the mass of a plate represented 1 amp-hr? The atomic weight of zinc is 65.4.

12.10. For an energy cost of 2¢ per kwhr, what is the cost of plating 4 lb of silver from a univalent silver solution with a supply voltage of 6 v? The atomic weight of silver is 107.88.

12.11. How many ampere-hours are required to deposit ½ lb of copper from a bivalent copper solution? The atomic weight of copper is 63.6.

12.12. Each tank in a certain refining plant is to be supplied with 300 amp at 18 v. A total of about 50 tanks is to be installed. A 230-v d-c generator is to be used as a supply. Specify the best arrangement of connections for the tanks. What should be the current rating of the generator?

12.13. A nickel-plating vat and a cadmium-plating vat are in series. During a period in which 100 g of nickel are deposited, how much cadmium will be deposited? Nickel has an atomic weight of 58.69 and a valence of 2; cadmium has an atomic weight of 112.41 and a valence of 2.

12.14. A certain object that has a surface area of 80 sq in. is to be cadmium-plated to a depth of $\frac{1}{32}$ in. A current density of 15 amp per sq ft is to be used. The density of the cadmium may be taken as 520 lb per cu ft. How much time is required for the plating if the current efficiency of the plating process is 85 per cent?

INDEX